1968

Differential and Integral Calculus

DIFFERENTIAL AND INTEGRAL CALCULUS

SIXTH EDITION

Clyde E. Love, Ph.D.

LATE PROFESSOR OF MATHEMATICS IN

THE UNIVERSITY OF MICHIGAN

Earl D. Rainville, Ph.D.

PROFESSOR OF MATHEMATICS IN

THE UNIVERSITY OF MICHIGAN

New York THE MACMILLAN COMPANY

First Printing

Library of Congress catalog card number: 62-7117

The Macmillan Company, New York
Brett-Macmillan Ltd., Galt, Ontario

Printed in the United States of America

Some material included in this book is from Rainville: *Elementary Differential Equations*, Second Edition, © 1958 by The Macmillan Company; Rainville: *A Short Course in Differential Equations*, Second Edition, © 1958 by The Macmillan Company; and Rainville: *Unified Calculus and Analytic Geometry*, © 1961 by The Macmillan Company.

PREFACE

In the present edition, as in the fourth and fifth editions of this calculus, the material is so arranged that integration can be taken up early (Chapter 8) or delayed until after the customary topics in differentiation have been completed. The latter arrangement is accomplished by inserting Chapter 8 between Chapters 17 and 18.

New material in this edition includes the following topics: remainder theorems on power series, additional comparison tests for infinite series, a study of the error function, the intermediate value theorem, curve tracing from parametric equations, vibration of a spring, of a pendulum, simple electric circuits. A few other minor topics are new.

Additional explanatory material is included in the over-all attempt to make the text more readable for the student and to stimulate his interest in continuing mathematical studies. In particular, increased space has been allotted to the study of continuity, integration, even and odd functions, parametric equations, partial differentiation, iterated integration, and infinite series.

I have attempted to effect a reasonable balance between the desire for rigor and the student's ability to appreciate it.

I have tried to state definitions and theorems with care, to prove some things rigorously, to present others with discussions aimed only at making the facts seem plausible. By means of what I hope are illuminating discussions in the text, I attempt to increase both the student's maturity and his knowledge of the subject. There are in this book not only a large number of illustrative examples but also well over four thousand exercises for the student. More than two thousand of the exercises are new with this edition. They have been constructed carefully and are supposed not only to develop gradually a considerable manipulative skill but also in numerous instances to add appreciably to the student's basic knowledge. The instructor will

v

notice many exercises clearly intended to prepare the student for specific problems which he may encounter in more advanced courses.

I have included a few topics which are not often discussed at this stage in the student's training. For example, the error function is studied in § 242 to show the student how easily some so-called nonelementary functions may be handled.

I am indebted to Professor Ralph L. Shively of Swarthmore College for an independent reading of the proof sheets. There is also the ever present indebtedness I feel toward those teachers with whom I have been in close contact regarding the exposition of elementary mathematics, particularly to the late Clyde E. Love, to Professors C. A. Hutchinson, and Jack R. Britton, both of the University of Colorado, and to Professors R. V. Churchill, R. C. F. Bartels, D. G. Dickson, and others of the University of Michigan.

Earl D. Rainville

CONTENTS

FUNCTIONS. LIMITS

1. *Functions*

When two quantities x and y are related so that for some range of values of x the value of y is determined by that of x, we say that y is a *function* of x. For a square with side of length c the area is given by

$$(1) \qquad\qquad A = c^2, \qquad c > 0.$$

Therefore A is a function of c, the range of values of c being determined by the physical meaning of the quantities involved.

There is nothing in the definition of the term function to require that the variables be related by an equation or by any set of formulas. The temperature at a specific spot on the earth's surface is a function of the time, as well as of many other variables, but no formula is known for that function.

The student is already familiar with a large number of specific functions. Recall, as examples, the six trigonometric functions, $\sin x$, $\cos x$, etc., the square root

$$(2) \qquad\qquad y = \sqrt{x}, \qquad x \geqq 0,$$

the linear polynomial

$$(3) \qquad\qquad y = mx + b,$$

and the quadratic polynomial

$$(4) \qquad\qquad y = Ax^2 + Bx + C.$$

In this book our attention will be confined almost entirely to the study of functions defined by equations. Such functions occur often in mathematics and in physical applications, and they furnish illuminating examples of the power of the tools to be developed throughout the present course of study. Except where the contrary is stated, the quantities with which we shall deal are restricted to real values.

It is frequently desirable, particularly in the development of the theory, to work with a large class of functions rather than with a specific one. Therefore we use a symbol such as $f(x)$, which is read "f of x," to denote a function of x. We write

(5) $$y = f(x)$$

to convey the fact that y is a function of x, without designating the particular manner in which y is related to x. Letters other than f are used in the same way: we may write

(6) $$z = w(v), \qquad u = s(v),$$

to indicate that z and u are both functions of v.

Although the function symbol is of most value when the function is not stipulated, a little work with specific functions is an aid in becoming familiar with the notation.

Example (*a*). Let $f(x) = x^2 + 3$. Find $f(2), f(-4), f(0), f(u - 1), f(-x)$. Since $f(x) = x^2 + 3$,

$$f(2) = 2^2 + 3 = 7.$$

In the same way,

$$f(-4) = (-4)^2 + 3 = 19,$$
$$f(0) = 0^2 + 3 = 3,$$
$$f(u - 1) = (u - 1)^2 + 3 = u^2 - 2u + 4,$$
$$f(-x) = (-x)^2 + 3 = x^2 + 3 = f(x).$$

Example (*b*). Let $g(y) = \cos 2y - 2 \sin y$. Find $g(\pi)$, $g(\frac{1}{2}\pi)$, $g(0)$, and $[g(x) + g(-x)]$.

From the definition of $g(y)$ it follows that

$$g(\pi) = \cos 2\pi - 2 \sin \pi = 1 - 0 = 1,$$
$$g(\tfrac{1}{2}\pi) = \cos \pi - 2 \sin \tfrac{1}{2}\pi = -1 - 2 = -3,$$
$$g(0) = \cos 0 - 2 \sin 0 = 1 - 0 = 1.$$

Since
$$g(x) = \cos 2x - 2 \sin x,$$
$$g(-x) = \cos (-2x) - 2 \sin (-x)$$
$$= \cos 2x + 2 \sin x.$$

Therefore
$$g(x) + g(-x) = 2 \cos 2x.$$

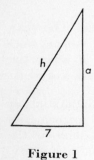

Figure 1

Example (*c*). A right triangle has a fixed base of length 7. Express the length of the altitude of the triangle as a function of the length of the hypotenuse.

With the notation in Fig. 1 the Theorem of Pythagoras yields

$$h^2 = 49 + a^2$$

or

(7) $$a = \sqrt{h^2 - 49}, \qquad h > 7.$$

In (7) a is expressed as a function (explicit) of h.

2. *Graph of a Function*

The curve

(1) $$y = f(x)$$

is called the graph of the function $f(x)$. Many properties of the function are made more vivid by this graphic representation.

The function $A = c^2$, $c > 0$, which was mentioned in § 1, is represented graphically by half of a parabola as exhibited in Fig. 2.

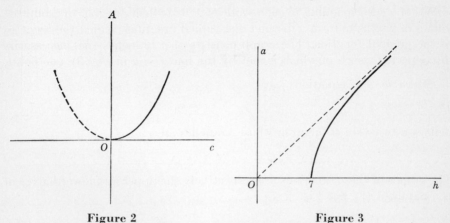

Figure 2   Figure 3

In Example (c) of § 1, we expressed the length of the altitude of a certain right triangle in terms of the length of the hypotenuse by means of the function shown in Fig. 3,

(2) $$a = \sqrt{h^2 - 49}, \qquad h > 7.$$

3. *Classification of Functions*

All functions are classed as either *algebraic* or *transcendental*. The algebraic functions are *rational integral functions*, or *polynomials; rational fractions*, or quotients of polynomials; and *irrational functions*, of which the simplest are those formed from rational functions by the extraction of roots. The elementary transcendental functions are *trigonometric* and *inverse trigonometric functions; exponential functions*, in which the variable occurs as an exponent; and *logarithms*.

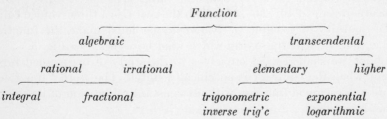

4. *One-valued and Many-valued Functions*

When the relation $y = f(x)$ is such that there is only one value of y for each admissible x, then $f(x)$ is said to be a *one-valued* function of x. The equivalent term *single-valued* function is also used. Graphically this means that if the function is defined for $x = a$, the vertical line $x = a$ intersects the curve in one and only one point.

Frequently, however, the law connecting x and y determines two or more values of y, in general distinct, for each value of x. Say that there are n values of y corresponding to each value of x. It is then possible to group the values of y so as to form n distinct one-valued functions, called the *branches* of the original function. The graph consists of n branches (not necessarily disconnected), each of which is met by the line $x = a$ in exactly one point.

Example. The equation

$$(1) \qquad\qquad y^2 = x, \qquad x \geqq 0,$$

defines a two-valued function whose branches are

$$y = \sqrt{x}, \qquad y = -\sqrt{x}.$$

The graphs of these functions are respectively the upper and lower halves of the parabola (1). See Fig. 4.

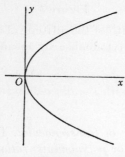
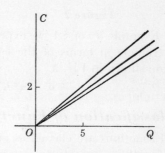

Figure 4   **Figure 5**

When a many-valued function arises, we must as a rule form from it a *one-valued function* by naming the particular branch from which the value of y is to be taken. The reason is easily seen: until this has been done, there is no way to tell which of the several possible values is meant. If three grades of gasoline are for sale at 40¢, 36¢, 33¢, then the cost C is a three-valued function of the quantity of gasoline Q. The customer must make the function definite (i.e., one-valued) by saying which kind he wants. See Fig. 5.

In this book we shall restrict ourselves to the study of one-valued functions except when the contrary is specifically stated. The word "function" is to denote a one-valued function without constant reiteration of its single-valued character.

5. *The Square Root*

Although every positive number of course has two square roots, one positive, one negative, by universal agreement the radical sign (or its equivalent the exponent $\frac{1}{2}$) is taken to mean invariably the *positive* root.* For example,

$$\sqrt{3} = 1.732 \cdots, \text{ not } \pm 1.732 \cdots; \qquad \sqrt{4} = 2, \text{ not } \pm 2;$$

$$\sqrt{a^2 - 2ab + b^2} = a - b \quad if \quad a \geqq b,$$
$$= b - a \quad if \quad a < b;$$

$$\sqrt{x^2} = x \quad if \quad x \geqq 0,$$
$$= -x \quad if \quad x < 0.$$

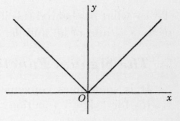

Figure 6

It follows that the graph of the function

$$y = \sqrt{x^2}$$

is not the 45°-line, but the two "half-lines" of Fig. 6.

6. *The Absolute-Value Symbol*

The symbol $|x|$, which may be read "absolute value of x," is defined by

$$(1) \qquad |x| = x, \qquad \text{for } x \geqq 0,$$
$$= -x, \qquad \text{for } x < 0.$$

Example (a). $|5| = |-5| = 5$.

Example (b). If $a > 0$, $|x| \leqq a$ is equivalent to $-a \leqq x \leqq a$.

By comparing the definition in (1) above with the discussion in § 5, we see that

$$(2) \qquad \sqrt{x^2} = |x|.$$

The graph of the curve $y = |x|$ is that shown in Fig. 6.

It is useful to recognize the geometric significance of $|a - b|$. Let the points associated with the real numbers a and b be marked on an axis in the usual manner; then $|a - b|$ is the positive distance between those points. For instance, let $a = -2$ and $b = 7$, as in Fig. 7.

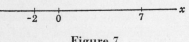

Figure 7

* The point should be emphasized that there is nothing new here; the student has always used these symbols exactly as here demanded. For instance, if $\tan \theta = \sqrt{3}$, we say that $\theta = 60°$ rather than $120°$, since $\tan 120° = -\sqrt{3}$.

To avoid any possible confusion, let us repeat that every positive number has two square roots; but to indicate the negative root, the minus sign must be written: if $x^2 = 4$, then $x = \sqrt{4} = 2$ or $x = -\sqrt{4} = -2$.

Then
$$|(-2) - 7| = |-9| = 9,$$

which checks with the distance between the points $x = -2$ and $x = 7$, as shown in Fig. 7.

A fundamental property of the absolute-value symbol is that *the absolute value of the sum of two numbers is never larger than the sum of their absolute values,*
$$|a + b| \leqq |a| + |b|.$$

To see what lies behind this inequality, consider the geometric interpretation of $|a + b|$ and of $|a|$ and $|b|$.

7. *The Signum Function*

It is sometimes convenient to make use of what is called the *signum* (Latin for "sign") function. In practice, signum is usually abbreviated to sgn. We define this function by

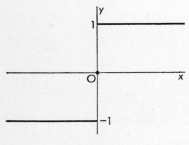

Figure 8

(1) $\operatorname{sgn} x = -1,$ for $x < 0,$
                  $= 0,$ for $x = 0,$
                  $= +1,$ for $x > 0.$

The graph of $y = \operatorname{sgn} x$ is shown in Fig. 8. Except at zero, the value of the signum function is determined by the algebraic sign of its argument. When the argument x is positive, sgn x has the value plus one; when x is negative, sgn x has the value minus one.

The signum function may be used to write in a single formula what would otherwise be given by two or more formulas. Suppose we wish to use the function $g(x)$ for values of $x < c$ and the function $h(x)$ for values of $x > c$. We write

(2) $F(x) = \frac{1}{2}[1 - \operatorname{sgn}\,(x - c)]g(x) + \frac{1}{2}[1 + \operatorname{sgn}\,(x - c)]h(x).$

Since $\operatorname{sgn}(x - c) = -1$ for $x < c$, and $\operatorname{sgn}\,(x - c) = +1$ for $x > c$, we may conclude that

(3) $F(x) = g(x),$ for $x < c,$
              $= \frac{1}{2}[g(c) + h(c)],$ for $x = c,$
              $= h(x),$ for $x > c.$

At $x = c$, $F(x)$ takes on the average value, the arithmetic mean of the values of $g(x)$ and $h(x)$.

Example. Sketch the curve

(4) $y = \frac{1}{2}(1 + \operatorname{sgn}\,x)\,\sin\,x.$

For $x < 0$, sgn $x = -1$, so $y = 0$. For $x = 0$, $y = 0$. For $x > 0$, $\frac{1}{2}(1 + \text{sgn } x) = +1$, so $y = \sin x$. Therefore the curve is as shown in Fig. 9.

The student may find it amusing to use the signum function to express in a single formula the domestic parcel post rate as a function of the weight of the package and the distance from point of departure to destination.

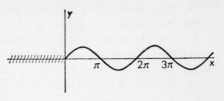

Figure 9

It follows from the definition of the absolute value function as given in § 6 that

(5) $$x = |x| \text{ sgn } x$$

and that

(6) $$|x| = x \text{ sgn } x.$$

EXERCISES

In Exs. 1–10, certain functions are explicitly defined. Perform the indicated operations in each exercise.

1. If $f(x) = x^2 - x + 3$, find $f(0)$, $f(2)$, $f(-4)$, $f(-2x)$.   *Ans.* $f(-4) = 23$.
2. If $f(x) = 7 - 2x + x^2$, find $f(0)$, $f(3)$, $f(-2)$, $f(-y)$.   *Ans.* $f(3) = 10$.
3. If $F(y) = y(y - 3)^2$, find $F(c)$, $F(0)$, $F(3)$, $F(-1)$, $F(x + 3)$.
   Ans. $F(x + 3) = x^2(x + 3)$.
4. If $F(b) = \dfrac{b - b^2}{1 + b^2}$, find $F(0)$, $F(1)$, $F(\frac{1}{2})$, $F(\tan x)$.
   Ans. $F(\tan x) = \sin x(\cos x - \sin x)$.
5. If $g(x) = 4x^4 - 3x^2 + 2x - 2$, find $g(2)$, $g(-2)$, $g(\frac{1}{2})$, $g(-x)$.
   Ans. $g(\frac{1}{2}) = -\frac{3}{2}$.
6. If $g(x) = x^4 - 2x^3 - 7x^2 + 8x + 16$, find $g(-1)$, $g(-2)$, $g(2)$, $g(3)$.
   Ans. 4.
7. If $\varphi(x) = \cos x$, find $\varphi(0)$, $\varphi(\frac{1}{2}\pi)$, $\varphi(\pi)$, $\varphi(-x)$, $\varphi(\pi - y)$.
8. If $H(y) = \cos y - \sin y$, find $H(0)$, $H(\frac{1}{2}\pi)$, $H(\pi)$, and also show that
$$H(\tfrac{1}{2}\pi + x) = H(\pi - x) = -H(-x).$$
9. If $\psi(x) = \tan x$, find $\psi(\pi/6)$, $\psi(x - \frac{1}{2}\pi)$, $\psi(-x)$, and express $\psi(2x)$ as a function of $\psi(x)$.
10. If $g(x) = \cos 2x$, find $g(\frac{1}{4}\pi)$, $g(\frac{1}{2}\pi)$, $g(-x)$, $g(\pi - x)$, $g(\pi + x)$, $g(x - \frac{1}{2}\pi)$.
11. For the function $f(x) = \tan x$, show that
$$f(x + y) - f(x) = \frac{\sec^2 x \tan y}{1 - \tan x \tan y}.$$

12. For the function $f(x) = \sin x$, show with the aid of the elementary formula $\sin^2 A = \frac{1}{2}(1 - \cos 2A)$ that
$$f(x + y) - f(x) = \cos x \sin y - 2 \sin x \sin^2 (\tfrac{1}{2}y).$$

In Exs. 13–25, express the function by a formula and draw the graph, indicating that portion of the graph which has a meaning in the problem.

13. The amount of \$1 at 4% simple interest, as a function of time.
14. The volume of a sphere as a function of the radius.
15. The radius of a sphere as a function of the volume.
16. The volume of a cube as a function of the length of an edge.
17. The surface area of a cube as a function of the length of an edge.
18. The length e of an edge of a cube as a function of the surface area A of the cube.

$$Ans.\ e = \sqrt{\frac{A}{6}}.$$

19. The surface area of a cube as a function of the volume of the cube.
20. Temperature in °F as a function of temperature in °C, (a) in general; (b) for a body of water in liquid form. $Ans.\ (a)\ F = \frac{9}{5}C + 32,\ C \geqq -273.$
21. The altitude of a right triangle as a function of the base, if the hypotenuse is given.
22. The hypotenuse of a right triangle as a function of the base, if the altitude is given.
23. The height of a cylindrical can as a function of the diameter, if 18π sq. in. of sheet metal are used. What kind of curve is this?
24. In Ex. 23, the diameter as a function of the height. What kind of curve is this? $Ans.\ D = -h + \sqrt{h^2 + 36}.$
25. The current I from a battery as a function of the external resistance R, the electromotive force E and internal resistance r being constant. (Current equals electromotive force divided by the sum of the two resistances.)
26. In Ex. 25, express R as a function of I, and draw the curve.
27. A man drives from Detroit to Chicago, say 300 mi., at an average speed of 60 mi. per hr., stops 1 hr. in Chicago, and returns at a speed of 50 mi. per hr. Neglecting variations of speed en route, write formulas expressing x (distance from Detroit) as a function of t, and draw the graph.
28. Use the signum function of § 7 to express the x of Ex. 27 as a function of t for $0 \leqq t \leqq 12$. $Ans.\ x = 300 + 5t - 30(t - 5)\ \text{sgn}\ (t - 5) - 25(t - 6)\ \text{sgn}\ (t - 6).$

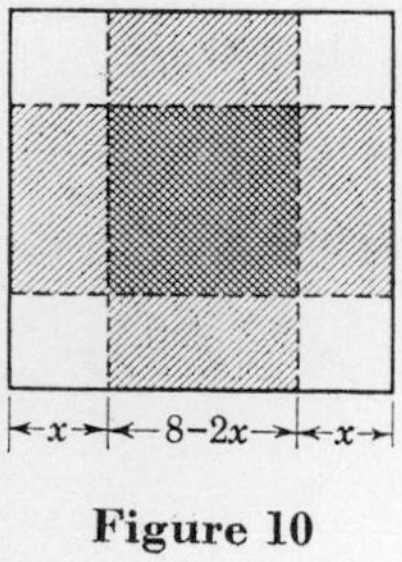

29. In Ex. 27, graph the speed v as a function of t.
30. In Ex. 27, graph the speed v as a function of x.
31. An open-top box is made by cutting equal squares of side x out of the corners of a piece of cardboard 8 in. square and turning up the sides (Fig. 10). Plot the volume V as a function of x. $Ans.\ V = 4x(4 - x)^2;\ 0 \leqq x \leqq 4.$
32. In Ex. 31, find x if $V = 37.5$ cu. in. $Ans.\ x_1 = 1.5;\ x_2 = 1.17$ in.

←x→←8-2x→←x→

Figure 10

33. Draw the graph of letter postage in the United States. What is the independent variable?

In Exs. 34–39, draw the curve.

34. $y = \frac{1}{2}(1 - \text{sgn}\ x)x^2.$
35. $y = x - |x|.$
36. $y = x^2 + \text{sgn}\ (x - 1).$
37. $y = x^2\ \text{sgn}\ (x - 1).$
38. $y = x|x|.$
39. $y = \sqrt{x^4 - 2x^2 + 1}.$

40. It is shown in physics that the attraction of a thin spherical shell of radius a upon a particle at distance b $(b \neq a)$ from the center is

$$A = \frac{k}{b^2}\left(1 - \frac{a - b}{\sqrt{a^2 - 2ab + b^2}} \right).$$

Show that

$$A = \frac{k}{b^2}[1 - \operatorname{sgn}(a - b)],$$

and that

$$A = 0 \quad \text{or} \quad A = \frac{2k}{b^2},$$

according as the particle is inside or outside the shell.

41. Draw the curve (a square) whose equation is $|x| + |y| = 1$.

42. The sides of three squares are $4, c, x$. If the area of the third square equals the difference in area of the other two, graph x as a function of c.

8. *Definition of a Limit*

Let $f(x)$ be a function of x and let a be constant. If there is a number L such that, *in order to make the value of $f(x)$ as close to L as may be desired, it is sufficient to choose x close enough to a, but different from a*, then we say that the limit of $f(x)$, as x approaches a, is L. We write

$$\operatorname*{Lim}_{x \to a} f(x) = L,$$

which is read "the limit of $f(x)$, as x approaches a, is L." The same idea is to be conveyed by writing:

$$\text{As } x \to a, f(x) \to L;$$

read "as x approaches a, $f(x)$ approaches L."

If efficient use is to be made of the definition of a limit, the phrases "as close to L as may be desired" and "close enough to a" must be expressed in mathematical symbols. Therefore we restate the definition as follows: We say that

(1) $$\operatorname*{Lim}_{x \to a} f(x) = L,$$

if for every positive number ϵ (arbitrarily small), there exists a number δ such that, in order to make

(2) $$|f(x) - L| < \varepsilon,$$

it is sufficient that x satisfy

(3) $$|x - a| < \delta, \qquad x \neq a.$$

The above concept of a limit is the mathematical refinement of an intuitive notion which is still of importance in rough everyday use, that the limit L is a number which $f(x)$ approaches as closely as may be desired, as

x creeps up on a. The idea of a moving point, x moving toward a, $f(x)$ moving toward L, is a relic of the Newtonian* calculus.

A graphical interpretation of the definition of a limit is helpful. Consider a sketch of the graph of $y = f(x)$ near $x = a$. In Fig. 11 is shown a representative graph in which $\underset{x \to a}{\text{Lim}} f(x)$ exists; in Fig. 12 is shown a graph in which $\underset{x \to a}{\text{Lim}} f(x)$ does not exist.

In Fig. 11, if it is desired to force $f(x)$ to differ from L by less than a prescribed quantity ϵ, $|f(x) - L| < \epsilon$, then all that is needed is to choose x anywhere within a certain amount δ of the value $x = a$, $0 < |x - a| < \delta$. That is, it is possible near $x = a$ on the curve in Fig. 11 to restrict the y variation to as little as may be desired by sufficiently narrowing the vertical band around $x = a$. For the curve of Fig. 11, $\underset{x \to a}{\text{Lim}} f(x) = L$.

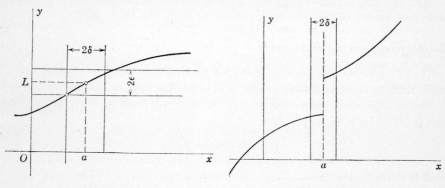

Figure 11   **Figure 12**

Now consider the situation near $x = a$ for the curve shown in Fig. 12. There, no matter how narrow a band be chosen about $x = a$, the y variation can never be made arbitrarily small. For the curve of Fig. 12, $\underset{x \to a}{\text{Lim}} f(x)$ does not exist.

The existence or nonexistence of $f(a)$, the value of $f(x)$ at $x = a$, has nothing whatever to do with the existence or nonexistence of the limit of $f(x)$ as x approaches a.

A major difference between calculus and the subjects which usually precede it in the mathematical curriculum is that calculus uses limiting processes.

Example (a). Show that

$$\underset{x \to 3}{\text{Lim}} (2x + 1) = 7.$$

* Sir Isaac Newton (1642–1727) and Gottfried Wilhelm Leibniz (1646–1716), independently of each other, developed the calculus. Before them, the nearest approach to calculus was a set of isolated, partially developed ideas, scattered throughout the mathematical literature.

Analysis of the Problem. Given an ϵ, we wish to satisfy the inequality

$$|(2x + 1) - 7| < \epsilon$$

by choosing x "sufficiently close" to 3. The inequality yields

$$|2x - 6| < \epsilon,$$

or

$$|x - 3| < \frac{\epsilon}{2}.$$

Proof of the Desired Limit Property. We are now in a position to choose the δ in (3) for this problem.

Let $\delta = \frac{\epsilon}{2}$. Then for all x such that

$$|x - 3| < \frac{\epsilon}{2}, \qquad x \neq 3,$$

it follows that

$$|2x - 6| < \epsilon,$$

from which

$$|(2x + 1) - 7| < \epsilon,$$

so that, by the definition of this section,

$$\operatorname*{Lim}_{x \to 3} (2x + 1) = 7,$$

as was desired.

Example (b). Show that

$$\operatorname*{Lim}_{x \to 2} (x^2 + 1) = 5.$$

Analysis. Since we wish to obtain

$$|x^2 + 1 - 5| < \epsilon,$$

we write it in the form

$$|x^2 - 4| < \epsilon,$$

or

$$|x - 2| \cdot |x + 2| < \epsilon.$$

Recall that one property of the absolute value symbol is that

$$|A + B| \leqq |A| + |B|.$$

Since $x + 2 = x - 2 + 4$, it follows that

$$|x + 2| \leqq |x - 2| + 4.$$

Thus, if we choose

$$|x - 2| < \delta,$$
$$|x + 2| < \delta + 4.$$

Therefore it is desirable to find a δ such that

$$\delta(\delta + 4) = \epsilon.$$

Since δ is required to be positive, we find that

$$\delta = -2 + \sqrt{4 + \epsilon}.$$

Proof of the Desired Limit Property. Choose

$$\delta = \sqrt{4 + \epsilon} - 2;$$

then, for

$$|x - 2| < \sqrt{4 + \epsilon} - 2,$$

it can be seen, because $|x + 2| \leqq |x - 2| + 4$, that

$$|x + 2| < \sqrt{4 + \epsilon} + 2.$$

By multiplication of corresponding members of the above two inequalities, we obtain

$$|x - 2| \cdot |x + 2| < (\sqrt{4 + \epsilon})^2 - (2)^2,$$

or

$$|x^2 - 4| < 4 + \epsilon - 4,$$

so that

$$|x^2 + 1 - 5| < \epsilon,$$

as desired.

Therefore

$$\underset{x \to 2}{\text{Lim}} (x^2 + 1) = 5.$$

The procedure used in Examples (*a*) and (*b*) above quickly grows tedious. Hence we proceed to obtain theorems to remove the necessity of going through all those details in the evaluation of limits.

9. *Theorems on Limits*

We shall need the following theorems on limits. Proofs are omitted, except that a proof of Theorem 1 can be found in the next section.

THEOREM 1. *The limit of the sum of two (or more) functions is equal to the sum of their limits:*

$$\underset{x \to a}{\text{Lim}} \left[u(x) + v(x) \right] = \underset{x \to a}{\text{Lim}} u(x) + \underset{x \to a}{\text{Lim}} v(x).$$

THEOREM 2. *The limit of the product of two (or more) functions is equal to the product of their limits:*

$$\underset{x \to a}{\text{Lim}} \left[u(x)v(x) \right] = \left[\underset{x \to a}{\text{Lim}} u(x) \right] \left[\underset{x \to a}{\text{Lim}} v(x) \right].$$

THEOREM 3. *The limit of the quotient of two functions is equal to the quotient of their limits, provided the limit of the denominator is not zero:*

$$\lim_{x \to a} \frac{u(x)}{v(x)} = \frac{\lim\limits_{x \to a} u(x)}{\lim\limits_{x \to a} v(x)}, \qquad \text{if } \lim_{x \to a} v(x) \neq 0.$$

In these theorems it is assumed that the limits of the two functions exist. However, even though neither function separately approaches a limit, the sum, product, or quotient may do so.

Theorem 3 tells us nothing about what happens to the ratio u/v if $v \to 0$. If u approaches a nonzero limit and $v \to 0$, the ratio u/v can be made to assume values numerically larger than any preassigned quantity. Let us prove that statement.

Let $u \to k \neq 0$ as $x \to a$. Then, by the definition of a limit, we may choose x close enough to a to make u lie between $\frac{1}{2}k$ and $\frac{3}{2}k$. For such values of x, $|u| > \frac{1}{2}|k|$. At the same time, since $v \to 0$, we may choose x close enough to a to make $|v| < \epsilon$, with ϵ as small as desired. Now let x be chosen closer to a than either of the above two choices. Then $|u| > \frac{1}{2}|k|$ and $|v| < \epsilon$ are both true, and it follows that $\left| \dfrac{u}{v} \right| > \dfrac{|k|}{2\epsilon}$, which can be made as large as we wish by choosing ϵ sufficiently small.

If $u \to 0$ and $v \to 0$ as $x \to a$, the limit of the ratio u/v may exist, as it does in Example (*b*) below. We shall find that the entire differential calculus is based upon limits of ratios whose numerators and denominators $\to 0$.

Example (a). Evaluate $\lim\limits_{x \to 3} (x^3 + 4x)$.

By Theorem 1,

$$\lim_{x \to 3} (x^3 + 4x) = \lim_{x \to 3} (x^3) + \lim_{x \to 3} (4x).$$

Then Theorem 2 yields

$$\lim_{x \to 3} (x^3 + 4x) = (\lim_{x \to 3} x)(\lim_{x \to 3} x)(\lim_{x \to 3} x) + (\lim_{x \to 3} 4)(\lim_{x \to 3} x)$$
$$= 3 \cdot 3 \cdot 3 + 4 \cdot 3 = 27 + 12 = 39.$$

Example (b). Evaluate $\lim\limits_{x \to 2} \dfrac{x^3 - 9x + 10}{x^2 - 4}$.

Repeated application of Theorems 1 and 2 shows that

$$\lim_{x \to 2} (x^3 - 9x + 10) = 0 \quad \text{and} \quad \lim_{x \to 2} (x^2 - 4) = 0.$$

Hence Theorem 3 cannot be applied at this stage.

A simple exercise in synthetic division, suggested by the fact that $x = 2$ is a zero of $(x^3 - 9x + 10)$, yields

$$x^3 - 9x + 10 = (x - 2)(x^2 + 2x - 5).$$

Recall that in the definition of a limit as $x \to a$, x is barred from taking on the value a. That is, $x \neq a$. For $x \neq 2$,

$$\frac{x^3 - 9x + 10}{x^2 - 4} = \frac{(x - 2)(x^2 + 2x - 5)}{(x - 2)(x + 2)} = \frac{x^2 + 2x - 5}{x + 2}.$$

Hence

$$\operatorname*{Lim}_{x \to 2} \frac{x^3 - 9x + 10}{x^2 - 4} = \operatorname*{Lim}_{x \to 2} \frac{x^2 + 2x - 5}{x + 2} = \frac{4 + 4 - 5}{2 + 2} = \frac{3}{4}.$$

10. *Proof of a Theorem on Limits*

Let us prove one of the results stated in § 9. Theorem 1 may be restated as follows.

THEOREM 1. *If*

(1)
$$\operatorname*{Lim}_{x \to a} f_1(x) = L_1$$

and

(2)
$$\operatorname*{Lim}_{x \to a} f_2(x) = L_2,$$

then

(3)
$$\operatorname*{Lim}_{x \to a} \left[f_1(x) + f_2(x) \right] = L_1 + L_2.$$

Proof. Because of (1) and the definition of a limit we know that for any $\epsilon_1 > 0$, there exists a δ_1 such that, if x satisfies

$$|x - a| < \delta_1, \qquad x \neq a,$$

then

$$|f_1(x) - L_1| < \epsilon_1.$$

Similarly, because of (2), for any $\epsilon_2 > 0$, there exists a δ_2 such that if x satisfies

$$|x - a| < \delta_2, \qquad x \neq a,$$

then

$$|f_2(x) - L_2| < \epsilon_2.$$

Now suppose we are given an ϵ for which we wish to make

(4)
$$|\{f_1(x) + f_2(x)\} - (L_1 + L_2)| < \epsilon.$$

We can choose $\epsilon_1 = \frac{1}{2}\epsilon$, $\epsilon_2 = \frac{1}{2}\epsilon$, and let δ be smaller than either of δ_1 and δ_2, the δ's which correspond respectively to ϵ_1 and ϵ_2. Then for all x which satisfy

$$|x - a| < \delta, \qquad x \neq a,$$

it is also true that $|x - a| < \delta_1$ and $|x - a| < \delta_2$, and therefore that

(5) $$|f_1(x) - L_1| < \frac{\epsilon}{2}$$

and

(6) $$|f_2(x) - L_2| < \frac{\epsilon}{2},$$

using the specific ϵ_1 and ϵ_2 which we chose.

Since

$$|f_1(x) + f_2(x) - (L_1 + L_2)| \leqq |f_1(x) - L_1| + |f_2(x) - L_2|,$$

it follows, using (5) and (6), that

$$|f_1(x) + f_2(x) - (L_1 + L_2)| < \frac{\epsilon}{2} + \frac{\epsilon}{2}$$

or

$$|f_1(x) + f_2(x) - (L_1 + L_2)| < \epsilon.$$

as desired.

By similar, sometimes more complicated, devices, the other theorems on limits which are quoted in § 9 can be proved.

11. *Right-Hand and Left-Hand Limits*

Once in a while it is convenient to employ a restricted version of limit as described below. We write

(1) $$\lim_{x \to a^+} f(x) = L,$$

and mean by $x \to a^+$ that each x involved is greater than a. A limit such as that in (1) is called a *right-hand* limit; the independent variable x approaches a from the right. A left-hand limit,

(2) $$\lim_{x \to a^-} f(x) = M,$$

with x remaining less than a, is also used.

If the ordinary limit exists, the right-hand and left-hand limits each exist and all three have the same value. If the right- and left-hand limits exist and have the same value, the limit itself exists and has that value.

12. *Limit of $\dfrac{\sin \alpha}{\alpha}$ as α Approaches Zero*

In Example (*b*), page 13, we evaluated the limit of a ratio u/v in which $u \to 0$ and $v \to 0$ by first removing from the numerator and denominator a common factor. To show that the problem is not always quite so simple, and at the same time to establish a result of great intrinsic importance, we obtain the following result.

THEOREM 4. *If α is measured in radians,*

(1)
$$\text{Lim}_{\alpha \to 0} \frac{\sin \alpha}{\alpha} = 1.$$

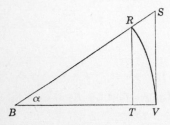

Figure 13

Consider Fig. 13 in which RV is a circular arc with radius r and with center at B. The angles RTB and SVB are right angles. Since the triangle RTB is contained in the sector RVB, and the sector is in turn contained in the larger triangle SVB, it follows that:

Area of $\triangle RTB <$ Area of sector RVB
$< $ Area of $\triangle SVB$.

Since

$$\text{Area of } \triangle RTB = \tfrac{1}{2}\overline{BT} \cdot \overline{RT} = \tfrac{1}{2}r \cos \alpha \cdot r \sin \alpha,$$

$$\text{Area of sector } RVB = \frac{\alpha}{2\pi} (\pi r^2) = \frac{1}{2} \alpha r^2,$$

and

$$\text{Area of } \triangle SVB = \tfrac{1}{2}\overline{BV} \cdot \overline{SV} = \tfrac{1}{2}r \cdot r \tan \alpha,$$

we may conclude that, for $0 < \alpha < \dfrac{\pi}{2}$,

(2)
$$\tfrac{1}{2}r^2 \cos \alpha \sin \alpha < \tfrac{1}{2}\alpha r^2 < \tfrac{1}{2}r^2 \tan \alpha.$$

Let us divide each member of the inequalities (2) by the positive quantity $\tfrac{1}{2}r^2 \sin \alpha$, and thus obtain

$$\cos \alpha < \frac{\alpha}{\sin \alpha} < \frac{1}{\cos \alpha},$$

which can be rewritten, by inverting each member, in the form

$$\frac{1}{\cos \alpha} > \frac{\sin \alpha}{\alpha} > \cos \alpha.$$

As α approaches zero, both $\cos \alpha$ and $\dfrac{1}{\cos \alpha}$ approach unity. Then $\dfrac{\sin \alpha}{\alpha}$, which is hemmed in between them, must also approach unity. That is,

$$\text{Lim}_{\alpha \to 0^+} \frac{\sin \alpha}{\alpha} = 1.$$

That the left-hand limit also has the value unity follows from the fact that

$$\frac{\sin \alpha}{\alpha} = \frac{\sin (-\alpha)}{(-\alpha)}.$$

This completes the proof of (1).

A variety of other important limits may be evaluated by judicious use of (1).

Example (a). Evaluate $\text{Lim}_{\theta\to0} \dfrac{\sin 3\theta}{\theta}$.

Since

$$\frac{\sin 3\theta}{\theta} \equiv 3 \cdot \frac{\sin 3\theta}{3\theta},$$

we take $\alpha = 3\theta$ in (1):

(3) $$\text{Lim}_{\theta\to0} \frac{\sin 3\theta}{\theta} = 3 \text{ Lim}_{\theta\to0} \frac{\sin 3\theta}{3\theta} = 3.$$

Lest anyone should think that (1) justifies us in assigning a value to the nonsense symbol $\dfrac{\sin 0}{0}$, we note that the "value" suggested by (1) would be in conflict with (3); see also Exs. 30, 33 below.

Example (b). Evaluate $\text{Lim}_{\alpha\to0} \dfrac{\tan \alpha}{\alpha}$.

We proceed as follows:

$$\text{Lim}_{\alpha\to0} \frac{\tan \alpha}{\alpha} = \text{Lim}_{\alpha\to0} \frac{\sin \alpha}{\alpha \cos \alpha} = \left(\text{Lim}_{\alpha\to0} \frac{\sin \alpha}{\alpha}\right)\left(\text{Lim}_{\alpha\to0} \frac{1}{\cos \alpha}\right) = 1 \cdot 1 = 1.$$

EXERCISES

Evaluate the limits in Exs. 1–28.

1. $\text{Lim}_{x\to4} (x^2 + 3x - 5)$.   *Ans.* 23.

2. $\text{Lim}_{x\to-1} (2x^2 + x + 4)$.   *Ans.* 5.

3. $\text{Lim}_{y\to3} (y^3 - 2y + 7)$.

4. $\text{Lim}_{y\to-2} (y^3 + 5y - 1)$.

5. $\text{Lim}_{t\to0} \dfrac{2t^2 + 1}{t^3 + 3t - 4}$.   *Ans.* $-\frac{1}{4}$.

6. $\text{Lim}_{t\to1} \dfrac{(t + 1)^2}{2(t^2 + 3)}$.   *Ans.* $\frac{1}{2}$.

7. $\text{Lim}_{w\to2} \dfrac{3w^2 - 4w + 2}{w^3 - 5}$.

8. $\text{Lim}_{w\to-1} \dfrac{3w^3 - 2w + 7}{w^2 + 1}$.

9. $\text{Lim}_{\theta\to\frac{1}{2}\pi} \dfrac{\sin^2 \theta}{\tan^3 \theta}$.   *Ans.* $\frac{1}{2}$.

10. $\text{Lim}_{\theta\to\frac{\pi}{6}} \dfrac{\sin 2\theta}{\sin \theta \tan \theta}$.   *Ans.* 3.

11. $\text{Lim}_{x\to1} \dfrac{x^2 - 1}{x^2 + 3x - 4}$.   *Ans.* $\frac{2}{5}$.

12. $\text{Lim}_{x\to3} \dfrac{x^2 + x - 12}{2x^2 - 7x + 3}$.   *Ans.* $\frac{7}{5}$.

13. $\text{Lim}_{x\to-1} \dfrac{2x^2 - x - 3}{3x^2 + 5x + 2}$.

14. $\text{Lim}_{x\to4} \dfrac{2x^2 - 7x - 4}{x^2 - x - 12}$.

15. $\text{Lim}_{y\to2} \dfrac{y^3 - y^2 - y - 2}{2y^3 - 5y^2 + 5y - 6}$.   *Ans.* $\frac{7}{9}$.

16. $\text{Lim}_{y\to3} \dfrac{y^3 - 13y + 12}{y^3 - 14y + 15}$.   *Ans.* $\frac{14}{13}$.

17. $\text{Lim}_{\beta\to3} \dfrac{\beta^3 + \beta^2 - 8\beta - 12}{\beta^3 - 4\beta^2 - 3\beta + 18}$.   *Ans.* No limit.

18. $\text{Lim}_{\beta\to3} \dfrac{\beta^3 - 7\beta - 6}{2\beta^3 - 11\beta^2 + 12\beta + 9}$.   *Ans.* No limit.

19. $\text{Lim}_{x \to \frac{1}{2}} \dfrac{4x^3 - 3x + 1}{12x^3 - 8x^2 - x + 1}.$ *Ans.* $\frac{3}{5}$.

20. $\text{Lim}_{\alpha \to 2} \dfrac{2\alpha^3 - 5\alpha^2 - 4\alpha + 12}{\alpha^3 - 12\alpha + 16}.$ *Ans.* $\frac{7}{6}$.

21. $\text{Lim}_{x \to -2} \dfrac{x^4 + 5x + 6}{x^4 + 5x - 6}.$ **22.** $\text{Lim}_{x \to 1} \dfrac{2x^4 - 2x^3 - x^2 + 1}{x^4 - x^2 - 2x + 2}.$

23. $\text{Lim}_{\theta \to 0} \dfrac{\tan \theta}{\sin 2\theta}.$ *Ans.* $\frac{1}{2}$.   **24.** $\text{Lim}_{\theta \to \frac{1}{2}\pi} \dfrac{\cos 2\theta}{\tan \theta}.$ *Ans.* 0.

25. $\text{Lim}_{y \to 0} \dfrac{1 - \cos y}{\sin^2 y}.$ **26.** $\text{Lim}_{y \to \pi} \dfrac{\sin^2 y}{1 + \cos y}.$

27. $\text{Lim}_{\alpha \to 0} \dfrac{\sin \alpha \sin 2\alpha}{1 - \cos \alpha}.$ *Ans.* 4.   **28.** $\text{Lim}_{\alpha \to 0} \dfrac{\sin^3 \alpha}{\sin \alpha - \tan \alpha}.$ *Ans.* -2.

Use Theorem 4, page 16, to evaluate the limits in Exs. 29–38.

29. $\text{Lim}_{\alpha \to 0} \dfrac{\sin \alpha^2}{\alpha^2}.$ *Ans.* 1.   **30.** $\text{Lim}_{\alpha \to 0} \dfrac{\sin \alpha^2}{\alpha}.$ *Ans.* 0.

31. $\text{Lim}_{\theta \to 0} \dfrac{\theta^2}{\sin \theta}.$ *Ans.* 0.   **32.** $\text{Lim}_{\theta \to 0} \dfrac{\theta}{\sin^2 \theta}.$ *Ans.* No limit.

33. $\text{Lim}_{x \to 0} \dfrac{\sin kx}{x}.$ *Ans.* k.   **34.** $\text{Lim}_{x \to 0} x \csc 3x.$ *Ans.* $\frac{1}{3}$.

35. $\text{Lim}_{x \to 0} \dfrac{\sin ax}{\tan bx}.$ *Ans.* $\dfrac{a}{b}$.   **36.** $\text{Lim}_{x \to 0} \dfrac{1 - \cos 4x}{1 - \cos 2x}.$ *Ans.* 4.

37. $\text{Lim}_{y \to \frac{1}{2}\pi} \dfrac{2y - \pi}{\cos y}.$ *Ans.* -2.   **38.** $\text{Lim}_{y \to \frac{1}{2}\pi} \dfrac{(y - \frac{1}{2}\pi)^2}{1 - \sin y}.$ *Ans.* 2.

39. Let $\alpha°$ denote the measure in degrees of an angle whose radian measure is α. Use the fact that $\sin \alpha° = \sin \alpha$, and that $\alpha° = \dfrac{180°}{\pi} \alpha$, together with Theorem 4, page 16, to show that

$$\text{Lim}_{\alpha° \to 0} \frac{\sin \alpha°}{\alpha°} = \frac{\pi}{180°}.$$

40. Show that, if $P(x)$ is a polynomial in x,

$$\text{Lim}_{x \to a} P(x) = P(a).$$

41. Show that, if $P_1(x)$ and $P_2(x)$ are polynomials,

$$\text{Lim}_{x \to a} \frac{P_1(x)}{P_2(x)} = \frac{P_1(a)}{P_2(a)}, \qquad P_2(a) \neq 0.$$

42. Under what circumstances may the limit in Ex. 41 exist when $P_2(a) = 0$? Give examples.

43. Show, by means of an example, that the limit in Ex. 41 does not always exist when $P_1(a) = P_2(a) = 0$.

44. Prove that

$$\lim_{x \to a} \sqrt{u} = \sqrt{\lim_{x \to a} u}, \qquad u > 0.$$

(Put $u = v^2$ and apply Theorem 2, page 12.)

45. Prove that, if p and q are integers,

$$\lim_{x \to a} (u^{\frac{p}{q}}) = (\lim_{x \to a} u)^{\frac{p}{q}}, \qquad u > 0.$$

Evaluate the limits in Exs. 46–51.

46. $\displaystyle\lim_{x \to 2^+} \frac{\sqrt{x - 2}}{\sqrt{x^2 - 4}}.$ *Ans.* $\frac{1}{2}$.   **47.** $\displaystyle\lim_{x \to 3^+} \frac{x - 3}{\sqrt{x^2 - 9}}.$ *Ans.* 0.

48. $\displaystyle\lim_{x \to 1} \frac{(1 - x^2)^{\frac{1}{3}}}{(1 - x^3)^{\frac{1}{3}}}.$ *Ans.* $(\frac{2}{3})^{\frac{1}{3}}$.   **49.** $\displaystyle\lim_{x \to 1^-} \frac{\sqrt{1 - x^3}}{\sqrt{1 - x^2}}.$ *Ans.* $\frac{1}{2}\sqrt{6}$.

50. $\displaystyle\lim_{x \to 2^+} \frac{(x^4 - 4x^3 + 5x^2 - 4x + 4)^{\frac{1}{4}}}{(x^2 - 3x + 2)^{\frac{1}{2}}}.$ *Ans.* $5^{\frac{1}{4}}$.

51. $\displaystyle\lim_{x \to 1^+} \frac{(x^2 + 4x - 5)^{\frac{1}{2}}}{(x^2 - 4x + 3)^{\frac{1}{3}}}.$ *Ans.* 0.

CONTINUITY

13. Definitions

A function $f(x)$ is said to be *continuous* at $x = a$ if all three of the following conditions are satisfied:

$$(1) \qquad\qquad f(a) \text{ exists};$$
$$(2) \qquad\qquad \underset{x \to a}{\text{Lim}} f(x) \text{ exists};$$
$$(3) \qquad\qquad \underset{x \to a}{\text{Lim}} f(x) = f(a).$$

Example (a). At $x = 2$, $f(x) = x^2 + 1$ is continuous because

$$\underset{x \to 2}{\text{Lim}} (x^2 + 1) = 5, \qquad f(2) = 2^2 + 1 = 5.$$

Indeed, by Ex. 40, page 18, every polynomial in x is continuous for every finite x.

If any one, or more, of conditions (1), (2), (3) is not satisfied, the function $f(x)$ is said to be *discontinuous* at $x = a$ or to have a *discontinuity* at $x = a$.

When $f(a)$ exists and

$$(4) \qquad\qquad \underset{x \to a^+}{\text{Lim}} f(x) = f(a)$$

the function $f(x)$ is said to have *right-hand continuity* at $x = a$. If $f(a)$ exists and

$$(5) \qquad\qquad \underset{x \to a^-}{\text{Lim}} f(x) = f(a)$$

$f(x)$ is said to have *left-hand continuity* at $x = a$.

Example (b). Examine $f(x) = \sqrt{x}$ at $x = 0$.

Here $f(0) = 0$. But $f(x)$ is not defined (we deal in real values only) for $x < 0$, so $\underset{x \to 0}{\text{Lim}} f(x)$ does not exist. However,

$$\underset{x \to 0^+}{\text{Lim}} \sqrt{x} = 0.$$

Hence, since $f(0)$ is also zero, $f(x) = \sqrt{x}$ has right-hand continuity at $x = 0$.

Continuity implies both right-hand and left-hand continuity. Since we are concerned with only single-valued functions, the existence of both right-hand and left-hand continuity at a point implies ordinary continuity at that point.

The following theorem is easily proved with the aid of Theorems 1, 2, 3, pages 12-13.

THEOREM 5. *If $u(x)$ and $v(x)$ are both continuous at $x = a$, it follows that $u(x) \cdot v(x)$ and $u(x) + v(x)$ are continuous at $x = a$, and that if $v(a) \neq 0$,*

$$\frac{u(x)}{v(x)}$$

is continuous at $x = a$.

14. *Missing-Point Discontinuities*

Consider a function $f(x)$ which is not defined when $x = a$, but such that $\lim\limits_{x \to a} f(x)$ exists,

(1) $$\lim_{x \to a} f(x) = L.$$

The function is discontinuous at $x = a$ because condition (1), § 13, is not satisfied. Graphically the curve appears, to the eye, to be continuous, but the single point $x = a$ is missing.

It is always possible to repair such missing-point discontinuities by replacing the original function $f(x)$ with another function $\varphi(x)$, defined as follows:

(2) $$\begin{cases} \varphi(x) = f(x), & x \neq a; \\ \varphi(x) = L, & x = a. \end{cases}$$

The function $\varphi(x)$ is the same as $f(x)$ wherever $f(x)$ was defined, but $\varphi(x)$ is continuous at $x = a$.

Example. The function

(3) $$f(x) = \frac{x^3 - 9x + 10}{x - 2}$$

is undefined when $x = 2$ because both numerator and denominator vanish at $x = 2$. But

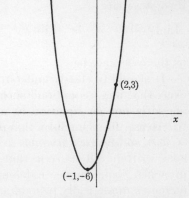

$$\lim_{x \to 2} \frac{x^3 - 9x + 10}{x - 2}$$
$$= \lim_{x \to 2} \frac{(x - 2)(x^2 + 2x - 5)}{x - 2}$$
$$= \lim_{x \to 2} (x^2 + 2x - 5) = 3.$$

Since

$$\frac{x^3 - 9x + 10}{x - 2} = x^2 + 2x - 5, \qquad x \neq 2,$$

Figure 14

the graph of $f(x)$ is the parabola $y = x^2 + 2x - 5$, except for an invisible break at $x = 2$.

15. *Finite Jumps*

It may happen that, at $x = a$, the function has both a left-hand and a right-hand limit, but the two are not equal:

$$\operatorname*{Lim}_{x \to a^-} f(x) = L_1, \quad \operatorname*{Lim}_{x \to a^+} f(x) = L_2, \quad L_1 \neq L_2.$$

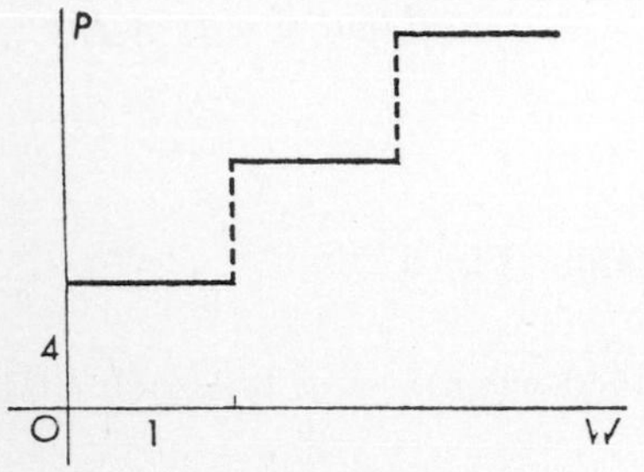

At such a point the function has a *finite jump*: the curve takes a vertical jump of width $L_2 - L_1$.

Figure 15

Example. The first-class postage P (in cents) is defined in terms of the weight W (in ounces) as follows:

$$P = 0, \qquad W = 0;$$
$$P = 4, \qquad 0 < W \leqq 1;$$
$$P = 8, \qquad 1 < W \leqq 2; \text{ etc.}$$

The function has finite discontinuities at $W = 0, 1, 2$, etc.*

16. *Infinite Discontinuities*

A frequently occurring type of discontinuity is that in which the function *increases numerically without bound* as x approaches a: we say that the function has an *infinite discontinuity* at $x = a$. Graphically this means that the curve approaches the line $x = a$, usually without ever reaching it, at the same time receding from the x-axis. It may happen that $f(x)$ becomes large and positive, or large and negative, on both sides of the line $x = a$ (Fig. 16); if so, we write

$$\operatorname*{Lim}_{x \to a} f(x) = \infty \quad \text{or} \quad \operatorname*{Lim}_{x \to a} f(x) = -\infty,$$

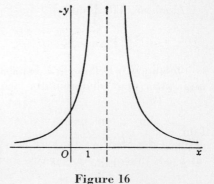

Figure 16

as the case may be.

It should be clearly understood, however, that any "equation" such as those above is not an equation at all, in the true sense, for the reason that *the symbol ∞ does not represent a number.* The symbols written tell us, not that $f(x)$ approaches some vague, indefinite, very large limiting value, but that it increases numerically beyond any limit whatever.

* Many familiar functions have a great number of relatively small finite discontinuities—e.g., the cost of a quantity of gasoline at 36 cents per gallon, jumping by 1 cent at intervals of $\frac{1}{36}$ gallon; price of a stock on the New York Exchange, changing by eighths at irregular time-intervals; etc. For most purposes such a function may be replaced by a function varying continuously.

Example (*a*). As x approaches 1, the function (Fig. 16)

$$y = \frac{1}{(x-1)^2}$$

increases without limit; i.e.,

$$\lim_{x \to 1} \frac{1}{(x-1)^2} = \infty.$$

Example (*b*). As x approaches 2, the function (Fig. 17)

$$y = \frac{x^2}{x-2}$$

becomes indefinitely large, positive if $x > 2$, negative if $x < 2$:

$$\lim_{x \to 2^+} \frac{x^2}{x-2} = \infty, \qquad \lim_{x \to 2^-} \frac{x^2}{x-2} = -\infty.$$

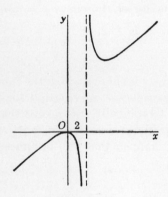

Figure 17

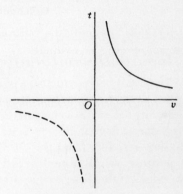

Figure 18

Example (*c*). The time required to travel 100 miles at a constant speed v is (Fig. 18)

$$t = \frac{100}{v}; \quad \lim_{v \to 0^+} \frac{100}{v} = \infty.$$

This states the fact that by moving slowly enough we could, theoretically at least, take any conceivable amount of time to cover the distance.*

17. *Function with Argument Approaching Infinity*

We frequently have to investigate the behavior of a function as the independent variable increases, or decreases, without bound.

If there is a constant c, such that $|f(x) - c|$ can be made as small as desired by choosing x sufficiently large, we write

* A glacier would require many centuries to travel 100 miles.

$$\text{Lim}_{x \to \infty} f(x) = c.$$

Graphically this means that the curve $y = f(x)$ approaches the line $y = c$, as $x \to \infty$.

In a similar manner, if there is a constant k, such that $|f(x) - k|$ can be made arbitrarily small by choosing x negative and of sufficiently great magnitude, we say that

$$\text{Lim}_{x \to -\infty} f(x) = k.$$

As x increases without bound, it may happen that $f(x)$ does likewise. If both are positive, we write

$$\text{Lim}_{x \to \infty} f(x) = \infty,$$

with appropriate changes in notation when either or both are negative.

Finally, it may be that $f(x)$ approaches no limit, finite or infinite, as $x \to \infty$, or as $x \to -\infty$. Consider the behavior of the curve $y = \tan x$, as $x \to \infty$ or as $x \to -\infty$.

Example (*a*). To evaluate

$$\text{Lim}_{x \to \infty} \frac{x^2 - 1}{x^2 + 1},$$

divide numerator and denominator by x^2:

$$\text{Lim}_{x \to \infty} \frac{x^2 - 1}{x^2 + 1} = \text{Lim}_{x \to \infty} \frac{1 - \dfrac{1}{x^2}}{1 + \dfrac{1}{x^2}} = 1.$$

The graph of the function is shown in Fig. 19.

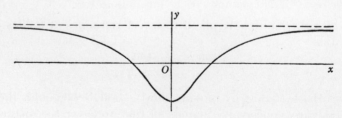

Figure 19

Example (*b*).

$$\text{Lim}_{x \to \infty} \frac{x^2}{x - 2} = \text{Lim}_{x \to \infty} \frac{x}{1 - \dfrac{2}{x}} = \infty,$$

$$\text{Lim}_{x \to -\infty} \frac{x^2}{x - 2} = -\infty.$$

Thus in this case no limit is approached as x increases without bound in either direction. (Fig. 17.)

Example (*c*). In Example (*c*), § 16,

$$t = \frac{100}{v}; \quad \lim_{v \to \infty} \frac{100}{v} = 0.$$

This merely says that if the speed could be made great enough, we could cover the distance in any desired time, no matter how short.* (Fig. 18.)

18. Rational Algebraic Functions

With regard to rational algebraic functions, the question of continuity is completely covered by the following theorems.

THEOREM 6. *A polynomial is continuous for all values of x.*

THEOREM 7. *A rational algebraic fraction is continuous except for those values of x for which the denominator vanishes.*

These theorems are immediate consequences of Exs. 40–41, page 18. Under Theorem 7, at a point where the denominator vanishes, only two kinds of discontinuity are possible: a missing-point discontinuity (§ 14), or an infinite discontinuity (§ 16).

In the above, it is understood that x is free to assume any real value. In applications where, owing to the nature of the problem, the variable is restricted in range, an entirely different situation may arise. This matter will be discussed in § 44.

EXERCISES

Find the points of discontinuity of the functions in Exs. 1–25.

1. $\dfrac{x^2 + 3}{x^2 - 16}$. *Ans.* $x = \pm 4$. **2.** $\dfrac{3x + 2}{x^2 - 6x + 9}$. *Ans.* $x = 3$.

3. $\dfrac{x - 2}{x^2 + 9}$. **4.** $\dfrac{x + 3}{4x^2 - x + 2}$.

5. $\dfrac{x^2 - 3x}{x^3 + 2x^2 + 5x}$. *Ans.* $x = 0$. **6.** $\dfrac{3(x + 2)^2}{x^3 + 4x^2 + x - 6}$.

7. $\dfrac{4}{x^3 - 4x^2 - 3x + 18}$. **8.** $\dfrac{x^3 + 2x - 1}{4x^4 + 4x^3 + 3x^2 - x - 1}$.

9. $\cos \theta$. *Ans.* None. **10.** $\sin \theta$.

11. $\csc \theta$. *Ans.* $\theta = n\pi$, n any integer.

12. $\sec \theta$. **13.** $(1 + x)^{\frac{1}{3}}$. **14.** $(1 + x)^{-\frac{1}{3}}$.

15. $(1 - x)^{-\frac{1}{2}}$. **16.** $\sqrt{x^2 - a^2}$.

* Light travels 100 miles in a very small fraction of a second.

17. $\sqrt{1 + \sqrt{x}}$.

18. $\dfrac{\sqrt{a + x}}{x^2 - a^2}$.

19. $\sqrt{x^2 - 2ax + a^2}$. *Ans.* None.

20. $\dfrac{\sqrt{2ax - x^2}}{a^2 - x^2}$.

21. The cost of sending a telegram, as a function of the number of words.
Ans. Everywhere discontinuous.

22. The weight of a U.S. coin, as a function of the value.

23. $y = x - |x|$.　　*Ans.* None.　　**24.** $y = \operatorname{sgn} x$.　　*Ans.* $x = 0$.

25. $y = -(1 + \operatorname{sgn} x) \sin x$.　　　　　　　　　*Ans.* None.

26. If $f(x)$ is continuous, is its square continuous? Is its reciprocal?

27. Show that as x approaches zero, the function $\sin \dfrac{\pi}{x}$ oscillates between -1 and 1, without approaching any limit.

28. Discuss the behavior of $\tan \dfrac{\pi}{x}$ near the origin.

29. Show that the function $y = x \sin \dfrac{1}{x}$ is discontinuous at the origin. What type of discontinuity is present?

30. Show that the function $y = x \tan \dfrac{1}{x}$ is discontinuous at the origin.

Evaluate the limits in Exs. 31–52.

31. $\underset{x \to \infty}{\operatorname{Lim}} \dfrac{4}{2x^2 - 3}$.

32. $\underset{x \to \infty}{\operatorname{Lim}} \dfrac{2x^2}{3x^2 + 5}$.

33. $\underset{x \to -\infty}{\operatorname{Lim}} \dfrac{x^2}{3x^2 - 4x + 1}$.　　*Ans.* $\frac{1}{3}$.

34. $\underset{x \to -\infty}{\operatorname{Lim}} \dfrac{2x^3}{7x^3 - 4x}$.　　*Ans.* $\frac{2}{7}$.

35. $\underset{x \to \infty}{\operatorname{Lim}} \dfrac{x^4}{(2x - 1)^3}$.　　　　　*Ans.* No limit ($\infty$).

36. $\underset{x \to -\infty}{\operatorname{Lim}} \dfrac{(x - 4)^3}{(3x + 1)^2}$.　　　　*Ans.* No limit ($-\infty$).

37. $\underset{x \to \infty}{\operatorname{Lim}} \dfrac{(x + 2)^3}{(x^2 - 4)^2}$.

38. $\underset{x \to -\infty}{\operatorname{Lim}} \dfrac{(x + 3)(x^2 - 7x + 1)}{4x^3 + 2x + 1}$.

39. $\underset{x \to \infty}{\operatorname{Lim}} 2^{\frac{1}{x}}$.　　*Ans.* 1.

40. $\underset{x \to -\infty}{\operatorname{Lim}} 2^{\frac{1}{x}}$.　　*Ans.* 1.

41. $\underset{x \to 0^+}{\operatorname{Lim}} 2^{\frac{1}{x}}$.　　*Ans.* No limit ($\infty$).

42. $\underset{x \to 0^-}{\operatorname{Lim}} 2^{\frac{1}{x}}$.　　*Ans.* 0.

43. $\underset{x \to \infty}{\operatorname{Lim}} \dfrac{1}{1 + 2^{\frac{1}{x}}}$.　　*Ans.* $\frac{1}{2}$.

44. $\underset{x \to -\infty}{\operatorname{Lim}} \dfrac{1}{1 + 2^{\frac{1}{x}}}$.　　*Ans.* $\frac{1}{2}$.

45. $\underset{x \to 0^+}{\operatorname{Lim}} \dfrac{1}{1 + 2^{\frac{1}{x}}}$.　　*Ans.* 0.

46. $\underset{x \to 0^-}{\operatorname{Lim}} \dfrac{1}{1 + 2^{\frac{1}{x}}}$.　　*Ans.* 1.

47. $\text{Lim}_{x \to \infty} \dfrac{2}{5 + 3^{\frac{1}{x}}}$.

48. $\text{Lim}_{x \to -\infty} \dfrac{3}{3 + 2^{\frac{1}{x}}}$.

49. $\text{Lim}_{x \to \infty} \sin x$.   *Ans.* No limit.

50. $\text{Lim}_{x \to \infty} \tan x$.   *Ans.* No limit.

51. $\text{Lim}_{x \to \infty} \dfrac{\sin x}{x}$.   *Ans.* 0.

52. $\text{Lim}_{x \to \infty} \dfrac{\tan x}{x}$.   *Ans.* No limit.

53. Sketch the curve $y = 2^{\frac{1}{x}}$. See Exs. 39–42.

54. Sketch the curve $y = \dfrac{1}{1 + 2^{\frac{1}{x}}}$. See Exs. 43–46.

55. In Ex. 40, page 9, graph A as a function of a with b held fixed.

56. Sketch the curve $y = \dfrac{2}{5 + 3^{\frac{1}{x}}}$.

19. *The Intermediate Value Theorem*

The function $f(x)$ is said to be continuous over the closed interval $a \leqq x \leqq b$ if $f(x)$ is continuous at every interior point $a < x < b$ and $f(x)$ has right-hand continuity at $x = a$ and left-hand continuity at $x = b$.

LEMMA 1. *If $f(x)$ is continuous over the closed interval $a \leqq x \leqq b$, if $f(a) < 0$ and $f(b) > 0$, there exists a number c in the open interval $a < c < b$ for which $f(c) = 0$.*

In Lemma 1 the signs of $f(a)$ and $f(b)$ may be reversed, as may be seen by applying the lemma to the negative of $f(x)$.

Proof of Lemma 1 belongs, in the author's opinion, in a more advanced course. Here we shall attempt in two ways to make the truth of the result plausible. Examine a representative graph such as that in Fig. 20. As x

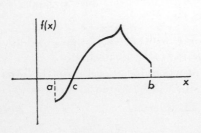

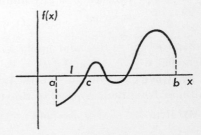

Figure 20   Figure 21

varies from a to b, the value of $f(x)$, starting with a negative value and proceeding without jumping (continuity) to a positive value, must somewhere take on the value zero for an x between a and b.

Consider next the following argument. Since $f(x)$ is continuous and is negative at $x = a$, there must exist an interval I of nonzero length, with a for its left endpoint, such that $f(x)$ is negative over that entire interval. But $f(b)$ is positive, so the interval I cannot occupy all the original interval $a \leqq x \leqq b$. Hence there is a point c (Fig. 21) such that for some $\epsilon > 0$

(1) $$f(x) < 0 \quad \text{for } x \text{ in the range } c - \epsilon < x < c$$

and

(2) $$f(x) > 0 \quad \text{for } x \text{ in the range } c < x < c + \epsilon.$$

That is, $f(x)$ is negative for all x near enough to c and to the left of c. Also $f(x)$ is positive for all x near enough to c and to the right of c.

Now $f(c)$ exists (continuity). But $f(c)$ cannot be positive because of (1), and $f(c)$ cannot be negative because of (2). Hence $f(c) = 0$ and c lies between a and b, $a < c < b$.

From Lemma 1 the intermediate value theorem follows at once.

THEOREM 8. *If the single-valued function $f(x)$ is continuous over the closed interval $a \leqq x \leqq b$, then in that interval $f(x)$ takes on every value between $f(a)$ and $f(b)$.*

If $f(a) = f(b)$, there is nothing to prove.
If $f(a) < f(b)$, let λ be any number between them,

$$f(a) < \lambda < f(b).$$

We need to show that there is a number c in $a < c < b$ such that $f(c) = \lambda$. Put $\varphi(x) = f(x) - \lambda$. Then $\varphi(x)$ is continuous over $a \leqq x \leqq b$. Also $\varphi(a) < 0$ and $\varphi(b) > 0$. Then Lemma 1 may be applied to $\varphi(x)$, thus yielding a number c such that $a < c < b$ and $\varphi(c) = 0$. But $\varphi(c) = 0$ means $f(c) = \lambda$, as desired.

If $f(a) > f(b)$, let μ be any number between them,

$$f(b) < \mu < f(a).$$

Use $\psi(x) = \mu - f(x)$ and apply Lemma 1 to $\psi(x)$ to obtain a number c such that $a < c < b$ and $\psi(c) = 0$. Thus $f(c) = \mu$, as desired.

Another important result, the proof of which is beyond us in this course, will now be stated. A proof of this theorem will be found in more advanced books.

THEOREM 9. *If $f(x)$ is continuous over the closed interval $a \leqq x \leqq b$, $f(x)$ takes on a greatest value and a least value in the closed interval.*

The theorem states that there is at least one point x_1 in $a \leqq x_1 \leqq b$ such that

$$f(x_1) \geqq f(x)$$

for all x in $a \leqq x \leqq b$. There may be many such points, each with the same maximum value for $f(x)$. The situation with regard to least (minimum) values is similar.

In Theorem 9 the interval must be a closed one for the conclusion to follow from the hypothesis. For example, $f(x) = 1/x$ has no greatest value in the open interval $0 < x < 1$, although $f(x)$ is continuous over that interval. The discontinuity at $x = 0$ causes the trouble. Of course a function may be discontinuous and still take on a greatest and a least value. Theorem 9 states that a function continuous over a closed interval must take on a greatest and a least value in that interval. If a function is discontinuous, it is on its own; the theorem simply yields no conclusion for that function.

The student should draw graphs illustrating the theorem and graphs showing some pertinent types of behavior for functions which fail to satisfy the hypothesis of the theorem.

The lemma and theorems stated in this section may well be considered obvious* by the student. We shall not argue that point. What we do state is that the theorems are true. That the obvious is not always true is commonplace in mathematics. Demonstration of such a statement is a bit elusive because what is obvious to one person may not be obvious to another.

A widely used example will now be exhibited. Many people consider the truth of the following statement to be obvious: "If arcs of two continuous curves approach each other in position, they do so in length."† Let us be more precise.

In an xy-plane the line segment along the x-axis from the origin to the point $(2, 0)$ has the length 2. Consider a sequence of curves

$$(3) \qquad\qquad y = f_n(x),$$

one for each positive integer n, with the following properties:

    (a) For each n, the curve (3) passes through the points $(0, 0)$ and $(2, 0)$;
    (b) For each n, the curve (3) is continuous over the closed interval $0 \leqq x \leqq 2$;
    (c) As $n \to \infty$, $f_n(x) \to 0$ for each x in $0 \leqq x \leqq 2$.

Our contention is that it is obvious, but not true, that the length of the curve (3) from $(0, 0)$ to $(2, 0)$ approaches 2 as $n \to \infty$.

Let the curves (3) be defined as follows. For $n = 1$, the curve is to be a semicircle (radius unity) with the segment from $(0, 0)$ to $(2, 0)$ as diameter. The length of the arc is π.

---

* The word "obvious" is a dangerous one. It is often said, not always facetiously, that when a mathematician says something is obvious, he means one of two things: either the statement isn't true or he can't prove it.

† The sad fact is that a continuous curve need not have a length in the sense in which length of an arc is defined in calculus. Unfortunately, continuous curves for which arc length does not exist are not elementary, so no such examples are given here.

For $n = 2$, the curve (3) is to consist of two semicircles, one with the segment from $(0, 0)$ to $(1, 0)$ as diameter, the other having the segment from $(1, 0)$ to $(2, 0)$ as diameter. Each semicircle has radius $\frac{1}{2}$ and length $\frac{1}{2}\pi$. The total length of arc from $(0, 0)$ to $(2, 0)$ is π.

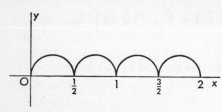

Figure 22

For general n, the curve (3) is to consist of n semicircles, each of radius $1/n$, side by side from $(0, 0)$ to $(2, 0)$. The total length of arc is $n(\pi/n) = \pi$. Figure 22 shows the curve for $n = 4$.

The curves (3), as described above, satisfy conditions (*a*) and (*b*) for each n. Since, for any n, the maximum value of $f_n(x)$ is $1/n$, it follows that (*c*) is also satisfied. But the length of arc is always π, so the length of arc does not approach 2 as $n \to \infty$.

THE DERIVATIVE. SLOPE.

RATE OF CHANGE

20. *The Derivative*

Given a continuous function

$$(1) \qquad y = f(x),$$

let us choose some fixed value of x, the corresponding value of y being given by (1). Now consider another value of x, differing from the first one by an amount (positive or negative) which we will call the *increment* of x, and will denote by the symbol Δx. For this value of x, y will have a new value, differing from the original by an amount Δy. In other words, *when x changes to the value $x + \Delta x$, y changes to the value $y + \Delta y$*, and we have

$$
\begin{aligned}
y + \Delta y &= f(x + \Delta x), \\
(2) \qquad \Delta y &= f(x + \Delta x) - f(x).
\end{aligned}
$$

Now let us form the ratio $\dfrac{\Delta y}{\Delta x}$, and investigate the behavior of this ratio when Δx approaches zero. Since $f(x)$ is continuous, the Δy of equation (2) also approaches zero. We have found that when both numerator and denominator of a fraction approach zero, the fraction itself may, or may not, approach a limit. In Fig. 23, let the curve AB represent the graph of the given function. The ratio $\dfrac{\Delta y}{\Delta x}$ is the slope of the line joining the points $P:(x,\,y)$ and $P':(x + \Delta x,\,y + \Delta y)$. As Δx approaches zero, P' approaches P along the curve, and in all ordinary cases the line PP' approaches a certain straight line (PT in the figure) as a limiting position. That is, for a sufficiently well-

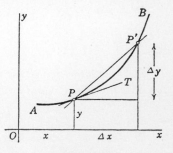

Figure 23

behaved curve, the ratio $\dfrac{\Delta y}{\Delta x}$ *approaches a limit*, the slope of the line PT. This limit is called the *derivative* of y with respect to x.

FUNDAMENTAL DEFINITION. *The* **derivative** *of y with respect to x is the limit of the ratio* $\dfrac{\Delta y}{\Delta x}$ *when* Δx *approaches zero.*

The derivative is designated by the symbol $\dfrac{dy}{dx}$:

$$\frac{dy}{dx} = \operatorname*{Lim}_{\Delta x \to 0} \frac{\Delta y}{\Delta x} = \operatorname*{Lim}_{\Delta x \to 0} \frac{f(x + \Delta x) - f(x)}{\Delta x}.$$

Other symbols for the derivative are y', $f'(x)$, $D_x y$, $\dfrac{d}{dx} f(x)$. But since the symbol y' does not explicitly indicate the independent variable, this notation should be used only when no confusion or ambiguity can arise.

Functions can be found which, though continuous, do not possess a derivative for any value of x. Such functions are unlikely to occur in elementary applications. Their importance is theoretical rather than practical.

The operation of finding the derivative is called **differentiation.** *Only differentiable functions* (those having a derivative) *are studied in this book.* When the derivative fails to exist for particular values of x, those values are either excluded or specially investigated. (See § 44.)

We have now listed three fundamental requirements of the calculus. Each function to be studied must, for some range of values of the independent variable, be *continuous, one-valued,* and *differentiable.*

21. *Determination of the Derivative*

Our first problem is to prove, for the elementary functions, the existence of the derivative—i.e., to prove that when Δx approaches zero, $\dfrac{\Delta y}{\Delta x}$ approaches a definite limit—and at the same time to derive formulas for the derivative in terms of x, for the various functions.

To obtain the derivative of any function, the general process is as follows:

1. *Replace x by* $x + \Delta x$, *and y by* $y + \Delta y$:

(1) $$y = f(x),$$
(2) $$y + \Delta y = f(x + \Delta x).$$

2. *By subtraction, eliminate y between* (1) *and* (2), *thus obtaining a formula for* Δy *in terms of x and* Δx:

(3) $$\Delta y = f(x + \Delta x) - f(x).$$

3. *By some suitable transformation, throw the right member of* (3) *into a form which contains* Δx *explicitly as a factor.*

4. *Divide through by* Δx:

$$\frac{\Delta y}{\Delta x} = \frac{f(x + \Delta x) - f(x)}{\Delta x}.$$

5. *Determine the limit as* Δx *approaches zero.*

The transformation required in step 3 varies with different classes of functions and must be discovered by trial. For the transcendental functions, evaluation of the limit in the final step is not always a simple problem. We shall see how to overcome these difficulties as they arise.

Example (a). Differentiate the function $y = x^3 - 2x$.

1. $y + \Delta y = (x + \Delta x)^3 - 2(x + \Delta x)$.
2. $\quad \Delta y = (x + \Delta x)^3 - 2(x + \Delta x) - x^3 + 2x$
3. $\quad\quad = x^3 + 3x^2 \Delta x + 3x (\Delta x)^2 + (\Delta x)^3 - 2x - 2 \Delta x - x^3 + 2x$
   $\quad\quad = 3x^2 \Delta x + 3x (\Delta x)^2 + (\Delta x)^3 - 2 \Delta x$.
4. $\quad \dfrac{\Delta y}{\Delta x} = 3x^2 + 3x \Delta x + (\Delta x)^2 - 2$.
5. $\quad y' = 3x^2 - 2$.

Example (b). Find the derivative of the function $x = \dfrac{1}{t}$.

1. $x + \Delta x = \dfrac{1}{t + \Delta t}$.
2. $\quad \Delta x = \dfrac{1}{t + \Delta t} - \dfrac{1}{t}$
3. $\quad\quad = \dfrac{t - (t + \Delta t)}{(t + \Delta t)t} = \dfrac{-\Delta t}{(t + \Delta t)t}$.
4. $\quad \dfrac{\Delta x}{\Delta t} = \dfrac{-1}{(t + \Delta t)t}$.
5. $\quad \dfrac{dx}{dt} = -\dfrac{1}{t^2}$.

Example (c). Differentiate the function

$$y = \sqrt{x} \qquad x > 0.$$

1. $y + \Delta y = \sqrt{x + \Delta x}$.
2. $\quad \Delta y = \sqrt{x + \Delta x} - \sqrt{x}$
3. $\quad\quad = (\sqrt{x + \Delta x} - \sqrt{x}) \cdot \dfrac{\sqrt{x + \Delta x} + \sqrt{x}}{\sqrt{x + \Delta x} + \sqrt{x}}$
   $\quad\quad = \dfrac{(x + \Delta x) - x}{\sqrt{x + \Delta x} + \sqrt{x}}$
   $\quad\quad = \dfrac{\Delta x}{\sqrt{x + \Delta x} + \sqrt{x}}$.
4. $\quad \dfrac{\Delta y}{\Delta x} = \dfrac{1}{\sqrt{x + \Delta x} + \sqrt{x}}$.
5. $\quad \dfrac{dy}{dx} = \dfrac{1}{2\sqrt{x}}$.

Example (*d*). Differentiate $y = \sin x$.

At once
$$y + \Delta y = \sin (x + \Delta x)$$
$$= \sin x \cos \Delta x + \cos x \sin \Delta x.$$

Then
$$\Delta y = \sin x \cos \Delta x + \cos x \sin \Delta x - \sin x$$
$$= \cos x \sin \Delta x - \sin x(1 - \cos \Delta x).$$

Eventually we shall let $\Delta x \to 0$. By Theorem 4,

$$\lim_{\alpha \to 0} \frac{\sin \alpha}{\alpha} = 1;$$

therefore we favor sine functions involving Δx. From trigonometry we know that $\sin^2 A = \frac{1}{2}(1 - \cos 2A)$. Hence

$$1 - \cos \Delta x = 2 \sin^2 (\tfrac{1}{2}\Delta x),$$

so that we may write

$$\Delta y = \cos x \sin \Delta x - 2 \sin x \sin^2 (\tfrac{1}{2}\Delta x).$$

This leads us to

$$\frac{\Delta y}{\Delta x} = \cos x \frac{\sin \Delta x}{\Delta x} - 2 \sin x \frac{\sin^2 (\tfrac{1}{2}\Delta x)}{\Delta x},$$

or

(4) $$\frac{\Delta y}{\Delta x} = \cos x \frac{\sin \Delta x}{\Delta x} - \sin x \frac{\sin (\tfrac{1}{2}\Delta x)}{\tfrac{1}{2}\Delta x} \sin (\tfrac{1}{2}\Delta x).$$

Now

$$\lim_{\Delta x \to 0} \frac{\sin \Delta x}{\Delta x} = 1, \qquad \lim_{\Delta x \to 0} \frac{\sin (\tfrac{1}{2}\Delta x)}{\tfrac{1}{2}\Delta x} = 1, \qquad \lim_{\Delta x \to 0} \sin (\tfrac{1}{2}\Delta x) = 0.$$

Thus, when we let $\Delta x \to 0$ in each member of (4), we obtain

$$y' = \cos x \cdot 1 - \sin x \cdot 1 \cdot 0,$$

or

(5) $$y' = \cos x.$$

EXERCISES

Differentiate the functions in Exs. 1–26.

1. $y = 4x^2 - 3x - 2$.   *Ans.* $y' = 8x - 3$.
2. $y = 3 + 4x - x^2$.   *Ans.* $y' = 4 - 2x$.
3. $y = x^3 - 5x + 2$.   *Ans.* $y' = 3x^2 - 5$.
4. $y = x^3 - 2x^2 + 6$.   *Ans.* $y' = 3x^2 - 4x$.

5. $x = y^4 - 2y^3$.   *Ans.* $\dfrac{dx}{dy} = 4y^3 - 6y^2$.

6. $x = \frac{1}{2}t^4 - 5t - 3.$ *Ans.* $\dfrac{dx}{dt} = 2t^3 - 5.$

7. $y = \frac{1}{2}(3x^2 + 1)^2.$ *Ans.* $y' = 6x(3x^2 + 1).$

8. $y = (x^2 - 2)^2.$ *Ans.* $y' = 4x(x^2 - 2).$

9. $y = \dfrac{1}{x + 7}.$ *Ans.* $\dfrac{dy}{dx} = \dfrac{-1}{(x + 7)^2}.$

10. $y = \dfrac{1}{4 - x}.$ *Ans.* $\dfrac{dy}{dx} = \dfrac{1}{(4 - x)^2}.$

11. $x = \dfrac{2y}{y - 1}.$ **12.** $x = \dfrac{t}{3 - t}.$

13. $y = 2 - 3x - \dfrac{1}{x}.$ *Ans.* $y' = -3 + \dfrac{1}{x^2}.$

14. $y = \dfrac{3x - 1}{2x + 5}.$ *Ans.* $\dfrac{dy}{dx} = \dfrac{17}{(2x + 5)^2}.$

15. $x = \dfrac{1}{t^2}.$ *Ans.* $\dfrac{dx}{dt} = \dfrac{-2}{t^3}.$ **16.** $v = \dfrac{4}{x^3}.$ *Ans.* $\dfrac{dv}{dx} = \dfrac{-12}{x^4}.$

17. $y = \sqrt{x + 2}.$ *Ans.* $\dfrac{dy}{dx} = \dfrac{1}{2\sqrt{x + 2}}.$

18. $y = \sqrt{2 - 3x}.$ *Ans.* $\dfrac{dy}{dx} = \dfrac{-3}{2\sqrt{2 - 3x}}.$

19. $y = \sqrt{a^2 + x^2}.$ *Ans.* $\dfrac{dy}{dx} = \dfrac{x}{\sqrt{a^2 + x^2}}.$

20. $v = \sqrt{a^2 - y^2}.$ *Ans.* $\dfrac{dv}{dy} = \dfrac{-y}{\sqrt{a^2 - y^2}}.$

21. $y = 3x - \sqrt{x}.$ *Ans.* $\dfrac{dy}{dx} = 3 - \dfrac{1}{2\sqrt{x}}.$

22. $x = 3t^2 - 2\sqrt{t}.$ *Ans.* $\dfrac{dx}{dt} = 6t - \dfrac{1}{\sqrt{t}}.$

23. $y = \dfrac{1}{\sqrt{x}}.$ *Ans.* $\dfrac{dy}{dx} = \dfrac{-1}{2x^{\frac{3}{2}}}.$ **24.** $u = t^{\frac{3}{2}}.$ *Ans.* $\dfrac{du}{dt} = \dfrac{3}{2}t^{\frac{1}{2}}.$

25. $y = \dfrac{1}{\sqrt{x - 2}}.$ **26.** $y = x\sqrt{x - 1}.$

27. For the function $y = \sqrt{2 - 3x}$ of Ex. 18 show that the derivative does not exist at $x = \frac{2}{3}$.

28. For the function $u = t^{\frac{3}{2}}$ of Ex. 24 show that the derivative does not exist at $t = 0$ but that the right-hand derivative exists at that point.

In Exs. 29–33 the method of Example (*d*) preceding these exercises will be found useful, as will the elementary formula

$$\tan (A + B) = \frac{\tan A + \tan B}{1 - \tan A \tan B}.$$

29. $y = \cos x.$ *Ans.* $y' = \sin x.$

30. $y = \tan x.$ (See Ex. 11, page 7.)   *Ans.* $y' = \sec^2 x.$

31. $y = \cot x = \dfrac{1}{\tan x}$.

Ans. $y' = -\csc^2 x$.

32. $y = \csc x$.

Ans. $y' = -\csc x \cot x$.

33. $y = \sec x$.

Ans. $y' = \sec x \tan x$.

22. Tangents to Plane Curves

A straight line that intersects a curve in two or more distinct points is called a *secant*.

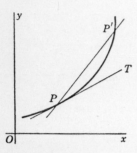

Figure 24

Let P be a fixed point of a plane curve, and P' a neighboring point. If P' be made to approach P along the curve, the secant PP' approaches, in general, a definite limiting position, PT in Fig. 24. If the secant line has such a limiting position, then the straight line which is that limit, PT in Fig. 24, is called the *tangent to the curve at P*, or is said to *touch the curve at P*. The point P is the *point of contact.*

The slope of the tangent to the curve at any point is called simply the *slope of the curve* at that point. When P' approaches P, the slope of the secant *approaches as its limit the slope of the curve.*

23. Derivative Interpreted as Slope

In Fig. 23, the slope of the secant PP' is $\dfrac{\Delta y}{\Delta x}$. As Δx approaches zero, P' approaches P along the curve, so that by § 22 the slope of the secant approaches as its limit the slope of the curve at P. But this limit has been defined as the derivative of y with respect to x. *The derivative of a function is identical with the slope of the graph of the function.*

More explicitly, this means that if, in the formula for y' we substitute any given value of x, the *number* thus obtained is the slope of the curve at the point whose abscissa is the given x.

Example. Find the slope of the curve $y = \frac{1}{4}x^3 - 2x$ at the point $P: (2, -2)$.

By the method of § 21, the derivative is

$$y' = \tfrac{3}{4}x^2 - 2.$$

When $x = 2$, this takes the value

$$y' = 1,$$

which is the slope at the given point (slope of the tangent PT, Fig. 25).

Let us verify that the term *slope of a curve* does not conflict with the previously used term *slope of a line*. The

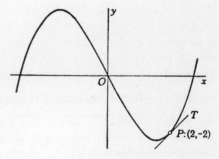

Figure 25

equation of a line of slope m can be written

(1)
$$y = mx + b.$$

From (1) we obtain

$$y + \Delta y = m(x + \Delta x) + b,$$
$$\Delta y = m\, \Delta x,$$

(2)
$$\frac{\Delta y}{\Delta x} = m.$$

Hence, for the straight line (1),

$$\frac{dy}{dx} = m;$$

the two uses of the word "slope" are in agreement.

24. *Rate of Change*

The idea of *rate of change* of a function occurs constantly in everyday experience. Such familiar expressions as miles per hour, miles per gallon, pressure per square inch, value per acre, price per ton, all represent rates.

Given a function

$$y = f(x),$$

let us assign to x an arbitrary increment Δx, thus causing in y a (positive or negative) change Δy. The ratio $\dfrac{\Delta y}{\Delta x}$ is called the *average* rate of change over the interval Δx. If we let Δx approach zero, this ratio in general approaches a limiting value, which is defined as the *rate of change of y corresponding to the given value of* x, or the *instantaneous rate*:

$$\frac{dy}{dx} = \operatorname*{Lim}_{\Delta x \to 0} \frac{\Delta y}{\Delta x} = \textit{rate of change of y with respect to x.}$$

In order to understand and appreciate these ideas, nothing more than ordinary experience is needed. As an illustration, suppose that two posts, at a measured distance apart, are set up beside a highway, and that a car is driven past them. Let Δx be the distance between the posts, and Δt the time required to pass. Then, if the car travels at a uniform speed, that speed is merely $\dfrac{\Delta x}{\Delta t}$. But if the speed is variable, this ratio is the *average* speed. If we wish to know the speed at a particular instant, say, when passing the first post, common sense would suggest that the posts be placed close together. For then Δt will be small, and there will not be time for the speed to change a great deal, so that the average will be nearly equal to the instantaneous speed. While in practice this process could not be pushed beyond a certain point, our ordinary idea of instantaneous speed is expressed exactly by $\dfrac{dx}{dt}$, the *limit* of $\dfrac{\Delta x}{\Delta t}$ as Δt approaches zero.

Comparing the definitions of derivative and rate of change, we have another fundamental relation: *The derivative of a function is identical with its rate of change.*

Thus in our future work it must always be borne in mind that the three quantities—derivative, slope of graph, rate of change—are all equal to each other.

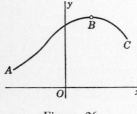

Figure 26

When the slope of a curve is positive (as on the arc AB), the ordinate y is increasing (as x increases), when the slope is negative (as on BC), the ordinate is decreasing. This says that a function increases or decreases according as its rate of change is positive or negative.

Example (a). Find the rate at which the reciprocal of a number changes as the number increases.

Let n equal the number, r its reciprocal:

$$r = \frac{1}{n}.$$

By the method of § 21 we find

$$\frac{dr}{dn} = -\frac{1}{n^2}.$$

At the instant, say, when n passes through the value 2, the reciprocal is diminishing one-fourth as fast as the number is increasing.

Example (b). The surface area of a sphere, initially zero, increases uniformly at the rate of 4 sq. in. per sec. Find the rate at which the radius is increasing at the end of 2 sec.

Let: t = time (sec.),
     r = radius of sphere (in.),
     S = surface area (sq. in.).

Since S is increasing at a constant rate, S is proportional to the elapsed time; indeed,

$$S = 4t.$$

But also, $S = 4\pi r^2$, so that $4t = 4\pi r^2$, from which it follows that

$$r = \frac{\sqrt{t}}{\sqrt{\pi}}.$$

By the method of § 21, we find

$$\frac{dr}{dt} = \frac{1}{2\sqrt{\pi}\cdot\sqrt{t}}.$$

When $t = 2$,

$$\frac{dr}{dt} = \frac{1}{2\sqrt{2\pi}} = 0.20 \text{ in. per sec.}$$

EXERCISES

In Exs. 1–10, find the slope of the curve at the given point.

1. $y = 2 - x^2$, $(3, -7)$.   *Ans.* -6.
2. $y = 3x^2 - 2x$, $(2, 8)$.   *Ans.* 10.
3. $y = 2x^3 - 3x$, $(-1, 1)$.   *Ans.* 3.

4. $y = x^2 - x^3$, $(1, 0)$.   *Ans.* -1.   5. $y = \dfrac{1}{x^2}$, $(2, \frac{1}{4})$.   *Ans.* $-\frac{1}{4}$.

6. $y = \dfrac{1}{x + 1}$, $(-2, -1)$.   *Ans.* -1.

7. $y^2 = 4x$, $(1, 2)$.   *Ans.* 1.   8. $y^2 = 4x$, $(1, -2)$.   *Ans.* -1.
9. $y^2 = 3x + 1$, $(1, 2)$.   *Ans.* $\frac{3}{4}$.
10. $y^2 = 3x + 1$, $(-\frac{1}{3}, 0)$.   *Ans.* Does not exist.

11. Find how fast (a) the circumference, (b) the area, of a circle increases when the radius increases.

12. Find how fast (a) the volume, (b) the surface area, (c) the diagonal, of a cube increases when the length of the edge increases.

13. Find how fast (a) the volume, (b) the surface area, of a sphere increases as the radius increases.

14. The radius of a sphere, initially zero, increases at the rate of 6 ft. per sec. Find how fast the volume is increasing after $\frac{1}{4}$ sec.   *Ans.* 54π cu. ft. per sec.

15. A right circular cylinder has a fixed height of 6 units. Find the rate of change of its volume V with respect to the radius r of its base.

$$Ans. \ \frac{dV}{dr} = 12\pi r.$$

16. In Ex. 15, find the rate of change of the total surface area A with respect to r.

$$Ans. \ \frac{dA}{dr} = 4\pi(r + 3).$$

17. The dimensions of a box are b, $b + 1$, $b + 4$. Find how fast the total surface area A increases as b increases.

$$Ans. \ \frac{dA}{db} = 12b + 20.$$

18. For the box of Ex. 17, find how fast the volume increases as b increases.

ALGEBRAIC FUNCTIONS

25. *Introduction*

In this and later chapters (9–11) we develop certain *standard formulas* by means of which any elementary function may be differentiated. The use of these formulas obviates the necessity of evaluating a special limit in every problem, thus effecting a great saving of time.

At present we confine our attention to algebraic functions. However, the formulas of §§ 27, 29 are direct consequences of the definition of the derivative, and are valid for all functions that are *continuous, one-valued*, and *differentiable*.

26. *Derivative of a Constant*

We note first that *the derivative of a constant is zero*:

(1) $$\frac{dc}{dx} = 0.$$

This result appears geometrically from the fact that the curve $y = c$ is a straight line parallel to Ox, so that the slope is everywhere zero. Likewise, since a constant never changes in value, its rate of change is always zero. Formally, if $y = c$, then $y + \Delta y = c$, and hence

$$\Delta y = 0, \qquad \frac{\Delta y}{\Delta x} = 0,$$

$$\frac{dy}{dx} = \operatorname*{Lim}_{\Delta x \to 0} \frac{\Delta y}{\Delta x} = 0.$$

27. *Derivative of a Sum; a Product; a Quotient*

If u and v are functions of x, the following formulas are true by the definition of the derivative (see proofs below):

(2) $$\frac{d}{dx}(u + v) = \frac{du}{dx} + \frac{dv}{dx},$$

(3) $$\frac{d}{dx}(uv) = u\frac{dv}{dx} + v\frac{du}{dx},$$

$$(4) \qquad \frac{d}{dx}\left(\frac{u}{v}\right) = \frac{v\dfrac{du}{dx} - u\dfrac{dv}{dx}}{v^2}.$$

These formulas may be stated in words as follows:

(2) *The derivative of the sum of two functions is equal to the sum of their derivatives.*

(3) *The derivative of the product of two functions is equal to the first function times the derivative of the second plus the second times the derivative of the first.*

(4) *The derivative of the quotient of two functions is equal to the denominator times the derivative of the numerator minus the numerator times the derivative of the denominator, all divided by the square of the denominator.*

Proof of (2): Let x assume an increment Δx, and denote by Δu and Δv the corresponding increments of u and v. Then

$$y = u + v,$$
$$y + \Delta y = u + \Delta u + v + \Delta v,$$
$$\Delta y = \Delta u + \Delta v,$$
$$\frac{\Delta y}{\Delta x} = \frac{\Delta u}{\Delta x} + \frac{\Delta v}{\Delta x},$$
$$\frac{dy}{dx} = \operatorname*{Lim}_{\Delta x \to 0} \frac{\Delta y}{\Delta x} = \frac{du}{dx} + \frac{dv}{dx}.$$

Proof of (3):

$$y = uv,$$
$$y + \Delta y = (u + \Delta u)(v + \Delta v),$$
$$\Delta y = u\,\Delta v + v\,\Delta u + \Delta u\,\Delta v,$$
$$\frac{\Delta y}{\Delta x} = u\frac{\Delta v}{\Delta x} + v\frac{\Delta u}{\Delta x} + \Delta u\frac{\Delta v}{\Delta x},$$
$$\frac{dy}{dx} = \operatorname*{Lim}_{\Delta x \to 0} \frac{\Delta y}{\Delta x} = u\frac{dv}{dx} + v\frac{du}{dx}.$$

Proof of (4):

$$y = \frac{u}{v},$$
$$y + \Delta y = \frac{u + \Delta u}{v + \Delta v},$$
$$\Delta y = \frac{u + \Delta u}{v + \Delta v} - \frac{u}{v} = \frac{uv + v\,\Delta u - uv - u\,\Delta v}{(v + \Delta v)v},$$
$$\frac{\Delta y}{\Delta x} = \frac{v\dfrac{\Delta u}{\Delta x} - u\dfrac{\Delta v}{\Delta x}}{(v + \Delta v)v},$$
$$\frac{dy}{dx} = \operatorname*{Lim}_{\Delta x \to 0} \frac{\Delta y}{\Delta x} = \frac{v\dfrac{du}{dx} - u\dfrac{dv}{dx}}{v^2}.$$

Formulas (2) and (3) can be extended to the case where n functions are involved. For three functions, (3) becomes

$$\frac{d}{dx} uvw = vw \frac{du}{dx} + wu \frac{dv}{dx} + uv \frac{dw}{dx}.$$

In the special case when $u = c$, a constant, (3) and (4) become

(3′)
$$\frac{d}{dx} cv = c \frac{dv}{dx},$$

(4′)
$$\frac{d}{dx} \frac{c}{v} = - \frac{c \frac{dv}{dx}}{v^2}.$$

All the formulas appearing in heavy type should be carefully memorized, preferably in words.

On pages 156–157 there is a collection of fundamental differentiation formulas, each of which is derived either in this chapter or in one of Chapters 9, 10, or 11. These basic formulas carry boldface (heavy type) equation numbers and retain those numbers throughout the various chapters involved.

28. *Derivative of* x^n

If

$$y = x^n,$$

then

(1)
$$\frac{dy}{dx} = nx^{n-1}.$$

When n is a positive integer, this formula may be established as follows:

$$y + \Delta y = (x + \Delta x)^n$$
$$= x^n + nx^{n-1} \Delta x + \frac{n(n - 1)}{2!} x^{n-2}(\Delta x)^2 + \cdots + (\Delta x)^n,$$
$$\Delta y = nx^{n-1} \Delta x + \frac{n(n - 1)}{2!} x^{n-2}(\Delta x)^2 + \cdots + (\Delta x)^n,$$
$$\frac{\Delta y}{\Delta x} = nx^{n-1} + \frac{n(n - 1)}{2!} x^{n-2} \Delta x + \cdots + (\Delta x)^{n-1},$$
$$\frac{dy}{dx} = \lim_{\Delta x \to 0} \frac{\Delta y}{\Delta x} = nx^{n-1}.$$

In particular, if $n = 1$, i.e., if $y = x$,

$$\frac{dx}{dx} = 1.$$

Although the above proof is valid only for positive integral values of n, formula (1) is true for all values of the exponent. The general proof will be given later; meanwhile the truth of the statement will be assumed.

Example (*a*). The derivative of

$$y = 2x^3 - 5x^2 + 3x + 2$$

is

$$y' = 6x^2 - 10x + 3.$$

Example (*b*). The derivative of

$$y = \frac{x^2 + 1}{4x + 3}$$

is

$$y' = \frac{(4x + 3)2x - (x^2 + 1)4}{(4x + 3)^2}$$

$$= \frac{4x^2 + 6x - 4}{(4x + 3)^2}.$$

Example (*c*). To differentiate

$$y = \frac{1}{\sqrt{x}},$$

we write

$$y = x^{-\frac{1}{2}},$$

from which we obtain

$$\frac{dy}{dx} = -\frac{1}{2} x^{-\frac{3}{2}} = \frac{-1}{2x^{\frac{3}{2}}}.$$

EXERCISES

Differentiate the functions in Exs. 1–28.

1. $y = 2x^3 - 7x + 1.$

2. $y = x^2 - 2x^4 - 3x^5.$

3. $y = 5 - 4x + 7x^3 - x^5.$

4. $y = x^6 + x^3 + 5x - 8.$
    Ans. $y' = -3x^{-2} + 8x^{-3}.$

5. $y = 3x^{-1} - 4x^{-2}.$

6. $y = 5x^{-2} + x^{-3}.$
    Ans. $y' = -10x^{-3} - 3x^{-4}.$

7. $y = \dfrac{3}{x} - \dfrac{5}{x^2}.$ See Ex. 5.
    Ans. $\dfrac{dy}{dx} = -\dfrac{3}{x^2} + \dfrac{10}{x^3}.$

8. $y = \dfrac{1}{v^2} - \dfrac{2}{v^4}.$ See Ex. 5.
    Ans. $\dfrac{dy}{dv} = -\dfrac{2}{v^3} + \dfrac{8}{v^5}.$

9. $w = \dfrac{1}{6} + \dfrac{2y}{5} - \dfrac{y^2}{3}.$
    Ans. $\dfrac{dw}{dy} = \dfrac{2}{5} - \dfrac{2y}{3}.$

10. $w = \dfrac{2}{3} - \dfrac{y^2}{5} + \dfrac{4y^3}{3}.$
    Ans. $\dfrac{dw}{dy} = -\dfrac{2y}{5} + 4y^2.$

11. $y = x^{\frac{1}{2}} - 4x^{-\frac{1}{2}}.$

12. $y = 2x^{-\frac{1}{2}} + 4x^{-\frac{1}{2}}.$

13. $x = \sqrt{t} - \dfrac{1}{\sqrt{t}}.$

14. $x = 2t\sqrt{t} + \dfrac{1}{\sqrt{t}}.$

15. $y = 6 - x^{-\frac{1}{3}}.$

16. $y = 6x^{\frac{1}{3}} - x^3.$

17. $y = (1 + x^2)(3 - 2x).$

18. $y = (v^2 + 3)(v^2 - v + 1).$　　　　　　*Ans.* $\dfrac{dy}{dv} = 4v^3 - 3v^2 + 8v - 3.$

19. $y = \dfrac{1}{3x - 2} \cdot$ Use (4′), § 27.　　　　*Ans.* $\dfrac{dy}{dx} = \dfrac{-3}{(3x - 2)^2}.$

20. $y = \dfrac{3}{1 + 2x} \cdot$ Use (4′), § 27.　　　　*Ans.* $\dfrac{dy}{dx} = \dfrac{-6}{(1 + 2x)^2}.$

21. $x = \dfrac{3}{t^2 + 1} \cdot$　　　　　　　*Ans.* $\dfrac{dx}{dt} = \dfrac{-6t}{(t^2 + 1)^2}.$

22. $x = \dfrac{4}{1 - 2t^3} \cdot$　　　　　　　*Ans.* $\dfrac{dx}{dt} = \dfrac{24t^2}{(1 - 2t^3)^2}.$

23. $y = \dfrac{x}{x^2 - 1} \cdot$　　　　　　*Ans.* $\dfrac{dy}{dx} = - \dfrac{x^2 + 1}{(x^2 - 1)^2}.$

24. $y = \dfrac{x^2}{x + 1} \cdot$　　　　　　*Ans.* $\dfrac{dy}{dx} = \dfrac{x^2 + 2x}{(x + 1)^2}.$

25. $f(x) = \dfrac{x^2 + 1}{x^2 - 1} \cdot$　　　　*Ans.* $f'(x) = \dfrac{-4x}{(x^2 - 1)^2}.$

26. $F(v) = \dfrac{1 + v}{3 - v^2} \cdot$　　　*Ans.* $F'(v) = \dfrac{v^2 + 2v + 3}{(3 - v^2)^2}.$

27. $\varphi(v) = \dfrac{3 - v^2}{1 + v} \cdot$　　　*Ans.* $\varphi'(v) = - \dfrac{v^2 + 2v + 3}{(1 + v)^2}.$

28. $\varphi(x) = \dfrac{x(x + 1)}{2x - 1} \cdot$　　　*Ans.* $\varphi'(x) = \dfrac{2x^2 - 2x - 1}{(2x - 1)^2}.$

In Exs. 29–34, find the slope at the point indicated.

29. $y = x^3 - 5x + 4,$ at $(1, 0).$　　　　　　　　*Ans.* $-2.$
30. $y = 7 - x^2 + 4x^3,$ at $(-1, 2).$　　　　　　*Ans.* $14.$

31. $y = \dfrac{x}{x^2 + 4},$ at $(2, \tfrac{1}{4}).$　　　　　　　*Ans.* $0.$

32. $y = \dfrac{1 - 3x + x^3}{x^2},$ at $(\tfrac{1}{2}, -\tfrac{3}{2})$　　　　*Ans.* $-3.$

33. $y = x^3 + 3x + 14,$ where the curve crosses $Ox.$　　　*Ans.* $15.$
34. $y = 2x^4 + 3x^3 + 2x^2 - 1,$ where the curve crosses $Ox.$　　*Ans.* $-3; 5.25.$

In Exs. 35–38, find the vertex of the parabola by means of the derivative. Check by completing the square and putting the equation of the parabola in standard form.

35. $y = x^2 + 6x + 7.$　　　　　　**36.** $y = 4x^2 - 4x + 3.$
37. $9x^2 + 6x - 18y - 35 = 0.$　　　**38.** $x^2 + 4x + 3y + 1 = 0.$

In Exs. 39–48, find the points where the tangent is parallel to $Ox.$

39. $y = x^3 + 6x^2 + 9x + 7.$　　　　　　*Ans.* $(-1, 3), (-3, 7).$
40. $y = 2x^3 - 3x^2 - 12x + 6.$　　　　　*Ans.* $(-1, 13), (2, -14).$
41. $y = 8x^4 - 16x^3 - 24x^2 + 32x + 8.$　*Ans.* $(\tfrac{1}{2}, \tfrac{33}{2}), (-1, -24), (2, -24).$
42. $y = x^4 - 8x^3 + 22x^2 - 24x + 9.$　　*Ans.* $(1, 0), (2, 1), (3, 0).$
43. $y = x^4 - 4x^3 + 16x + 3.$　　　　*Ans.* $(-1, -8), (2, -13)$ twice.
44. $y = 8x^4 - 16x^3 + 12x^2 - 4x + 1.$　　　*Ans.* $(\tfrac{1}{2}, \tfrac{1}{2})$ three times.

45. $y = x^4 - 4x^2 - 16x + 24$.   *Ans.* $(2, -8)$.
46. $y = x^4 - 4x^3 + 8x^2 + 32x + 10$.   *Ans.* $(-1, -9)$.

47. $y = \dfrac{x - 1}{x^2 - 2x + 5}$.   *Ans.* $(-1, -\frac{1}{4})$, $(3, \frac{1}{4})$.

48. $y = \dfrac{x + 3}{(x + 1)(x + 4)}$.   *Ans.* None.

49. The force between two magnetic poles at a distance r apart is $F = \dfrac{k}{r^2}$. Find the rate at which F changes with respect to r, when $r = 3$.

50. Find the rate at which the radius r of a sphere increases as the volume V increases.

$$Ans. \quad \frac{dr}{dV} = (4\pi)^{-\frac{1}{3}}(3V)^{-\frac{2}{3}}.$$

51. A body of gas is contained in a vessel of volume v; the pressure is given by the formula $p = \dfrac{k}{v}$. Find the rate at which pressure increases with decreasing volume, at the instant when $v = 4$.

52. Suppose the container of Ex. 51 is a cube with its edge c units in length. Find the rate at which the pressure p varies with varying edge length, when $c = 3$ units.

$$Ans. \quad \frac{dp}{dc} = -\frac{k}{27}.$$

53. Use (4′) of § 27 to prove that (1) of § 28 holds for negative integral values of n.

29. *The Chain Rule*

Given y as a function of x, it is frequently convenient to think of y as a function of an auxiliary variable u, where u in turn is a function of x. For example, the formula of § 28 would fail entirely to find the derivative of such a function as

$$y = \sqrt{x^2 + 1};$$

it will appear presently that the difficulty may be overcome by merely putting $y = \sqrt{u}$, where $u = x^2 + 1$.

Let

$$y = f(u), \text{ where } u = \varphi(x).$$

Assign to x an increment Δx, and denote by Δu and Δy the corresponding changes in u and y. Then

$$\frac{\Delta y}{\Delta x} = \frac{\Delta y}{\Delta u} \cdot \frac{\Delta u}{\Delta x},$$

and when Δx approaches zero, we find (assuming that the limits of all three ratios exist)

$$\operatorname*{Lim}_{\Delta x \to 0} \frac{\Delta y}{\Delta x} = \operatorname*{Lim}_{\Delta x \to 0} \frac{\Delta y}{\Delta u} \cdot \operatorname*{Lim}_{\Delta x \to 0} \frac{\Delta u}{\Delta x},$$

or

(5)
$$\frac{dy}{dx} = \frac{dy}{du} \cdot \frac{du}{dx}.$$

Equation (5) is called the *chain rule*. It is an extremely useful tool and will be employed over and over again throughout much of the remainder of this book.

Two other formulas follow very quickly. Writing (5) in the form

$$\frac{dy}{du} = \frac{\dfrac{dy}{dx}}{\dfrac{du}{dx}},$$

let us interchange u and x:

(5')
$$\frac{dy}{dx} = \frac{\dfrac{dy}{du}}{\dfrac{dx}{du}}, \qquad \frac{dx}{du} \neq 0.$$

In (5'), put $u = y$:

(5'')
$$\frac{dy}{dx} = \frac{1}{\dfrac{dx}{dy}}, \qquad \frac{dx}{dy} \neq 0.$$

Formula (5'') says that the rate of change of y with respect to x and the rate of change of x with respect to y are reciprocals. This fact appears constantly in ordinary experience. Say that a car is traveling at a speed (time-rate of change of distance) of 30 mi. per hr. Then time is elapsing at a rate (distance-rate of change of time) of 2 min. ($\frac{1}{30}$ hr.) per mile:

$$\frac{dx}{dt} = 30, \qquad \frac{dt}{dx} = \frac{1}{30}.$$

30. *The General Power Formula*

Formula (1) of § 28 enables us to differentiate any power of x. By means of the chain rule, we are able to differentiate *any power of any function of x*. To do this, let

$$y = u^n, \qquad \text{where } u = \varphi(x).$$

Then by (1), § 28,

$$\frac{dy}{du} = nu^{n-1},$$

and we have by the chain rule (5)

(6)
$$\frac{d}{dx} u^n = nu^{n-1} \frac{du}{dx}.$$

An important special case of this formula is the case $n = \frac{1}{2}$:

(6′)
$$\frac{d}{dx} \sqrt{u} = \frac{\dfrac{du}{dx}}{2 \sqrt{u}}.$$

Example (*a*). Find the derivative of

$$y = (3x^2 + 1)^4.$$

This function is of the form u^n, with $u = 3x^2 + 1$, $n = 4$. Hence (6) gives

$$y' = 4(3x^2 + 1)^3 \cdot 6x$$
$$= 24x(3x^2 + 1)^3.$$

Example (*b*). Differentiate the function

$$x = \sqrt{t^2 + 1}.$$

By (6′), we have

$$\frac{dx}{dt} = \frac{2t}{2 \sqrt{t^2 + 1}} = \frac{t}{\sqrt{t^2 + 1}}.$$

Example (*c*). Differentiate

$$f(y) = y^2(16 - y^2)^{-\frac{1}{2}}.$$

By (3) and (6) we have

$$f'(y) = 2y(16 - y^2)^{-\frac{1}{2}} - \frac{1}{2}(-2y)y^2(16 - y^2)^{-\frac{3}{2}}$$
$$= 2y(16 - y^2)^{-\frac{1}{2}} + y^3(16 - y^2)^{-\frac{3}{2}}$$
$$= y(16 - y^2)^{-\frac{3}{2}}[2(16 - y^2) + y^2]$$
$$= y(32 - y^2)(16 - y^2)^{-\frac{3}{2}}.$$

31. *Higher Derivatives*

The derivative of y with respect to x is itself a function of x, and may in turn be differentiated. The derivative of the first derivative is called the *second derivative* and is written $\dfrac{d^2y}{dx^2}$; further differentiations give $\dfrac{d^3y}{dx^3}$, $\dfrac{d^4y}{dx^4}$, etc. Other symbols for the higher derivatives are y'', y''', $y^{(4)}$, $\cdots$, and $f''(x), f'''(x), f^{(4)}(x), \cdots$.

Since y'' is the derivative of y', we see by § 24 that *the second derivative of a function is the rate of change of slope of the graph.*

Example. In Example (*b*), § 30,

$$\frac{dx}{dt} = \frac{t}{\sqrt{t^2 + 1}},$$

so that, by (4),

$$\frac{d^2x}{dt^2} = \frac{\sqrt{t^2+1} \cdot 1 - \dfrac{t \cdot 2t}{2\sqrt{t^2+1}}}{t^2+1}$$

$$= \frac{1}{(t^2+1)^{\frac{3}{2}}}.$$

It is sometimes necessary to express $\dfrac{d^2y}{dx^2}$ in terms of the derivatives of x with respect to y. To do this, let us in (5′), § 29, replace u by y and y by y':

$$(1) \qquad \frac{dy'}{dx} = \frac{\dfrac{dy'}{dy}}{\dfrac{dx}{dy}}.$$

But by (5″),

$$\frac{dy'}{dy} = \frac{d}{dy}\left(\frac{1}{\dfrac{dx}{dy}}\right) = -\frac{\dfrac{d^2x}{dy^2}}{\left(\dfrac{dx}{dy}\right)^2}.$$

Substituting in (1), we find

$$(2) \qquad \frac{d^2y}{dx^2} = -\frac{\dfrac{d^2x}{dy^2}}{\left(\dfrac{dx}{dy}\right)^3}, \qquad \frac{dx}{dy} \neq 0.$$

Suppose $f(x)$ contains $(x-a)$ as a factor precisely n times. Then

$$(3) \qquad f(x) = (x-a)^n g_0(x), \qquad g_0(a) \neq 0.$$

From (3), with the aid of the formula for the derivative of a product, we obtain

$$f'(x) = (x-a)^n g_0'(x) + n(x-a)^{n-1} g_0(x)$$
$$= (x-a)^{n-1}[(x-a)g_0'(x) + ng_0(x)].$$

Hence

$$(4) \qquad f'(x) = (x-a)^{n-1} g_1(x), \qquad g_1(a) \neq 0.$$

That is, the derivative of $f(x)$ contains $(x-a)$ as a factor one time less than did $f(x)$. Iteration of this fact yields the following result.

THEOREM 10. *If $f(x)$ contains $(x-a)$ as a factor precisely n times, the kth derivative of $f(x)$ contains $(x-a)$ as a factor precisely $(n-k)$ times. That is, if*

$$(5) \qquad f(x) = (x-a)^n g_0(x), \qquad g_0(a) \neq 0,$$

$$(6) \qquad f^{(k)}(x) = (x-a)^{n-k} g_k(x), \qquad g_k(a) \neq 0.$$

EXERCISES

In Exs. 1–40, find the first derivative.

1. $y = (3x + 4)^2.$ Ans. $y' = 6(3x + 4).$

2. $y = (1 - 2x)^3.$ Ans. $y' = -6(1 - 2x)^2.$

3. $x = \frac{1}{3}(1 - 5t)^6.$ Ans. $\dfrac{dx}{dt} = -10(1 - 5t)^5.$

4. $x = \frac{1}{2}(4t - 1)^3.$ Ans. $\dfrac{dx}{dt} = 6(4t - 1)^2.$

5. $y = a^4(a - x)^{-3}.$ Ans. $\dfrac{dy}{dx} = 3a^4(a - x)^{-4}.$

6. $y = 6\sqrt{4 + x}.$ Ans. $\dfrac{dy}{dx} = \dfrac{3}{\sqrt{4 + x}}.$

7. $x = (3 - 2y)^{\frac{5}{2}}.$ Ans. $\dfrac{dx}{dy} = -5(3 - 2y)^{\frac{3}{2}}.$

8. $x = \dfrac{4}{(1 + 3y)^2}.$ Ans. $\dfrac{dx}{dy} = -\dfrac{24}{(1 + 3y)^3}.$

9. $a^4y = (x^2 + a^2)^{\frac{5}{2}}.$ Ans. $a^4y' = 5x(x^2 + a^2)^{\frac{3}{2}}.$

10. $u = (8 - t^6)^{-\frac{3}{2}}.$ Ans. $\dfrac{du}{dt} = 9t^5(8 - t^6)^{-\frac{5}{2}}.$

11. $y = \sqrt{2ax - x^2}.$ Ans. $\dfrac{dy}{dx} = \dfrac{a - x}{\sqrt{2ax - x^2}}.$

12. $v = (z^4 - 2z + 1)^{\frac{3}{2}}.$ Ans. $\dfrac{dv}{dz} = 3(2z^3 - 1)(z^4 - 2z + 1)^{\frac{1}{2}}.$

13. $y = x^2(x + 1)^3.$ Ans. $y' = x(x + 1)^2(5x + 2).$

14. $f(x) = x^3(x^2 - a^2)^{\frac{1}{2}}.$ Ans. $f'(x) = x^2(4x^2 - 3a^2)(x^2 - a^2)^{-\frac{1}{2}}.$

15. $f(v) = v(v^2 + b^2)^{-\frac{1}{2}}.$ Ans. $f'(v) = b^2(v^2 + b^2)^{-\frac{3}{2}}.$

16. $y = x(a^2 - x^2)^{\frac{3}{2}}.$ Ans. $y' = (a^2 - 4x^2)(a^2 - x^2)^{\frac{1}{2}}.$

17. $y = x^{-1}(a^2 + x^2)^{\frac{1}{2}}.$ Ans. $y' = -a^2x^{-2}(a^2 + x^2)^{-\frac{1}{2}}.$

18. $\psi = \dfrac{3}{\sqrt{16 + t^4}}.$ Ans. $\dfrac{d\psi}{dt} = \dfrac{-6t^3}{(16 + t^4)^{\frac{3}{2}}}.$

19. $y = \dfrac{(1 - 2x)^2}{x}.$ Ans. $y' = -x^{-2} + 4.$

20. $y = \dfrac{(x + 1)^3}{x^2}.$ Ans. $y' = 1 - 3x^{-2} - 2x^{-3}.$

21. $y = \dfrac{(x - 2)^3}{x^2}.$ Use three methods and check your answers against one another. *Hint*: Consider y as a product, as a quotient, or with the binomial expanded.

22. $x = \dfrac{t}{\sqrt{a^2 - t^2}}.$ Ans. $\dfrac{dx}{dt} = \dfrac{a^2}{(a^2 - t^2)^{\frac{3}{2}}}.$

23. $y = (a^{\frac{2}{3}} - x^{\frac{2}{3}})^{\frac{3}{2}}.$ Ans. $y' = -x^{-\frac{1}{3}}(a^{\frac{2}{3}} - x^{\frac{2}{3}})^{\frac{1}{2}}.$

24. $y = \dfrac{1}{(5 - 2x)^3}.$ Ans. $\dfrac{dy}{dx} = \dfrac{6}{(5 - 2x)^4}.$

25. $f(x) = (2 + x)^2(1 - x)^3.$ Ans. $f'(x) = -(2 + x)(1 - x)^2(4 + 5x).$

26. $\psi(v) = (3v + 1)^3(2v - 3)^4$.   *Ans.* $\psi'(v) = (3v + 1)^2(2v - 3)^3(42v - 19)$.

27. $y = (2x - 1)^3(1 - 3x)^5$.   *Ans.* $y' = 3(2x - 1)^2(1 - 3x)^4(7 - 16x)$.

28. $z = (1 + t^2 + t^4)^3(3t - 1)^2$.

$$\text{Ans. } \frac{dz}{dt} = 6(1 + t^2 + t^4)^2(3t - 1)(7t^4 - 2t^3 + 4t^2 - t + 1).$$

29. $y = (3x + 1)^2(x^2 - 1)^{\frac{1}{2}}$.   *Ans.* $y' = (3x + 1)(9x^2 + x - 6)(x^2 - 1)^{-\frac{1}{2}}$.

30. $y = (4x - 1)^3(x^2 - 1)^{\frac{2}{3}}$.   *Ans.* $y' = 3(4x - 1)^2(8x^2 - x - 4)(x^2 - 1)^{\frac{1}{3}}$.

31. $x = \dfrac{(y^2 - 1)^2}{y^2 + 1}$.   *Ans.* $\dfrac{dx}{dy} = 2y(y^2 - 1)(y^2 + 3)(y^2 + 1)^{-2}$.

32. $\varphi(x) = \dfrac{2x^2}{\sqrt{x + 1}}$.   *Ans.* $\varphi'(x) = x(3x + 4)(x + 1)^{-\frac{3}{2}}$.

33. $H(y) = \dfrac{1}{y^2(y + 2)^3}$.   *Ans.* $H'(y) = -(5y + 4)y^{-3}(y + 2)^{-4}$.

34. $F(x) = \dfrac{1}{(x + 1)^3(3x - 1)^2}$.   *Ans.* $F'(x) = -3(5x + 1)(x + 1)^{-4}(3x - 1)^{-3}$.

35. $z = [1 + (x^2 - 1)^3]^{\frac{3}{2}}$.   *Ans.* $z' = 9x(x^2 - 1)^2 \sqrt{1 + (x^2 - 1)^3}$.

36. $f(x) = \sqrt{1 + \sqrt{1 - x}}$.   *Ans.* $f'(x) = \dfrac{-1}{4\sqrt{1 - x}\sqrt{1 + \sqrt{1 - x}}}$.

37. $y = \dfrac{1}{(1 + \sqrt{1 - x})^2}$.   *Ans.* $y' = \dfrac{1}{\sqrt{1 - x}(1 + \sqrt{1 - x})^3}$.

38. $y = \left(\dfrac{u}{1 - u}\right)^{\frac{1}{2}}$.   *Ans.* $\dfrac{dy}{du} = \dfrac{1}{2}u^{-\frac{1}{2}}(1 - u)^{-\frac{3}{2}}$.

39. $y = \left(\dfrac{w^3}{a - w}\right)^{\frac{1}{2}}$.   *Ans.* $\dfrac{dy}{dw} = \dfrac{1}{2}(3a - 2w)w^{\frac{1}{2}}(a - w)^{-\frac{3}{2}}$.

40. $y = x^2(x - 1)^3(2x - 5)^2$.   *Ans.* $y' = x(x - 1)^2(2x - 5)(x - 2)(14x - 5)$.

In Exs. 41–44, find the slope of the curve at the given point.

41. $y = \sqrt{25 - x^2}$, $(4, 3)$.   *Ans.* $-\frac{4}{3}$.

42. $y = x(4x - 1)^2$, $(\frac{1}{2}, \frac{1}{2})$.   *Ans.* 5.

43. $y = \dfrac{x}{x^2 + 1}$, $(1, \frac{1}{2})$.   *Ans.* 0.

44. $y = (2x - 1)^2(x - 2)^3$, $(1, -1)$.   *Ans.* -1.

In Exs. 45–52, find the second derivative.

45. $y = (x^2 + x + 1)^2$.   *Ans.* $y'' = 6(2x^2 + 2x + 1)$.

46. $y = x(2x + 1)^3$.   *Ans.* $y'' = 12(2x + 1)(4x + 1)$.

47. The y of Ex. 11.   *Ans.* $y'' = -a^2(2ax - x^2)^{-\frac{3}{2}}$.

48. $x = \dfrac{1}{\sqrt{1 - t^2}}$.   *Ans.* $\dfrac{d^2x}{dt^2} = \dfrac{1 + 2t^2}{(1 - t^2)^{\frac{5}{2}}}$.

49. $x = \dfrac{(1 + t)^2}{t^2}$.   *Ans.* $\dfrac{d^2x}{dt^2} = \dfrac{6}{t^4} + \dfrac{4}{t^3}$.

50. $y = (2x - 1)^3(x + 2)^2$.   *Ans.* $y'' = 10(2x - 1)(8x^2 + 16x + 5)$.

51. The y of Ex. 38. $Ans. \dfrac{d^2y}{du^2} = \left(u - \dfrac{1}{4}\right) u^{-\frac{3}{2}}(1 - u)^{-\frac{5}{2}}.$

52. The y of Ex. 39. $Ans. \dfrac{d^2y}{dw^2} = \dfrac{3}{4} a^2 w^{-\frac{1}{2}}(a - w)^{-\frac{3}{2}}.$

53. Let t be constant. Find $\dfrac{d^2y}{dx^2}$ from the equation $y = \sqrt{1 - 2xt + t^2}.$

$$Ans. \dfrac{d^2y}{dx^2} = -t^2(1 - 2xt + t^2)^{-\frac{3}{2}}.$$

54. Let x be held constant. Find $\dfrac{d^2y}{dt^2}$ from the equation of Ex. 53.

$$Ans. \dfrac{d^2y}{dt^2} = (1 - x^2)(1 - 2xt + t^2)^{-\frac{3}{2}}.$$

55. For the curve $y = \dfrac{(1 - x)^2}{x}$, find the rate of change of slope at $(2, \frac{1}{2})$.

$$Ans. \tfrac{1}{4}.$$

56. Given any parabola with axis parallel to Oy, show that the rate of change of slope is constant.

57. If $y = (4x - 1)^{\frac{1}{2}}$, find y'''. $Ans. y''' = 24(4x - 1)^{-\frac{5}{2}}.$

58. If $\varphi(x) = (ax + b)^{\frac{3}{2}}$, find $\varphi^{(4)}(x)$. $Ans. \varphi^{(4)}(x) = \dfrac{9a^4}{16} (ax + b)^{-\frac{5}{2}}.$

59. If $y = uv$, where u and v are any functions of x, derive the formula

$$y'' = uv'' + 2u'v' + u''v.$$

Obtain the formula for y'''.

32. *Implicit Functions*

In general, an equation involving x and y determines a value (or values) of y corresponding to each value of x in some range, and therefore determines y as a function of x. Hitherto we have been concerned with functions defined *explicitly* by an equation of the form

$$(1) \qquad\qquad y = f(x).$$

It may happen, however, that x and y are connected by an equation not solved for y; for example,

$$x^3 + y^3 = 3axy.$$

Then y is called an *implicit function* of x.

In contrast to (1), an implicit relation between x and y will be written

$$(2) \qquad\qquad F(x, y) = 0.$$

In equation (2), $F(x, y)$ is a function of two *arguments*, or variables, x and y. Later (Chapter 27) we shall devote considerable attention to the study of functions of two, or more than two, arguments.

33. *Derivatives in Implicit Form*

To find the derivative of a function defined implicitly, we apply the following procedure.

RULE. *Differentiale each term of the equation*

$$F(x, y) = 0$$

with respect to x, bearing in mind that y is a function of x.

In this connection it must be remembered that, by (6), the derivative of y^n with respect to x is $ny^{n-1}\dfrac{dy}{dx}$.

Example (*a*). Find y', if

$$x^3 + y^3 - 3axy = 0.$$

Differentiating each term in turn, we have

$$3x^2 + 3y^2y' - 3a(xy' + y) = 0,$$

so that

$$(y^2 - ax)y' + x^2 - ay = 0,$$

$$y' = -\frac{x^2 - ay}{y^2 - ax}.$$

A little experience soon shows that it is sometimes more convenient to treat a function by means of an implicit relation than it is to use an explicit form of the function, even when the explicit form is obtainable by elementary means.

Example (*b*). Find the slope of the curve

(1) $$x^2 - 3xy + y^2 - 4x + 2y + 1 = 0$$

at the point $(1, -1)$.

That the point $(1, -1)$ lies on the hyperbola (1) is easily verified. The problem makes sense.

From (1) it follows at once that

(2) $$2x - 3y - 3xy' + 2yy' - 4 + 2y' = 0.$$

We shall denote the slope at $(1, -1)$ by m, to distinguish between the general y' and one of its numerical values. Using $x = 1$, $y = -1$, and $y' = m$ in (2), we arrive at

$$2 + 3 - 3m - 2m - 4 + 2m = 0; \quad 3m = 1.$$

Therefore, at the point $(1, -1)$ the slope of the hyperbola (1) is $m = \frac{1}{3}$.

Next let us solve the same problem by first expressing the y of (1) as an explicit function of x. Equation (1) may be written

$$y^2 - (3x - 2)y + (x^2 - 4x + 1) = 0$$

from which, by the usual formula for the solution of a quadratic equation, we get

$$y = \tfrac{1}{2}(3x - 2) \pm \tfrac{1}{2}\sqrt{(3x - 2)^2 - 4(x^2 - 4x + 1)},$$

or

(3) $$y = \tfrac{1}{2}(3x - 2) \pm \tfrac{1}{2}\sqrt{5x^2 + 4x}.$$

In (3), y is expressed as a two-valued function of x. We need to select the correct branch of that function. Since we seek the slope at $(1, -1)$, y must take on the value minus one when $x = 1$. Therefore, of the two values given by (3), we must choose the branch

(4) $$y = \tfrac{1}{2}(3x - 2) - \tfrac{1}{2}\sqrt{5x^2 + 4x}.$$

Equation (4) yields

(5) $$y' = \frac{3}{2} - \frac{5x + 2}{2\sqrt{5x^2 + 4x}}.$$

Hence, at $(1, -1)$, we get

$$m = \frac{3}{2} - \frac{7}{2\sqrt{9}} = \frac{9 - 7}{6} = \frac{1}{3},$$

as desired.

Most people would choose the first, rather than the second, of the above methods of solving this problem.

Example (c). Find y'', if $x^2 - y^2 = a^2$.

At once, $2x - 2yy' = 0$, from which we obtain

(6) $$y' = \frac{x}{y}.$$

A second differentiation gives

(7) $$y'' = \frac{y - xy'}{y^2}.$$

Employing the value of y' from (6), we rewrite (7) as

$$y'' = \frac{y - \dfrac{x^2}{y}}{y^2} = \frac{y^2 - x^2}{y^3};$$

since $x^2 - y^2 = a^2$, this reduces to

$$y'' = -\frac{a^2}{y^3}.$$

EXERCISES

In Exs. 1–14, find the derivative of y with respect to x. Use the given relation in its implicit form.

1. $x^2 + y^2 = a^2$.   Ans. $y' = -\dfrac{x}{y}$.   2. $x^3 + y^3 = a^3$.   Ans. $y' = -\dfrac{x^2}{y^2}$.

3. $x^2 + 4y^2 = 4ay$.   Ans. $y' = \dfrac{x}{2(a - 2y)}$.

4. $y^2(x + 2y) = c^3$.   Ans. $y' = \dfrac{-y}{2(x + 3y)}$.

5. $x^2 + 4xy + y^2 = 1$.   Ans. $y' = -\dfrac{x + 2y}{2x + y}$.

6. $x^2 - 2xy + y^2 - 6x + 2y = 0$.   Ans. $y' = \dfrac{x - y - 3}{x - y - 1}$.

7. $(x + y)^2 = 2ay$.   Ans. $\dfrac{dy}{dx} = \dfrac{x + y}{a - x - y}$.

8. $(x - y)^2 = 2ax$.   Ans. $\dfrac{dy}{dx} = \dfrac{x - y - a}{x - y}$.

9. $x^{\frac{1}{2}} + y^{\frac{1}{2}} = a^{\frac{1}{2}}$.   Ans. $y' = -x^{-\frac{1}{2}}y^{\frac{1}{2}}$.
10. $x^{\frac{2}{3}} + y^{\frac{2}{3}} = a^{\frac{2}{3}}$.   Ans. $y' = -x^{-\frac{1}{3}}y^{\frac{1}{3}}$.

11. $(x^2 - y^2)^2 = 4ay^3$.   Ans. $\dfrac{dy}{dx} = \dfrac{x(x^2 - y^2)}{y(x^2 - y^2 + 3ay)}$.

12. $(x^2 - y^2)^3 = 3a^4x^2$.   Ans. $\dfrac{dy}{dx} = \dfrac{x(x^2 - y^2 - a^2)(x^2 - y^2 + a^2)}{y(x^2 - y^2)^2}$.

13. $(x^2 + y^2)^2 = ay^3$.   Ans. $\dfrac{dy}{dx} = \dfrac{4x(x^2 + y^2)}{y(3ay - 4x^2 - 4y^2)}$.

14. $(x^2 + y^2)^3 = a^4x^2$.   Ans. $\dfrac{dy}{dx} = \dfrac{x[a^4 - 3(x^2 + y^2)^2]}{3y(x^2 + y^2)^2}$.

15. If $x = t^3 - 3t^2$, find $\dfrac{dt}{dx}$.   Ans. $\dfrac{dt}{dx} = \dfrac{1}{3t(t - 2)}$.

16. If $y = (x^3 + 1)^2$, find $\dfrac{dx}{dy}$.   Ans. $\dfrac{dx}{dy} = \dfrac{1}{6x^2(x^3 + 1)}$.

17. If $z^2 - 2zy + 3y^2 = 4$, find $\dfrac{dz}{dy}$.   Ans. $\dfrac{dz}{dy} = \dfrac{z - 3y}{z - y}$.

18. If $4c^2\theta t = (\theta^2 - t^2)^2$ find $\dfrac{d\theta}{dt}$.   Ans. $\dfrac{d\theta}{dt} = \dfrac{t\theta^2 - t^3 + c^2\theta}{\theta^3 - t^2\theta - c^2t}$.

19. If $y^2 = 4ax$, find y''.   Ans. $y'' = \dfrac{-4a^2}{y^3}$.

20. If $x^2 = 4ay$, find y''.

21. If $x^2 + y^2 = a^2$, find y''.   Ans. $y'' = \dfrac{-a^2}{y^3}$.

22. If $x^3 - y^3 = a^3$, find y''.   Ans. $y'' = -2a^3xy^{-5}$.

23. If $u^3 = a^2t$, find $\dfrac{d^2u}{dt^2}$.   Ans. $\dfrac{d^2u}{dt^2} = -\dfrac{2a^4}{9u^5}$.

24. If $x^3 = at^2$, find $\dfrac{d^2x}{dt^2}$.   *Ans.* $\dfrac{d^2x}{dt^2} = -\dfrac{2a}{9x^2}$.

25. If $x^{\frac{1}{2}} + y^{\frac{1}{2}} = a^{\frac{1}{2}}$, find $\dfrac{d^2y}{dx^2}$.   *Ans.* $\dfrac{d^2y}{dx^2} = \frac{1}{2}a^{\frac{1}{2}}x^{-\frac{3}{2}}$.

26. If $x^{\frac{2}{3}} + y^{\frac{2}{3}} = a^{\frac{2}{3}}$, find $\dfrac{d^2y}{dx^2}$.   *Ans.* $\dfrac{d^2y}{dx^2} = \frac{1}{3}a^{\frac{2}{3}}x^{-\frac{4}{3}}y^{-\frac{1}{3}}$.

In Exs. 27–37, find the slope of the curve at the given point.

27. $x^2 + y^2 - 12x + 4y - 5 = 0$ at $(0, 1)$.   *Ans.* 2.

28. $x^2 + 2y^2 - 3x - 4y + 2 = 0$ at $(1, 2)$.   *Ans.* $\frac{1}{4}$.

29. $(x + 2y)^2 = x + 10$ at $(-1, 2)$.   *Ans.* $-\frac{5}{12}$.

30. $(3x - y)^2 = 6x + 2y + 23$ at $(1, -2)$.   *Ans.* 2.

31. $x(x^2 - y^2) = 3$ at $(-1, 2)$.   *Ans.* $\frac{1}{4}$.

32. $y(3x - y^2) = 10$ at $(3, 2)$.   *Ans.* 2.

33. $y(3x - y^2) = 16$ at $(4, 2)$.   *Ans.* Slope does not exist.

34. $y^2 = \dfrac{b^3}{2x + b}$ at $(0, b)$.   *Ans.* -1.

35. $y^2 = \dfrac{2a^3x}{x^2 + a^2}$ at (a, a).   *Ans.* 0.

36. $y^3 = \dfrac{2ax^3}{x + a}$ at (a, a).   *Ans.* $\frac{5}{6}$.

37. $y^2 = \dfrac{x^3}{2a - x}$ at (a, a).   *Ans.* 2.

POLYNOMIAL CURVES

34. Tangents and Normals to Plane Curves

The equation of a line of slope m through the point (x_1, y_1) is

$$(1) \qquad\qquad y - y_1 = m(x - x_1).$$

Hence, to find the tangent at any point of a plane curve we have only to find the slope of the curve (i.e., the value of y') at that point, and substitute for m in the above formula.

The normal* to a curve at the point (x_1, y_1) is defined to be the line through that point and perpendicular to the tangent line there.

The equation of the normal is found from that of the tangent by recalling that if two lines are perpendicular, the slope of one is the negative reciprocal of the slope of the other.

Example (a). Find the tangent and normal to the ellipse

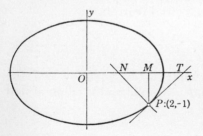

Figure 27

$$(2) \qquad\qquad 4x^2 + 9y^2 = 25$$

at the point $P:(2, -1)$.

Differentiation of both members of the equation of the ellipse yields

$$(3) \qquad\qquad 8x + 18yy' = 0.$$

At the point of contact $(2, -1)$ x has the value 2, y the value (-1), and we shall denote the slope there by m. Thus at $(2, -1)$ equation (3) yields

$$16 - 18m = 0; \quad m = \tfrac{8}{9}.$$

---

* The word "normal" is used in advanced mathematics to mean "perpendicular." It is in this sense rather than in the sense of "natural" or "usual" that the word is used here.

By (1) the equation of the tangent line is

$$y + 1 = \tfrac{8}{9}(x - 2),$$

or

(4) $8x - 9y = 25.$

The normal line is perpendicular to the line (4) and passes through $(2, -1)$. Hence that normal is

(5) $9x + 8y = 10.$

   Example (b). Find the tangent to the ellipse

(6) $\dfrac{x^2}{a^2} + \dfrac{y^2}{b^2} = 1$

at any point (x_1, y_1) on the curve.
   From (6) we obtain

$$\frac{2x}{a^2} + \frac{2yy'}{b^2} = 0,$$

$$y' = -\frac{b^2 x}{a^2 y}.$$

Hence, at the point (x_1, y_1), the slope is

$$m = -\frac{b^2 x_1}{a^2 y_1}.$$

We may now substitute the value of m into equation (1) and arrive at the equation

$$y - y_1 = -\frac{b^2 x_1}{a^2 y_1}(x - x_1),$$

or, after clearing of fractions, dividing by $a^2 b^2$, and rearranging,

(7) $\dfrac{x_1 x}{a^2} + \dfrac{y_1 y}{b^2} = \dfrac{x_1^2}{a^2} + \dfrac{y_1^2}{b^2}.$

   Nowhere in the above work have we imposed the condition that the point (x_1, y_1) be on the ellipse (6). The point (x_1, y_1) is on the ellipse if and only if its coordinates satisfy the equation

(8) $\dfrac{x_1^2}{a^2} + \dfrac{y_1^2}{b^2} = 1.$

Using the condition (8) on the right in equation (7), we may conclude that the equation of the tangent at any point (x_1, y_1) on the ellipse is

(9) $\dfrac{x_1 x}{a^2} + \dfrac{y_1 y}{b^2} = 1.$

Putting $b = a$, we deduce the further result that the tangent at any point (x_1, y_1) of the circle

$$x^2 + y^2 = a^2$$

is

(10)
$$x_1 x + y_1 y = a^2.$$

Example (c). Find the tangents of slope 2 to the circle

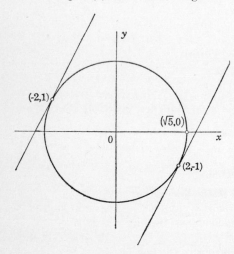

Figure 28

(11)
$$x^2 + y^2 = 5.$$

From equation (11) it follows that

(12)
$$x + yy' = 0.$$

The slope of the tangent line is to be 2. Therefore, the coordinates of the point of contact must satisfy the equation

(13)
$$x + 2y = 0,$$

found by using $y' = 2$ in equation (12).

The coordinates of the point of contact must also satisfy the equation of the original curve (11). By solving the simultaneous equations (11) and (13), we determine the points of contact $(-2, 1)$ and $(2, -1)$.

Each point of contact, together with the given slope 2, yields the equation of one of the desired tangent lines. With the aid of the point-slope form (1) of the equation of a line, the desired tangents may now be found to be

$$2x - y = -5, \quad 2x - y = 5.$$

EXERCISES

In Exs. 1–18, find the equations of the tangent and the normal at the point indicated.

1. $y = 3x^2 - 2x + 1$ at $(1, 2)$.
    Ans. Tangent: $4x - y = 2$; Normal: $x + 4y = 9$.

2. $y = x^3 - 3x^2 - 2$ at $(1, -4)$.
    Ans. Tangent: $3x + y = -1$.

3. $y = 2 + 4x - x^3$ at $x = -1$.
    Ans. Normal: $y = -x - 2$.

4. $x^2 - 6x + 2y - 8 = 0$ at $x = 3$.
    Ans. Normal: $x = 3$.

5. $x^2 + y^2 - 6x + 2y = 0$ at $(0, 0)$.
    Ans. Tangent: $y = 3x$.

6. $y = (2x - 1)^3$ at $x = 1$.
    Ans. Tangent: $6x - y = 5$.

7. $y = x^2 - 2x$ at its points of intersection with the line $y = 3$.
    Ans. Tangents: $4x - y = 9, 4x + y = -1$.

8. $y = x^3 - 7x + 6$ at its points of intersection with the x-axis.
Ans. Tangents: $4x + y = 4$, $5x - y = 10$, $20x - y = -60$.

9. $a^2y = x^3$ at (a, a). *Ans.* Normal: $x + 3y = 4a$.

10. $xy^2 = a^3$ at its points of intersection with the line $x = \frac{1}{4}a$.
Ans. Tangents: $4x - y = 3a$, $4x + y = 3a$.

11. $2xy + 5x - 3y = 0$ at $x = 4$. *Ans.* Tangent: $3x - 5y = 32$.

12. $x^2 - xy + 2y - 2 = 0$ at $x = -2$. *Ans.* Tangent: $7x - 8y = -10$.

13. $(x - y)^2 + 4x - 1 = 0$ at $(0, 1)$. *Ans.* Tangent: $x + y = 1$.

14. $(x - 3y)^2 + 8x + 12 = 0$ at $(-2, 0)$.

15. The *cissoid* $y^2 = \dfrac{x^3}{2a - x}$ at (a, a). *Ans.* Tangent: $2x - y = a$.

16. The *trisectrix* $y^2 = \dfrac{x^2(3a - x)}{a + x}$ at (a, a).

17. The *folium* $x^3 + y^3 = 3axy$ at $(\frac{3}{2}a, \frac{3}{2}a)$. *Ans.* Normal: $x - y = 0$.

18. The hypocycloid of four cusps $x^{\frac{2}{3}} + y^{\frac{2}{3}} = a^{\frac{2}{3}}$ at its first quadrant intersection with the line $y = x$.

Ans. Tangent: $x + y = \dfrac{a}{\sqrt{2}}$.

In Exs. 19–36, find tangent lines as directed.

19. To the ellipse $x^2 + 4y^2 = 8$ parallel to the line $x + 2y = 6$.
Ans. $x + 2y = \pm 4$.

20. To the parabola $y^2 = 6x - 3$ perpendicular to the line $x + 3y = 7$.
Ans. $3x - y = 1$.

21. To the ellipse $x^2 + 2y^2 = 9$ perpendicular to the line $4x - y = 6$.
Ans. $x + 4y = \pm 9$.

22. To the ellipse $x^2 - xy + 2y^2 - 4x + 2y + 2 = 0$ parallel to the line $x - 4y = 2$. *Ans.* $x - 4y = -2$, $x - 4y = 6$.

23. To the parabola $(x + 2y)^2 + 2x - y - 3 = 0$ parallel to the line $4x + 3y = 2$. *Ans.* $4x + 3y = 4$.

24. To the cubic $y = x^3 - 2x + 3$ parallel to the line $10x - y = 3$.
Ans. $10x - y = 13$, $10x - y = -19$.

25. To the cubic $y = x^3 + 6x^2 + 10x + 8$ parallel to the line $y = x$.
Ans. $y = x + 4$, $y = x + 8$.

26. To the curve $y = x^4 - 14x^2 + 17x + 40$ perpendicular to the line $x = 7y + 4$. *Ans.* $7x + y = 51$, $7x + y = 48$, $7x + y = -77$.

27. To the curve $y = x^4 + 2x^3 - 2x^2 - 3x + 3$ perpendicular to the line $x - 3y = 2$. *Ans.* $3x + y = 3$, $3x + y = -5$, $48x + 16y = 45$.

28. To the curve $y = x^4 - 4x^3 + 2x^2 - 4x + 15$ perpendicular to the line $x + 8y = 7$. *Ans.* $8x - y = 30$.

29. To the curve $y = x^4 - 4x^3 - 2x^2 + 16x - 10$ parallel to the line $y = 4x - 1$. *Ans.* $4x - y = 3$, $4x - y = 19$ (twice).

30. To the curve $y = \frac{1}{4}x^4 + x^3 + x^2 - 2x - 3$ parallel to the line $2x + y = 1$. *Ans.* $8x + 4y = -11$, $2x + y = -3$ (twice).

31. To the curve $y = x^4 - 4x^3 + 6x^2 - 4x + 3$ with slope zero.
Ans. $y = 2$ (three times).

32. To the curve $y = x^4 + 4x^3 - 8x^2 + 3x + 70$ with slope 3.
Ans. $3x - y = -70$, $3x - y = -67$, $3x - y = 58$.

33. To the curve $y = x^2(x^2 + 2x - 2)$ parallel to the x-axis.
$$Ans.\ y = 0,\ y = -8,\ y = -\tfrac{3}{16}.$$

34. To the parabola $y^2 = 4ax$, with slope m. $\qquad Ans.\ y = mx + \dfrac{a}{m}.$

35. To the ellipse $\dfrac{x^2}{a^2} + \dfrac{y^2}{b^2} = 1$, with slope m. $\quad Ans.\ y = mx \pm \sqrt{a^2m^2 + b^2}.$

36. To the hyperbola $2xy = a^2$, with slope m; $(m < 0)$.
$$Ans.\ y = mx \pm a\sqrt{-2m}.$$

37. Find a normal of slope $\tfrac{2}{3}$ to the hyperbola $3x^2 - 4y^2 = 8$.
$$Ans.\ 2x - 3y = \pm 7.$$

38. Find a normal of slope 2 to the ellipse $x^2 + 2y^2 = 3$. $\quad Ans.\ 2x - y = \pm 1.$

39. Find a normal of slope $(-\tfrac{1}{2})$ to the cubic $y = x^3 - 10x - 7$.
$$Ans.\ x + 2y = 8,\ x + 2y = -36.$$

40. Find a normal of slope $\tfrac{1}{3}$ to the cubic $ay^2 = x^3$. $\quad Ans.\ x - 3y = 28a.$

In Exs. 41–44, determine the coefficients a, b, c, etc., so that the curve will satisfy the stipulated conditions.

41. Make the parabola $y = ax^2 + bx + c$ pass through $(2, 1)$ and be tangent to the line $y = 2x + 4$ at $(1, 6)$. $\qquad Ans.\ y = -7x^2 + 16x - 3.$

42. Make the parabola $y = ax^2 + bx + c$ pass through $(3, 13)$ and be tangent to the line $8x - y = 15$ at $(2, 1)$. $\qquad Ans.\ y = 4x^2 - 8x + 1.$

43. Make the cubic $y = ax^3 + bx^2 + cx + d$ pass through the points $(0, -6)$, $(1, -2)$ and be tangent to the line $3x - y = 6$ at $(2, 0)$.
$$Ans.\ y = x^3 - 4x^2 + 7x - 6.$$

44. Make the cubic $y = ax^3 + bx^2 + cx + d$ be tangent to the line $y = 12x + 13$ at $(-1, 1)$ and have a horizontal tangent line at the point $(1, 5)$.
$$Ans.\ y = 2x^3 - 3x^2 + 6.$$

45. Find the x-intercept of each of the lines (9), (10), § 34; hence deduce a ruler-and-compass construction for the tangent at any point of an ellipse.

In Exs. 46–51, (a) plot the curve; (b) get the equation of the tangent at (x_1, y_1); (c) find the x-intercept of the tangent; (d) from the result of (c), show how to construct the tangent by ruler and compass.

46. The parabola $y^2 = 4ax$. $\qquad Ans.\ (b)\ y_1 y = 2ax + 2ax_1.$

47. The hyperbola $2xy = a^2$. $\qquad Ans.\ (b)\ y_1 x + x_1 y = a^2;\ (c)\ 2x_1.$

48. $a^2 y = x^3$. $\qquad Ans.\ (c)\ \tfrac{2}{3}x_1.$ $\qquad$ **49.** $y^3 = ax^2$. $\qquad Ans.\ (c)\ -\tfrac{1}{2}x_1.$

50. $a^{n-1} y = x^n$. Cf. Exs. 46–49. $\qquad\qquad Ans.\ (c)\ \dfrac{n-1}{n}x_1.$

51. The hyperbola $\dfrac{x^2}{a^2} - \dfrac{y^2}{b^2} = 1$. $\qquad Ans.\ (b)\ \dfrac{x_1 x}{a^2} - \dfrac{y_1 y}{b^2} = 1.$

52. Find (a) the normal to the parabola $y^2 = 4ax$ at (x_1, y_1), and (b) its x-intercept; hence construct the normal and tangent.
$$Ans.\ (a)\ y_1 x + 2ay = y_1(x_1 + 2a).$$

53. Show that the tangent to the hyperbola $2xy = a^2$ forms with the axes a triangle of constant area. (Ex. 47.)

35. *Graphs*

In constructing the graph of a given function, the beginner relies chiefly on the rudimentary method of plotting by separate points. This method, although useful in giving an accurate detail of some portion of the curve in which we may be specially interested, fails to exhibit the general properties of the function. In analytic geometry, by observing the algebraic properties of the equation and then interpreting these properties geometrically, we are able to discover the general appearance of the curve, in many cases, with very little point plotting. We are now in position to develop still stronger methods for attacking the problem. These methods will rest chiefly on a study of the first and second derivatives of the function.

For simplicity, we shall in this chapter confine our attention to the graphs of polynomials. A fuller treatment of the subject of curve tracing will be given in Chapter 16.

In drawing a curve, it is well to begin by finding the points of intersection with the axes, provided this can be done without great difficulty.

The behavior of a function for large values of x, both positive and negative, can usually be determined at once by inspection. This question should always be investigated; the result is of great value in interpreting the data.

36. *Increasing and Decreasing Functions*

Consider a function

$$(1) \qquad\qquad y = f(x)$$

which has a continuous derivative on some range of x values. We know ($\S$ 24) that the derivative y' is the rate of change of y with respect to x. If $y' > 0$ in some x interval, the rate of change of y is positive, so that y increases as x increases in that interval. If $y' < 0$ in some interval, y decreases as x increases in that interval. The same conclusions are exhibited vividly by the graph of the function because y' is also the slope of the

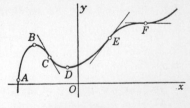

Figure 29

curve (1). In Fig. 29, as x increases, *the curve rises if the slope is positive*, as on the arc AB; *it falls if the slope is negative*, as along BD:

$$If\ y' > 0,\ y\ increases;$$
$$If\ y' < 0,\ y\ decreases.$$

The above results are useful not only as employed in this chapter but also in demonstrating the validity of certain inequalities which are valuable in many phases of advanced mathematics. In $\S\S$ 63, 79, some of those inequalities will be obtained.

37. *Maxima and Minima*

At a point such as B (Fig. 29), where the function is algebraically greater than at any neighboring point, the function is said to have a *maximum value*, and the point is called a *maximum point*. Similarly, at D the function has a *minimum value*. *At such points the tangent is parallel to Ox;* i.e.,

$$y' = 0.$$

But the vanishing of the derivative does not mean that the function is necessarily a maximum or a minimum; the tangent is parallel to Ox at F, yet the function is neither a maximum nor a minimum there. From the figure, we deduce the following test:

At a point where $y' = 0$, if y changes from positive to negative (as x increases), y is a maximum; if y' changes from negative to positive, y is a minimum; if y' does not change sign, y is neither a maximum nor a minimum.

The points at which $y' = 0$ are called *critical points*, and the corresponding values of x are the *critical values of x*: in Fig. 29, B, D, F are critical points. Maxima and minima collectively are called *extremes*: in the figure, B and D are extremes.

An extreme is not necessarily the greatest (or least) value that the function attains anywhere in its range. The ordinate of F, for example, is greater than that of B. An extreme is merely greater (or less) than any *neighboring* value. The greatest value that the function can assume anywhere in its range (if such a value exists) is the *absolute maximum*; a maximum (such as at B) that is greater than any other in the neighborhood is a *relative maximum*.

In the majority of applications, we are concerned with the absolute maximum or minimum. When the function is a polynomial there can never be an absolute extreme if x is unrestricted; but even in the case of polynomials such extremes frequently occur in practical problems, owing to the fact that x is limited in range. This matter will be discussed in § 44.

Example. Locate and classify the critical points of

$$y = \tfrac{1}{3}x^3 - \tfrac{1}{2}x^2 - 2x + 2.$$

We find

$$y' = x^2 - x - 2 = (x + 1)(x - 2).$$

Setting

$$y' = 0,$$

we get the critical values $x = -1$ or 2, and the critical points $(-1, \tfrac{19}{6})$, $(2, -\tfrac{4}{3})$. Now as x (increasing) passes through -1, y' changes from positive to negative: thus y assumes the maximum value $\tfrac{19}{6}$. As x passes through 2, y' changes from negative to positive: y assumes the minimum value $-\tfrac{4}{3}$. The curve is shown in Fig. 30, page 66.

38. *Concavity*

The second derivative is the rate of change of the first derivative. It follows that when y'' is positive, y' is increasing; as x increases, the tangent turns in a counterclockwise sense and the curve is *concave upward*. When y'' is negative, y' decreases; the curve is *concave downward*.

At a maximum point the curve is concave downward, and hence y'', if it is not zero, must be negative. At a minimum, if not zero, y'' must be positive. If the second derivative is easily obtained and if y'' does not happen to be zero at the critical point in question, it is usually more convenient to determine whether we have a maximum or a minimum by finding the sign of y''; but the test of § 37 has the advantage of being perfectly general.

In summary, the test is as follows:

At a point where $y' = 0$, if $y'' < 0$, y is a maximum; if $y'' > 0$, y is a minimum; if $y'' = 0$, the test fails.

Example (a). Examine the function

$$y = \tfrac{1}{3}x^3 - \tfrac{1}{2}x^2 - 2x + 2$$

for maxima and minima. (See the example, § 37.)

We have

$$y' = x^2 - x - 2 = (x + 1)(x - 2),$$
$$y'' = 2x - 1.$$

At $x = -1$, $y'' = -3$; y is a maximum. At $x = 2$, $y'' = 3$; y is a minimum.

Example (b). Examine the function

$$y = x(x - 1)^3$$

for maxima and minima.

We find

$$y' = 3x(x - 1)^2 + (x - 1)^3 = (x - 1)^2(4x - 1),$$
$$y'' = 4(x - 1)^2 + 2(x - 1)(4x - 1) = 6(x - 1)(2x - 1).$$

The critical points ($y' = 0$) are $(\tfrac{1}{4}, -\tfrac{27}{256})$, $(1, 0)$. When $x = \tfrac{1}{4}$, $y'' = \tfrac{9}{4}$; y is a minimum. When $x = 1$, $y'' = 0$; the test fails. Turning to the test of § 37, we find that as x passes through 1, y' does not change sign; the point is neither a maximum nor a minimum. The curve is shown in Fig. 31, page 66.

The results of this and the preceding section give useful information regarding the behavior of a function as determined by the behavior of its derivatives. However, we shall find in the next chapter that in specific applications of the theory, the nature of the various critical values can often be determined very easily by inspection. In such a case, of course, it is unnecessary to apply either of the above tests, except perhaps as a check.

In the exercises below, it is advised that no attempt be made to trace the curve; this is better postponed until our analysis is complete (§§ 39–40).

EXERCISES

In Exs. 1–16, locate the critical points, and determine the maxima and minima by the tests of §§ 37–38.

1. $y = 4 - 6x + x^2$.　　　　　　　2. $y = 4x^2 + 16x + 9$.

3. $y = (2x - 1)^2$.　　　　　　　　4. $y = -4(x + 2)^2$.

5. $y = 2 + 12x - x^3$.　　　　*Ans.* $(-2, -14)$ minimum; $(2, 18)$ maximum.

6. $y = x^3 - 3x^2 - 9x + 20$.　　*Ans.* $(-1, 25)$ maximum; $(3, -7)$ minimum.

7. $y = x^3 - 3x^2 + 4x + 5$.　　　　　　　　　　*Ans.* No critical point.

8. $y = x^3 - 6x^2 + 12x$.　　　　　　　　　　　　*Ans.* No extreme.

9. $y = x^4 + 2x^2 + 8x + 3$.　　　　　　　*Ans.* $(-1, -2)$ minimum.

10. $y = 16x + 4x^2 - x^4$.　　　　　　　　*Ans.* $(2, 32)$ maximum.

11. $y = x^2(x - 2)^2$.　　　*Ans.* $(0, 0)$ and $(2, 0)$ minima; $(1, 1)$ maximum.

12. $a^3 y = x^4$.　　　　　　　　　　　　*Ans.* $(0, 0)$ minimum.

13. $9a^3 y = x(4a - x)^3$.　　　　　　　　*Ans.* $(a, 3a)$ maximum.

14. $a^3 y = x^2(2a^2 - x^2)$.　　*Ans.* $(0, 0)$ minimum; (a, a) and $(-a, a)$ maxima.

15. $a^3 y = x^3(4a - 3x)$.　　　　　　　　　*Ans.* (a, a) maximum.

16. $a^5 y = x^4(3a^2 - 2x^2)$.

In Exs. 17–22, determine the coefficients a, b, c, etc. so that the curve will satisfy the stipulated conditions.

17. Make the curve $y = ax^3 + bx^2 + cx + d$ have critical points at $(0, 4)$ and $(2, 0)$.　　　　　　　　　　　　　　　　*Ans.* $y = x^3 - 3x^2 + 4$.

18. Make the curve $y = ax^3 + bx^2 + cx + d$ have critical points at $(1, 0)$ and $(-2, 27)$.　　　　　　　　　　　*Ans.* $y = 2x^3 + 3x^2 - 12x + 7$.

19. Make the curve $y = ax^3 + bx^2 + cx + d$ pass through the points $(0, 1)$ and $(-3, 7)$ and have a critical point at $(-1, 3)$.　　*Ans.* $y = -x^3 - 4x^2 - 5x + 1$.

20. Make the curve $y = ax^3 + bx^2 + cx + d$ have a critical point at $(0, -2)$ and also be tangent to the line $3x + y + 3 = 0$ at $(-1, 0)$.

Ans. $y = x^3 + 3x^2 - 2$.

21. Make the curve $y = ax^4 + bx^3 + cx^2 + dx + e$ pass through the point $(1, -9)$ and have critical points at $(0, 0)$ and $(-1, -1)$.　　*Ans.* $y = -x^2(x + 2)^2$.

22. Make the curve $y = ax^4 + bx^3 + cx^2 + dx + e$ pass through $(-1, 8)$, be tangent to the line $y = 11x - 5$ at $(1, 6)$, and have a critical point at $(0, 3)$.

Ans. $y = 3x^4 - x^3 + x^2 + 3$.

23. What is the condition that the cubic $y = ax^3 + bx^2 + cx + d$ shall have two extremes?　　　　　　　　　　　　　　　　*Ans.* $b^2 - 3ac > 0$.

39. *Points of Inflection*

A *point of inflection* is a point at which the curve changes from concave upward to concave downward, or vice versa (the points C, E, F in Fig. 29, page 61).

At a point of inflection the tangent reverses the sense in which it turns, which means that y' changes from an increasing to a decreasing function, or vice versa. Hence at such a point y'' changes sign and, if it is continuous, must vanish. Conversely, *a point at which y'' vanishes is a point of inflection, provided y'' changes sign at that point.*

Since y'', the rate of change of the slope, is zero at a point of inflection, the tangent is sometimes said to be *stationary for an instant* at such a point, and in the neighborhood of the point it turns very slowly. Hence the inflectional tangent agrees more closely with the curve near its point of contact than does an ordinary tangent; it is therefore especially useful in tracing the curve to *draw the tangent at each point of inflection.*

A point at which y'' vanishes without changing sign is not a point of inflection; the result means that near that point the tangent turns even more slowly than near a point of inflection.

As noted in §§ 37–38, a point where $y' = 0$ is a maximum or a minimum, provided $y'' \neq 0$. If y' and y'' both equal zero, the point is in general a point of inflection with a horizontal tangent (the point F in Fig. 29); but if y'' vanishes without changing sign, the point is a maximum or minimum.

By combining Theorem 10, page 48, with the above discussion, we obtain the following useful result.

THEOREM 11. *If $x = a$ is a root of odd order—simple, triple, etc.—of the equation $y' = 0$, then $x = a$ is a maximum or minimum; if $x = a$ is a root of even order, $x = a$ is a point of inflection with horizontal tangent.*

40. *Sketching Polynomial Curves*

The theory in §§ 35–39 may now be summarized in the form of a definite sequence of steps, as follows:

1. *Find the points of intersection with the axes.*
2. *Determine the behavior of y for large values of x.*
3. *Locate the points where $y' = 0$, and determine the maxima and minima.*
4. *Locate the points where $y'' = 0$ (points of inflection, in most cases), and draw the tangent at each of those points.*
5. *If necessary, plot a few additional points.*

Any step that leads to serious algebraic difficulties may be omitted, provided sufficient information is obtainable without it.

Example (a). Sketch the curve

$$y = \tfrac{1}{3}x^3 - \tfrac{1}{2}x^2 - 2x + 2.$$

1. When $x = 0$, $y = 2$. The x-intercepts are irrational and will not be determined.

2. When x is numerically large, the sign of y is the same as the sign of the highest-degree term in x. Hence, when x is large and negative, y is large and negative; when x is large and positive, y is large and positive.

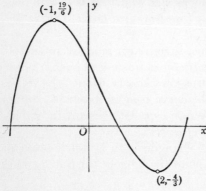

Figure 30

3. $y' = x^2 - x - 2$
$$= (x + 1)(x - 2):$$

the critical points are $(-1, \frac{19}{6})$, $(2, -\frac{4}{3})$. Without reference to previous examples (§§ 37–38), the situation at once becomes clear when the result of step 2 is considered. Since y is large and negative when x is large and negative, the curve must come up through the third quadrant, rise to a maximum at $(-1, \frac{19}{6})$, fall to a minimum at $(2, -\frac{4}{3})$, and then rise indefinitely (since when x is large and positive y is large and positive).

4. $y'' = 2x - 1$.

Equating this to zero, we get $x = \frac{1}{2}$; the point $(\frac{1}{2}, \frac{11}{12})$ is a point of inflection, the slope at that point being $-\frac{9}{4}$.

Example (b). Sketch the curve $y = x(x - 1)^3$.

1. When $x = 0$, $y = 0$; when $y = 0$, $x = 0$ or 1.
2. When x is large and either positive or negative, y is large and positive.
3. $y' = (x - 1)^3 + 3x(x - 1)^2 = (x - 1)^2(4x - 1)$.

Thus the critical points are $(\frac{1}{4}, -\frac{27}{256})$, $(1, 0)$. The result of step 2 shows that the former point is a minimum, the latter a point of inflection with horizontal

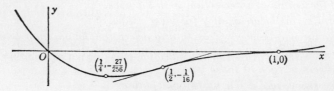

Figure 31

tangent. This last is verified by the fact that $x = 1$ is a *double root* of $y' = 0$ (Theorem 11).

4. $y'' = 2(x - 1)(4x - 1) + 4(x - 1)^2$
$$= 6(x - 1)(2x - 1).$$

The points of inflection are $(\frac{1}{2}, -\frac{1}{16})$, with slope $\frac{1}{4}$, and $(1, 0)$, with slope zero.

EXERCISES

In Exs. 1–39, sketch the curve, choosing a suitable scale in each problem.

1. $y = x^3 - 3x$.   2. $y = x^3 - 3x^2$.

3. $y = x^3 + 3x^2 + 3x$.   4. $y = 36 + 12x - x^3$.

5. $y = 2x^3 - 9x^2 + 12x - 2$.   6. $y = 28 - 15x + 6x^2 - x^3$.

7. $y = (x - 6)^2(9 - x)$.   8. $6y = x^3 + 9x^2 + 12$.

9. $y = 2x^3 + 3x^2 - 12x + 7$.   10. $a^2y = 27x^2(x - a)$.

11. $y = x^4 - 2x^3$.   12. $y = x^4 - 4x^3 + 8x$.

13. $y = x^4 - 6x^2 - 7$.   14. $y = x^4 - 6x^2 - 8x$.

15. $y = x(x^3 - 8x^2 + 24x - 32)$.   16. $y = 4x(1 - 3x + 4x^2 - 2x^3)$.

17. $y = 4x(x^3 - 2x^2 + 2)$.   18. $y = 4(x^4 + 2x^3 + 1)$.

19. $y = x^4 + 2x^3 - 10x - 9$.   20. $y = 8x + 2x^3 - x^4$.

21. $y = 4x^2(x^2 + 3x + 3)$.   22. $y = x^2(3x^2 + 8x + 16)$.

23. $y = x^4 + 2x^3 - 10x - 20$.   24. $y = 4x(x^3 + 8x^2 + 12x + 8)$.

25. $y = x^4 - 6x^3 + 12x^2 - 8x + 1$.

26. $y = x^4 - 8x^3 + 18x^2 - 8x - 3$.

27. $y = x^5 - 5x$.   28. $y = x^5 - 20x^2$.

29. $4y = 20x^3 - 3x^5$.   30. $a^4y = x^4(4x - 5a)$.

31. $y = 3x^5 - 10x^3 + 15x$.   32. $y = (2x - 1)^5 + 32$.

33. $8y = 3x^5 - 50x^3 + 135x$.   34. $y = x^3(6x^2 - 15x + 10)$.

35. $y = x^5 - 5x^4 + 20x^2$.   36. $y = 64x^3(x - 1)^3$.

37. $a^4y = x(x^2 - 15a^2)^2$.   38. $y = x^2(x - 1)^4$.

39. $a^5y = x^5(6a - 5x)$; $[(0.8)^5 = 0.33]$.

40. Plot the curves $y = x$, $y = x^2$, $y = x^3$, $y = x^4$, $y = x^5$, all on the same axes, in the interval $-1 \leqq x \leqq 1$.

41. Make the curve $y = ax^3 + bx^2 + cx + d$ pass through $(0, 3)$ and have at $(1, 2)$ a point of inflection with a horizontal tangent.

$$Ans. \ y = -x^3 + 3x^2 - 3x + 3.$$

42. Make the curve $y = ax^3 + bx^2 + cx + d$ pass through $(-1, -1)$ and have at $(1, 3)$ an inflection point with inflectional tangent $4x - y = 1$.

$$Ans. \ 2y = -x^3 + 3x^2 + 5x - 1.$$

43. Make the curve $y = ax^3 + bx^2 + cx + d$ pass through $(1, 4)$ and have at $(-1, 2)$ an inflection point with inflectional tangent $3x + y = -1$.

44. Make the curve $y = ax^4 + bx^3 + cx^2 + dx + e$ pass through the points $(0, 3)$, $(-2, 7)$ and have at $(-1, 4)$ an inflection point with a horizontal tangent.

$$Ans. \ y = x^4 + 2x^3 - 2x + 3.$$

45. Make the curve $y = ax^4 + bx^3 + cx^2 + dx + e$ have a critical point at $(0, 3)$ and have an inflection point at $(1, 2)$ with inflectional tangent $6x + y = 8$.

$$Ans. \ y = 9x^4 - 22x^3 + 12x^2 + 3.$$

46. Prove that the cubic $y = ax^3 + bx^2 + cx + d$ is symmetric with respect to its point of inflection. (Find the point of inflection; translate to that point as new origin.)

APPLICATIONS OF THE

DERIVATIVE

41. *Applications of Maxima and Minima*

It was shown in § 37 that at a point where its first derivative vanishes, a function assumes an extreme value, provided the derivative changes sign at that point. This result finds application in a great variety of problems, some of which will now be considered.

When the derivative is equated to zero, it may happen, of course, that several critical values are obtained. In practice, the value that gives the desired maximum or minimum can often be selected at once by inspection.

Example (a). A box is to be made of a piece of cardboard 16 × 10 in. by cutting equal squares out of the corners and turning up the sides. Find the volume of the largest box that can be made in this way. (Fig. 32.)

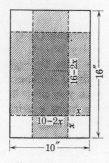
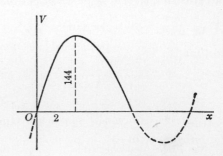

Figure 32   Figure 33

Let x be the length of the side of each of the squares cut out. Then the volume of the box is

$$V = x(10 - 2x)(16 - 2x), \qquad 0 \le x \le 5$$
$$= 160x - 52x^2 + 4x^3,$$

whence
$$V' = 160 - 104x + 12x^2$$
$$= 4(x - 2)(3x - 20).$$

Setting
$$V' = 0,$$

we get the critical values $x = 2$, $\frac{20}{3}$. By the nature of the problem x is restricted to values between 0 and 5, so that the value $\frac{20}{3}$ must be rejected. Since the volume is zero when $x = 0$ and again when $x = 5$, it must reach a maximum at some intermediate point; it therefore follows without the application of further tests that the critical value $x = 2$ gives the required maximum volume (Fig. 33):

$$V_{\text{max.}} = 2(10 - 4)(16 - 4) = 144 \text{ cu. in.}$$

The minimum volume, of course, is $V = 0$, occurring at the endpoints $x = 0$, $x = 5$. The reason why our analysis fails to show these minima is that V is discontinuous at $x = 0, 5$, and all our present theory rests on the assumption that $f(x)$ and $f'(x)$ are continuous. Extremes occurring in connection with discontinuities will be discussed in § 44.

Example (b). Find the area of the largest rectangle that can be inscribed in a given circle.

The area of the rectangle is

(1) $A = 4xy,$

where x and y are connected by the relation

(2) $x^2 + y^2 = a^2.$

Substituting $y = \sqrt{a^2 - x^2}$ in (1), we find

(3) $A = 4x \sqrt{a^2 - x^2},$

so that

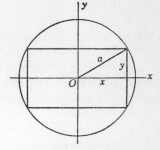

Figure 34

$$A' = 4 \sqrt{a^2 - x^2} - \frac{4x^2}{\sqrt{a^2 - x^2}} = \frac{4a^2 - 8x^2}{\sqrt{a^2 - x^2}}.$$

Setting $A' = 0$, we get $4a^2 - 8x^2 = 0$, $x = \frac{1}{2} \sqrt{2}\, a$.
Substitute in (3):
$$A_{\text{max.}} = 2a^2.$$

Example (c). Find the altitude of the largest circular cylinder that can be inscribed in a circular cone of radius r and height h.

The volume of the cylinder is

$$V = \pi x^2 y.$$

Figure 35 shows a section by a plane through the axis. By similar triangles,

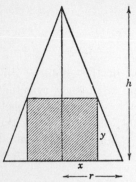

Figure 35

$$\frac{x}{r} = \frac{h - y}{h}, \quad x = \frac{r}{h}(h - y),$$

so that

$$V = \frac{\pi r^2}{h^2}(h - y)^2 y,$$

$$\frac{dV}{dy} = \frac{\pi r^2}{h^2}[(h - y)^2 - 2(h - y)y]$$

$$= \frac{\pi r^2}{h^2}(h - y)(h - 3y).$$

To make V a maximum, set $V' = 0$. Then $y = h$ or $y = \frac{1}{3}h$. But $y = h$ leads to $V = 0$, surely not the largest V. That $y = \frac{1}{3}h$ yields the maximum V is intuitively reasonable and can be checked by noting that

$$\frac{d^2 V}{dy^2} = \frac{\pi r^2}{h^2}(-4h + 6y)$$

is negative for $y = \frac{1}{3}h$.

42. *Use of an Auxiliary Variable*

If the function under consideration is most readily expressed in terms of two variables, a relation between these two variables must be found from the conditions of the problem. By means of this relation one of the variables can be eliminated, after which the maximum or minimum can be found as in § 41. However, it is often more convenient not to perform the elimination but to proceed as in the following examples.

Example (a). Find the shape of the largest rectangle that can be inscribed in a given circle. (See Fig. 34, page 69.)

The area of the rectangle is

$$(1) \qquad\qquad A = 4xy,$$

where x and y are connected by the relation

$$(2) \qquad\qquad x^2 + y^2 = a^2.$$

Differentiating the A of (1) with respect to x and equating the derivative to zero, we have

$$A' = 4(xy' + y) = 0,$$

or

$$y' = -\frac{y}{x}.$$

Differentiating each member of (2), we get, since a is constant,

$$2x + 2yy' = 0, \qquad y' = -\frac{x}{y}.$$

Equating values of y', we find

$$-\frac{y}{x} = -\frac{x}{y},$$

from which it follows that

(3) $$y = x:$$

the maximum rectangle is a square.

If it is desired to find the actual maximum value of A, we solve the simultaneous equations (2), (3), which yield

$$x = y = \tfrac{1}{2}\sqrt{2}\, a,$$

and

$$A_{\text{max.}} = 2a^2.$$

Example (*b*). A cylindrical tin boiler, open at the top, has a copper bottom. If sheet copper is five times as expensive as tin, per unit area, find the most economical proportions.

Let r denote the radius, h the height; let k be the unit cost of tin. Then the cost C, which is to be a minimum, is

(4) $$C = 2\pi krh + 5\pi kr^2 = \pi k(2rh + 5r^2).$$

The volume

(5) $$V = \pi r^2 h$$

is to be held constant.

From (4) we get

(6) $$\frac{dC}{dr} = \pi k \left(2r\frac{dh}{dr} + 2h + 10r \right)$$

and from (5) it follows that

(7) $$\pi \left(r^2 \frac{dh}{dr} + 2rh \right) = 0,$$

since V is constant.

Seeking a minimum cost, we may set $\dfrac{dC}{dr} = 0$, eliminate $\dfrac{dh}{dr}$ with the aid of (7), and thus arrive at $h = 5r$. This is certainly an easy way to solve the problem, but it has one disadvantage in that it tempts us to rely on intuition to see that $h = 5r$ actually leads to the minimum C. An alternative procedure follows.

From (7) we obtain $r \dfrac{dh}{dr} = -2h$ so that (6) may now be written in the form

$$(8) \qquad\qquad \frac{dC}{dr} = 2\pi k(5r - h).$$

Now set $C' = 0$ and obtain $h = 5r$. But also note that (8) yields

$$(9) \qquad\qquad \frac{d^2C}{dr^2} = 2\pi k\left(5 - \frac{dh}{dr}\right) = 2\pi k\left(5 + \frac{2h}{r}\right).$$

Thus C'' is positive for $h = 5r$. We may then conclude that C is a minimum at $h = 5r$.

It is just as reasonable to attack this problem by holding the cost fixed and seeking a maximum volume. Either method leads eventually to the two equations $C' = 0$ and $V' = 0$.

We must, however, hold either C or V constant. With no restrictions on V or C, surely the minimum cost is attained by not building the boiler; i.e., $r = h = 0$ yields a minimum C for V unrestricted. This type of "solution" is not popular in industry.

Example (c). A man in a rowboat 6 mi. from shore desires to reach a point on the shore at a distance of 10 mi. from his present position. If he can walk 4 mi. per hr. and row 2 mi. per hr., in what direction should he row in order to reach his destination in the shortest possible time?

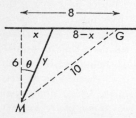

Figure 36

Let x and y be distances defined by Fig. 36, with the man starting at M. Since he rows the distance y at 2 mi. per hr. and walks the distance $(8 - x)$ at 4 mi. per hr., the time required for him to reach his goal G is

$$T = \frac{y}{2} + \frac{8 - x}{4},$$

with

$$y^2 = x^2 + 36.$$

To find the minimum time, we have

$$T' = \tfrac{1}{2}y' - \tfrac{1}{4} = 0, \qquad y' = \tfrac{1}{2};$$
$$2yy' = 2x, \qquad\qquad y' = \frac{x}{y}.$$

Equating the values of y' and noting that

$$\frac{x}{y} = \sin\theta,$$

we find $\theta = 30°$.

EXERCISES

1. What number exceeds its square by the maximum amount? *Ans.* $\frac{1}{2}$.

2. What positive number added to its reciprocal gives the minimum sum?

3. The sum of two numbers is k. Find the minimum value of the sum of their squares. *Ans.* $\frac{1}{2}k^2$.

4. The sum of two numbers is k. Find the minimum value of the sum of their cubes. *Ans.* $\frac{1}{4}k^3$.

5. The sum of two positive numbers is 2. Find the smallest value possible for the sum of the cube of one number and the square of the other. *Ans.* $\frac{256}{27}$.

6. Find two numbers whose sum is a, if the product of one by the square of the other is to be a maximum. *Ans.* $\frac{1}{3}a$, $\frac{2}{3}a$.

7. Find two numbers whose sum is a, if the product of one by the cube of the other is to be a maximum. *Ans.* $\frac{1}{4}a$, $\frac{3}{4}a$.

8. Find two numbers whose sum is a, if the product of the square of one by the cube of the other is to be a maximum. *Ans.* $\frac{2}{5}a$, $\frac{3}{5}a$.

9. What should be the shape of a rectangular field of given area, if it is to be enclosed by the least amount of fencing? *Ans.* A square.

10. A rectangular field of given area is to be fenced off along the bank of a river. If no fence is needed along the river, what is the shape of the rectangle requiring the least amount of fencing? *Ans.* Width $= \frac{1}{2} \times$ length.

11. A rectangular lot is to be fenced off along a highway. If the fence on the highway costs m dollars per yd., on the other sides n dollars per yd., find the area of the largest lot that can be fenced off for k dollars.

12. A rectangular field of fixed area is to be enclosed and divided into three lots by parallels to one of the sides. What should be the relative dimensions of the field to make the amount of fencing a minimum? *Ans.* Width $= \frac{1}{2} \times$ length.

13. Do Ex. 12 with the words "three lots" replaced by "five lots."

14. A rectangular lot is bounded at the back by a river. No fence is needed along the river and there is to be a 24-ft. opening in front. If the fence along the front costs $1.50 per ft., along the sides $1 per ft., find the dimensions of the largest lot which can be thus fenced in for $300. *Ans.* 84 by 112 ft.

15. A box is to be made of a piece of cardboard 9 in. square by cutting equal squares out of the corners and turning up the sides. Find the volume of the largest box that can be made in this way. *Ans.* 54 cu. in.

16. Find the volume of the largest box that can be made by cutting equal squares out of the corners of a piece of cardboard of dimensions 15 in. by 24 in., and then turning up the sides. *Ans.* 486 cu. in.

17. Find the depth of the largest box that can be made by cutting equal squares of side x out of the corners of a piece of cardboard of dimensions $6a$, $6b$, ($b \leqq a$), and then turning up the sides. To select that value of x which yields a maximum volume, apply the test of § 38; or, as an exercise in algebra, show that

$$(a + b + \sqrt{a^2 - ab + b^2}) \geqq 3b.$$

Check Exs. 15, 16. *Ans.* Depth $= a + b - \sqrt{a^2 - ab + b^2}$.

18. The strength of a rectangular beam is proportional to the breadth and the square of the depth. Find the shape of the strongest beam that can be cut from a log of given size. *Ans.* Depth $= \sqrt{2} \times$ breadth.

19. The stiffness of a rectangular beam is proportional to the breadth and the cube of the depth. Find the shape of the stiffest beam that can be cut from a log of given size.   *Ans.* Depth $= \sqrt{3} \times$ breadth.

20. Compare for strength and stiffness, against both edgewise and sidewise thrust, two beams of equal length, one 2 in. by 8 in., the other 4 in. by 6 in. (See Exs. 18–19.) Which shape is more often used for floor joists? Why?

21. Find the rectangle of maximum perimeter inscribed in a given circle.

  Ans. A square.

22. If the hypotenuse of a right triangle is given, show that the area is a maximum when the triangle is isosceles.

23. Find the most economical proportions for a covered box of fixed volume whose base is a rectangle with one side three times as long as the other.

  Ans. Altitude $= \frac{3}{2} \times$ shorter side of base.

24. Solve Ex. 23 if the box has an open top.

  Ans. Altitude $= \frac{3}{4} \times$ shorter side of base.

25. Find the most economical proportions for a quart can.

  Ans. Diameter = height.

26. Find the most economical proportions for a cylindrical cup.

  Ans. Radius = height.

27. Find the most economical proportions for a box with an open top and a square base.   *Ans.* Side of base $= 2 \times$ altitude.

28. The perimeter of an isosceles triangle is P in. Find the maximum area.

29. The sum of the length and girth of a container of square cross-section is a in. Find the maximum volume.   *Ans.* $\frac{1}{108}a^3$ cu. in.

30. Find the proportions of the circular cylinder of largest volume that can be inscribed in a given sphere.   *Ans.* Diameter $= \sqrt{2} \times$ height.

31. In Ex. 30, find the shape of the cylinder if its convex surface area is to be a maximum.   *Ans.* Diameter = height.

32. Find the dimensions of the largest rectangular building that can be placed on a right-triangular lot, facing one of the perpendicular sides. (Fig. 37.)   *Ans.* $x = \frac{1}{2}a$.

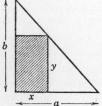

Figure 37

33. A lot has the form of a right triangle, with perpendicular sides 60 and 80 ft. long. Find the length and width of the largest rectangular building that can be erected, facing the hypotenuse of the triangle.   *Ans.* 50 ft. by 24 ft.

34. Solve Ex. 33 if the lengths of the perpendicular sides are a, b.

  Ans. $\dfrac{ab}{2\sqrt{a^2 + b^2}}, \dfrac{\sqrt{a^2 + b^2}}{2}.$

35. A page is to contain 24 sq. in. of print. The margins at top and bottom are 1.5 in., at the sides 1 in. Find the most economical dimensions for the page.

36. A Norman window consists of a rectangle surmounted by a semicircle. What shape gives the most light for a given perimeter?   *Ans.* Breadth = height.

37. Solve Ex. 36 if the semicircle is of stained glass admitting only half the normal amount of light.

38. A cylindrical glass jar has a plastic top. If the plastic is half as expensive as glass, per unit area, find the most economical proportions for the jar.

  Ans. Height $= \frac{3}{2} \times$ radius of the base.

39. A trapezoidal gutter is to be made from a strip of tin by bending up the edges. If the cross-section has the form shown in Fig. 38, what width across the top gives maximum carrying capacity?

Ans. 2a.

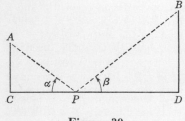

40. Solve Ex. 39, if the strip is 11 in. wide and the base 7 in. wide.   *Ans.* 8 in.

Figure 38

41. In Ex. 39, if the strip is L in. wide, and the width across the top is T in. $(T < L)$, what base width gives the maximum capacity?

42. From a strip of tin 14 in. wide a trapezoidal gutter is to be made by bending up the sides at an angle of 45°. Find the width of the base for greatest carrying capacity.   *Ans.* 3.17 in.

43. A ship lies 6 mi. from shore, and opposite a point 10 mi. farther along the shore another ship lies 18 mi. offshore. A boat from the first ship is to land a passenger and then proceed to the other ship. What is the least distance the boat can travel?

Ans. 26 mi.

44. Two posts, one 8 ft. high and the other 12 ft. high, stand 15 ft. apart. They are to be stayed by wires attached to a single stake at ground level, the wires running to the tops of the posts. Where should the stake be placed, to use the least amount of wire?   *Ans.* 6 ft. from the shorter post.

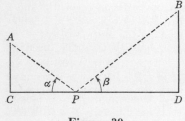

Figure 39

45. A ray of light travels, as in Fig. 39, from A to B via the point P on the mirror CD. Prove that the length $(\overline{AP} + \overline{PB})$ will be a minimum if and only if $\alpha = \beta$.

46. Given a point on the conjugate axis of an equilateral hyperbola, find the shortest distance to the curve.

Ans. For curve $x^2 - y^2 = a^2$, point $(0, k)$, ordinate of nearest point is $y = \frac{1}{2}k$.

47. Find the point on the curve $a^2y = x^3$ that is nearest the point $(4a, 0)$.   *Ans.* (a, a).

In Exs. 48–52, find the shortest distance from the given point to the given curve.

48. $(5, 0)$; $2y^2 = x^3$.   *Ans.* $\sqrt{13}$.   **49.** $(0, 8a)$; $ax^2 = y^3$.   *Ans.* $2a\sqrt{11}$.

50. $(4, 2)$; $x^2 + 3y^2 = 12$.   *Ans.* $\sqrt{2}$.

51. $(1 + n, 0)$; $y = x^n$, $n > 0$.   *Ans.* $\sqrt{1 + n^2}$.

52. $(0, 5)$; $3y^2 = x^3$.   *Ans.* $\sqrt{13}$.

53. Cut the largest possible rectangle from a circular quadrant, as shown in Fig. 40.   *Ans.* $x = 0.54a$.

54. A cylindrical tin boiler, open at the top, has a copper bottom. If sheet copper is m times as expensive as tin, per unit area, find the most economical proportions.

Ans. Height $= m \times$ radius.

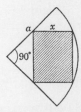

55. Solve Ex. 54 if the boiler is to have a tin cover. Deduce the answer directly from that of Ex. 54.

56. The base of a covered box is a square. The bottom and back are made of pine, the remainder of oak. If oak is m times as expensive as pine, find the most economical proportions.

Figure 40

57. A silo consists of a cylinder surmounted by a hemisphere. If the floor, walls, and roof are equally expensive per unit area, find the most economical proportions. *Ans.* Diameter = total height.

58. For the silo of Ex. 57, find the most economical proportions, if the floor is twice as expensive as the walls, per unit area, and the roof is three times as expensive as the walls, per unit area. *Ans.* Diameter = $\frac{2}{7}$ × total height.

59. An oil can consists of a cylinder surmounted by a cone. If the diameter of the cone is five-sixths of its height, find the most economical proportions.

Ans. Height of cone = 2 × height of cylinder.

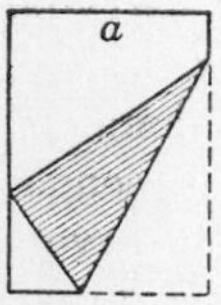

60. One corner of a leaf of width a is folded over so as just to reach the opposite side of the page. Find the width of the part folded over when the length of the crease is a minimum. See Fig. 41. *Ans.* $\frac{3}{4}a$.

61. Solve Ex. 60 if the area folded over is to be a minimum.

Ans. $\frac{2}{3}a$.

62. Inscribe a circular cylinder of maximum convex surface area in a given circular cone. *Ans.* Diameter of cylinder = radius of cone.

Figure 41

63. Find the circular cone of maximum volume inscribed in a sphere of radius a. *Ans.* Altitude = $\frac{4}{3}a$.

64. A sphere is cut to the shape of a circular cone. How much of the material can be saved? (Ex. 63.) *Ans.* 30%.

65. Find the circular cone of minimum volume circumscribed about a sphere of radius a. *Ans.* Altitude = 4a.

66. Find the largest right pyramid with a square base that can be inscribed in a sphere of radius a. *Ans.* Altitude = $\frac{4}{3}a$.

67. An Indian tepee is made by stretching skins or birch bark over a group of poles tied together at the top. If poles of given length are to be used, what shape gives maximum volume? *Ans.* Radius = $\sqrt{2}$ × height.

68. Solve Ex. 67 if poles of any length can be found, but only a limited amount of covering material is available. *Ans.* Height = $\sqrt{2}$ × radius.

69. A man on an island 12 mi. south of a straight beach wishes to reach a point on shore 20 mi. east. If a motorboat, making 20 mi. per hr., can be hired at a rate of $2.00 per hr. for the time it is actually used, and the cost of land transportation is $0.06 per mi., how much must he pay for the trip? *Ans.* $2.16.

70. A man in a motorboat at A (Fig. 42) receives a message at noon, calling him to B. A bus making 40 mi. per hr. leaves C, bound for B, at 1:00 P.M. If $AC = 40$ mi., what must be the speed of the boat to enable the man to catch the bus? *Ans.* At least 28.3 mi. per hr.

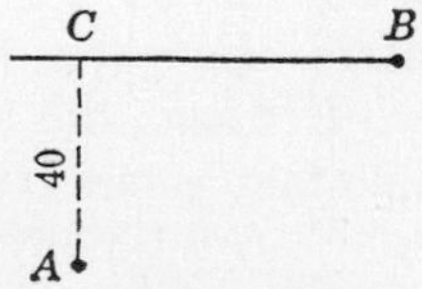

71. In Ex. 70, if the speed of the boat is 30 mi. per hr., what is the greatest distance offshore from which the bus can be caught? *Ans.* $\frac{120}{7}\sqrt{7} = 45.3$ mi.

Figure 42

72. A light is to be placed above the center of a circular area of radius a. What height gives the best illumination on a circular walk surrounding the area? (When light from a point-source strikes a surface obliquely, the intensity of illumination is $I = \dfrac{k \sin \theta}{d^2}$, where θ is the angle of incidence and d the distance from the source.)

Ans. $h = \frac{1}{2}\sqrt{2}\,a$.

73. It is shown in the theory of attraction that a wire bent in the form of a circle of radius a exerts upon a particle in the axis of the circle (i.e., in the line through the center of the circle perpendicular to its plane) an attraction proportional to $\dfrac{h}{(a^2 + h^2)^{\frac{3}{2}}}$, where h is the height of the particle above the plane of the circle. Find h, for maximum attraction. (Compare with Ex. 72.)   *Ans.* $h = \frac{1}{2}\sqrt{2}\,a$.

74. In Ex. 73, if the wire has instead the form of a square of side $2l$, the attraction is proportional to $\dfrac{h}{(h^2 + l^2)\sqrt{h^2 + 2l^2}}$. Find h, for maximum attraction.

43. *Time-Rates*

The fact that the derivative of a function is identical with its rate of change leads to a great variety of applications; those in which time is the independent variable are especially important.

Example (*a*). A balloon, leaving the ground 60 ft. from an observer, rises vertically at the rate of 10 ft. per sec. How fast is the balloon receding from the observer, after 8 sec.?

In time t, the balloon rises a distance $10t$, so that

$$s = \sqrt{3600 + 100t^2},$$
$$\frac{ds}{dt} = \frac{100t}{\sqrt{3600 + 100t^2}}.$$

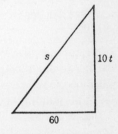

When $t = 8$,

$$\frac{ds}{dt} = \frac{800}{\sqrt{3600 + 6400}} = 8 \text{ ft. per sec.}$$

Figure 43

Note that the given value $t = 8$ is employed only *after the differentiation has been performed.*

Example (*b*). As a man walks across a bridge at the rate of 5 ft. per sec., a boat passes directly beneath him at 10 ft. per sec. If the bridge is 30 ft. above the water, how fast are the man and the boat separating 3 sec. later?

In t sec., the man covers a distance $5t$, the boat a distance $10t$. By elementary geometry, the distance between them is

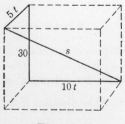

$$s = \sqrt{(5t)^2 + (10t)^2 + (30)^2}$$
$$= \sqrt{125t^2 + 900};$$
$$\frac{ds}{dt} = \frac{125t}{\sqrt{125t^2 + 900}}.$$

After 3 sec.,

Figure 44

$$\frac{ds}{dt} = \frac{375}{\sqrt{2025}} = \tfrac{25}{3} \text{ ft. per sec.}$$

Frequently, the problem of rates is most conveniently solved by expressing the variable whose rate of change is to be found, in terms of another variable whose rate is *known*, and then differentiating *with respect to time* the equation connecting them. It will be recalled that a similar device was employed in § 42.

Example (c). A man on a wharf 20 ft. above the water pulls in a rope, to which a boat is attached, at the rate of 4 ft. per sec. At what rate is the boat approaching the wharf when there is 25 ft. of rope out?

Let x denote the distance of the boat from the wharf, r the length of rope. Then, *given* $\dfrac{dr}{dt}$, we have *to find* $\dfrac{dx}{dt}$. To do this, as suggested above, we express x in terms of r (implicitly or explicitly) and differentiate with respect to t:

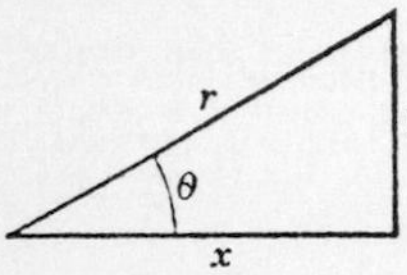

$$x = \sqrt{r^2 - 400}, \quad \frac{dx}{dt} = \frac{r\,\dfrac{dr}{dt}}{\sqrt{r^2 - 400}}.$$

Substitute $r = 25$, $\dfrac{dr}{dt} = -4$:

$$\frac{dx}{dt} = \frac{-100}{\sqrt{225}} = -\tfrac{20}{3} \text{ ft. per sec.}$$

Figure 45

Example (d). Water is flowing into a conical reservoir 20 ft. deep and 10 ft. across the top, at the rate of 15 cu. ft. per min. Find how fast the surface is rising when the water is 8 ft. deep.

The volume of water is

$$V = \tfrac{1}{3}\pi r^2 h.$$

By similar triangles,

$$\frac{r}{h} = \frac{5}{20}, \quad r = \frac{1}{4} h.$$

Hence

$$V = \frac{\pi h^3}{48}, \quad \frac{dV}{dt} = \frac{\pi h^2}{16} \frac{dh}{dt}.$$

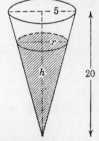

Figure 46

The rate of change of the volume of water with respect to time is

$$\frac{dV}{dt} = 15,$$

so that

$$\frac{\pi h^2}{16} \frac{dh}{dt} = 15, \quad \frac{dh}{dt} = \frac{240}{\pi h^2}.$$

When $h = 8$,

$$\frac{dh}{dt} = \frac{15}{4\pi} = 1.19 \text{ ft. per min.}$$

EXERCISES

1. Water is flowing into a vertical cylindrical tank at the rate of 24 cu. ft. per min. If the radius of the tank is 4 ft., how fast is the surface rising?

Ans. 0.48 ft. per min.

2. Water flows into a vertical cylindrical tank at 12 cu. ft. per min.; the surface rises 6 in. per min. Find the radius of the tank.　　　　　*Ans.* 2.76 ft.

3. A rectangular trough is 10 ft. long and 3 ft. wide. Find how fast the surface rises, if water flows in at the rate of 12 cu. ft. per min.　　　*Ans.* 0.4 ft. per min.

4. A triangular trough 10 ft. long is 4 ft. across the top, and 4 ft. deep. If water flows in at the rate of 3 cu. ft. per min., find how fast the surface is rising when the water is 6 in. deep.　　　　　　　　　　　　　　*Ans.* 0.6 ft. per min.

5. A triangular trough is 10 ft. long, 6 ft. across the top, and 3 ft. deep. If water flows in at the rate of 12 cu. ft. per min., find how fast the surface is rising when the water is 6 in. deep.　　　　　　　　　　　*Ans.* 1.2 ft. per min.

6. A ladder 20 ft. long leans against a vertical wall. If the top slides downward at the rate of 2 ft. per sec., find how fast the lower end is moving when it is 16 ft. from the wall.　　　　　　　　　　　　　　　*Ans.* 1.5 ft. per sec.

7. In Ex. 6, find the rate of change of the slope of the ladder.

Ans. $-\frac{25}{128}$ per sec.

8. A man 6 ft. tall walks away from a lamp post 16 ft. high at the rate of 5 mi. per hr. How fast does the end of his shadow move?　　*Ans.* 8 mi. per hr.

9. In Ex. 8, how fast does the shadow lengthen?

10. A boy on a bike rides north 5 mi., then turns east (Fig. 47). If he rides 10 mi. per hr., at what rate was his distance to the starting point S changing 2 hr. after he left that point?

Ans. 3 $\sqrt{10}$ mi. per hr.

Figure 47

11. A train, starting at noon, travels north at 40 mi. per hr. Another train, starting from the same point at 2 P.M., travels east at 50 mi. per hr. Find, to the nearest mile per hour, how fast the two trains are separating at 3 P.M.

Ans. 56 mi. per hr.

12. In Ex. 10, how fast are the trains separating after a long time?

Ans. 64 mi. per hr.

13. A trapezoidal trough is 10 ft. long, 4 ft. wide at the top, 2 ft. wide at the bottom, and 2 ft. deep. If water flows in at 10 cu. ft. per min., find how fast the water surface is rising, when the water is 6 in. deep.　　*Ans.* 0.4 ft. per min.

14. For the trough of Ex. 13, find how fast the water surface is rising, when the water is one foot deep.　　　　　　　　　　　　*Ans.* $\frac{1}{3}$ ft. per min.

15. A light at eye level stands 20 ft. from a house and 15 ft. from the path leading from the house to the street. A man walks along the path at 6 ft. per sec. How fast does his shadow move along the wall when he is 5 ft. from the house?

Ans. 8 ft. per sec.

16. In Ex. 15, when the man is 5 ft. from the house, find the time-rate of change of that portion of his shadow which lies on the ground.　　*Ans.* 9.9 ft. per sec.

17. A light is placed on the ground 30 ft. from a building. A man 6 ft. tall walks from the light toward the building at the rate of 5 ft. per sec. Find the rate at which the length of his shadow on the wall is changing when he is 15 ft. from the building.

Ans. −4 ft. per sec.

18. Solve Ex. 17, if the light is 10 ft. above the ground.   *Ans.* $\frac{8}{3}$ ft. per sec.

19. One city, A, is 30 mi. north and 55 mi. east of another city, B. At noon, a car starts west from A at 40 mi. per hr.; at 12:10 P.M., another car starts east from B at 60 mi. per hr. Find, in two ways, when the cars will be nearest together.

Ans. 12:39 P.M.

20. For the conditions of Ex. 19, draw the appropriate figures for times before 12:39 P.M. and after that time. Show that in terms of time after noon, the formulas for distance between the two cars (one formula associated with each figure) are equivalent.

21. For Ex. 19, compute the time-rate of change of the distance between the cars at: (*a*) 12:15 P.M.; (*b*) 12:30 P.M.; (*c*) 1:15 P.M.

Ans. (*a*) −80 mi. per hr.; (*c*) 89.4 mi. per hr.

22. One city, C, is 30 mi. north and 35 mi. east of another city, D. At noon, a car starts north from C at 40 mi. per hr.; at 12:10 P.M., another car starts east from D at 60 mi. per hr. Find when the cars will be nearest together.   *Ans.* 12:17 P.M.

23. For the conditions of Ex. 22, draw the appropriate figures for times before 12:45 P.M. and after that time. Show that in terms of time after noon, the formulas for distance between the two cars (one formula associated with each figure) are equivalent.

24. For Ex. 22, compute the time-rate of change of the distance between the cars at: (*a*) 12:15 P.M.; (*b*) 12:45 P.M.   *Ans.* (*a*) −4 mi. per hr.

25. One city, E, is 20 mi. north and 20 mi. east of another city, F. At noon, a car starts south from E at 40 mi. per hr.; at 12:10 P.M., another car starts east from F at 60 mi. per hr. Find the rate at which the cars approach each other between 12:10 P.M. and 12:30 P.M. What happens at 12:30 P.M.?   *Ans.* 72.1 mi. per hr.

26. A kite is 40 ft. high, with 50 ft. of cord out. If the kite moves horizontally at 5 mi. per hr. directly away from the boy flying it, how fast is the cord being paid out?

Ans. 4.4 ft. per sec.

27. In Ex. 26, find the rate at which the slope of the cord is decreasing.

28. At noon a car drives from A (Fig. 48) toward C at 60 mi. per hr. Another car, starting from B at the same time, drives toward A at 30 mi. per hr. If $AB = 42$ mi., find when the cars will be nearest each other.

Ans. 12:24 P.M.

29. Solve Ex. 28 if the car from B leaves at noon but the car from A leaves at 12:07 P.M.   *Ans.* 12:29 P.M.

30. Two railroad tracks intersect at right angles. At noon there is a train on each track approaching the crossing at 40 mi. per hr., one being 100 mi., the other 200 mi. distant. Find (*a*) when they will be the nearest together, and (*b*) what will be their minimum distance apart.   *Ans.* (*a*) 3:45 P.M.; (*b*) 70.7 mi.

Figure 48

31. An elevated train on a track 30 ft. above the ground crosses a street at the rate of 20 ft. per sec. at the instant that a car, approaching at the rate of 30 ft. per sec., is 40 ft. up the street. Find how fast the train and the car are separating 1 sec. later.   *Ans.* $\frac{5}{7} \sqrt{14} = 2.67$ ft. per sec.

32. In Ex. 31, find when the train and the car are nearest together.

33. From a car traveling east at 40 mi. per hr., an airplane traveling horizontally

north at 100 mi. per hr. is visible 1 mi. east, 2 mi. south, and 2 mi. up. Find when
the two will be nearest together.　　　　　　　　　　　　*Ans.* $1\frac{7}{29}$ min.

34. In Ex. 33, find how fast the two will be separating after a long time.

Ans. $20\sqrt{29} = 107.7$ mi. per hr.

35. An arc light hangs at a height of 30 ft. above the center of a street 60 ft. wide.
A man 6 ft. tall walks along the sidewalk at the rate of 4 ft. per sec. How fast is his
shadow lengthening when he is 40 ft. up the street?　　　　*Ans.* 0.8 ft. per sec.

36. In Ex. 35, how fast is the tip of the shadow moving?　　*Ans.* 5 ft. per sec.

37. A ship sails east 20 mi. and then turns N. 30° W. If the ship's speed is 10 mi.
per hr., find how fast it will be leaving the starting point 6 hr. after the start.

Ans. 8.66 mi. per hr.

38. Solve Ex. 37 if the ship turns N. 30° E.　　　　*Ans.* 9.45 mi. per hr.

44. *Discontinuous Derivatives*

Our treatment of maxima, minima, and inflection points has centered
on functions which have continuous first and second derivatives. Since
continuity of $f(x)$ requires only that

$$\underset{\Delta x \to 0}{\text{Lim}} \, [f(x + \Delta x) - f(x)] = 0$$

and differentiability of $f(x)$ requires that

$$\underset{\Delta x \to 0}{\text{Lim}} \, \frac{f(x + \Delta x) - f(x)}{\Delta x}$$

exists, we know that continuity does not imply the existence of the derivative. In particular, a continuous function $f(x)$ may have a derivative which
is discontinuous. If $f(x)$ and $f'(x)$ are continuous, $f''(x)$, the derivative of
$f'(x)$, may be discontinuous.

When discontinuities are present in a derivative, the location of extremes
or inflection points of the corresponding graph should be examined with
even more than customary caution. At a point of discontinuity of y or y'
the graph of

$$y = f(x)$$

may have an extreme even though y' does not vanish or even exist, as in
Example (*b*) below. In order to produce an inflection point, the essential
thing is that y'' change sign, not that it vanish. If y'' is discontinuous, it
may change sign by jumping over the value zero, as in Example (*a*) below.

Example (a). The function

(1)　　　　　　　　　　　$y = x^{\frac{1}{3}}$

is everywhere continuous, but the curve comes in to the origin tangent to
the y-axis; thus the slope,

$$y' = \frac{1}{3x^{\frac{2}{3}}},$$

has an infinite discontinuity at that point. The graphs of y and y' are shown in Fig. 49. The curve (1) has a point of inflection at the origin. Since

$$y'' = \frac{-2}{9x^{\frac{4}{3}}},$$

it is clear that y'' changes sign, not by vanishing but by virtue of an infinite discontinuity:

$$\text{Lim}_{x \to 0^-} y'' = +\infty, \quad \text{Lim}_{x \to 0^+} y'' = -\infty.$$

An inflection effected by a finite jump occurs in Ex. 19 below. It is even possible for an extreme and an inflection to occur at the same point (Ex. 14 below).

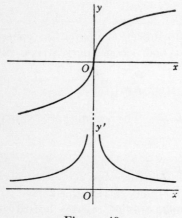

Figure 49

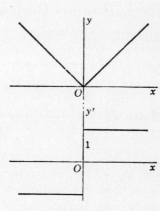

Figure 50

Example (b). The function

(2) $$y = |x|$$

is everywhere continuous, but the slope y' jumps from -1 to 1 at $x = 0$. Both y and y' are shown in Fig. 50. The function $|x|$ assumes its minimum value zero at $x = 0$, although the derivative does not vanish (or exist) there.

If a function $f(x)$ and its first derivative $f'(x)$ are both continuous, the function is said to be smooth. A smooth function may, of course, have a

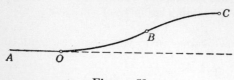

Figure 51

discontinuous second derivative. An important instance of this occurs in highway or railroad construction. Say that a level highway AO begins at O to climb a grade OBC. The pavement must be unbroken (y continuous) and smooth (y' continuous), but in general y''—rate of change of grade—will be discontinuous at O and B. A similar situation arises in connection with horizontal turns. The turn would usually be "eased"—y' continuous—but the rate of change of direction may jump abruptly.

In practical applications, as we have seen many times, the independent variable is usually confined, by the nature of the problem, to a limited range. Then, a function which would be continuous if x were unrestricted has only one-sided continuity at the ends of the interval, and in many cases assumes extreme values at those points, although as a rule the derivative does not vanish there.

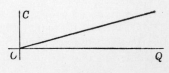

Example (*a*). The cost of a quantity of gasoline at \$0.30 per gallon is, in dollars,

Figure 52

$$C = 0.30Q.$$

The minimum cost is zero, occurring at $Q = 0$, although

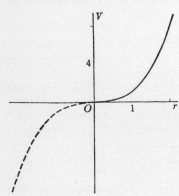

$$\frac{dC}{dQ} = 0.30.$$

Example (*b*). The volume of a sphere is (Fig. 53)

$$V = \frac{4}{3}\pi r^3, \quad \frac{dV}{dr} = 4\pi r^2.$$

The minimum volume is zero, occurring at $r = 0$. Here it is true that $\dfrac{dV}{dr} = 0$ when $r = 0$, but the theory of § 38 (here inapplica-

Figure 53

ble of course) would show this to be not a minimum but a point of inflection.

Similar remarks apply to most of our problems in maxima and minima (§§ 41–42, and in the exercises following). In any practical case the situation would almost always be just as clear as in the above examples.

EXERCISES

In Exs. 1–8, examine the curve for maxima and minima. Rationalize the equation and plot the curve; indicate the portion representing the original equation.

1. $y = x^{\frac{2}{3}}$.

2. $y = (9 - x^2)^{\frac{1}{3}}$.

3. $y = -\sqrt{4 + x}$.

4. $y = (1 - x)^{\frac{2}{3}}$.

5. $y = \sqrt{x^2 - a^2}$.

6. $y = \sqrt{2ax - x^2}$.

7. $y = \sqrt{1 - \sqrt{x}}$.

8. $y = \sqrt{1 + \sqrt{x}}$.

In Exs. 9–16, draw the graphs of y, y', and y''. The function sgn x was defined in § 7.

9. $y = x - |x|$.   10. $y = x^2 \operatorname{sgn} x$.

11. $y = x - \operatorname{sgn} x$.   12. $y = (x^2 - 1) \operatorname{sgn} (x - 1)$.

13. $y = x(1 - \operatorname{sgn} x) + x^2 \operatorname{sgn} x$.   14. $y = \sqrt{x^4 - 2x^2 + 1}$.

15. $y = \sqrt{1 + |x|}$.   16. $y = \sqrt{|x| - 1}$.

17. A cone with radius of base R and height H is given. A cylinder of height h is inscribed in the cone. Show that the volume of the cylinder is given by

$$V = \pi R^2 H^{-2} h (H - h)^2.$$

Draw the curve representing V as a function of h, and indicate that portion of the curve which has physical meaning in the problem.

18. A box is to be made from a rectangular piece of cardboard of dimensions 4 in. by 10 in., by cutting equal squares out of the corners, and turning up the sides. Graph the volume of the box as a function of the length of side of the squares cut out, and indicate the portion of the graph which has physical meaning.

19. In Fig. 51, let the coordinates of B, C with O as origin be (5, 25), (10, 50), the x-unit being 100 ft., the y-unit 1 ft. If OB, BC are parabolic arcs with equations of the form $y = ax^2 + bx + c$, the slope being zero at O and C, determine y as a function of x; investigate y'' for continuity; find the maximum grade.

Ans. $y = x^2$, $0 \leqq x \leqq 5$; $y = -x^2 + 20x - 50$, $5 \leqq x \leqq 10$; maximum grade 10 %.

20. Graph the difference in area between a square of side 3 and a square of side c.

21. Graph the difference in volume between a sphere of radius r and a cylinder of radius r with height 2.

22. Graph the difference in volume between a sphere of radius c and a cylinder of radius 2 with height c.

23. Graph the difference in volume between two boxes of dimensions c, 3, 3 and 3, c, c. Discuss the extremes.

24. Sketch the curve

$$y = \sqrt{x + \sqrt{x - \tfrac{1}{4}}} + \sqrt{x - \sqrt{x - \tfrac{1}{4}}}.$$

Hint: Examine the curve for $x < \tfrac{1}{4}$, $\tfrac{1}{4} \leqq x \leqq \tfrac{1}{2}$, $\tfrac{1}{2} < x$; rationalize the equation.

In Exs. 25–28, a cylinder is to be cut from a sphere of diameter 1 ft. and then packed in a rectangular box. Find the volume of the largest cylinder that can be handled in this way, if the dimensions of the box are as given.

25. Box 10 in. by 10 in. by 8 in.   *Ans.* $V = 96 \sqrt{3}\, \pi = 166.3\pi$ cu. in.

26. Box 10 in. by 8 in. by 8 in.   *Ans.* $V = 64 \sqrt{5}\, \pi = 143.1\pi$ cu. in.

27. Box 12 in. by 12 in. by 6 in.   *Ans.* $V = 162\pi$ cu. in.

28. Box 10 in. by 6 in. by 4 in.   *Ans.* $V = 40\pi$ cu. in.

29. Express $\cos 3\theta$ as a function of $\cos \theta$ by the addition formula. Putting $x = \cos \theta$, $y = \cos 3\theta$, graph $\cos 3\theta$ as a function of $\cos \theta$; find the extremes.

Ans. $\cos 3\theta = 4 \cos^3 \theta - 3 \cos \theta$; $(\pm\tfrac{1}{2}, \mp 1)$, $(\pm 1, \pm 1)$.

30. Solve Ex. 29 for the functions $\sin 3\theta$, $\sin \theta$.

Ans. $\sin 3\theta = 3 \sin \theta - 4 \sin^3 \theta$; $(\pm\tfrac{1}{2}, \pm 1)$, $(\pm 1, \mp 1)$.

In Exs. 31–34, find the abscissa of that point of the curve that is nearest the point $(k, 0)$. Draw the graphs of x and $\dfrac{dx}{dk}$ as functions of k.

31. The parabola $y^2 = 4ax$.   *Ans.* $x = 0,\ k \leqq 2a;\ x = k - 2a,\ k > 2a$.

32. The hyperbola $x^2 - y^2 = a^2$.

Ans. $x = \tfrac{1}{2}k,\ k < -2a;\ x = -a,\ -2a \leqq k < 0;\ x = \pm a,\ k = 0;\ x = a,$
$$0 < k \leqq 2a;\ x = \tfrac{1}{2}k,\ k > 2a.$$

33. The ellipse $\dfrac{x^2}{a^2} + \dfrac{y^2}{b^2} = 1$.   *Ans.* $x = -a,\ k < \dfrac{b^2 - a^2}{a}$;

$$x = \frac{a^2 k}{a^2 - b^2},\ \frac{b^2 - a^2}{a} \leqq k \leqq \frac{a^2 - b^2}{a};\ x = a,\ k > \frac{a^2 - b^2}{a}.$$

34. The circle $x^2 + y^2 = a^2$.

Ans. $x = -a,\ k < 0;\ -a \leqq x \leqq a,\ k = 0;\ x = a,\ k > 0$.

35. Solve Ex. 31 by analytic geometry. Write the equation of a circle of arbitrary radius with center at $(k, 0)$ and make it touch the parabola. (Eliminate y between the two equations; equate to zero the discriminant of the resulting quadratic in x.)

36. Solve Ex. 32 by the method suggested in Ex. 35.

THE DIFFERENTIAL

45. *Differentials*

Consider an interval in which a curve relating x and y has a slope y'. Let $P:(x, y)$ be a point on the curve, as shown in Figs. 54 and 55. A change Δx in the value of x changes y by some amount Δy. In the figures P' is the point $(x + \Delta x, y + \Delta y)$; Δy is the distance QP'. Unless the equation of the curve is particularly simple, it may be difficult to compute Δy. We seek for Δy an approximation which must satisfy two requirements: First it must be possible for us to prove that the difference between the approximation and Δy can be made arbitrarily small by taking Δx sufficiently small; second, the approximation must be easy to compute.

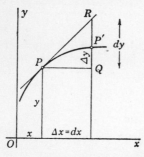

Figure 54

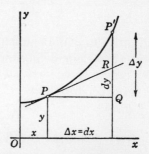

Figure 55

In Figs. 54 and 55 the tangent line at P intersects the ordinate through P' at the point R. Examination of the figures shows that it is plausible that the length QR is an approximation to $QP' = \Delta y$ for small Δx. Let us see whether QR satisfies our two requirements.

At P the slope of the curve is $\dfrac{QR}{PQ}$. Now $PQ = \Delta x$, so that we obtain

(1) $$QR = y' \, \Delta x.$$

We already know how easy it is to compute the slope y'. Hence our second requirement is satisfied by QR.

The difference between QR and QP' is given by

$$P'R = QR - QP' = y' \, \Delta x - \Delta y.$$

Our first requirement demands that we show that $P'R \to 0$ as $\Delta x \to 0$. We shall do even better by showing that $\dfrac{P'R}{\Delta x} \to 0$ as $\Delta x \to 0$. Indeed,

$$(2) \qquad \lim_{\Delta x \to 0} \frac{P'R}{\Delta x} = \lim_{\Delta x \to 0} \left(y' - \frac{\Delta y}{\Delta x} \right) = y' - y' = 0$$

because

$$\lim_{\Delta x \to 0} \frac{\Delta y}{\Delta x} = y'$$

since we are working in an interval where the slope exists. In a sense (2) shows that $P'R \to 0$ more rapidly than $\Delta x \to 0$.

The quantity QR is called the *differential* of y and is denoted by dy. By equation (1)

$$(3) \qquad dy = y' \, \Delta x.$$

Theoretically, we are still at liberty to define dx—i.e., the differential of the independent variable—in any way we please. But if in (3) we put

$$y = x, \qquad y' = 1,$$

the result is

$$(4) \qquad dx = \Delta x.$$

Thus in order to avoid conflict when (3) is applied to the function $y = x$, we adopt (4) as our definition. That is, the *differential of the independent variable is equal to the increment of that variable.*

We may therefore write

$$(5) \qquad dy = y' \, dx = y' \, \Delta x,$$

and state the definition as follows:

*The **differential** of any function is equal to its derivative multiplied by the differential of the independent variable.*

Starting with page 32, we have been using $\dfrac{dy}{dx}$ (as well as y') to denote the derivative of y with respect to x. Our two newly defined quantities dy and dx are such that their ratio is the derivative $\dfrac{dy}{dx}$. If that were not true, we would be forced to abandon one or the other of the notations. From now on the derivative may be looked upon as the single quantity $\dfrac{dy}{dx}$ or as the ratio dy divided by dx, whichever suits our purpose. No attempt is made to carry this idea to higher derivatives; from our standpoint there is no meaning to d^2y by itself.

It follows from the above definitions that *all the fundamental formulas for derivatives become differential formulas if we merely multiply through by* dx. For instance, the product formula is

$$d(uv) = u\, dv + v\, du;$$

in words, the differential of the product of two functions is equal to the first function times the differential of the second plus the second times the differential of the first.

Example (a).
$$y = x^3 - 2x,$$
$$dy = 3x^2\, dx - 2dx.$$

Example (b).
$$y = \frac{z^2 - 1}{z^2 + 1},$$
$$dy = \frac{(z^2 + 1)2z\, dz - (z^2 - 1)2z\, dz}{(z^2 + 1)^2}$$
$$= \frac{4z\, dz}{(z^2 + 1)^2}.$$

Example (c).
$$y^3 + 2xy = 3.$$
$$3y^2\, dy + 2x\, dy + 2y\, dx = 0,$$
$$dy = \frac{-2y\, dx}{3y^2 + 2x}.$$

Here we have an excellent example in support of the statement made in the first paragraph of this chapter to the effect that it may be difficult to compute Δy. From
$$y^3 + 2xy = 3$$
and
$$(y + \Delta y)^3 + 2(x + \Delta x)(y + \Delta y) = 3$$
it follows rapidly that
$$(\Delta y)^3 + 3y(\Delta y)^2 + (3y^2 + 2x + 2\Delta x)(\Delta y) + 2y\, \Delta x = 0.$$

The determination of Δy from the above cubic is surely not simple compared with the determination of dy as accomplished at the beginning of this example.

We see now that the technique of differentiation is the same, except for a slight change in form, whether derivatives or differentials are used. It follows that differentials would hardly be worth bothering with, if they were to be used merely as an additional tool in differentiation. The importance of differentials lies elsewhere, as will become apparent in several places later in the book.

46. *Differential of Arc Length*

To obtain the length of an arc of a curve, the average person might well bend a wire to fit that arc, then straighten the wire and measure its length. We wish to replace that intuitive concept with a mathematical definition of arc length. Actually, we now define only the differential of arc length and leave until later (§ 159) the computation of lengths of curves.

We shall use Fig. 56 to guide us to a desirable definition. Let s denote the length of the arc of the curve measured from some initial point P_0 to the point $P:(x, y)$, and suppose for definiteness that s increases as x increases. For the change Δs in arc length from P to P' we obtain

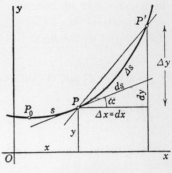

Figure 56

$$\frac{\Delta s}{\Delta x} = \frac{\Delta s}{PP'} \cdot \frac{PP'}{\Delta x} = \frac{\Delta s}{PP'} \cdot \frac{\sqrt{(\Delta x)^2 + (\Delta y)^2}}{\Delta x}$$

$$= \frac{\Delta s}{PP'} \cdot \sqrt{1 + \left(\frac{\Delta y}{\Delta x}\right)^2},$$

in which PP' is the length of the chord from $P:(x, y)$ to $P':(x + \Delta x, y + \Delta y)$. If the curve is well behaved near P, it is reasonable to expect that

$$\operatorname*{Lim}_{\Delta x \to 0} \frac{\Delta s}{PP'} = 1,$$

which yields

(1) $$\frac{ds}{dx} = \operatorname*{Lim}_{\Delta x \to 0} \frac{\Delta s}{\Delta x} = \sqrt{1 + \left(\frac{dy}{dx}\right)^2}.$$

If s decreases as x increases, then

$$\frac{\Delta s}{\Delta x} = -\frac{\Delta s}{PP'} \cdot \sqrt{1 + \left(\frac{\Delta y}{\Delta x}\right)^2},$$

(2) $$\frac{ds}{dx} = -\sqrt{1 + \left(\frac{dy}{dx}\right)^2}.$$

Equations (1) and (2) furnish us with a desirable starting point. We define the differential of arc length ds by (1) and (2) and conclude that

(3) $$(ds)^2 = (dx)^2 + (dy)^2.$$

Thus $|ds|$ is the hypotenuse of the right triangle with sides $|dx|$ and $|dy|$.

If the tangent to the curve at P makes an angle α with Ox, then

(4) $$\cos \alpha = \frac{dx}{ds}, \qquad \sin \alpha = \frac{dy}{ds}.$$

The formula for differential of arc length in polar coordinates will be derived in § 159. From equation (3) and the relations $x = r \cos \theta$, $y = r \sin \theta$, it will be found that

(5)
$$(ds)^2 = (dr)^2 + r^2(d\theta)^2.$$

We are in no position now to make use of the above definitions and results. They do, however, play a significant role in several later developments. See §§ 159–160.

EXERCISES

In Exs. 1–24 find the differential of the given function.

1. $y = 3x^4 - 5x^3 + x - 4$.
  Ans. $dy = 12x^3\,dx - 15x^2\,dx + dx = (12x^3 - 15x^2 + 1)\,dx$.

2. $z = (1 - 2v + v^4)^{-\frac{3}{2}}$.   *Ans.* $dz = 3(1 - 2v^3)(1 - 2v + v^4)^{-\frac{5}{2}}\,dv$.

3. $x = (5t - 2)^4$.   **4.** $y = (1 - x^5)^2$.

5. $z = \sqrt{4 - 3x}$.   **6.** $\beta = \dfrac{3}{\sqrt{1 - 2\alpha}}$.

7. $u = \sqrt{2y - y^2}$.   *Ans.* $du = (1 - y)(2y - y^2)^{-\frac{1}{2}}\,dy$.

8. $x = \dfrac{1}{3}t^3 - \sqrt{t} + \dfrac{1}{t^2}$.   *Ans.* $dx = \left(t^2 - \dfrac{1}{2\sqrt{t}} - \dfrac{2}{t^3} \right) dt$.

9. $y = x(3 + 2x)^4$.   **10.** $w = x^2(1 - x^2)^{\frac{1}{2}}$.

11. $u = \dfrac{v^3}{v + 2}$.   **12.** $x = \dfrac{t^2}{\sqrt{1 - t}}$.

13. $y = \sqrt{x^2 - a^2}$, *a* held constant.
  Ans. $dy = \dfrac{x\,dx}{\sqrt{x^2 - a^2}}$.

14. $y = \sqrt{x^2 - a^2}$, *x* held constant.
  Ans. $dy = \dfrac{-a\,da}{\sqrt{x^2 - a^2}}$.

15. $x = t^2(t^2 + 4)^{\frac{3}{2}}$.   **16.** $x = y^3(9 - y^2)^{\frac{1}{2}}$.

17. $r = \dfrac{s}{\sqrt{1 - s^2}}$.   **18.** $r = \dfrac{\sqrt{1 - s^2}}{s}$.

19. $y = (1 + \sqrt{x})^4$.   **20.** $y = \sqrt{1 + \sqrt{x}}$.

21. $x = \dfrac{t}{(2 - 3t)^4}$.   *Ans.* $dx = \dfrac{(9t + 2)\,dt}{(2 - 3t)^5}$.

22. $y = \dfrac{(1 - x)^2}{(1 - 2x)^2}$.   *Ans.* $dy = \dfrac{2(1 - x)\,dx}{(1 - 2x)^3}$.

23. $r = \sqrt{\dfrac{1 - s}{1 + s}}$.   *Ans.* $dr = \dfrac{-ds}{(1 - s)^{\frac{1}{2}}(1 + s)^{\frac{3}{2}}}$.

24. $y = \dfrac{(x^3 - x)^2}{x + 1}$.   *Ans.* $dy = x(x - 1)(5x^2 + x - 2)\,dx$.

In Exs. 25–33, find dy.

25. $y^2 = 4ax$.   *Ans.* $dy = \dfrac{2a\,dx}{y}$.   **26.** $\dfrac{x^2}{a^2} - \dfrac{y^2}{b^2} = 1$.   *Ans.* $dy = \dfrac{b^2x\,dx}{a^2y}$.

27. $x^2 + xy + y^2 = 4$.

28. $3x^2 - 6xy + 3y^2 - 7x + 2y - 1 = 0$.

29. $x^{\frac{2}{3}} + y^{\frac{2}{3}} = a^{\frac{2}{3}}$.   **30.** $y^2 = \dfrac{x^2}{x^2 - a^2}$.

31. $y^2 = \dfrac{x^3}{2a - x}$.   **32.** $y^3 = \dfrac{x^2}{a - x}$.

33. $x^3 + y^3 - 3axy = 0$.   *Ans.* $dy = -\dfrac{(x^2 - ay)\,dx}{y^2 - ax}$.

47. *Approximate Formulas*

Very often we wish to compute, or to estimate within safe limits, the change in the value of a function caused by a small change in the value of the independent variable. When Δx is small, dy and Δy are, in general, nearly equal, and in many cases *the value of dy furnishes a sufficiently good approximation to the value of Δy.*

In any approximate computation, the amount by which the computed value of the function differs from the true value is called the *error* of the computation. Of course, in using any approximate formula, we should make sure that the error committed is within the allowable limit of error for the problem in hand. This question will be considered more fully in § 236.

Example (a). Find an approximate formula for the area of a narrow circular ring.

The area of a circle of radius r is

$$A = \pi r^2.$$

When the radius increases by an amount Δr, the area increases by an amount ΔA which is approximated by

$$dA = 2\pi r\,dr = 2\pi r\,\Delta r.$$

(Since r is the independent variable, $dr = \Delta r$.) Hence the area of a narrow circular ring is approximately the *product of the circumference by the width.*

Example (b). Find an approximate value for $\sqrt{8.73}$.

Put $y = \sqrt{x}$, from which

(1) $$dy = \frac{dx}{2\sqrt{x}}.$$

For x we choose a number which is close to 8.73 and for which we know the square root. Choose

$$x = 9 \quad \text{and} \quad \Delta x = dx = -0.27$$

so that $x + dx = 8.73$. From (1) it follows that

$$dy = \frac{-0.27}{2\sqrt{9}} = \frac{-0.27}{6} = -0.045.$$

Then

$$\sqrt{8.73} = y + dy = 3 - 0.045 = 2.955$$

approximately. To five decimal places the correct value is 2.95466.

EXERCISES

1. Find approximately the volume of a thin spherical shell.

Ans. Surface area × thickness.

2. Find an approximate formula for the volume of a thin cylindrical shell of given height. *Ans. Circumference × height × thickness.*

3. Find approximately the volume of wood required to make a cubical box, of edge length 6 ft., using boards $\frac{1}{2}$ in. thick. *Ans. 4.5 cu. ft.*

4. The base of a right triangle is fixed at 3 ft., the hypotenuse is 5 ft. long and subject to change. Find the approximate change in altitude when the hypotenuse is changed by a small amount Δh. *Ans. 1.25 Δh.*

5. The diameter of a circle is measured and found to be 6 ft. with a maximum error of 0.1 in. Find the approximate maximum error in the computed area.

Ans. 11.3 sq. in.

6. The diameter of a sphere is measured and found to be 3 ft. with a maximum error of 0.1 in. Find the approximate maximum error in the computed volume.

Ans. 204 cu. in.

7. Find the approximate maximum error in computing the surface area of the sphere of Ex. 6. *Ans. 22.6 sq. in.*

8. The diameter of a circle is to be measured, and its area computed. If the diameter can be measured with a maximum error of 0.001 in., and the area must be accurate to within 0.1 sq. in., find the largest diameter for which the process can be used. *Ans. Nearly 64 in.*

9. The diameter of a sphere is to be measured, and its volume computed. If the diameter can be measured with a maximum error of 0.001 in., and the volume must be accurate to within 0.1 cu. in., find the largest diameter for which the process can be used. *Ans. Nearly 8 in.*

10. Find approximately the change in the reciprocal of a number x produced by a small change in the number. Investigate also the case when the number itself is small.

11. Divide 1 by 9.81. Use Ex. 10. *Ans. 0.1019.*

12. Divide 1 by 25.2. *Ans. 0.0397.*

13. The volume of a body of gas is measured; the pressure is then computed from the formula

$$p = \frac{k}{v}.$$

If the allowable error in p is $0.001k$, and the maximum error in measuring v is 0.6 cu. ft., what is the volume of the smallest container to which the process can be applied? *Ans. 24.5 cu. ft.*

14. Suppose that the container in Ex. 13 is a cube of edge length s. Find the approximate error in the computed value of p due to a small error in measuring s.

15. In Ex. 14, if $s = 10 \pm 0.2$, how accurately can p be determined?

Ans. $dp \leqq 6(10)^{-5}k$.

16. The attraction between two magnetic poles is inversely proportional to the square of the distance between them: $F = \dfrac{k}{r^2}$. If the distance is slightly increased, how is the attraction affected?

17. The attraction between two magnetic poles is measured, and the distance between them computed (cf. Ex. 16). If $k = 1$ and $F = 7.5 \pm 0.1$, find r.

Ans. 0.3652 ∓ 0.0024.

18. Find the change in the lateral surface area of a right circular cone, with radius of base fixed as r, when the altitude h changes by a small amount Δh.

$$Ans. \ \frac{\pi r h \, \Delta h}{\sqrt{r^2 + h^2}}.$$

19. Solve Ex. 18 if the radius changes (altitude fixed).

$$Ans. \ \frac{\pi(h^2 + 2r^2)\, \Delta r}{\sqrt{r^2 + h^2}}.$$

20. Find the lateral surface area of a right circular cone of radius 5 ft. and height 12 ft., if the radius is uncertain by $\frac{1}{8}$ in. See Ex. 19.   *Ans. 204.2 ± 0.5 sq. ft.*

21. For what values of x may $\sqrt[3]{x+1}$ be replaced by $\sqrt[3]{x}$, if the allowable error is 0.01?   *Ans. $x > 192$.*

22. For what values of x may $(x+1)^{\frac{1}{4}}$ be replaced by $x^{\frac{1}{4}}$ if the allowable error is 0.01?   *Ans. $x > 73$.*

23. A 16-lb. shot is made of iron weighing 444 lb. per cu. ft. If the weight must be accurate within 1 oz., find the radius.   *Ans. 2.459 ± 0.003 in.*

24. A hollow sphere of outer radius 1 ft. is made of metal weighing about 400 lb. per cu. ft. The volume of metal is found by weighing to be 2 cu. ft., with an uncertainty of 0.1 cu. ft. due to the uncertain density. Find the inner radius.

Ans. 9.67 ∓ 0.15 in.

In Exs. 25–36, use differentials to approximate to the desired number.

25. The square root of 627.   *Ans. 25.04.*
26. The square root of 398.   *Ans. 19.95.*
27. The square root of 193.   *Ans. 13.89.*
28. The square root of 287.   *Ans. 16.94.*
29. The square root of 0.253.   *Ans. 0.5030.*
30. The square root of 98.8.   *Ans. 9.940.*
31. The cube root of 26.   *Ans. 2.963.*
32. The cube root of 0.009.   *Ans. 0.208.*
33. The cube root of 1.35.   *Ans. 1.105.*
34. The cube root of 3.3.   *Ans. 1.489.*
35. The fourth root of 17.   *Ans. 2.031.*
36. The fourth root of 255.   *Ans. 3.996.*

INTEGRATION

48. *The Indefinite Integral*

We have been occupied up to this point with the problem: Given a function, to find its derivative (or differential). Many of the most important applications of the calculus lead to the inverse problem: *Given the derivative of a function, to find the function.* The required function is called an *integral* of the given derivative, and the process of finding it is called *integration.* The given function is the *integrand.*

If $f(x)$ is a given function and $F(x)$ is a function whose derivative is $f(x)$, the relation between them is expressed by writing

$$F(x) = \int f(x) \, dx,$$

where the symbol $\int$, called the *integral sign*, indicates that we are to perform the operation of integration upon $f(x) \, dx$: that is, we are to find a function whose derivative is $f(x)$ or whose differential is $f(x) \, dx$. For reasons that will appear later, we always write after the integral sign the differential $f(x) \, dx$ rather than the derivative $f(x)$.

Example (a). Evaluate $\int x^2 \, dx$.

Since differentiation reduces the exponent by 1, integration must *increase* the exponent by 1 (in order that, upon differentiating our answer, we may return to the original exponent). Thus our first guess at the answer might be x^3. Since

$$d(x^3) = 3x^2 \, dx,$$

an unwanted factor 3 presents itself. To correct this, we amend our first guess by dividing by 3. Now, $d(\frac{1}{3}x^3) = x^2 \, dx$, but the addition of any constant whatever to $(\frac{1}{3}x^3)$ does not alter the differential. Hence

(1) $$\int x^2 \, dx = \tfrac{1}{3}x^3 + C,$$

where C is an arbitrary constant. Equation (1) is equivalent to the statement that $d(\frac{1}{3}x^3 + C) = x^2 \, dx$.

It is natural to inquire whether there may be other correct, and essentially different, functions for the right member of (1); i.e., whether any function can have the differential $(x^2 \, dx)$ and differ from $\frac{1}{3}x^3$ by other than a constant. The answer, contained in the following theorem, is "No!".

THEOREM 12. *Two functions having the same derivative differ only by a constant.*

Let $\varphi(x)$ and $\psi(x)$ be the two functions, and place

$$y = \varphi(x) - \psi(x).$$

By hypothesis,

$$y' = \varphi'(x) - \psi'(x) = 0.$$

The rate of change of y with respect to x is everywhere zero; hence y is constant.

In the following examples, the student should try to obtain the answer for himself, by intelligent guesswork, and should finally verify by differentiation.

Example (b). $\displaystyle \int \sqrt{1 + 5x} \, dx = \tfrac{2}{15}(1 + 5x)^{\frac{3}{2}} + C.$

Example (c). $\displaystyle \int (a^2 - y^2)^6 y \, dy = -\tfrac{1}{14}(a^2 - y^2)^7 + C.$

Example (d). $\displaystyle \int \frac{dt}{\sqrt{1 - t}} = \int (1 - t)^{-\frac{1}{2}} \, dt = -2(1 - t)^{\frac{1}{2}} + C.$

It is now clear that a function whose derivative is given is not completely determined, since it contains an arbitrary additive constant, the *constant of integration.* For this reason, the function $\displaystyle \int f(x) \, dx$ is called the *indefinite integral* of $f(x)$.

49. *General Properties of Indefinite Integrals*

The following properties of indefinite integrals are easily verified by differentiation.

$$\int du = u + C.$$

$$\int (du + dv + \cdots + dz) = \int du + \int dv + \cdots + \int dz.$$

$$\int c \, du = c \int du.$$

The first formula is the definition of an integral.

The second formula states that if the integrand consists of a sum of terms, each term may be integrated separately.

The third formula says that if the integrand contains a constant factor, that factor may be written before the integral sign. As a corollary, we may *introduce a constant factor into the integrand*, provided we place its reciprocal before the integral sign. But it is *never* allowable to introduce variable factors by this rule, for the reason that an answer obtained in this way cannot possibly be correct. Given

(1) $$F(x) = \int f(x)\ dx,$$

write

(2) $$F(x) = \frac{1}{u} \int uf(x)\ dx,$$

or

$$uF(x) = \int uf(x)\ dx.$$

Differentiate:

(3) $$uF'(x)\ dx + F(x)\ du = uf(x)\ dx.$$

But, from (1), $F'(x) = f(x)$, so that (3) becomes

$$F(x)\ du = 0.$$

Since $F(x) \neq 0$, we must have $du = 0$, $u = C$ if (2) is to be true.

50. *The Power Formula*

In the formula
$$d(u^n) = nu^{n-1}\ du,$$

let us replace n by $n + 1$:

$$d(u^{n+1}) = (n + 1)u^n\ du.$$

Divide by $n + 1$ (since this is impossible when $n = -1$, that value must be excluded), and reverse the equation to obtain

$$u^n\ du = \frac{d(u^{n+1})}{n + 1}.$$

Integrating, we obtain the *general power-formula of integration*:

(1) $$\int u^n\ du = \frac{u^{n+1}}{n + 1} + C, \qquad n \neq -1.$$

This formula, *correctly applied*, serves to evaluate each of the examples of § 48, and in fact every integral occurring in this chapter. (In Chapter 18, analogous formulas will be developed for the other types of elementary integrals.) Thus the hit-or-miss method of § 48 may now be replaced by straightforward use of the formula. But aside from mere algebraic mistakes, it often happens, especially at first, that the student interprets the formula incorrectly; thus it is just as important as ever that each answer be checked by differentiation.

Example (a).

$$\int \left(3x^3 + 1 + \frac{1}{2x^2}\right) dx = 3 \int x^3\, dx + \int dx + \frac{1}{2} \int x^{-2}\, dx$$

$$= \frac{3x^4}{4} + x - \frac{1}{2} x^{-1} + C$$

$$= \frac{3x^4}{4} + x - \frac{1}{2x} + C.$$

After a little practice the answer can be written at once, both intermediate steps being omitted.

Example (b). Evaluate $\int (a^2 - y^2)^5 y\, dy$.

This resembles (1) with $u = a^2 - y^2$, $n = 5$. Since

$$d(a^2 - y^2) = -2y\, dy,$$

we introduce the factor -2 under the integral sign, with its reciprocal in front:

$$\int (a^2 - y^2)^5 y\, dy = -\tfrac{1}{2} \int (a^2 - y^2)^5(-2y)\, dy = -\frac{(a^2 - y^2)^6}{12} + C.$$

This integral could also be evaluated by expanding $(a^2 - y^2)^5$ and integrating the resulting row of powers; but this would be an exceedingly slow and tiresome method.

Example (c). Evaluate $\int (a^2 - x^2)^2\, dx$.

This resembles Example (b), but only superficially. In any attempt to use formula (1) directly, it is found that when we choose $u = a^2 - x^2$, $n = 2$, then the differential

$$du = d(a^2 - x^2) = -2x\, dx$$

is not present in our integrand. The (-2) can be inserted, but nothing can be done about that missing factor x.

We are therefore forced to have recourse to expansion of $(a^2 - x^2)^2$, followed by a term-by-term integration. Thus the integral can be evaluated as follows:

$$\int (a^2 - x^2)^2\, dx = \int (a^4 - 2a^2x^2 + x^4)\, dx$$

$$= a^4 x - \tfrac{2}{3}a^2x^3 + \tfrac{1}{5}x^5 + C.$$

Example (d). Evaluate $\int (2x + 3)\, dx$.

First method: $\int (2x + 3)\, dx = x^2 + 3x + C$.

Second method:

$$\int (2x + 3)\, dx = \frac{1}{2} \int (2x + 3)2\, dx = \frac{(2x + 3)^2}{4} + C_1.$$

This simple example is introduced to exhibit a very common phenomenon. We shall meet many integrations in which two answers, both correct, differ widely in appearance; yet it will always be possible to show that they differ at most by a constant, however improbable this may seem at first sight. Here, we have only to expand the second form:

$$\frac{(2x + 3)^2}{4} + C_1 = x^2 + 3x + \frac{9}{4} + C_1 = x^2 + 3x + C.$$

This shows that the arbitrary constants C, C_1 differ by $\frac{9}{4}$.

In the exercises, when the result of an integration is given, it is not implied that the one given is the only correct form or even necessarily better than any other.

EXERCISES

Evaluate the following integrals; check by differentiation.

1. $\int (x^3 - 4x)\, dx$.

2. $\int (2x - x^2)\, dx$.

3. $\int (6x^3 - 4x + 1)\, dx$.

4. $\int (15x^4 - 6x^2 + 2)\, dx$.

5. $\int \dfrac{dv}{v^2}$.
   $\qquad\qquad$ *Ans.* $-\dfrac{1}{v} + C$.

6. $\int \dfrac{6\, dz}{z^4}$.
   $\qquad\qquad$ *Ans.* $-\dfrac{2}{z^3} + C$.

7. $\int \left(\sqrt{t} - \dfrac{1}{\sqrt{t}} \right) dt$.
   $\qquad\qquad$ *Ans.* $\frac{2}{3}t^{\frac{3}{2}} - 2t^{\frac{1}{2}} + C$.

8. $\int \left(u^{\frac{3}{2}} + \dfrac{1}{u^{\frac{3}{2}}} \right) du$.
   $\qquad\qquad$ *Ans.* $\frac{2}{5}u^{\frac{5}{2}} - 2u^{-\frac{1}{2}} + C$.

9. $\int (3 - 2y^{-2})\, dy$.

10. $\int (y^{-4} - y^{-3})\, dy$.

11. $\int (z + 3)^4\, dz$.

12. $\int (a - x)^3\, dx$.

13. $\int \dfrac{dx}{(x - 5)^2}$.

14. $\int \dfrac{dv}{(v + 7)^3}$.

15. $\int (4x + 1)^2\, dx.$ *Ans.* $\frac{1}{12}(4x + 1)^3 + C.$

16. $\int \dfrac{dx}{(2x - 7)^4}.$ *Ans.* $-\frac{1}{6}(2x - 7)^{-3} + C.$

17. $\int \dfrac{du}{(4u + a)^{\frac{3}{2}}}.$ 18. $\int \dfrac{dv}{\sqrt{3v - 2a}}.$

19. $\int \sqrt{3y - 7}\, dy.$ 20. $\int (5 - 3y)^{\frac{3}{2}}\, dy.$

21. $\int (x^3 + a^3)^2\, dx.$ 22. $\int (x^5 - 3a^2 x^3)\, dx.$

23. $\int \left(y + \dfrac{1}{y}\right)^2 dy.$ 24. $\int \dfrac{y^2\, dy}{(1 + y^3)^2}.$

25. $\int x(1 - x^2)^3\, dx.$ 26. $\int x(2 - x)^2\, dx.$

27. $\int \dfrac{dz}{(2z - 5)^4}.$ 28. $\int \dfrac{dy}{(2y - 1)^{\frac{3}{4}}}.$

29. $\int \dfrac{y\, dy}{\sqrt{a^2 - y^2}}.$ 30. $\int \dfrac{z\, dz}{\sqrt{4z^2 + a^2}}.$

31. $\int (1 - x^2)^3\, dx.$ 32. $\int x^2(x^2 + a^2)^2\, dx.$

33. $\int x(x^2 + 3)^3\, dx.$ 34. $\int x^2(x^3 - 1)^4\, dx.$

35. $\int \dfrac{x^4 + a^4}{x^3}\, dx.$ 36. $\int \dfrac{x^2 - a^2}{x^2}\, dx.$

37. $\int (x^6 - 7x)^4\, dx.$ 38. $\int (x - 4x^8)^6\, dx.$

In Exs. 39–42, integrate by two different methods and show that your answers are equivalent.

39. $\int y(4 + y^2)\, dy.$ 40. $\int y^2(2 - y^3)^2\, dy.$

41. $\int \dfrac{(2 + \sqrt{x})^2\, dx}{\sqrt{x}}.$ 42. $\int \dfrac{(1 - \sqrt{x})^3\, dx}{\sqrt{x}}.$

51. *The Definite Integral*

Let $f(x)$ be a given continuous function, $F(x)$ an integral of $f(x)$, and $x = a$ and $x = b$ two given values of x. The *change in the value of the integral* $F(x)$ as x changes from a to b, i.e., the quantity $F(b) - F(a)$, is called the *definite integral of* $f(x)$ *between the "limits"* a *and* b, or simply the *definite integral from* a *to* b, and is denoted by the symbol $\int_a^b f(x)\, dx$. It is called the *definite* integral because its value is independent of the constant of integration.

The numbers a and b are called the *lower limit* and the *upper limit*, respectively. Thus the definite integral is *the value of the indefinite integral at the upper limit, minus its value at the lower limit.* The symbol $\left[F(x)\right]_a^b$ means $F(b) - F(a)$:

(1)
$$\int_a^b f(x)\,dx = \left[F(x)\right]_a^b = F(b) - F(a).$$

Since the constant of integration disappears, there is no object in writing it at all.

The assumption of continuity is introduced temporarily for simplicity. See § 150.

Example (a). $\displaystyle\int_0^1 (x+1)^2\,dx = \left[\frac{(x+1)^3}{3}\right]_0^1 = \frac{8}{3} - \frac{1}{3} = \frac{7}{3}.$

Example (b). $\displaystyle\int_{-a}^a (a^2 - t^2)\,dt = \left[a^2 t - \tfrac{1}{3}t^3\right]_{-a}^a$

$$= a^3 - \tfrac{1}{3}a^3 - (-a^3 + \tfrac{1}{3}a^2) = \tfrac{4}{3}a^3.$$

Example (c). $\displaystyle\int_0^a z(a^2 - z^2)^3\,dz = -\left[\frac{(a^2 - z^2)^4}{8}\right]_0^a = \frac{a^8}{8}.$

The variable whose differential occurs—respectively x, t, z, in the examples—is called the *variable of integration.*

52. *General Properties of Definite Integrals*

The following properties are possessed by all definite integrals:

(1)
$$\int_a^b f(x)\,dx = -\int_b^a f(x)\,dx;$$

(2)
$$\int_a^b f(x)\,dx = \int_a^c f(x)\,dx + \int_c^b f(x)\,dx;$$

(3)
$$\int_a^b f(x)\,dx = \int_a^b f(z)\,dz.$$

In words, these formulas say respectively:

(1) Interchanging the limits changes the sign of the integral.

(2) The interval of integration may be broken up into any number of subintervals, and the integration performed over each interval separately.

Although the theorem is usually employed in this way, it is true whether or not c lies between a and b.

(3) It makes no difference what letter is used for the variable of integration; i.e., *the definite integral of a given integrand is independent of the variable of integration.*

The first two are established very easily by writing out, by the defining formula (1), § 51, the values of the various integrals. The truth of (3) appears from a glance at that same formula, where the result involves the limits a and b but not the variable of integration x. Thus in Example (a), § 51,

$$\int_0^1 (x+1)^2 \, dx = \int_0^1 (y+1)^2 \, dy = \int_0^1 (t+1)^2 \, dt = \tfrac{7}{3}.$$

53. *Even and Odd Functions*

A function that *remains unchanged* when x is replaced by $-x$, i.e., such that

(1) $f(-x) = f(x),$

is called an *even function*. This means geometrically that the curve

$$y = f(x)$$

is symmetric with respect to the y-axis. Familiar examples of even functions are x^{2n} (n an integer), $\cos\theta$, $t\sin t$, etc.

A function such that

(2) $f(-x) = -f(x)$

is called an *odd function*. Geometrically, the curve $y = f(x)$ is symmetric with respect to the origin. Examples are x^{2n+1}, $x^{\frac{1}{3}}$, $\sin\theta$, $\tan\theta$.

There are a few very simple but useful facts about even and odd functions which will now be stated and proved.

THEOREM 13. *Any function defined throughout an interval* $-a \leqq x \leqq a$ *can be expressed as the sum of an even function and an odd function in that interval.*

Proof. We prove that this can be done by doing it. For x in the interval $-a \leqq x \leqq a$, write

(3) $f(x) = \tfrac{1}{2}[f(x) + f(-x)] + \tfrac{1}{2}[f(x) - f(-x)],$

an identity. The introduction of $f(-x)$ is permissible because our interval is symmetric with respect to $x = 0$; both $f(x)$ and $f(-x)$ exist for any x in that interval.

It is important that the separation (3) of a function into its even and odd parts is unique.

THEOREM 14. *If $E_1(x)$ and $E_2(x)$ are even functions of x and $O_1(x)$ and $O_2(x)$ are odd functions of x, then from*

(4)
$$E_1(x) + O_1(x) = E_2(x) + O_2(x)$$

in some interval, it follows that in the same interval

(5)
$$E_1(x) = E_2(x), \qquad O_1(x) = O_2(x).$$

Proof. In (4) change x to $(-x)$ to get

(6)
$$E_1(x) - O_1(x) = E_2(x) - O_2(x).$$

Add and subtract the members of (4) and (6) to arrive at (5).

THEOREM 15. *If $f(x)$ is an even function of x and $f(x)$ has a derivative $f'(x)$, then $f'(x)$ is an odd function of x.*

THEOREM 16. *If $f(x)$ is an odd function of x and $f(x)$ has a derivative $f'(x)$, then $f'(x)$ is an even function of x.*

Proof of Theorems 15 and 16. We know that

(7)
$$f'(x) = \lim_{\Delta x \to 0} \frac{f(x + \Delta x) - f(x)}{\Delta x}$$

and, directly from the definition of a limit, that

(8)
$$\lim_{h \to 0} g(h) = \lim_{h \to 0} g(-h).$$

From (7) and (8) it follows that

$$f'(-x) = \lim_{\Delta x \to 0} \frac{f(-x + \Delta x) - f(-x)}{\Delta x}$$
$$= \lim_{\Delta x \to 0} \frac{f(-x - \Delta x) - f(-x)}{-\Delta x}.$$

If $f(x)$ is an even function of x, $f(-x - \Delta x) = f(x + \Delta x)$ and therefore

$$f'(-x) = \lim_{\Delta x \to 0} \frac{f(x + \Delta x) - f(x)}{-\Delta x} = -f'(x),$$

so that $f'(x)$ is an odd function of x. If $f(x)$ is an odd function of x,

$$f(-x - \Delta x) = -f(x + \Delta x),$$

and therefore

$$f'(-x) = \lim_{\Delta x \to 0} \frac{-f(x + \Delta x) + f(x)}{-\Delta x} = f'(x),$$

so that $f'(x)$ is an even function of x.

The student should prove the following lemma by first separating $H(x)$ into its even and odd parts and then employing Theorems 14, 15, 16.

LEMMA 2. *If $H'(x)$ is an even function of x, $H(x)$ is the sum of a constant $H(0)$ and an odd function of x; if $H'(x)$ is an odd function of x, $H(x)$ is an even function of x.*

THEOREM 17. *If $f(x)$ is an even function of x,*

$$\int_{-a}^{a} f(x)\, dx = 2 \int_{0}^{a} f(x)\, dx.$$

THEOREM 18. *If $f(x)$ is an odd function of x,*

$$\int_{-a}^{a} f(x)\, dx = 0.$$

In Theorems 17 and 18 it is assumed that the integrals involved exist.

Proof of Theorems 17 and 18. Let the indefinite integral of $f(x)\, dx$ be denoted by

$$(9) \qquad \int f(x)\, dx = H(x) + C.$$

We know that $H'(x) = f(x)$ and that

$$(10) \qquad \int_{-a}^{a} f(x)\, dx = H(a) - H(-a).$$

If $f(x)$ is an even function in the interval $-a \leqq x \leqq a$, $H'(x)$ is an even function and, by Lemma 2, $H(x)$ is an odd function of x plus the constant $H(0)$. Put

$$(11) \qquad H(x) = O(x) + H(0).$$

Then, by (10),

$$\int_{-a}^{a} f(x)\, dx = O(a) + H(0) - O(-a) - H(0) = 2O(a)$$

or

$$\int_{-a}^{a} f(x)\, dx = 2[H(a) - H(0)] = 2 \int_{0}^{a} f(x)\, dx,$$

by (11).

If $f(x)$ is an odd function of x, $H'(x)$ is odd, so $H(x)$ is an even function of x. Then $H(-a) = H(a)$ and Theorem 18 follows from equation (10).

Since many integrals of these precise types occur, the theorems are frequently applicable. Theorem 17 saves time and reduces the danger of mistake. Theorem 18 is even more useful, since whenever it applies there is no need to find the indefinite integral at all.

When the integrand of a definite integral with limits $(-a)$ to a consists of several terms, some odd and some even, the odd terms may be dropped at once. See Example (c) below.

Example (a).

$$\int_{-a}^{a} (a^2 - t^2)\, dt = 2 \int_{0}^{a} (a^2 - t^2)\, dt$$

$$= 2 \left[a^2 t - \tfrac{1}{3} t^3 \right]_{0}^{a} = \tfrac{4}{3} a^3.$$

[Compare with Example (b), § 51.]

Example (b). $\displaystyle \int_{-1}^{1} \frac{x\, dx}{\sqrt{2 - x^8}} = 0.$

This is a so-called elliptic integral: The indefinite integral is not only beyond our present reach—it can never be evaluated in terms of elementary functions. But Theorem 18 gives the value of the definite integral at a glance.

Example (c).

$$\int_{-2}^{2} (x^5 - 3x^3 + 2x^2 - x)\, dx = 4 \int_{0}^{2} x^2\, dx$$

$$= \left[\frac{4x^3}{3} \right]_{0}^{2} = \frac{32}{3}.$$

EXERCISES

Evaluate the definite integrals in Exs. 1–26.

1. $\displaystyle \int_{1}^{2} x^4\, dx.$ *Ans.* $\frac{31}{5}$.   2. $\displaystyle \int_{1}^{3} (y - 2)^2\, dy.$ *Ans.* $\frac{2}{3}$.

3. $\displaystyle \int_{0}^{1} (y^2 - y^3)\, dy.$ *Ans.* $\frac{1}{12}$.   4. $\displaystyle \int_{0}^{2} (x - 3x^2)\, dx.$ *Ans.* -6.

5. $\displaystyle \int_{-1}^{2} x(1 - 2x)\, dx.$ *Ans.* $-\frac{9}{2}$.   6. $\displaystyle \int_{\frac{1}{2}}^{1} \sqrt{2\beta - 1}\, d\beta.$ *Ans.* $\frac{1}{3}$.

7. $\displaystyle \int_{-1}^{2} x^2(3 - 2x)\, dx.$ *Ans.* $\frac{3}{2}$.   8. $\displaystyle \int_{-2}^{-1} (3 + 2u)\, du.$ *Ans.* 0.

9. $\displaystyle \int_{1}^{2} (3x - 7)(x - 3)\, dx.$ 10. $\displaystyle \int_{1}^{2} (3x - 4)(x - 6)\, dx.$

11. $\displaystyle \int_{-3}^{-2} \frac{dx}{(4 + x)^3}.$ *Ans.* $\frac{3}{8}$.   12. $\displaystyle \int_{0}^{2} \frac{dx}{(3 + x)^2}.$ *Ans.* $\frac{2}{15}$.

13. $\displaystyle \int_{0}^{1} (1 + \alpha^2)^2\, d\alpha.$ *Ans.* $\frac{28}{15}$.   14. $\displaystyle \int_{0}^{1} x(1 - x^2)\, dx.$ *Ans.* $\frac{1}{4}$.

15. $\displaystyle \int_{0}^{1} \frac{dy}{(1 + 3y)^2}.$ *Ans.* $\frac{1}{4}$.   16. $\displaystyle \int_{0}^{1} \frac{dy}{(1 + 2y)^3}.$ *Ans.* $\frac{1}{3}$.

17. $\displaystyle \int_{1}^{2} \left(1 - \frac{1}{u^2} \right)^2\, du.$ *Ans.* $\frac{7}{24}$.   18. $\displaystyle \int_{\frac{1}{2}}^{1} \left(1 + \frac{1}{u^2} \right)^2\, du.$ *Ans.* $\frac{29}{6}$.

19. $\displaystyle\int_1^4 \frac{(1-y)\,dy}{\sqrt{y}}.$ *Ans.* $-\frac{8}{3}.$ **20.** $\displaystyle\int_1^3 \frac{v^4+1}{v^2}\,dv.$ *Ans.* $\frac{28}{3}.$

21. $\displaystyle\int_0^a x^3(a^4-x^4)^{\frac{1}{2}}\,dx.$ *Ans.* $\frac{1}{6}a^6.$ **22.** $\displaystyle\int_0^a y^2(a^3-y^3)^{\frac{1}{3}}\,dy.$ *Ans.* $\frac{1}{4}a^4.$

23. $\displaystyle\int_0^{\frac{1}{2}a} \frac{y\,dy}{(a^2-y^2)^{\frac{3}{2}}}.$ *Ans.* $\dfrac{2-\sqrt{3}}{a\sqrt{3}}.$

24. $\displaystyle\int_0^a \frac{x^3\,dx}{\sqrt{a^4+x^4}}.$ *Ans.* $\frac{1}{2}a^2(\sqrt{2}-1).$

25. $\displaystyle\int_{\frac{1}{4}}^1 \frac{\sqrt{1-\sqrt{y}}}{\sqrt{y}}\,dy.$ *Ans.* $\frac{1}{3}\sqrt{2}.$

26. $\displaystyle\int_0^1 (1-x^{\frac{3}{2}})^4\sqrt{x}\,dx.$ *Ans.* $\frac{2}{15}.$

In Exs. 27–35, use the properties of integrals with odd, or even, functions as integrands, to simplify the evaluation of the integral.

27. $\displaystyle\int_{-2}^2 (x^3-7x^5)\,dx.$ *Ans.* 0.   **28.** $\displaystyle\int_{-a}^a x^3\sqrt{a^2-x^2}\,dx.$ *Ans.* 0.

29. $\displaystyle\int_{-1}^1 (6y^2-5y^4)\,dy.$ *Ans.* 2.   **30.** $\displaystyle\int_{-2}^2 (1-\frac{1}{4}t^2)^2\,dt.$ *Ans.* $\frac{32}{15}.$

31. $\displaystyle\int_{-4}^4 (2v^3+\frac{3}{8}v^2-17v-3)\,dv.$ *Ans.* $-8.$

32. $\displaystyle\int_{-a}^a x^2(7x^3+15ax^2-13a^2x+6a^3)\,dx.$ *Ans.* $10a^6.$

33. $\displaystyle\int_{-2}^2 x(9-x^6)^{\frac{1}{2}}\,dx.$ *Ans.* 0.

34. $\displaystyle\int_{-1}^1 (u^7+1)(3u^2+1)\,du.$ *Ans.* 4.

35. $\displaystyle\int_{-2}^2 (x^5-x^3+3x^2-4)\,dx.$ *Ans.* 0.

36. Show that the product or quotient of two odd functions is even.

37. Show that the product or quotient of an odd function by an even function is odd.

38. Prove Lemma 2, page 103.

54. *The Sigma Notation*

We shall have frequent occasion to speak of *sums* of a considerable number of terms, usually an unspecified number n:

$$u_1 + u_2 + u_3 + \cdots + u_n.$$

To save the bother of writing out such expressions always in full, a single

symbol is commonly used in mathematics. The symbol $\sum\limits_{i=1}^{n}$ means that we
are to substitute $i = 1, 2, 3, \cdot\cdot\cdot, n$ successively in the expression following, and add the results; for example,

$$\sum_{i=1}^{n} u_i = u_1 + u_2 + u_3 + \cdot\cdot\cdot + u_n,$$

$$\sum_{k=0}^{n} a_k x^{n-k} = a_0 x^n + a_1 x^{n-1} + \cdot\cdot\cdot + a_{n-1} x + a_n.$$

55. *Plane Area*

Calculus grew out of the attempts, eventually successful in the seven-
teenth century, of mathematicians* to solve two major problems. The first
problem was to obtain the tangent line to a curve at a given point on it;
that was solved by introducing and applying the notion of a derivative.
The second problem was to obtain the area bounded by a curve $y = f(x)$,
the x-axis, and two ordinates $x = a$ and $x = b$.

This second problem is solved by a judicious extension of the elementary
concept of the area of a rectangle as the product of its base and its altitude.

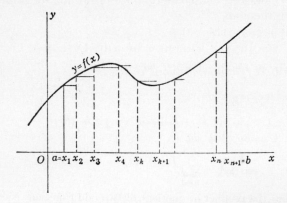

Figure 57

In Fig. 57, let the interval $a \leqq x \leqq b$ be divided into n parts in any
manner, the divisions being at $x_1, x_2, x_3, \cdot\cdot\cdot, x_{n+1}$, with $x_1 = a$, $x_{n+1} = b$.
Erect rectangles using the ordinates at $x_1, x_2, x_3, \cdot\cdot\cdot, x_n$, as shown in
the figure. In order to have a simple notation for the width of the bases
of these rectangles, let $\Delta x_1 = x_2 - x_1$, $\Delta x_2 = x_3 - x_2$, $\cdot\cdot\cdot$; i.e., let
$\Delta x_k = x_{k+1} - x_k$, for $k = 1, 2, 3, \cdot\cdot\cdot, n$.

* Particularly Sir Isaac Newton, 1642–1727, and Gottfried Wilhelm Leibnitz (or
Leibniz), 1646–1716; these two men, independently of each other, produced the great
bulk of basic ideas and techniques which form the elementary calculus.

It is reasonable that if the maximum width of the rectangles shown be taken sufficiently small, and the number of rectangles correspondingly large, then the sum of the areas of the rectangles will approximate, as closely as desired, a quantity which agrees with our intuitive concept of the required area.

Even the oft-quoted average man on the street would, if presented with the curve $y = f(x)$ drawn carefully on graph paper, obtain an approximation to the area we wish by counting the squares enclosed by its boundaries. We wish to replace his rough idea by a specific formula.

Therefore, we proceed to lay down as our definition of the area A bounded by the curve $y = f(x)$, the x-axis, and the ordinates $x = a$ and $x = b$, the following:

$$(1) \qquad A = \operatorname*{Lim}_{\text{max. } \Delta x_k \to 0} \sum_{k=1}^{n} f(x_k)\, \Delta x_k,$$

in which, since the widths Δx_k of the rectangles approach zero, the number of them, n, must approach infinity.

At once we are confronted with the question of whether the limit in (1) exists, and, if it does exist, with the problem of determining how to compute that limit. A sufficient condition for the existence of the limit in (1), together with a remarkably simple method for obtaining its value, is contained in the following theorem.

The Fundamental Theorem of the Integral Calculus

THEOREM 19. *If $f(x)$ is continuous in the interval $a \leqq x \leqq b$,*

$$\text{if } a = x_1 < x_2 < x_3 < \cdots < x_n < x_{n+1} = b,$$

and if $\Delta x_k = x_{k+1} - x_k$, for $k = 1, 2, 3, \cdots, n$, then

$$(2) \qquad \operatorname*{Lim}_{\text{max. } \Delta x_k \to 0} \sum_{k=1}^{n} f(x_k)\, \Delta x_k = \int_a^b f(x)\, dx.$$

From equations (1) and (2) above, it follows that the area A is given by

$$(3) \qquad A = \int_a^b f(x)\, dx,$$

which is the basic formula we needed for the computation of the area shown in Fig. 57.

Proof of Theorem 19 will be omitted; a rigorous analytic approach to our subject properly belongs in advanced calculus or in a course in functions of a real variable. Here we content ourselves with the discussion in the next section, a treatment intended to make Theorem 19 plausible, not to prove it.

56. *Plane Area: An Intuitive Approach*

Consider the area bounded by the continuous curve $y = f(x)$, the x-axis, the fixed ordinate $x = a$, and a variable ordinate $x = x$, as shown in Fig. 58. For the moment, let the function $f(x)$ be increasing with increasing x. Then, when x is increased by an amount Δx, the area A will increase by an amount ΔA, the area $KLRP$. Now,

$$\text{Area } KLQP < \text{Area } KLRP < \text{Area } KLRS,$$

and

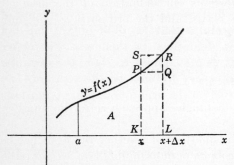

Figure 58

$$\text{Area } KLQP = \overline{KP} \cdot \overline{KL} = f(x)\,\Delta x,$$
$$\text{Area } KLRP = \Delta A,$$
$$\text{Area } KLRS = f(x + \Delta x)\,\Delta x.$$

Therefore, we have

$$f(x)\,\Delta x < \Delta A < f(x + \Delta x)\,\Delta x,$$

$$(1) \qquad f(x) < \frac{\Delta A}{\Delta x} < f(x + \Delta x).$$

In the inequalities (1), let $\Delta x \to 0$. Then $f(x)$ stays fixed and $f(x + \Delta x) \to f(x)$ because $f(x)$ is continuous.

Since $\dfrac{\Delta A}{\Delta x}$ is pinned in between two quantities, $f(x)$ and the quantity $f(x + \Delta x)$ which approaches $f(x)$ (because of continuity), then $\dfrac{\Delta A}{\Delta x}$ must also approach $f(x)$. Since $\dfrac{\Delta A}{\Delta x} \to \dfrac{dA}{dx}$, as $\Delta x \to 0$, we can conclude that

$$(2) \qquad \frac{dA}{dx} = f(x).$$

Because the derivative of A is $f(x)$, it follows that

$$A = \int f(x)\,dx = F(x) + C.$$

Since the position of the fixed ordinate $x = a$ is given, the constant of integration may be determined by the fact that $A = 0$ when $x = a$:

$$0 = F(a) + C,$$
$$C = -F(a),$$
$$(3) \qquad A = F(x) - F(a).$$

For the area bounded by $y = f(x)$, the x-axis, and the ordinates $x = a$ and $x = b$, equation (3) becomes

$$(4) \qquad A = F(b) - F(a).$$

In view of the definition of the definite integral, equation (4) yields

(5) $$A = \int_a^b f(x) \, dx,$$

in agreement with the formula for area given in Theorem 19.

The above discussion is readily modified to apply to a function which steadily decreases with increasing x, or which remains constant. If the interval between the ordinates $x = a$ and $x = b$ can be broken up into subintervals, on each of which the function increases, decreases, or remains constant, the argument leading to (5) goes through just as easily.

For brevity and simplicity in this first course, we shall make free use of intuitive reasoning. All the many formulas that we shall obtain will fall into one or the other of two classes, definitions or theorems. For many theorems we shall omit formal proofs, being content to show the meaning and reasonableness of the result; but every formula or theorem that we accept on this basis can be shown to rest on the firm foundation of analysis.

57. *Simple Verifications*

Let us verify that the definition of area presented in § 55 yields the desired result ($\frac{1}{2}$ base $\times$ altitude) for a right triangle. Figure 59 shows a right triangle bounded by the x-axis, the vertical line $x = b$, and the line

$$y = \frac{hx}{b}.$$

In the definition of area

(1) $$A = \operatorname*{Lim}_{\substack{\text{max. } \Delta x_k \to 0}} \sum_{k=1}^{n} f(x_k) \, \Delta x_k$$

we choose to use n intervals of equal length. Put

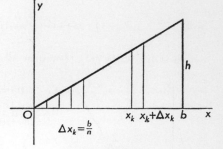

Figure 59

$$f(x) = \frac{hx}{b}, \qquad x_k = \frac{(k-1)b}{n}, \qquad \Delta x_k = \Delta x = \frac{b}{n}.$$

Then (1) becomes

$$A = \operatorname*{Lim}_{\Delta x \to 0} \sum_{k=1}^{n} \frac{h}{b} \cdot \frac{(k-1)b}{n} \cdot \frac{b}{n},$$

or

(2) $$A = \operatorname*{Lim}_{n \to \infty} \frac{bh}{n^2} \sum_{k=1}^{n} (k-1).$$

In algebra* we found that the sum of any arithmetic progression is one-half the product of the number of terms by the sum of the first term and the last term·

(3) $$\sum_{k=1}^{n} [a + (k - 1)d] = \tfrac{1}{2}n[2a + (n - 1)d].$$

For $a = 0$, $d = 1$, equation (3) yields

(4) $$\sum_{k=1}^{n} (k - 1) = \tfrac{1}{2}n(n - 1).$$

Then equation (2) becomes

$$A = \operatorname*{Lim}_{n\to\infty} \frac{bh}{n^2} \cdot \frac{n(n - 1)}{2} = \frac{1}{2}\, bh \operatorname*{Lim}_{n\to\infty} \frac{n - 1}{n} = \frac{1}{2}\, bh,$$

as desired.

Because of Theorem 19, page 107, we may obtain the desired area more simply by employing a definite integral. Since, in this example,

$$f(x) = \frac{hx}{b},$$

it follows that

$$A = \int_0^b f(x)\, dx = \frac{h}{b} \int_0^b x\, dx = \frac{h}{b} \left[\frac{1}{2}\, x^2 \right]_0^b = \frac{1}{2}\, bh.$$

Next let us verify Theorem 19 for the area exhibited in Fig. 60. Again we use only the one choice of intervals of equal length. The desired area is that bounded by the x-axis, the vertical line $x = 1$, and the pertinent arc of the parabola

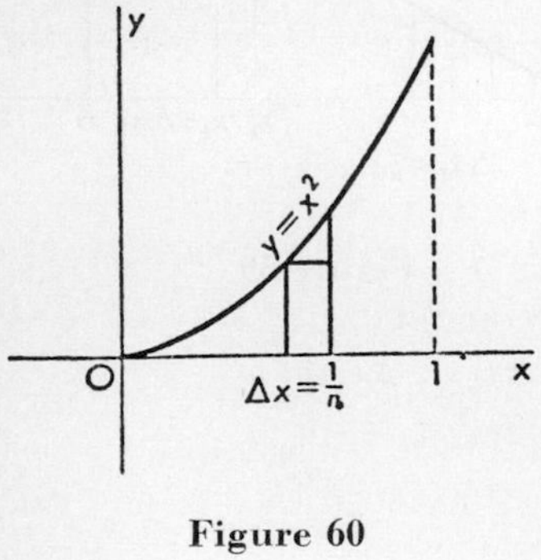

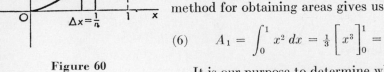

(5) $$y = x^2.$$

Here $f(x) = x^2$ and the definite integral method for obtaining areas gives us

(6) $$A_1 = \int_0^1 x^2\, dx = \tfrac{1}{3} \left[x^3 \right]_0^1 = \tfrac{1}{3}.$$

Figure 60

It is our purpose to determine whether the result in (6) agrees, as Theorem 19 states it does, with the result given by

(7) $$A_2 = \operatorname*{Lim}_{\Delta x_k \to 0} \sum_{k=1}^{n} f(x_k)\, \Delta x_k.$$

* See any college algebra; for example, J. R. Britton and L. C. Snively, *Algebra for College Students*, 2nd ed., New York, Rinehart and Co., 1954, page 292.

For this example,

$$f(x) = x^2, \qquad x_k = \frac{k-1}{n}, \qquad \Delta x_k = \Delta x = \frac{1}{n}.$$

Hence (7) yields

$$A_2 = \operatorname*{Lim}_{n \to \infty} \sum_{k=1}^{n} \left(\frac{k-1}{n} \right)^2 \frac{1}{n} = \operatorname*{Lim}_{n \to \infty} \frac{1}{n^3} \sum_{k=1}^{n} (k-1)^2.$$

It is easy to show by induction that

$$(8) \qquad \sum_{k=1}^{n} (k-1)^2 = \frac{n(n-1)(2n-1)}{6},$$

or the result may be obtained by replacing n by $(n-1)$ in Ex. 11 on page 287 of Britton and Snively's *Algebra for College Students* cited near the beginning of this section.

With the aid of equation (8) we may write

$$A_2 = \operatorname*{Lim}_{n \to \infty} \frac{n(n-1)(2n-1)}{6n^3} = \operatorname*{Lim}_{n \to \infty} \frac{2n^2 - 3n + 1}{6n^2} = \frac{1}{3}.$$

Therefore the A_1 of (6) and A_2 of (7) are equal, as predicted by Theorem 19.

EXERCISES

In each exercise compute by the two methods employed in this section the area bounded by the given curves and straight lines. Use equation (1) of § 55 and recompute the area by formula (3) of § 55. In your work, equations (4) and (8) of the present section and the sum

$$(9) \qquad \sum_{k=1}^{n} (k-1)^3 = \tfrac{1}{4}n^2(n-1)^2$$

may be used. A set of formulas equivalent to (4), (8), and (9) is

$$(10) \qquad \sum_{k=1}^{n} 1 = n, \qquad \sum_{k=1}^{n} k = \tfrac{1}{2}n(n+1),$$

$$\sum_{k=1}^{n} k^2 = \tfrac{1}{6}n(n+1)(2n+1), \qquad \sum_{k=1}^{n} k^3 = \tfrac{1}{4}n^2(n+1)^2.$$

1. $y = x^3, y = 0, x = 1.$ *Ans.* $\frac{1}{4}$.
2. $y = 4x(1 - x), y = 0.$ *Ans.* $\frac{2}{3}$.
3. $y = x^2, y = 0, x = 1, x = 2.$ *Ans.* $\frac{7}{3}$.
4. $y = 2x - 3, y = 0, x = 2, x = 5.$ *Ans.* 12.
5. $y = x^2, y = 0, x = 1, x = 3.$ *Ans.* $\frac{26}{3}$.

58. *Computation of Plane Areas*

The formula for area in § 55, properly extended, enables us to compute areas bounded, in any manner whatever, by curves whose equations are given in rectangular coordinates. We merely take an element, parallel to either axis according to convenience, express its area in terms of the coordinates, and integrate over the whole region. The process is best explained by means of examples.

In plane-area problems, a rough check on the answer may be obtained by circumscribing about the area a rectangle with its sides parallel to the axes and comparing the area of the rectangle with the result obtained by integration. In problems where the numerical work is simple, so that the answer is apt to be either correct or widely incorrect, this check is especially valuable.

In every problem the student should *make a sketch of the area to be found, draw an element in a general position, and obtain the area of the element directly from the figure.*

Example (a). Find the area in the first quadrant bounded by the parabola $y^2 = 4ax$, the x-axis, and the line $x = a$. (Fig. 61.)

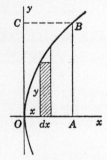   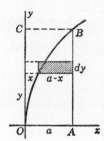

Figure 61   Figure 62

With the element parallel to Oy, we have

$$A = \int_0^a y\, dx = 2a^{\frac{1}{2}} \int_0^a x^{\frac{1}{2}}\, dx = \tfrac{4}{3}a^{\frac{1}{2}} \left[x^{\frac{3}{2}} \right]_0^a = \tfrac{4}{3}a^2.$$

Since the area $OABC$ is $2a^2$, the result is roughly checked.

Example (b). Find the above area by another method.

Take the element parallel to Ox (Fig. 62). The base of the rectangle is $a - x$, the altitude dy, whence

$$A = \int_0^{2a} (a - x)\, dy = \int_0^{2a} \left(a - \frac{y^2}{4a} \right) dy$$

$$= \left[ay - \frac{y^3}{12a} \right]_0^{2a} = \frac{4}{3}\, a^2.$$

59. *Integral with Negative Integrand*

In the definite integral $\int_a^b f(x)\, dx$, let the limits be so chosen that the lower limit is algebraically less than the upper limit. With this convention x increases, so that dx is positive.

Suppose first that the integrand $f(x)$ keeps the same sign, either positive or negative, throughout the interval. Then, when the integral is evaluated, the result will have the same sign as $f(x)$. For, in Theorem 19, each of the terms occurring in the summation will have the same sign as $f(x)$, and the limit of the sum must have that same sign.

Now, if we are using the integral to compute an area in the ordinary sense of elementary geometry, the formula must always be so written that the element is positive, since area is positive.

Example. Find the area in the second quadrant bounded by the curve

$$y = x^3 + 1.$$

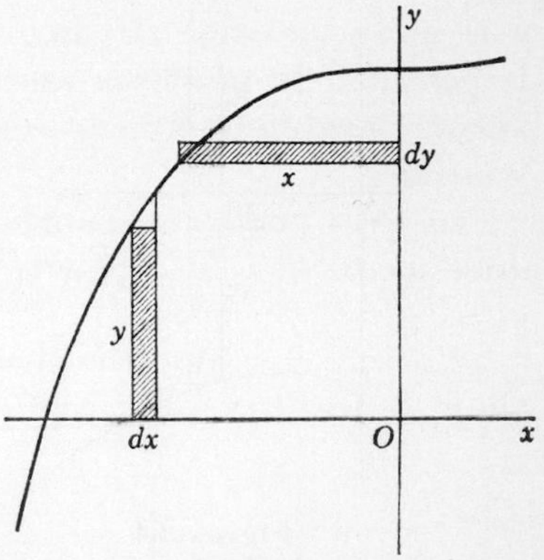

Figure 63

With vertical rectangles,

$$A = \int_{-1}^{0} y\, dx = \int_{-1}^{0} (x^3 + 1)\, dx$$

$$= \left[\frac{1}{4} x^4 + x \right]_{-1}^{0} = \frac{3}{4}.$$

With horizontal rectangles, since x is negative, the area of the element is $(-x)\, dy$, and

$$A = \int_{0}^{1} (-x)\, dy$$

$$= -\int_{0}^{1} (y - 1)^{\frac{1}{3}}\, dy$$

$$= -\frac{3}{4} \left[(y - 1)^{\frac{4}{3}} \right]_{0}^{1} = \frac{3}{4}.$$

If the curve crosses the axis within the interval of integration, and we wish to find the area in the above sense, we integrate over the positive and negative regions separately, changing the sign in the latter. Of course considerations of symmetry may enable us to shorten the process.

60. *Area Between Two Curves*

In finding the area between two curves, uncertainty as to signs sometimes arises when some of the coordinates are negative. It need not, if we merely remember that in analytic geometry all coordinates are *directed* line segments. In Fig. 64, the height of the element is

$$QP = QM + MP = MP - MQ = y_h - y_l.$$

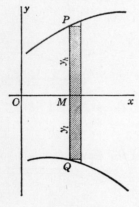

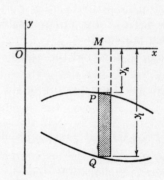

Figure 64   Figure 65

In Fig. 65, the height is

$$QP = QM - PM = MP - MQ = y_h - y_l.$$

Always, a vertical element will be positive, if we use the *y of the higher point minus the y of the lower point.*

A horizontal element will be positive if we use the *x of the right-hand point minus the x of the left-hand point*, as is done in Example (c) below.

Example (a). Find the area between the curves (Fig. 66)

$$x^2 = 2ay, \qquad x^2 = 4ay - a^2.$$

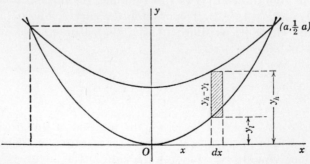

Figure 66

We easily find that these parabolas intersect at $(\pm a, \frac{1}{2}a)$. The area of a vertical element is $(y_h - y_l)\,dx$, where y_h and y_l are the ordinates of the higher and lower curves, respectively. Instead of integrating from $-a$ to a, we may, because of the symmetry with respect to Oy, integrate from 0 to a and multiply by 2:

$$A = \int_{-a}^{a} (y_h - y_l)\,dx = 2\int_0^a \left(\frac{x^2}{4a} + \frac{a}{4} - \frac{x^2}{2a}\right)\,dx$$

$$= 2\int_0^a \left(\frac{a}{4} - \frac{x^2}{4a}\right)\,dx = \frac{1}{2}\left[ax - \frac{x^3}{3a}\right]_0^a = \frac{1}{3}\,a^2.$$

The area of the circumscribing rectangle is a^2, which yields a rough check on our result.

Example (b). Find the area bounded by the curve $x^2 + 4y - 8 = 0$ and the line $x = 2y$.

First, put the equation of the parabola into the standard form,

$$x^2 = -4(y - 2),$$

in order to sketch it. Obtain the intersections of the given curves, by solving

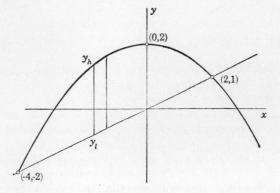

Figure 67

their equations simultaneously. In this example, the intersections are found to be at $(2, 1)$ and $(-4, -2)$. Then sketch the curves, Fig. 67, and draw in an appropriate element, as shown. Using that element, we arrive at the desired areas as follows:

$$A = \int_{-4}^{2} (y_h - y_l)\,dx$$

$$= \int_{-4}^{2} (2 - \tfrac{1}{4}x^2 - \tfrac{1}{2}x)\,dx$$

$$= \left[2x - \frac{x^3}{12} - \frac{x^2}{4}\right]_{-4}^{2}$$

$$= 4 - \tfrac{2}{3} - 1 - (-8 + \tfrac{16}{3} - 4) = 9.$$

Example (*c*). Find the area bounded by the curve $x = y^2 - 1$ and the line $y = x - 1$.

As in Example (*a*), we find the intersections and sketch the figure, Fig. 68. This time a horizontal element is suggested by the figure. The length of the element is the x-coordinate on the right (that of the straight line) minus the x-coordinate on the left (that of the parabola). Therefore we conclude that

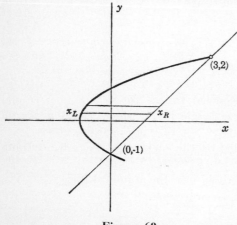

Figure 68

$$A = \int_{-1}^{2} (x_R - x_L) \, dy$$

$$= \int_{-1}^{2} (y + 1 - y^2 + 1) \, dy$$

$$= \left[2y + \frac{y^2}{2} - \frac{y^3}{3} \right]_{-1}^{2} = \frac{9}{2}.$$

EXERCISES

1. Find the area bounded by the curve $y = 9 - x^2$ and the x-axis. Solve in two ways.   *Ans.* 36.

2. Find the area bounded by the curve $a^2 y = x^3$, the x-axis, and the line $x = 2a$. Solve in two ways.   *Ans.* $4a^2$.

3. Find the area bounded by the curve $y^2 - 3x + 3 = 0$ and the line $x = 4$.
Ans. 12.

4. Find the area bounded by the curve $ay = x^2$ and the lines $y = a$ and $y = 4a$.
Ans. $\frac{28}{3}a^2$.

5. Find the area bounded by the curve $y^2 + x - 4y = 5$ and the y-axis.
Ans. 36.

6. A trapezoid has its vertices at $(0, 0)$, (a, h), $(a + b_1, h)$, $(b_2, 0)$, with all letters denoting positive quantities. Set up a single integral for the area of the trapezoid, evaluate the integral, and compare your answer with the known elementary formula $A = \frac{1}{2}h(b_1 + b_2)$.

7. Find the area bounded by a parabola and any right chord. (Use the parabola $y^2 = 4ax$, chord $x = x_1$.)   *Ans.* Two-thirds of the circumscribing rectangle.

8. Solve Ex. 7 by another method.

9. Find the area in the third quadrant bounded by the curve $x = y^2 + 2y$.
Ans. $\frac{4}{3}$.

10. Find the area bounded by the curve $x = y^2 + 2y$ and the line $x = 3$.

11. Find the area bounded by the curve $y^2 + 2x - 2y - 3 = 0$ and the y-axis.
Ans. $\frac{16}{3}$.

12. Find the area bounded by the curve $y = 3x(x - 2)^2$ and the x-axis.
Ans. 4.

13. Find the area bounded by the curve $y = x(x - 1)^2$, the y-axis, and the line $y = 2$.   *Ans.* $\frac{10}{3}$.

14. Find the area in the second quadrant bounded by the curve $2x^2 + 4x + y = 0$.   *Ans.* $\frac{8}{3}$.

15. Find the area bounded by the curve $y = 4x - x^2$ and the line $y = 3$.

Ans. $\frac{4}{3}$.

16. Find the area bounded by the curve $y = 4x - x^2$ and the lines $x = 0$ and $y = 4$. Solve in two ways.   *Ans.* $\frac{8}{3}$.

17. Find the area bounded by the curve $y = 4x - x^2$ and the lines $x = -2$ and $y = 4$.   *Ans.* $\frac{64}{3}$.

18. Find the area bounded by the curve $y = 3x - x^3$ and the line $y = 2$.

Ans. $\frac{27}{4}$.

19. Find each of the two areas bounded by the curves $y = x^3 - 4x$ and $y = x^2 + 2x$.   *Ans.* $\frac{16}{3}$, $\frac{63}{4}$.

20. Find the area bounded by the curve $a^3y = (x^2 - a^2)^2$ and the x-axis.

Ans. $\frac{16}{15}a^2$.

21. Find the area, in the first quadrant, bounded by the curve $x^2y = a^3$, the lines $x = 2a$, $y = 4a$, and the axes.   *Ans.* $\frac{7}{2}a^2$.

In Exs. 22–38, find the area between the two curves.

22. $2x^2 + 4x + y = 0$, $y = 2x$.   *Ans.* 9.
23. $y^2 = -4x$, $y = 2(x + 2)$.   *Ans.* 9.
24. $y^2 = 2x + 3$, $y = x$.   *Ans.* $\frac{16}{3}$.   25. $y = x^4$, $y = 5x + 6$.   *Ans.* 18.9.
26. A parabola and a chord through the vertex. (Use $y^2 = 4ax$, $y = mx$.)

Ans. $\dfrac{8a^2}{3m^3}$.

27. $x^2 = ay$, $a^2y = x^3$.   28. $y = x$, $a^2y = x^3$.
29. $y = x^2 + 2x$, $x - 2y = 1$. Check by Ex. 26.   *Ans.* $\frac{1}{48}$.
30. $y^2 = 1 + x$, $y = 1 - x$.   *Ans.* $\frac{9}{2}$.
31. $y^2 = x$, $x^2 - 2x + 3y = 2$.   *Ans.* 6.
32. $y^2 = -x$, $x^2 = 6 - 5y$.   *Ans.* 5.4.
33. $y^2 = -x$, $x^2 + 3y + 4x + 6 = 0$.   *Ans.* $\frac{5}{3}$.
34. $y = x^2(x - 3)$, $y = x^2$.   *Ans.* $\frac{64}{3}$.
35. $y = x^2(x - 3)$, $y = 4(x - 3)$; the total area.   *Ans.* 32.75.
36. $x^2 = y + 1$, $x = (y + 1)^2$. Solve in two ways.   *Ans.* $\frac{1}{3}$.
37. $y = x^2(x - 3)$, $y^2 + 8y - 16x + 48 = 0$.   *Ans.* $\frac{17}{12}$.
38. $y = x^3 + 3x^2 - 4$, $y = 2x^3$.   *Ans.* $\frac{27}{4}$.

39. Find the area bounded by $y^2 = 4a(y - x)$, $y^2 = 2a(x + 2y - 3a)$, and the x-axis.   *Ans.* $2a^2$.

40. Evaluate $\displaystyle\int_0^a \sqrt{a^2 - x^2}\, dx$ by considering the geometric meaning of the integral.   *Ans.* $\frac{1}{4}\pi a^2$.

41. Find the area of an ellipse. (Set up the integral; then see Ex. 40.)   *Ans.* πab.

TRIGONOMETRIC FUNCTIONS

61. *Elementary Properties*

The trigonometric functions are one-valued and continuous for all values of the argument x, except that the tangent and secant become infinite when $x = \pm(n + \frac{1}{2})\pi$, the cotangent and cosecant become infinite when $x = \pm n\pi$, where n is zero or a positive integer. The sine and cosine, and their reciprocals the cosecant and secant, are periodic with the period 2π; the tangent and cotangent are periodic with the period π.

A student of calculus may save himself a great deal of time and trouble by memorizing thoroughly the fundamental facts and formulas of trigonometry. It is strongly recommended that such a review be made before proceeding further.

62. *Derivative of* sin *x*

The derivative of

$$y = \sin x$$

was obtained in Example (d), page 34, in which we found that

$$\frac{dy}{dx} = \frac{d}{dx} \sin x = \cos x.$$

If u is any function of x, it follows by the chain rule of § 29 that

$$\frac{d}{dx} \sin u = \frac{d}{du} \sin u \cdot \frac{du}{dx},$$

or

(7)
$$\frac{d}{dx} \sin u = \cos u \, \frac{du}{dx}.$$

Radian measure of angles is almost always used in calculus in preference

118

to degree measure of angles. In Ex. 39, page 18, it was found that

$$\lim_{\alpha^\circ \to 0} \frac{\sin \alpha^\circ}{\alpha^\circ} = \frac{\pi}{180^\circ}.$$

With the aid of the above limit, it can be seen that if x° is measured in degrees,

$$\frac{d}{dx^\circ} \sin x^\circ = \frac{\pi}{180^\circ} \cos x^\circ.$$

The highly undesirable factor $\left(\frac{\pi}{180^\circ}\right)$ would also appear in the derivatives of the other trigonometric functions, if degree measure were to be used. Therefore, in calculus we use radian measure whenever feasible, although in numerical studies (surveying, etc.) it is common practice to retain degree measure of angles.

63. *Derivatives of* cos *x,* tan *x, Etc.*

The derivatives of the other trigonometric functions may also be obtained directly from the definition of the derivative (Exs. 29–33, page 35), but they are more easily found from (7) above.

To differentiate cos x, we write

$$\frac{d}{dx} \cos x = \frac{d}{dx} \sin \left(\frac{\pi}{2} - x\right) = - \cos \left(\frac{\pi}{2} - x\right)$$
$$= - \sin x.$$

If u is any function of x, we find by the chain rule of § 29 that

$$(8) \qquad \frac{d}{dx} \cos u = - \sin u \frac{du}{dx}.$$

The remaining trigonometric functions may be differentiated by expressing them in terms of the sine and cosine. If u is any function of x, the results are:

$$(9) \qquad \frac{d}{dx} \tan u = \sec^2 u \frac{du}{dx},$$

$$(10) \qquad \frac{d}{dx} \cot u = - \csc^2 u \frac{du}{dx},$$

$$(11) \qquad \frac{d}{dx} \sec u = \sec u \tan u \frac{du}{dx},$$

$$(12) \qquad \frac{d}{dx} \csc u = - \csc u \cot u \frac{du}{dx}.$$

Example (a). If $y = \sin 4x^2$, then

$$\frac{dy}{dx} = 8x \cos 4x^2.$$

Example (b). If $z = \tan \frac{1}{2}y$, then

$$\frac{dz}{dy} = \frac{1}{2} \sec^2 \frac{1}{2}y.$$

Example (c). If $r = (2 + 3 \cot 4\theta)^5$, then

$$\frac{dr}{d\theta} = 5(2 + 3 \cot 4\theta)^4 \cdot 3 \cdot (-4 \csc^2 4\theta)$$

$$= -60 \csc^2 4\theta(2 + 3 \cot 4\theta)^4.$$

Example (d). Show that $\sin \varphi > \dfrac{2\varphi}{\pi}$ for $0 < \varphi < \frac{1}{2}\pi$.

Put

(1) $$y = \sin \varphi - \frac{2\varphi}{\pi}.$$

The desired inequality will be obtained by showing that y is positive for the given range of φ values.

From (1) it follows that

(2) $$y' = \cos \varphi - \frac{2}{\pi},$$

(3) $$y'' = -\sin \varphi.$$

Since $\sin \varphi$ is positive in the range $0 < \varphi < \frac{1}{2}\pi$, equation (3) tells us that the y curve is concave downward throughout that range. Therefore, since y is zero at $\varphi = 0$ and at $\varphi = \frac{1}{2}\pi$, the direction of concavity of the curve (1) shows that y must be positive between $\varphi = 0$ and $\varphi = \frac{1}{2}\pi$.

As a check note that at $\varphi = 0$, $y' = 1 - \dfrac{2}{\pi}$ is positive, so that y is increasing for small positive φ. The known continuity of y and its derivatives is being used several times in the argument presented. The student should sketch the pertinent portion of the curve (1).

EXERCISES

In Exs. 1–44, find the first derivative of the given function.

1. $y = \sin 3x$.   *Ans.* $y' = 3 \cos 3x$.

2. $x = \cos 4t$.   *Ans.* $\dfrac{dx}{dt} = -4 \sin 4t$.

3. $w = \tan 2\theta$.   *Ans.* $\dfrac{dw}{d\theta} = 2 \sec^2 2\theta$.

4. $z = \sec \frac{1}{2}y$.   *Ans.* $\dfrac{dz}{dy} = \frac{1}{2} \sec \frac{1}{2}y \tan \frac{1}{2}y$.

5. $y = \cot 5x$.   *Ans.* $y' = -5 \csc^2 5x$.

6. $y = \csc 7x$.   *Ans.* $y' = -7 \csc 7x \cot 7x$.

7. $v = 3 \cos 2u$.   8. $x = -4 \tan 3\theta$.

9. $w = 2 \csc (1 - 3x)$.   10. $y = 4 \cot \frac{1}{4}x$.

11. $y = 6 \sec 3x$.

12. $y = 12 \sin \frac{1}{2}x$.

13. $y = \tan (\frac{1}{4}\pi - \frac{1}{2}x)$.

14. $y = \sin (\frac{1}{4}\pi - \frac{1}{3}x)$.

15. $z = \cos^3 2x$.

16. $u = \sin^2 3t$.

17. $x = \sec^3 2t$.

18. $y = \tan^2 4t$.

19. $y = \cot^2 \frac{1}{4}x$.

20. $y = \csc^4 2x$.

21. $y = x^2 \sin \frac{1}{2}x$.

22. $y = x^2 \cos^2 3x$.

23. $w = \sec 2v + \tan 2v$.

24. $w = \csc 2v - \cot 2v$.

25. $y = \sin \beta \cos^2 \beta$.

26. $y = \sec^3 \beta \tan^2 \beta$.

27. $f(x) = \tan x - x$.

28. $F(x) = x + \cot x$.

29. $y = \cos^4 t - \sin^4 t$.   *Ans.* $\dfrac{dy}{dt} = -2 \sin 2t$.

30. $y = \sec^2 \theta - \tan^2 \theta$.   *Ans.* $\dfrac{dy}{d\theta} = 0$.

31. $y = \sec^4 \theta - \tan^4 \theta$.   *Ans.* $\dfrac{dy}{d\theta} = 4 \tan \theta \sec^2 \theta$.

32. $r = \cos \theta \cot \theta$.   *Ans.* $\dfrac{dr}{d\theta} = - \cos \theta (1 + \csc^2 \theta)$.

33. $w = \sin^4 y \cos^4 y$.   *Ans.* $\dfrac{dw}{dy} = \dfrac{1}{2} \sin^3 2y \cos 2y$.

34. $x = 2 \cos^2 \dfrac{t}{2}$.   *Ans.* $\dfrac{dx}{dt} = - \sin t$.

35. $y = \sin (\cos x)$.   *Ans.* $y' = - \sin x \cos (\cos x)$.

36. $y = \tan (x \sin x)$.   *Ans.* $y' = (x \cos x + \sin x) \sec^2 (x \sin x)$.

37. $v = (1 + \sin^4 y)^{\frac{3}{4}}$.

38. $v = (1 - 4 \cos 5y)^{-\frac{1}{2}}$.

39. $r = (2 \tan^3 2\theta - 1)^{\frac{1}{4}}$.

40. $r = \dfrac{\cos 2\theta}{1 - \sin 2\theta}$.

41. $y = \dfrac{\tan 2x}{1 - \cot 2x}$.

42. $x = \dfrac{1 - \tan^2 v}{\tan^4 v}$.

43. $y = \left(\dfrac{1 - \cos \theta}{1 + \cos \theta}\right)^3$.

44. $r = \dfrac{1}{(\sin \varphi - \cos \varphi)^2}$.

45. From the equation $y = \cos ax$, find the first four derivatives of y with respect to x.

46. Find y'' and $y^{(4)}$ from the equation $y = \sin 2x$.

47. Let A, B, and k be constants. From $y = A \cos kx + B \sin kx$, show that $\dfrac{d^2y}{dx^2} = -k^2y$.

48. From each of the three trigonometric formulas for $\cos 2x$, deduce by differentiation the trigonometric formula for $\sin 2x$.

49. From the trigonometric formula for $\sin (x + \alpha)$, deduce by differentiation the trigonometric formula for $\cos (x + \alpha)$.

50. From the trigonometric formula for $\tan 2x$, deduce by differentiation the trigonometric formula for $\cos 2x$.

51. Show that $\tan x$ increases as x increases, for all values of x for which $\tan x$ is defined.

52. Derive (9) from the fact that $\tan x = \dfrac{\sin x}{\cos x}$.

53. Derive (10).   **54.** Derive (11).   **55.** Derive (12).

56. Assuming that you know $\dfrac{d}{dx} \sin x = \cos x$, find $\dfrac{d}{dx} \cos x$ from the relation $\cos^2 x = 1 - \sin^2 x$.

57. Assuming that you know $\dfrac{d}{dx} \sin u = \cos u \dfrac{du}{dx}$, find $\dfrac{d}{dx} \cos x$ from the relation $\cos x = 1 - 2 \sin^2 (\tfrac{1}{2}x)$.

58. Show that
$$\sin x + \cos x > 1 \text{ for } 0 < x < \tfrac{1}{2}\pi.$$

59. Show that
$$12\pi \sin x > (24 + \pi^2)x - 4x^3 \text{ for } 0 < x < \tfrac{1}{2}\pi.$$

60. Use the method, but not the result, of Example (d) to show that
$$\cos x > 1 - \frac{2x}{\pi} \text{ for } 0 < x < \frac{\pi}{2}.$$

64. *Graphs of Trigonometric Functions*

To draw the graph of the function
$$y = \sin x,$$
we may proceed as in § 40. On account of the periodicity of the sine function, it will be sufficient to determine the appearance of the curve in the interval from $x = 0$ to $x = 2\pi$; the remainder of the curve must consist of repetitions of this portion.

1. When $x = 0$, $y = 0$; when $y = 0$, $x = 0$, π, 2π.
2. Large values of x need not be considered.
3. $y' = \cos x$; hence the critical points are $(\tfrac{1}{2}\pi,\ 1)$, a maximum, and $(\tfrac{3}{2}\pi,\ -1)$, a minimum.

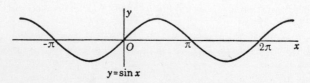

$y = \sin x$

Figure 69

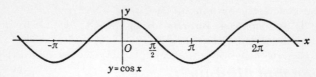

$y = \cos x$

Figure 70

4. $y'' = -\sin x$: the points of inflection are $(0, 0)$, with slope 1, $(\pi, 0)$, with slope -1, and $(2\pi, 0)$, with slope 1.

The curve consists of an infinite succession of waves along the x-axis, as shown in Fig. 69.

The graphs of the cosine and tangent are shown in Figs. 70 and 71; they are obtained in a similar way, except that in the case of the tangent

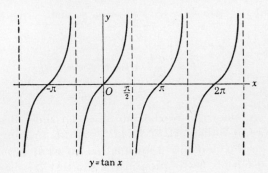

Figure 71

the points of discontinuity $x = \pm(n + \frac{1}{2})\pi$ must be specially investigated in addition to the usual discussion.

EXERCISES

Trace the curve in each exercise.

1. $y = \sec x.$
2. $y = \csc x.$
3. $y = \cot x.$
4. $y = 4 \tan 2x.$
5. $y = 2 \cos \frac{1}{2}x.$
6. $y = \frac{1}{4} \sin 2x.$
7. $y = -3 \sin \frac{1}{3}x.$
8. $y = 4 \cos 2x.$
9. $y = \sin^2 x.$
10. $y = \cos^2 x.$
11. $y = \cos^2 2x.$
12. $y = \sin^2 2x.$
13. $y = \cos^3 x.$
14. $y = \sin^3 x.$
15. $y = \sin^2 x - \sin x.$
16. $y = \cos^2 x + \cos x.$
17. $x = 1 - 2 \sin 2t.$
18. $x = 1 - 3 \cos \frac{1}{2}t.$
19. $y = 2 + \sin x - 2 \cos 2x.$
20. $y = 1 + \sin x - \cos \frac{1}{2}x.$
21. $y = \cos x - x.$
22. $y = x - \sin x.$
23. $y = \cos 2x - x.$
24. $y = 2x + \cos x.$
25. $y = \dfrac{\cos x}{x}.$
26. $y = \dfrac{\sin x}{x}.$
27. $y = \dfrac{\tan x}{x}.$
23. $y = x - \tan x.$

65. *Maxima and Minima*

Many problems requiring the determination of maxima and minima may be solved very neatly by expressing the function in terms of trigonometric functions of an angle.

Example (*a*). Find the shape of the largest rectangle that can be in-scribed in a given circle. [Example (*a*), § 42.]

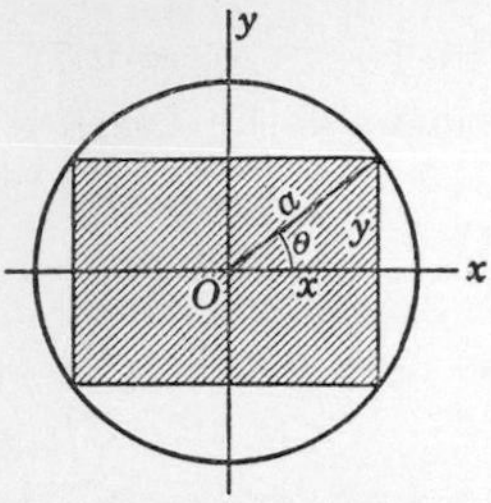

The area of the rectangle is

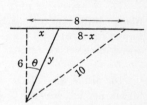

$$A = 4xy.$$

But $\qquad x = a \cos \theta, \qquad y = a \sin \theta,$

$$A = 4a^2 \cos \theta \sin \theta = 2a^2 \sin 2\theta:$$

$$\frac{dA}{d\theta} = 4a^2 \cos 2\theta = 0, \qquad \theta = \frac{\pi}{4},$$

Figure 72

$$y = x.$$

Example (*b*). A man in a rowboat 6 mi. from shore desires to reach a point on the shore at a distance of 10 mi. from his present position. If he can walk 4 mi. per hr. and row 2 mi. per hr., in what direction should he row in order to reach his destination in the shortest possible time? [Example (*c*), § 42.]

The time required is

$$T = \frac{y}{2} + \frac{8 - x}{4}.$$

Let us express the time *T* as a function of the angle *θ*. We obtain

$$y = 6 \sec \theta, \qquad x = 6 \tan \theta,$$

$$T = \frac{6 \sec \theta}{2} + \frac{8 - 6 \tan \theta}{4}$$

$$= 3 \sec \theta + 2 - \tfrac{3}{2} \tan \theta,$$

$$\frac{dT}{d\theta} = 3 \sec \theta \tan \theta - \tfrac{3}{2} \sec^2 \theta$$

$$= 3 \sec^2 \theta \,(\sin \theta - \tfrac{1}{2}) = 0,$$

$$\theta = 30°.$$

Figure 73

EXERCISES

Solve the following exercises by making use of trigonometric functions.

1. Find the shape of the rectangle of maximum perimeter inscribed in a circle.
Ans. A square.

2. A cylinder is inscribed in a given sphere. Find the shape of the cylinder if its convex surface area is a maximum. *Ans.* Diameter = height.

3. Find the weight of the heaviest circular cylinder that can be cut from a 16-lb. shot. *Ans.* 9.2 lb.

4. The stiffness of a rectangular beam is proportional to the breadth and the cube of the depth. Find the shape of the stiffest beam that can be cut from a log of given size. *Ans.* Depth = $\sqrt{3}$ × breadth.

5. The strength of a rectangular beam is proportional to the breadth and the square of the depth. Find the shape of the strongest beam that can be cut from a log of given size. *Ans.* Depth = $\sqrt{2}$ × breadth.

6. A trapezoidal gutter is to be made, from a strip of metal 22 in. wide, by bending up the edges. If the base is 14 in. wide, what width across the top gives the greatest carrying capacity?   *Ans.* 16 in.

7. Solve Ex. 6, if the strip is 13 in. wide and the base width 7 in.   *Ans.* 9 in.

8. Solve Ex. 6, if the strip is 9 in. wide and the base width 3 in.   *Ans.* 6 in.

9. Solve Ex. 6, if the strip width is w and the base width b.

$$Ans. \tfrac{1}{2}[b + \sqrt{b^2 + 2(w - b)^2}].$$

10. Find the largest conical tent that can be constructed having a given slant height.   *Ans.* $r = \sqrt{\tfrac{2}{3}}\, s$.

11. A gutter having a triangular cross-section is to be made by bending a strip of tin in the middle. Find the angle between the sides when the carrying capacity is a maximum.   *Ans.* 90°.

12. Find the altitude of the circular cone of maximum convex surface inscribed in a sphere of radius a.   *Ans.* Altitude = $\tfrac{4}{3}a$.

13. A sphere is cut in the shape of a circular cone. How much of the material can be saved?   *Ans.* About 30%.

14. A wall 10 ft. high is 8 ft. from a house. Find the length of the shortest ladder that will reach the house, when one end rests on the ground outside the wall.

Ans. 25.4 ft.

15. Solve Ex. 14, if the height of the wall is b and its distance from the house is c.

Ans. $(b^{\frac{2}{3}} + c^{\frac{2}{3}})^{\frac{3}{2}}$.

16. Solve Ex. 72, page 76.

17. A man in a motorboat at A receives a message at noon, calling him to B. A bus making 40 mi. per hr. leaves C, bound for B, at 1:00 P.M. If $AC = 30$ mi., what must be the speed of the boat, to enable the man to catch the bus?

Ans. 24 mi. per hr.

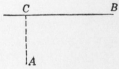

Figure 74

18. Solve Ex. 17, if $AC = 20$ mi., and the bus makes 50 mi. per hr., leaving C at 12:18 P.M., bound for B.

Ans. 40 mi. per hr.

19. A man on an island a mi. south of a straight beach wishes to reach a point on shore b mi. east of his present position. If he can row r mi. per hr. and walk w mi. per hr., in what direction should he row, to reach his destination as soon as possible? See Fig. 75.

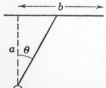

Figure 75

Ans. If $r < w$, and if $b > \dfrac{ra}{\sqrt{w^2 - r^2}}$, $\sin \theta = \dfrac{r}{w}$;

otherwise, directly toward his destination.

20. A pole 27 ft. long is carried horizontally along a corridor 8 ft. wide and into a second corridor at right angles to the first. How wide must the second corridor be?

Ans. $5\sqrt{5} = 11.18$ ft.

21. Solve Ex. 20, if the pole is of length L and the first corridor is of width C.

Ans. $(L^{\frac{2}{3}} - C^{\frac{2}{3}})^{\frac{3}{2}}$.

22. A sphere of radius a is dropped into a conical vessel full of water. Find the altitude of the smallest cone that will permit the sphere to be entirely submerged.

Ans. Altitude = $4a$.

23. A sphere is cut in the form of a right pyramid with a square base. How much of the material can be saved? *Ans.* 19%.

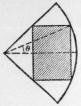

24. Find the area of the largest rectangle that can be cut from a circular quadrant as in Fig. 76.

$$Ans.\ \theta = 22\tfrac{1}{2}^\circ;\ A = (\sqrt{2} - 1)a^2 = 0.414a^2.$$

25. In Ex. 24, draw the graph of A as a function of θ, indicating the portion of the curve that has a meaning.

26. A corridor 4 ft. wide opens into a room 100 ft. long and 32 ft. wide, at the middle of one side. Find the length of the longest thin rod that can be carried horizontally into the room.

$$Ans.\ 20\sqrt{5} = 44.72\ \text{ft.}$$

Figure 76

27. Solve Ex. 26 if the room is 56 ft. long. *Ans.* 43.86 ft.

INVERSE TRIGONOMETRIC

FUNCTIONS

66. *Inverse Functions*

Consider an equation solved explicitly for x in terms of y

$$(1) \qquad\qquad x = \varphi(y).$$

Except where φ is independent of y, equation (1) will also define y as a function of x

$$(2) \qquad\qquad y = f(x).$$

When two functions $\varphi(y)$ and $f(x)$ are connected in this way, each is said to be the inverse of the other. Note that here "inverse" does not mean "reciprocal."

If $\varphi(y)$ is an algebraic function, $f(x)$ can sometimes be explicitly expressed in algebraic symbols. In fact, nothing is new in such cases except the name "inverse function," because the situation has been familiar to us since the days of elementary algebra. For example,

$$(a) \qquad\qquad \text{If} \quad x = 2y + 4, \quad \text{then} \quad y = \tfrac{1}{2}x - 2;$$
$$(b) \qquad\qquad \text{If} \quad x = y^2, \qquad \text{then} \quad y = \pm \sqrt{x}.$$

67. *Inverse Trigonometric Functions*

Let y be defined as a function of x by the equation

$$\sin y = x;$$

i.e., x is the sine of y, or, what is exactly the same thing, y *is an angle whose sine is x*. When this equation is solved for y, a new kind of function, neither algebraic nor trigonometric, is obtained; we must therefore devise a new symbol to denote this function.

An *angle whose sine is x* is represented by the symbol arcsin x or $\sin^{-1} x$:

$$y = \textbf{arcsin } x \quad \textit{if} \quad \sin y = x.$$

127

That is, the function arcsin x is the *inverse* of the sine, by the definition of § 66.

Similarly, we lay down the definitions

$$y = \textbf{arccos } x \quad if \quad \textbf{cos } y = x;$$
$$y = \textbf{arctan } x \quad if \quad \textbf{tan } y = x;$$

etc. The new functions here defined are called *inverse trigonometric functions*.

The graph of the inverse function

(1) $y = \text{arcsin } x$

is obtained by interchanging the roles of x and y in the graph (Fig. 69, page 122) of $y = \sin x$. Thus the graph of (1) can be found by reflecting the graph of

(2) $y = \sin x$

in the line $y = x$. The curve (1) consists of an infinite succession of waves along the y-axis, as shown in Fig. 77.

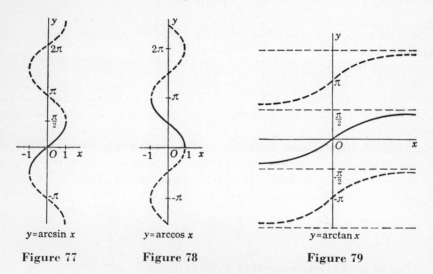

$y=$arcsin x	$y=$arccos x	$y=$arctan x
Figure 77	**Figure 78**	**Figure 79**

The curves $y = \text{arccos } x$, $y = \text{arctan } x$ appear in Figs. 78, 79. They are obtained, of course, by reflection of Figs. 70, 71.

68. *Restriction to a Single Branch*

When either the given or the inverse function is one-valued, it by no means follows that the other is one-valued. Both were so in (a), § 66, but in (b), the given function was one-valued, the inverse two-valued; and in fact, examples are easily found to illustrate any sort of combination.

When an angle is given, its sine, cosine, etc., are uniquely determined; the trigonometric functions are one-valued. On the other hand, if the sine is given, the angle is not uniquely determined; for instance, there are infinitely many angles whose sine is $\frac{1}{2}$, viz. $\frac{\pi}{6}, \frac{5\pi}{6}$, or an angle differing from one of these by any multiple of 2π. The inverse trigonometric functions are *infinitely many-valued*; corresponding to a given value of the variable there are infinitely many values of the function. Geometrically this means that a line $x = k$, if it meets the curve at all, meets it in an infinite number of points; the truth of this statement is evident from a glance at Figs. 77–79.

We shall in the future, unless the contrary is noted, *confine our attention to a single branch* of each of these functions; the branch chosen is the one drawn full in each figure. In order to distinguish between the single-valued function and its infinitely many-valued counterpart, we use a *capital letter to denote the single-valued function*. Thus in our future work the three principal inverse trigonometric functions are subject to the following restrictions:

(1) $$-\frac{\pi}{2} \leqq \mathbf{Arcsin}\ x \leqq \frac{\pi}{2};$$

(2) $$0 \leqq \mathbf{Arccos}\ x \leqq \pi;$$

(3) $$-\frac{\pi}{2} < \mathbf{Arctan}\ x < \frac{\pi}{2}.$$

With (1) in effect, we have now, uniquely,

$$\text{Arcsin}\ \frac{1}{2} = \frac{\pi}{6}.$$

Any other angle whose sine is $\frac{1}{2}$ is readily expressed in terms of Arcsin $\frac{1}{2}$:

$$\frac{5\pi}{6} = \pi - \text{Arcsin}\ \frac{1}{2}; \quad \frac{13\pi}{6} = 2\pi + \text{Arcsin}\ \frac{1}{2};\ \text{etc.}$$

Also,

$$\text{Arcsin}\ (-1) = -\frac{\pi}{2}, \quad \text{not}\ \frac{3\pi}{2};$$

$$\text{Arccos}\ \frac{1}{2}\sqrt{2} = \frac{\pi}{4}, \quad \text{Arccos}\left(-\frac{1}{2}\sqrt{2}\right) = \frac{3\pi}{4};$$

$$\text{Arctan}\ (-1) = -\frac{\pi}{4}, \quad \text{not}\ \frac{3\pi}{4}.$$

The student must note these conventions carefully, since failure to observe them leads to frequent errors.*

---

* It must be clearly understood that in calculus, just as surely as in trigonometry, there are infinitely many angles corresponding to a given value of the sine. We have merely agreed that the symbol Arcsin x shall denote *that one* of these angles (there will always be one and only one) that lies in the interval between $-\frac{\pi}{2}$ and $\frac{\pi}{2}$.

In dealing with the other three functions, we shall restrict ourselves to *positive values of* x. The conventions are as follows:

$$0 \leqq \text{Arccot } x \leqq \frac{\pi}{2}, \qquad x \geqq 0;$$

$$0 \leqq \text{Arcsec } x \leqq \frac{\pi}{2}, \qquad x \geqq 1;$$

$$0 \leqq \text{Arccsc } x \leqq \frac{\pi}{2}, \qquad x \geqq 1.$$

These last three functions are distinctly troublesome when x is negative. For instance, it will appear presently that

(4) $$\text{Arccot } x = \frac{\pi}{2} - \text{Arctan } x, \qquad x > 0;$$

also that

(5) $$\text{Arccot } x = \text{Arctan } \frac{1}{x}, \qquad x > 0.$$

These are useful formulas to have; yet no convention can be laid down under which both formulas are true when x is negative. (For instance, try $x = -1$.) Thus our agreement to consider these functions only for positive x makes greatly for simplicity.*

This book will make very little use of the three minor functions, chiefly because of the difficulty just mentioned.

69. *Elementary Properties*

Discovery of the elementary properties of the inverse trigonometric functions will be left largely to the student. However, since this new language may be troublesome at first, numerous examples are provided.

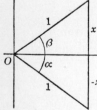

Figure 80

Example (a). Prove that

$$\text{Arcsin } (-x) = - \text{Arcsin } x.$$

This formula is nearly self-evident. Put

$$\alpha = \text{Arcsin } (-x), \quad \beta = \text{Arcsin } x,$$

so that

$$\sin \alpha = -x, \quad \sin \beta = x.$$

By (1), § 68, both α and β are acute angles, one negative, the other positive,

---

* The restriction is not serious. Of course it is possible to avoid the three minor functions completely; on the rather infrequent occasions when it seems simpler to use them, x is usually positive. If they are to be used when x is negative, great care must be exercised.

so that they may be represented as in Fig. 80. The truth of the formula appears from a glance at the figure.

Example (b). Prove that

$$\text{Arccot } x = \tfrac{1}{2}\pi - \text{Arctan } x.$$

Put

$$\alpha = \text{Arccot } x, \quad \beta = \text{Arctan } x.$$

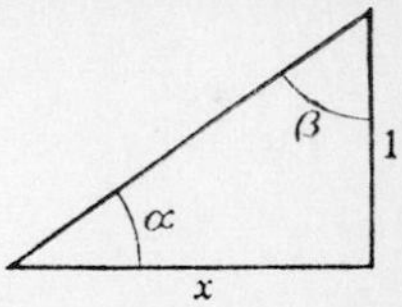

Figure 81

By § 68, both are positive acute and may be represented as in Fig. 81. Then α and β are complementary angles: $\alpha + \beta = \tfrac{1}{2}\pi$.

Example (c). Prove that

$$\sin (2 \text{ Arcsin } x) = 2x \sqrt{1 - x^2}.$$

Put

$$\alpha = \text{Arcsin } x,$$
$$\sin \alpha = x.$$

By trigonometry,

$$\cos \alpha = \pm \sqrt{1 - \sin^2 \alpha} = \pm \sqrt{1 - x^2}.$$

But since (§ 68) α lies in either the first or the fourth quadrant, the cosine is positive and we have definitely

$$(1) \qquad\qquad \cos \alpha = \sqrt{1 - x^2},$$

$$\sin (2 \text{ Arcsin } x) = \sin 2\alpha = 2 \sin \alpha \cos \alpha = 2x \sqrt{1 - x^2}.$$

Example (d). Simplify the expression $(\text{Arctan } 2 + \text{Arctan } 3)$.
Put

$$\alpha = \text{Arctan } 2, \quad \beta = \text{Arctan } 3,$$

from which

$$\tan \alpha = 2, \quad \tan \beta = 3,$$

and let

$$\gamma = \text{Arctan } 2 + \text{Arctan } 3 = \alpha + \beta.$$

Then

$$\tan \gamma = \tan (\alpha + \beta) = \frac{\tan \alpha + \tan \beta}{1 - \tan \alpha \tan \beta}$$
$$= \frac{2 + 3}{1 - 2 \cdot 3} = -1.$$

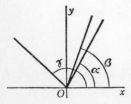

Figure 82

The sum of two positive acute angles must lie in either the first or the second quadrant. Our γ has a negative tangent. It must lie in the second quadrant. Therefore

$$\text{Arctan } 2 + \text{Arctan } 3 = \tfrac{3}{4}\pi.$$

This example, typical of many similar situations, shows that when $\tan \gamma = -1$, we must not hastily conclude that $\gamma = -\tfrac{1}{4}\pi$.

Example (*e*). Simplify the equation

(2) $\text{Arcsin } x + \text{Arcsin } y = \tfrac{1}{3}\pi.$

Put

(3) $\alpha = \text{Arcsin } x, \qquad \beta = \text{Arcsin } y,$

so that (2) becomes

(4) $\alpha + \beta = \tfrac{1}{3}\pi.$

From (3),

$$\sin \alpha = x, \qquad \cos \alpha = \sqrt{1 - x^2};$$
$$\sin \beta = y, \qquad \cos \beta = \sqrt{1 - y^2}.$$

It can be shown by trial (see Ex. 60 below) that in simplifying the sum of two Arcsines or two Arccosines, the best procedure is to take the cosine of the sum. (To simplify the sum of an Arcsine and an Arccosine, it is best to take the sine of the sum.) Hence, taking the cosine of both members of (4), we get

$$\sqrt{1 - x^2} \cdot \sqrt{1 - y^2} - xy = \tfrac{1}{2},$$

or, after isolating the radical, squaring, and simplifying,

(5) $4x^2 + 4xy + 4y^2 = 3.$

Thus, from equation (2), equation (5) follows. Therefore, every point on the curve (2) must lie on the curve (5), but by no means do the coordinates of all points on the locus (5) need to satisfy equation (2). Equation (2) consists of only a part of the ellipse (5). For instance, the point $(-\tfrac{1}{2}, -\tfrac{1}{2})$ is on the ellipse; its coordinates satisfy equation (5). Because of the principal value convention,

$$\text{Arcsin}\left(-\frac{1}{2}\right) = -\frac{\pi}{6},$$

so that, for $x = y = -\tfrac{1}{2}$, the left member of equation (2) becomes

$$-\frac{\pi}{6} - \frac{\pi}{6} = -\frac{\pi}{3} \neq \frac{\pi}{3}.$$

The point $(-\tfrac{1}{2}, -\tfrac{1}{2})$ satisfies equation (5) but not equation (2). Similar remarks apply to Exs. 54–59 below.

EXERCISES

1. Find Arcsin 0, Arcsin $(\tfrac{1}{2}\sqrt{2})$, Arcsin 1, Arcsin $(-\tfrac{1}{2}\sqrt{3})$.
2. Find Arctan 0, Arctan 1, Arctan $(-\tfrac{1}{3}\sqrt{3})$, Arctan $\sqrt{3}$.
3. Find Arccos (-1), Arccos (0), Arccos $(-\tfrac{1}{2}\sqrt{3})$, Arccos $(\tfrac{1}{2})$.
4. Find Arcsec $(\sqrt{2})$, Arccot $(\sqrt{3})$, Arcsec 2.

Establish the formulas in Exs. 5–22.

5. $\operatorname{Arctan} (-x) = -\operatorname{Arctan} x.$ **6.** $\operatorname{Arccos} (-x) = \pi - \operatorname{Arccos} x.$

7. $\operatorname{Arccos} x = \frac{1}{2}\pi - \operatorname{Arcsin} x.$ **8.** $\operatorname{Arctan} \dfrac{1}{x} = \operatorname{Arccot} x.$

9. $\operatorname{Arcsin} \dfrac{1}{x} = \operatorname{Arccsc} x.$ **10.** $\operatorname{Arccos} \dfrac{1}{x} = \operatorname{Arcsec} x.$

11. $\operatorname{Arcsin} \dfrac{x}{\sqrt{1 + x^2}} = \operatorname{Arctan} x.$ **12.** $\operatorname{Arctan} \dfrac{x}{\sqrt{1 - x^2}} = \operatorname{Arcsin} x.$

13. $\sin (\operatorname{Arccos} x) = \sqrt{1 - x^2}.$ **14.** $\cos (\operatorname{Arctan} x) = \dfrac{1}{\sqrt{1 + x^2}}.$

15. $\tan (2 \operatorname{Arctan} x) = \dfrac{2x}{1 - x^2}.$ **16.** $\sin (2 \operatorname{Arccos} x) = 2x \sqrt{1 - x^2}.$

17. $\cos (2 \operatorname{Arccos} x) = 2x^2 - 1.$ **18.** $\cos (2 \operatorname{Arctan} x) = \dfrac{1 - x^2}{1 + x^2}.$

19. $\sin (2 \operatorname{Arctan} x) = \dfrac{2x}{1 + x^2}.$ **20.** $\cos (2 \operatorname{Arcsin} x) = 1 - 2x^2.$

21. $\tan (2 \operatorname{Arcsin} x) = \dfrac{2x \sqrt{1 - x^2}}{1 - 2x^2}.$

22. $\tan (2 \operatorname{Arccos} x) = \dfrac{2x \sqrt{1 - x^2}}{2x^2 - 1}.$

In Exs. 23–32, evaluate the given expression.

23. $\tan (\operatorname{Arctan} \frac{1}{3} + \operatorname{Arctan} \frac{1}{7}).$ *Ans.* $\frac{1}{2}.$

24. $\tan (\operatorname{Arctan} \frac{2}{3} - \operatorname{Arctan} \frac{1}{5}).$ *Ans.* $\frac{7}{17}.$

25. $\tan (\operatorname{Arctan} \frac{1}{3} - \operatorname{Arctan} \frac{1}{4}).$ *Ans.* $\frac{1}{13}.$

26. $\cos (\operatorname{Arcsin} \frac{12}{13} - \operatorname{Arccos} \frac{3}{5}).$ *Ans.* $\frac{63}{65}.$

27. $\cos (\operatorname{Arctan} \frac{5}{12} + \operatorname{Arcsin} \frac{4}{5}).$ *Ans.* $\frac{16}{65}.$

28. $\tan (\operatorname{Arcsin} \frac{3}{5} + \operatorname{Arctan} 3).$ *Ans.* $-3.$

29. $\sin (\operatorname{Arctan} \frac{2}{9} + \operatorname{Arctan} \frac{6}{7}).$ *Ans.* $\frac{4}{5}.$

30. $\sin (\operatorname{Arctan} \frac{9}{8} - \operatorname{Arctan} \frac{2}{5}).$ *Ans.* $\frac{1}{5} \sqrt{5}.$

31. $\tan (\operatorname{Arctan} \frac{11}{7} - \operatorname{Arctan} \frac{1}{7} + \operatorname{Arctan} \frac{1}{2}).$ *Ans.* $4.$

32. $\tan (\operatorname{Arctan} \frac{11}{2} + \operatorname{Arctan} \frac{7}{6} - \operatorname{Arctan} \frac{4}{3}).$ *Ans.* $4.$

In Exs. 33–53, simplify the given expression, in the sense of Example (d) above.

33. $\operatorname{Arctan} 4 - \operatorname{Arctan} \frac{3}{5}.$ *Ans.* $\frac{1}{4}\pi.$

34. $\operatorname{Arctan} \frac{1}{3} + \operatorname{Arctan} \frac{1}{2}.$ *Ans.* $\frac{1}{4}\pi.$

35. $\operatorname{Arctan} 3 - \operatorname{Arctan} \frac{1}{2}.$ *Ans.* $\frac{1}{4}\pi.$

36. $\operatorname{Arccos} \frac{4}{5} + \operatorname{Arctan} \frac{1}{7}.$ *Ans.* $\frac{1}{4}\pi.$

37. $\operatorname{Arccos} \frac{1}{7} + \operatorname{Arcsin} \frac{13}{14}.$ *Ans.* $\frac{5}{6}\pi.$

38. $\operatorname{Arctan} \frac{3}{2} + \operatorname{Arctan} 5.$ *Ans.* $\frac{3}{4}\pi.$

39. $\operatorname{Arctan} 13 + \operatorname{Arctan} \frac{7}{6}.$ *Ans.* $\frac{3}{4}\pi.$

40. $\operatorname{Arcsin} \frac{5}{13} + \operatorname{Arcsin} \frac{12}{13}.$ *Ans.* $\frac{1}{2}\pi.$

41. $\operatorname{Arccos} \frac{4}{5} + \operatorname{Arctan} \frac{4}{3}.$ *Ans.* $\frac{1}{2}\pi.$

42. Arctan $\frac{5}{12}$ + Arcsin $\frac{12}{13}$. *Ans.* $\frac{1}{2}\pi$.

43. Arctan $\frac{1}{2}$ + Arctan $\frac{7}{6}$. *Ans.* Arctan 4.

44. Arctan $\dfrac{x+2}{x}$ + Arctan $(x+1)$; $x > 0$. *Ans.* $\frac{3}{4}\pi$.

45. Arctan $\dfrac{x}{x+2}$ + Arctan $\dfrac{1}{x+1}$; $x > 0$. *Ans.* $\frac{1}{4}\pi$.

46. 2 Arctan 2 + Arctan $\frac{4}{3}$. *Ans.* π.

47. 2 Arctan $\frac{1}{2}$ − Arctan $\frac{4}{3}$. *Ans.* 0.

48. 2 Arctan $\frac{1}{2}$ − Arctan $\frac{1}{7}$. *Ans.* $\frac{1}{4}\pi$.

49. Arctan $\frac{4}{3}$ − 2 Arctan 3. *Ans.* $-\frac{1}{2}\pi$.

50. Arctan $\frac{1}{3}$ + Arctan $\frac{5}{3}$ + Arctan $\frac{11}{7}$. *Ans.* $\frac{3}{4}\pi$.

51. Arctan $\frac{12}{5}$ + Arctan $\frac{1}{5}$ − Arctan $\frac{2}{3}$. *Ans.* $\frac{1}{4}\pi$.

52. 2 Arctan 2 + Arctan $\frac{11}{2}$ − Arctan $\frac{1}{2}$. *Ans.* π.

53. Arctan 2 + Arctan 4 + Arctan 13. *Ans.* $\frac{5}{4}\pi$.

In Exs. 54–59, change the equation to algebraic form, with the realization that the new form may contain points not satisfying the original equation. Identify the resulting curve by name, when you can, and point out what steps in your procedure may introduce extraneous portions of the curve.

54. Arcsin x + Arcsin $y = \frac{1}{2}\pi$. *Ans.* $x^2 + y^2 = 1$.

55. Arctan x + Arctan $y = \frac{1}{4}\pi$. *Ans.* $xy + x + y = 1$.

56. Arccos x + Arcsin $y = \frac{1}{6}\pi$. *Ans.* $4x^2 - 4xy + 4y^2 = 3$.

57. 2 Arcsin x + Arcsin $y = \pi$. *Ans.* $y^2 = 4x^2(1 - x^2)$.

58. Arctan x − 2 Arctan $y = \pi$. *Ans.* $xy^2 = x - 2y$.

59. Arctan x + Arctan $y = \frac{1}{2}\pi$. *Ans.* $xy = 1$.

60. In Example (*e*) § 69, simplify by taking the sine of both members.

70. *Derivatives of the Inverse Trigonometric Functions*

To differentiate the function
$$y = \text{Arcsin } x,$$
let us pass to the form

(1) $$\sin y = x.$$

Equation (1) yields
$$\cos y \frac{dy}{dx} = 1,$$
$$\frac{dy}{dx} = \frac{1}{\cos y}.$$

Since $\sin y = x$, and $-\frac{1}{2}\pi \leqq y \leqq \frac{1}{2}\pi$, it follows that
$$\cos y = \sqrt{1 - \sin^2 y} = \sqrt{1 - x^2},$$
so that
$$\frac{d}{dx} \text{Arcsin } x = \frac{1}{\sqrt{1 - x^2}}.$$

Differentiation of the other functions is left to the reader. If u is any function of x, the general formulas for the three principal functions are:

$$(13) \qquad \frac{d}{dx} \text{Arcsin } u = \frac{\dfrac{du}{dx}}{\sqrt{1 - u^2}};$$

$$(14) \qquad \frac{d}{dx} \text{Arccos } u = -\frac{\dfrac{du}{dx}}{\sqrt{1 - u^2}};$$

$$(15) \qquad \frac{d}{dx} \text{Arctan } u = \frac{\dfrac{du}{dx}}{1 + u^2}.$$

Example (a). If $\theta = \text{Arctan } \frac{1}{3}t$,

$$\frac{d\theta}{dt} = \frac{\frac{1}{3}}{1 + \frac{1}{9}t^2} = \frac{3}{9 + t^2}.$$

Example (b). If $y = \text{Arcsin } (2 \cos \theta)$,

$$\frac{dy}{d\theta} = \frac{-2 \sin \theta}{\sqrt{1 - 4 \cos^2 \theta}}.$$

Example (c). A man on a wharf 20 ft. above the water pulls in a rope to which a boat is tied, at the rate of 4 ft. per sec. Find the rate of change of the angle θ (Fig. 83) when there is 25 ft. of rope out.

By the figure,

$$\theta = \text{Arcsin } \frac{20}{r},$$

$$\frac{d\theta}{dt} = \frac{-\dfrac{20}{r^2}\dfrac{dr}{dt}}{\sqrt{1 - \dfrac{400}{r^2}}} = \frac{-20\dfrac{dr}{dt}}{r\sqrt{r^2 - 400}}.$$

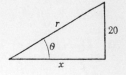

Figure 83

The length of rope out is decreasing at the rate of 4 ft. per sec. Hence

$$\frac{dr}{dt} = -4,$$

so that when $r = 25$,

$$\frac{d\theta}{dt} = \frac{16}{75} \text{ rad. per sec.}$$

This example may also be solved very neatly by using the equations

$$\csc \theta = \frac{r}{20};$$

$$-\csc \theta \cot \theta \frac{d\theta}{dt} = \frac{1}{20} \frac{dr}{dt}; \text{ etc.}$$

EXERCISES

In Exs. 1–32, find the first derivative of the function given.

1. $y = \text{Arcsin } 4x.$

$Ans. \dfrac{dy}{dx} = \dfrac{4}{\sqrt{1 - 16x^2}}.$

2. $\theta = \text{Arctan } 3\varphi.$

$Ans. \dfrac{d\theta}{d\varphi} = \dfrac{3}{1 + 9\varphi^2}.$

3. $u = \text{Arctan } \dfrac{x}{a}.$

$Ans. \dfrac{du}{dx} = \dfrac{a}{a^2 + x^2}.$

4. $u = \text{Arcsin } \dfrac{x}{a}, a > 0.$

$Ans. \dfrac{du}{dx} = \dfrac{1}{\sqrt{a^2 - x^2}}.$

5. $f(w) = \text{Arctan } (1 + 4w).$

$Ans. f'(w) = \dfrac{2}{1 + 4w + 8w^2}.$

6. $x = \text{Arcsin } (1 - 2v).$

$Ans. \dfrac{dx}{dv} = \dfrac{-1}{\sqrt{v - v^2}}.$

7. $x = \text{Arctan } (t^2).$ **8.** $x = (\text{Arctan } t)^2.$
9. $y = (\text{Arcsin } x)^3.$ **10.** $y = \text{Arcsin } (x^3).$
11. $\theta = \text{Arccos } 3\varphi.$ **12.** $\theta = \text{Arccos } \sqrt{1 - \varphi}.$
13. $x = \text{Arcsin } \sqrt{t}.$ **14.** $x = \text{Arctan } \sqrt{t}.$
15. $y = x \text{ Arcsin } 2x.$ **16.** $y = x \text{ Arctan } 4x.$
17. $u = x^2 \text{ Arcsin } x.$ **18.** $w = \dfrac{\text{Arcsin } \alpha}{\alpha}.$

19. $y = \dfrac{\text{Arctan } 2x}{x}.$ **20.** $y = \dfrac{\text{Arcsin } (x^2)}{x^2}.$

21. $y = (1 + x^2) \text{ Arctan } x - x.$ $Ans. y' = 2x \text{ Arctan } x.$

22. $y = \text{Arctan}^2 (x^3).$ $Ans. y' = \dfrac{6x^2 \text{ Arctan } (x^3)}{1 + x^6}.$

23. $y = \sqrt{\text{Arcsin } x}.$ $Ans. \dfrac{dy}{dx} = \dfrac{1}{2 \sqrt{1 - x^2} \cdot \sqrt{\text{Arcsin } x}}.$

24. $y = \text{Arcsin } \sqrt{1 + \dfrac{1}{x}}.$ (Note that x must be negative, so that in simplifying

the answer we must use $\sqrt{x^2} = -x.$) $Ans. \dfrac{dy}{dx} = \dfrac{1}{2x \sqrt{-x - 1}}.$

25. $y = (x - 1) \sqrt{2x - x^2} + \text{Arcsin } (x - 1).$ $Ans. y' = 2 \sqrt{2x - x^2}.$

26. $y = 2 \text{ Arcsin } \sqrt{\dfrac{x}{2}}.$ $Ans. y' = \dfrac{1}{\sqrt{2x - x^2}}.$

27. $y = x \text{ Arcsin } x + \sqrt{1 - x^2}.$ $Ans. y' = \text{Arcsin } x.$

28. $y = \dfrac{x}{\sqrt{a^2 - x^2}} - \text{Arcsin } \dfrac{x}{a}.$ $Ans. \dfrac{dy}{dx} = \dfrac{x^2}{(a^2 - x^2)^{\frac{3}{2}}}.$

29. $y = a^2 \operatorname{Arcsin} \dfrac{x}{a} - x \sqrt{a^2 - x^2}.$ *Ans.* $\dfrac{dy}{dx} = \dfrac{2x^2}{\sqrt{a^2 - x^2}}.$

30. $y = \operatorname{Arcsin} \dfrac{x}{a} + \dfrac{\sqrt{a^2 - x^2}}{x}.$ *Ans.* $y' = -\dfrac{\sqrt{a^2 - x^2}}{x^2}.$

31. $y = \operatorname{Arcsin} \dfrac{a}{x}.$ *Ans.* $\dfrac{dy}{dx} = \dfrac{-a}{x \sqrt{x^2 - a^2}}, x > a; \dfrac{dy}{dx} = \dfrac{a}{x \sqrt{x^2 - a^2}}, x < -a.$

32. $y = \operatorname{Arctan} \dfrac{a}{x}.$ *Ans.* $y' = \dfrac{-a}{a^2 + x^2}.$

33. Derive the formula $\dfrac{d}{dx} \operatorname{Arccot} u = \dfrac{-\dfrac{du}{dx}}{1 + u^2}, \quad u > 0.$

34. Derive the formula $\dfrac{d}{dx} \operatorname{Arcsec} u = \dfrac{\dfrac{du}{dx}}{u \sqrt{u^2 - 1}}, \quad u > 1.$

35. Derive the formula $\dfrac{d}{dx} \operatorname{Arccsc} u = \dfrac{-\dfrac{du}{dx}}{u \sqrt{u^2 - 1}}, \quad u > 1.$

36. If $\tan \theta = \dfrac{y}{x}$, where x and y are functions of t, show that

$$\frac{d\theta}{dt} = \frac{x \dfrac{dy}{dt} - y \dfrac{dx}{dt}}{x^2 + y^2}.$$

37. A ladder 15 ft. long leans against a vertical wall. If the top slides down at 2 ft. per sec., how fast is the angle of elevation of the ladder decreasing, when the lower end is 12 ft. from the wall? *Ans.* $\frac{1}{6}$ rad. per sec.

38. A ship, moving 8 mi. per hr., sails north for 30 min., then turns east. If a searchlight at the point of departure follows the ship, how fast is the light rotating 2 hr. after the start? *Ans.* 0.2 rad. per hr.

39. A balloon, leaving the ground 60 ft. from an observer, rises 10 ft. per sec. How fast is the angle of elevation of the line of sight increasing, after 8 sec.?

Ans. 0.06 rad. per sec.

40. The base of a right triangle grows 2 ft. per sec., the altitude grows 4 ft. per sec. If the base and altitude are originally 10 ft. and 6 ft., respectively, find the time-rate of change of the base angle, when that angle is 45°. *Ans.* $\frac{1}{14}$ rad. per sec.

41. Prove that an angle is a maximum or minimum when its tangent is a maximum or minimum, and conversely. (Let $\theta = \operatorname{Arctan} m$, where m is a function of x; compare the conditions for extreme θ and extreme m.)

42. Prove that an acute angle is a maximum or minimum when its sine is a maximum or minimum, and conversely.

43. Prove that an acute angle is a maximum or minimum when its cosine is a minimum or maximum, and conversely.

44. A rowboat is pushed off from a beach at 8 ft. per sec. A man on shore holds a rope, tied to the boat, at a height of 4 ft. Find how fast the angle of elevation of the rope is decreasing, after 1 sec. *Ans.* $\frac{2}{5}$ rad. per sec.

45. A kite is 60 ft. high, with 100 ft. of cord out. If the kite is moving horizontally 4 mi. per hr. directly away from the boy flying it, find the rate of change of the angle of elevation of the cord. *Ans.* $-\frac{22}{625}$ rad. per sec.

46. A ship, moving at 8 mi. per hr., sails E. for 2 hr., then turns N. 30° W. A searchlight, placed at the starting point, follows the ship. Find how fast the light is rotating, (*a*) 3 hr. after the start; (*b*) just after the turn.

Ans. (*a*) $\frac{1}{3}\sqrt{3}$ rad. per hr.; (*b*) $\frac{1}{4}\sqrt{3}$ rad. per hr.

47. In Ex. 46, find when the light rotates most rapidly. *Ans.* After 3 hr.

48. Prove that the results in Exs. 46–47 are independent of the speed of the ship.

49. A ship, moving at 10 mi. per hr., sails E. for 2 hr., then turns N. 30° E. A searchlight, placed at the starting point, follows the ship. Find how fast the light is rotating (*a*) 4 hr. after the start; (*b*) just after the turn.

Ans. (*a*) $\frac{1}{12}\sqrt{3}$ rad. per hr.; (*b*) $\frac{1}{4}\sqrt{3}$ rad. per hr.

50. Using the methods of § 44, show that in Ex. 49 the maximum rate of rotation of the light occurs at the time the ship turns.

51. Show that the answers to Exs. 49–50 are independent of the speed of the ship.

52. A car drives S. at 20 mi. per hr. Another car, starting from the same point at the same time and traveling 40 mi. per hr., goes E. for 30 min., then turns N. Find the rate of rotation of the line joining the cars (*a*) 1 hr. after the start; (*b*) at the time the second car makes its turn. *Ans.* (*a*) 0.6 rad. per hr.; (*b*) 2.4 rad. per hr.

53. Prove that the results in Ex. 52 are independent of the speed of the cars, if the second car travels twice as fast as the first car.

54. Two points are moving horizontally in space at different heights above the earth. Show that the angle of elevation of the line joining them is greatest when the distance between them is least.

55. The lower edge of a picture is *a* ft., the upper edge *b* ft., above the eye of an observer. At what horizontal distance should he stand, if the vertical angle subtended by the picture is to be greatest? *Ans.* $\sqrt{ab}$ ft.

EXPONENTIAL AND

LOGARITHMIC FUNCTIONS

71. *The Exponential Function*

The number $a^n (a > 0)$ is defined in algebra for all rational values of n. In calculus it becomes necessary to attach a meaning to the function

$$y = a^x, \qquad a > 0$$

as x varies continuously.

Let x_0 be any irrational number. Then a^{x_0} is defined as the limit of a^x, where x is rational, as x approaches x_0. That the limit exists is proved in more advanced texts. The function

$$y = a^x, \qquad a > 0,$$

called the *exponential function*, thus becomes defined for all values of x. It is one-valued and continuous, and obeys the laws of exponents:

(1) $$a^x \cdot a^t = a^{x+t},$$
(2) $$(a^x)^t = a^{xt}.$$

The exponential function is positive for all values of x.

72. *The Logarithm*

The inverse of the exponential function is the *logarithm*, defined by the statement that

$$y = \log_a x \quad if \quad x = a^y, \qquad a > 1.$$

This function is one-valued and continuous for all *positive* values of x. The number a is called the *base* of the system of logarithms. The assumption $a > 1$ is introduced for simplicity; this condition is satisfied in all cases of practical importance.

The following facts concerning the function

$$y = \log_a x$$

follow at once from the definition:

(a) *Negative numbers have no (real) logarithms.*
(b) *Numbers between 0 and 1 have negative logarithms.*
(c) *Numbers greater than 1 have positive logarithms.*
(d) *As $x \rightarrow 0^+$, $y \rightarrow -\infty$.*
(e) *The logarithm of 1 is 0.*
(f) *As $x \rightarrow \infty$, $y \rightarrow \infty$.*

It is easily discovered that some of these properties would not hold if a were less than 1.

73. *Fundamental Properties of Logarithms*

Further important properties of the logarithmic function are as follows:

(1) $$\log_a xy = \log_a x + \log_a y;$$

(2) $$\log_a \frac{x}{y} = \log_a x - \log_a y;$$

(3)* $$\log_a x^n = n \log_a x;$$

(4) $$\log_a a^x = x;$$

(5) $$a^{\log_a x} = x.$$

Since (1), (2), and (3) have been met in the study of trigonometry, their proofs will be omitted. Formulas (4) and (5) are restatements of the definition of logarithm. To prove (5) formally, set

$$a^{\log_a x} = t,$$

and take logarithms to the base a on each side:

$$\log_a x = \log_a t,$$

whence

$$t = x.$$

74. *Change of Base*

Given a table of logarithms to any base b, the logarithm of any number x to the base a can be found by the *formula for change of base*:

(1) $$\log_a x = \frac{\log_b x}{\log_b a}.$$

To prove this, let

$$m = \log_a x \quad \text{and} \quad n = \log_b x;$$

then

$$x = a^m = b^n.$$

---

* If n is a positive or negative even integer, the function $\log_a x^n$ has a meaning even when x is negative, and this case frequently arises. With proper modification, (3) still applies:

$$\log x^n = n \log (-x) \text{ if } x < 0, n = \pm 2, \pm 4, \pm 6, \cdots.$$

Taking logarithms to the base b, we get

$$m \log_b a = n,$$

which gives the formula at once.

Taking $x = b$ in (1), we obtain the formula

(2) $$\log_a b = \frac{1}{\log_b a}.$$

75. The Number e

It will be found, in § 78 below, that the problem of differentiating $y = \log_a x$ leads to a need for evaluation of

(1) $$\lim_{z \to \infty} \left(1 + \frac{1}{z}\right)^z.$$

First, let z take on only positive integral values. Consider the sequence of numbers v_n (i.e., $v_1, v_2, v_3, \cdots, v_n, v_{n+1}, \cdots$),

(2) $$v_n = \left(1 + \frac{1}{n}\right)^n; \qquad n \text{ integral, } n > 0.$$

We wish to show that v_n approaches* a limit, as $n \to \infty$.

Application of the binomial theorem to (2) yields

$$v_n = \left(1 + \frac{1}{n}\right)^n = 1 + \sum_{k=1}^{n} \frac{n(n-1)(n-2) \cdots (n-k+1)}{k!} \left(\frac{1}{n}\right)^k$$

$$= 1 + \frac{n}{1}\left(\frac{1}{n}\right) + \sum_{k=2}^{n} \frac{1 \cdot \left(1 - \frac{1}{n}\right)\left(1 - \frac{2}{n}\right) \cdots \left(1 - \frac{k-1}{n}\right)}{k!}.$$

Hence, for $n > 2$,

(3) $$v_n = 2 + \sum_{k=2}^{n} \frac{1 \cdot \left(1 - \frac{1}{n}\right)\left(1 - \frac{2}{n}\right) \cdots \left(1 - \frac{k-1}{n}\right)}{k!}.$$

---

* The student may find it helpful to examine v_n numerically as n increases. From (2) it follows that

$$\log_{10} v_n = n \log_{10}\left(1 + \frac{1}{n}\right).$$

In the table below the v_n for $n > 3$ were computed with the aid of a seven-place log table.

n	1	2	3	10	100	1000
v_n	2	2.25	2.37	2.594	2.705	2.717

From (3) we obtain the next number v_{n+1} in the sequence in the form

$$(4) \quad v_{n+1} = 2 + \sum_{k=2}^{n+1} \frac{1 \cdot \left(1 - \frac{1}{n+1}\right)\left(1 - \frac{2}{n+1}\right) \cdots \left(1 - \frac{k-1}{n+1}\right)}{k!}.$$

Since

$$1 - \frac{j}{n+1} > 1 - \frac{j}{n}$$

for each of $j = 1, 2, \cdots, (k-1)$, we may conclude that each term in the summation in (4) is larger than the corresponding term in the summation in (3), and (4) has an extra term, that in which $k = n + 1$. Hence

$$(5) \qquad v_{n+1} > v_n;$$

the v_n increase steadily as n increases.

Furthermore, equation (3) yields

$$(6) \qquad v_n < 2 + \sum_{k=2}^{n} \frac{1}{k!}.$$

But $k! = 1 \cdot 2 \cdot 3 \cdots k > 2^{k-1}$, so

$$v_n < 2 + \sum_{k=2}^{n} \frac{1}{2^{k-1}} = 2 + \left(1 - \frac{1}{2^{n-1}}\right).$$

Hence

$$(7) \qquad v_n < 3 - \frac{1}{2^{n-1}}.$$

Therefore

$$(8) \qquad v_n < 3.$$

We now know that the elements v_n of the sequence (2) steadily increase and are always less than 3. Then the v_n approaches a limit; call that limit e.

LEMMA 3. *For integral n,*

$$(9) \qquad \lim_{n \to \infty} \left(1 + \frac{1}{n}\right)^n = e.$$

We have shown that $e \leq 3$. Actually

$$e = 2.718 \quad 281 \quad 828 \quad 5 \cdots.$$

With the aid of Lemma 3 we may now obtain the desired result.

THEOREM 20. $\lim_{z \to \infty} \left(1 + \frac{1}{z}\right)^z = e.$

Proof. At any stage, z lies between two consecutive integers,

(10)
$$n \leqq z < n + 1.$$

From (10) it follows that

$$\frac{1}{n+1} < \frac{1}{z} \leqq \frac{1}{n}.$$

and

(11)
$$1 + \frac{1}{n+1} < 1 + \frac{1}{z} \leqq 1 + \frac{1}{n}.$$

From (10) and (11) we get

(12)
$$\left(1 + \frac{1}{n+1}\right)^n < \left(1 + \frac{1}{z}\right)^z \leqq \left(1 + \frac{1}{n}\right)^{n+1}.$$

Now, because of the result in Lemma 3,

$$\lim_{n \to \infty} \left(1 + \frac{1}{n+1}\right)^n = \frac{\lim_{n \to \infty} \left(1 + \frac{1}{n+1}\right)^{n+1}}{\lim_{n \to \infty} \left(1 + \frac{1}{n+1}\right)} = \frac{e}{1} = e$$

and

$$\lim_{n \to \infty} \left(1 + \frac{1}{n}\right)^{n+1} = \left[\lim_{n \to \infty} \left(1 + \frac{1}{n}\right)^n\right]\left[\lim_{n \to \infty} \left(1 + \frac{1}{n}\right)\right] = e \cdot 1 = e.$$

Hence, by (12), $\left(1 + \frac{1}{z}\right)^z$ lies between two numbers, each of which is approaching e as z (and therefore also n) approaches ∞. Thus $\left(1 + \frac{1}{z}\right)^z$ must also $\to e$ as $z \to \infty$.

The function

(13)
$$y = e^x$$

is of great importance in calculus and its applications. A table of values of e^x and its reciprocal e^{-x} will be found on pp. 560–565; with the help of the table the curve (13) is easily plotted by points. See Fig. 84, page 144.

76. *Natural Logarithms*

Only two systems of logarithms are of actual importance in practice. Logarithms to the base 10, called *common logarithms*, possess the great advantage that the "mantissa," or fractional part of the logarithm, is independent of the position of the decimal point in the given number; common logarithms are therefore used very generally in computing. However, in the applications of calculus it is more convenient to use the base e.

Logarithms to the base e are called *natural logarithms*, and e is the *natural base*. The reason for these names will appear in § 78. Since the natural logarithm enters our work often, it is worth while to use a special symbol for it. We write ln x for $\log_e x$; that is,

$$(1) \qquad\qquad \ln\ x = \log_e x.$$

A table of common logarithms gives

$$\log_{10} e = \log_{10} 2.71828 = 0.43429.$$

This important number, called the *modulus* of the common system, will hereafter be noted by M:

$$\log_{10} e = M = 0.43429;$$
$$\ln\ 10 = \frac{1}{M} = 2.30259.$$

We thus derive from (1), § 74, the following formulas:

$$(2) \qquad\qquad \log_{10} x = M \ln x, \quad \ln x = \frac{1}{M} \log_{10} x.$$

A brief table of natural logarithms will be found on pp. 558–559. For numbers beyond the range of the table, or with no table of natural logarithms at hand, any natural logarithm may be found from a table of common logarithms with the help of (2).

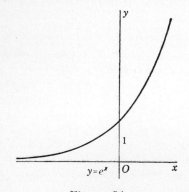

Figure 84

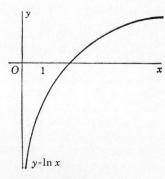

Figure 85

The curve

$$y = \ln x$$

is shown in Fig. 85. It can be obtained from the curve $y = e^x$ of Fig. 84 by interchanging the roles of x and y; i.e., by reflection in the line $y = x$.

Example (a). Find x, if

$$\ln x = \ln 2 - 2 \ln 3 + \tfrac{1}{2} \ln 5.$$

By (3), § 73,

$$2 \ln 3 = \ln 9,$$
$$\tfrac{1}{2} \ln 5 = \ln \sqrt{5},$$
$$\ln x = \ln 2 - \ln 9 + \ln \sqrt{5}.$$

Hence,* by (1) and (2), § 73,

$$\ln x = \ln \frac{2 \sqrt{5}}{9},$$
$$x = \frac{2 \sqrt{5}}{9}.$$

Example (*b*). Find the inverse of the function

(3) $$y = \sin 5e^{x^3}.$$

The problem means, of course, that we are to solve the equation for x (§ 66). Pass to the inverse trigonometric form:†

$$\arcsin y = 5e^{x^3}.$$

Take the natural logarithm:

$$\ln \arcsin y = \ln 5 + \ln e^{x^3} = \ln 5 + x^3,$$
$$x = (\ln \arcsin y - \ln 5)^{\frac{1}{3}}.$$

EXERCISES

In Exs. 1–13, find x without using a table.

1. (*a*) $\log_{10} x = 2$; (*b*) $\log_{10} x = -3$; (*c*) $\log_{10} x = \tfrac{1}{2}$.
2. (*a*) $\ln x = 3$; (*b*) $\ln x = \tfrac{2}{3}$; (*c*) $\ln x = -2$.
3. (*a*) $\log_a x = 0$; (*b*) $\log_a x = 1$; (*c*) $\log_a x = -3$; (*d*) $\log_a x = \tfrac{2}{3}$.
4. $\ln x = \ln 2 + \ln 3 + \ln 5$.   *Ans.* 30.
5. $\ln x = \ln 12 + \ln 13 - \ln 3$.   *Ans.* 52.
6. $\log_{10} x = \log_{10} 12 + \log_{10} 13 - \log_{10} 3$.
7. $\ln x = 3 \ln 2 - \ln 6 + 2 \ln 3$.   *Ans.* 12.
8. $\ln x = 2 \ln \tfrac{1}{2} - \ln 2 + \ln 5 + \ln 12$.   *Ans.* 7.5.
9. $\ln x = 3 + \ln 5$.   *Ans.* $5e^3$.   10. $\log_{10} x = 3 + \log_{10} 5$.
11. $\ln x = \tfrac{3}{2} \ln 6 - \tfrac{1}{2} \ln 3 - 4$.   *Ans.* $6e^{-4} \sqrt{2}$.
12. $\ln x = \tfrac{3}{2} \ln 6 - \ln 2 - 3$.   *Ans.* $3e^{-3} \sqrt{6}$.
13. $\log_{10} x = \tfrac{1}{2} + \tfrac{3}{2} \log_{10} 5 - \tfrac{1}{2} \log_{10} 2$.   *Ans.* 25.
14. Show that negative numbers have no (real) logarithms.
15. Show that numbers between 0 and 1 have negative logarithms.
16. Show that numbers greater than 1 have positive logarithms.

* After a little practice, we shall be able to write the result almost instantly, performing all intermediate steps mentally.

† Since, in (3), the quantity $5e^{x^3}$ may represent any angle whose sine is y—not necessarily the acute angle—what is needed here is the many-valued function arcsin y, not the single-valued function Arcsin y.

In Exs. 17–21, simplify the given expressions.

17. (a) $e^{\ln 4}$; (b) $e^{-\ln x}$; (c) $e^{3 \ln y}$.   *Ans.* (a) 4; (b) x^{-1}; (c) y^3.

18. (a) $e^{-3 \ln 2}$; (b) $e^{3y+\ln y}$; (c) $e^{-2y+3 \ln y}$.   *Ans.* (a) $\frac{1}{8}$; (b) ye^{3y}; (c) $y^3 e^{-2y}$.

19. (a) $e^{2-2 \ln 3}$; (b) $e^{3x-\ln x}$; (c) $e^{-x+2 \ln x}$.

20. (a) $\ln e^{4x}$; (b) $\ln (4e^{2x})$; (c) $\ln (9x^3)^{\frac{1}{2}}$.

Ans. (a) $4x$; (b) $2x + 2 \ln 2$; (c) $\frac{3}{2} \ln x + \ln 3$.

21. (a) $\ln (xe^{5x})$; (b) $\ln (3e^{-4x})$; (c) $\ln (4x^2 e^{-\cos x})$.

In Exs. 22–33, find the inverse of the given function; i.e., solve the equation for x.

22. $y = e^{4x}$.   *Ans.* $x = \frac{1}{4} \ln y$.   **23.** $y = 4e^{-3x}$.   *Ans.* $x = -\frac{1}{3} \ln \left(\frac{1}{4}y\right)$.

24. $y = 10^{x-2}$.   *Ans.* $x = 2 + \log_{10} y$.

25. $y = 10^{1-2x}$.   *Ans.* $x = \frac{1}{2}(1 - \log_{10} y)$.

26. $y = \sin 3x$.   *Ans.* $x = \frac{1}{3} \arcsin y$.

27. $y = 2 \tan 4x$.   *Ans.* $x = \frac{1}{4} \arctan \frac{1}{2}y$.

28. $y = \arctan e^{-x}$.   *Ans.* $x = -\ln \tan y$.

29. $y = 2 \arcsin (x - 1)$.   *Ans.* $x = 1 + \sin \frac{1}{2}y$.

30. $y = \ln (2x - 3)$.   *Ans.* $x = \frac{1}{2}(3 + e^y)$.

31. $y = \frac{1}{4} \ln (2x)$.   *Ans.* $x = \frac{1}{2}e^{4y}$.

32. $y = \ln \sin x$.   **33.** $y = 5 + \frac{1}{4} \ln \tan 3x$.

34. Show that the function $y = \text{Arcsin } e^{x^2}$ is imaginary except at one point.

35. Show that the curve $y = \text{Arcsin } e^{\sin^2 x}$ consists of a set of isolated points.

In Exs. 36–42, break up the given expression into sums and differences of simpler logarithms.

36. $\ln \dfrac{x^2 - 9}{x(x + 4)^2}$.   *Ans.* $\ln (x - 3) + \ln (x + 3) - \ln x - 2 \ln (x + 4)$.

37. $\ln \dfrac{4x^5 e^{-x}}{(x + 1)^3}$.   *Ans.* $2 \ln 2 + 5 \ln x - x - 3 \ln (x + 1)$.

38. $\ln \dfrac{e^{3x} - e^{-3x}}{x^4(e^{3x} + e^{-3x})}$.   *Ans.* $\ln (e^{3x} - e^{-3x}) - 4 \ln x - \ln (e^{3x} + e^{-3x})$.

39. $\ln \dfrac{x(2x - 3)}{x^2 - 4}$.   **40.** $\ln \dfrac{x^2 - 1}{x^3(x + 2)^4}$.

41. $\ln \dfrac{9x^3}{x^2 - 3x + 2}$.   **42.** $\ln \sqrt{\dfrac{x^5}{x - 3}}$.

In Exs. 43–50, solve for x by first taking logarithms of each member of the equation.

43. $5^x = 7$.   *Ans.* $x = \dfrac{\ln 7}{\ln 5}$.   **44.** $3^x = 4$.   *Ans.* $x = \dfrac{2 \ln 2}{\ln 3}$.

45. $5 \cdot 2^{3x} = 7$.   **46.** $7 \cdot 3^{-2x} = 8$.

47. $3^{2x} = 2^{3x-1}$.   *Ans.* $x = \dfrac{-\ln 2}{\ln 9 - \ln 8}$.

48. $3^{3x} = 2^{2x+3}$.   **49.** $10^x = 5^{2x-3}$.

50. $a^{x^x} = (a^x)^x$, $a > 0$.   *Ans.* $x = 1$; $x = 2$.

51. Show that, for $0 < a < x$,
$$\ln (x - \sqrt{x^2 - a^2}) = 2 \ln a - \ln (x + \sqrt{x^2 - a^2}).$$

52. Show that, for $a > 0$, $x > 0$,
$$\ln (\sqrt{x + a} + \sqrt{x}) = \ln a - \ln (\sqrt{x + a} - \sqrt{x}).$$

53. Show that, for $-\frac{1}{2}\pi < \theta < \frac{1}{2}\pi$,
$$\ln (\sec \theta - \tan \theta) = - \ln (\sec \theta + \tan \theta).$$

54. Let $\alpha = \left(1 + \dfrac{1}{n + 1}\right)^{\frac{1}{n}}$, $\alpha > 1$. Show that

(A)
$$n\alpha^n > \sum_{k=0}^{n-1} \alpha^k.$$

Add n times the right member of (A) to each member of (A) to obtain

$$n \sum_{k=0}^{n} \alpha^k > (n + 1) \sum_{k=0}^{n-1} \alpha^k,$$

or

(B)
$$n(\alpha^{n+1} - 1) > (n + 1)(\alpha^n - 1).$$

Use the fact that $\alpha^n = 1 + \dfrac{1}{n + 1}$ to conclude that

$$\alpha^{n+1} > 1 + \frac{1}{n}$$

and from it that $v_{n+1} > v_n$, in which v_n is defined by equation (2), § 75.

Of the statements in Exs. 55–58, which ones are true, and why?

55. If $t^2 = k$, and $x^2 = k$, then $t = x$.   *Ans.* False.
56. If $\sin t = k$, and $\sin x = k$, then $t = x$.   *Ans.* False.
57. If $\log_a x = k$, and $\log_a t = k$, then $t = x$.
58. If $k = a^x$, and $k = a^t (a \neq 1)$, then $t = x$. Take the logarithm in each equation.

77. *Exponential and Logarithmic Equations*

Equations involving exponential functions only, or logarithms only, may in simple cases be solved by applying the theory of §§ 72–73.

Example (a). Solve for x the equation
$$e^x - e^{-x} = 2.$$

Multiplying by e^x, we get
$$e^{2x} - 1 = 2e^x,$$
$$e^{2x} - 2e^x - 1 = 0.$$

This is a quadratic equation in e^x as the unknown quantity, whose solution is found by elementary algebra to be

$$e^x = 1 + \sqrt{2}.$$

(The root $e^x = 1 - \sqrt{2}$ must be rejected, since e^x is never negative.) Hence

$$x = \ln (1 + \sqrt{2}).$$

Check:

$$e^{\ln (1+\sqrt{2})} - e^{-\ln(1+\sqrt{2})} = 1 + \sqrt{2} - \frac{1}{1 + \sqrt{2}}$$

$$= 1 + \sqrt{2} - \frac{1 - \sqrt{2}}{(1 + \sqrt{2})(1 - \sqrt{2})}$$

$$= 1 + \sqrt{2} + 1 - \sqrt{2}$$

$$= 2.$$

Example (*b*). Solve the equation

$$\ln (2x + 7) - \ln (x - 1) = \ln 5.$$

Combining the logarithms in the left member, we get

$$\ln \frac{2x + 7}{x - 1} = \ln 5,$$

whence

(1) $$\frac{2x + 7}{x - 1} = 5,$$

and

$$x = 4.$$

Check: $\ln 15 - \ln 3 = \ln 5$.

EXERCISES

Solve the equations in Exs. 1–18.

1. $e^x + 6e^{-x} = 5$.   *Ans.* $x = 0.693, 1.099$.
2. $e^x + 10e^{-x} = 7$.   *Ans.* $x = 0.693, 1.609$.
3. $4e^x + 3e^{-x} = 13$.   *Ans.* $x = -1.386, 1.099$.
4. $3e^x + 2 = e^{-x}$.   *Ans.* $x = -1.099$.
5. $e^{2x} + 20e^{-x} = 21$.   *Ans.* $x = 0, 1.386$.
6. $1 - 3e^x = 4e^{-x}(e^{-x} + 1)$.   *Ans.* No real solutions.
7. $3^x + 8 \cdot 3^{-x} = 6$.   *Ans.* $x = 0.631, 1.262$.
8. $4^x + 2 \cdot 4^{-x} = 3$.   *Ans.* $x = 0, 0.5$.
9. $\ln (x + 1) + \ln (x - 2) = \ln 4$.   *Ans.* 3.
10. $\ln (x + 3) + \ln (x - 2) = \ln 6$.   *Ans.* 3.
11. $\ln (2 - x) + \ln (6 + x) = \ln 15$.   *Ans.* $x = -1, -3$.
12. $\ln (3 - x) + \ln (5 + 2x) = \ln 14$.   *Ans.* $x = 1, -\frac{1}{2}$.

13. $2 \log_{10} (3x - 2) - \log_{10} (x + 1) = 1 + \log_{10} 2.$ *Ans.* $x = 4.$
14. $2 \ln (x + 1) - \ln (5x + 1) + \ln (x - 1) = \ln 2.$ *Ans.* $x = 3.$
15. $\ln (x^2 + 3x + 1) - \ln (1 - x) + \ln (2 - x) = \ln 6.$
Ans. $x = -4, \frac{1}{2}(3 - \sqrt{5}).$
16. $\log_{10} (x + 6) + \log_{10} 5 - \log_{10} x + \log_{10} (x + 3) = 2.$ *Ans.* $x = 2, 9.$
17. $\ln x + \ln (x - 2) + \ln (x + 1) - \ln (x^2 - 2x - 1) = \ln 5 - \ln 2.$
Ans. No solutions.
18. $\ln (x^2 + 3) - \ln (x^2 - x + 2) + \ln (2 - x) = \ln 3.$ *Ans.* $x = 0, 0, -1.$

In Exs. 19–23, write the equation in a form free from logarithms. State the range of values of x and y for which the original equation is valid.

19. $\ln x + \ln y - \ln (x - y) = 2 \ln 2.$
Ans. $xy - 4x + 4y = 0,$ for $x > y > 0.$
20. $\ln (1 - x) - 2 \ln (1 + x) + 3 \ln y = 3 \ln 2.$
Ans. $y^3(1 - x) = 8(1 + x)^2,$ for $|x| < 1, y > 0.$
21. $\frac{1}{2} \ln (x - a) - \frac{1}{2} \ln (x + a) - \ln y + \ln a = 0.$
Ans. $y^2(x + a) = a^2(x - a),$ for $x > a > 0, y > 0.$
22. $\ln (x^2 + 4) - 2 \ln y + 3 = 0.$ *Ans.* $y^2 = e^3(x^2 + 4),$ for $y > 0.$
23. $x + \ln x + \ln y = 0.$ *Ans.* $xy = e^{-x},$ for $x > 0, y > 0.$

In Exs. 24–32, find the inverse of the given function.

24. $y = \frac{1}{2}(e^{4x} - e^{-4x}).$ *Ans.* $x = \frac{1}{4} \ln (y + \sqrt{y^2 + 1}).$
25. $y = \frac{1}{2}(e^{3x} + e^{-3x}).$ *Ans.* $x = \pm \frac{1}{3} \ln (y + \sqrt{y^2 - 1}).$
26. $4y = e^x - 8e^{-x}.$ *Ans.* $x = \ln (y + \sqrt{y^2 + 2}) + \ln 2.$
27. $y = \ln (x + 1) - \ln (x - 1).$ *Ans.* $x = \dfrac{e^y + 1}{e^y - 1}.$
28. $y = \ln (x + 1) + \ln (x - 1).$ *Ans.* $x = \sqrt{1 + e^y}.$
29. $y = 2 \ln x - \ln (x + 1).$ *Ans.* $x = \frac{1}{2}e^y(1 + \sqrt{1 + 4e^{-y}}).$
30. $y = \ln (e^{2x} - 1).$ *Ans.* $x = \frac{1}{2} \ln (1 + e^y).$
31. $y = \frac{1}{2} \ln (3e^{\frac{1}{2}x} - 2).$ *Ans.* $x = 2 \ln (e^{2y} + 2) - 2 \ln 3.$
32. $y = \ln (1 - \sqrt{4 - x^2}).$ *Ans.* $x = \pm \sqrt{(1 + e^y)(3 - e^y)},$ for $y \leqq 0.$

78. *Derivative of the Logarithm*

To obtain the derivative of the logarithm we proceed by the method of § 21:

$$y = \log_a x,$$
$$y + \Delta y = \log_a (x + \Delta x),$$
$$\Delta y = \log_a (x + \Delta x) - \log_a x = \log_a \frac{x + \Delta x}{x}$$
$$= \log_a \left(1 + \frac{\Delta x}{x}\right).$$

Thus

$$\frac{\Delta y}{\Delta x} = \frac{1}{\Delta x} \log_a \left(1 + \frac{\Delta x}{x}\right).$$

Let us multiply and divide by x and then employ (3), § 73:

$$\frac{\Delta y}{\Delta x} = \frac{1}{x} \cdot \frac{x}{\Delta x} \log_a \left(1 + \frac{\Delta x}{x} \right)$$

$$= \frac{1}{x} \log_a \left(1 + \frac{\Delta x}{x} \right)^{\frac{x}{\Delta x}}.$$

Hence

(1) $$\frac{dy}{dx} = \lim_{\Delta x \to 0} \frac{\Delta y}{\Delta x} = \frac{1}{x} \lim_{\Delta x \to 0} \log_a \left(1 + \frac{\Delta x}{x} \right)^{\frac{x}{\Delta x}}$$

(2) $$= \frac{1}{x} \log_a \left[\lim_{\Delta x \to 0} \left(1 + \frac{\Delta x}{x} \right)^{\frac{x}{\Delta x}} \right],$$

making use of the continuity of the logarithmic function.

Now, putting

$$\frac{x}{\Delta x} = z,$$

we see that the limit occurring in (2) is, if $\Delta x > 0$,

$$\lim_{z \to \infty} \left(1 + \frac{1}{z} \right)^z = e,$$

by Theorem 20. (The argument must be slightly modified for negative Δx.) Therefore

(3) $$\frac{d}{dx} \log_a x = \frac{1}{x} \log_a e.$$

In order to remove the undesirable factor $\log_a e$, choose the base a so that $\log_a e = 1$; i.e., take $a = e$. Then $\log_a x$ becomes $\ln x$, $\log_a e$ becomes unity, and equation (3) simplifies to the form

$$\frac{d}{dx} \ln x = \frac{1}{x}.$$

This is the reason for the use of logarithms to the base e in calculus.*

By the chain rule of § 29, if u is any function of x,

$$\frac{d}{dx} \log_a u = \frac{\frac{du}{dx}}{u} \cdot \log_a e,$$

---

* Since the awkward factor $\log_a e$ has appeared in consequence of an intrinsic property of the logarithmic function, with no way of removing it except by adoption of e as base, the terms "natural base" and "natural logarithm" are seen to be justified. While it is clearly a nuisance to have to use two systems of logarithms—one for computing, the other in applications of calculus—it would be a much greater nuisance to use (3) every time a logarithm is differentiated. Compare with similar remarks in § 62 concerning the use of radian measure of angles—which, in the same line of thought, might be called "natural measure."

and as special cases,

(16)
$$\frac{d}{dx} \ln u = \frac{\frac{du}{dx}}{u},$$

(17)
$$\frac{d}{dx} \log_{10} u = \frac{M \frac{du}{dx}}{u}.$$

In differentiating the logarithm of a complicated expression, a great deal of labor may often be saved by making judicious use of (1), (2), and (3) of § 73.

Example (*a*). Differentiate $y = \ln \sqrt{1 + 3x}$.

Let us write y in the form

$$y = \tfrac{1}{2} \ln (1 + 3x).$$

Then

$$y' = \frac{1}{2} \cdot \frac{3}{1 + 3x} = \frac{3}{2 + 6x}.$$

Example (*b*). Differentiate $x = \ln \dfrac{z^3 (z^2 - 1)^2}{(z^2 + 1)^2}$.

Write

$$x = 3 \ln z + 2 \ln (z^2 - 1) - 2 \ln (z^2 + 1);$$
$$\frac{dx}{dz} = \frac{3}{z} + \frac{4z}{z^2 - 1} - \frac{4z}{z^2 + 1}$$
$$= \frac{3(z^4 - 1) + 4z^2(z^2 + 1) - 4z^2(z^2 - 1)}{z(z^4 - 1)}$$
$$= \frac{3z^4 + 8z^2 - 3}{z(z^4 - 1)}.$$

EXERCISES

In Exs. 1–38, find the derivative of the given function. When necessary, use M to denote $\log_{10} e$.

1. $y = \ln (7 - 3x).$ **2.** $y = \ln (5x + 4).$

3. $y = \ln (cx).$ **4.** $y = \ln (2x^3 + x - 1).$

5. $y = \ln (a^2 - x^2)^{\frac{3}{2}}.$ **6.** $y = \ln (3x - x^3).$ **7.** $\theta = \ln \tan \varphi.$

8. $\theta = \ln \sin 4\varphi.$ **9.** $u = \ln \sec t.$ **10.** $u = \ln \cos 3t.$

11. $y = \log_{10} \sin \dfrac{x}{a}.$ *Ans.* $\dfrac{dy}{dx} = \dfrac{M}{a} \cot \dfrac{x}{a}.$

12. $\alpha = \log_{10} (1 - 4 \tan \beta).$ *Ans.* $\dfrac{d\alpha}{d\beta} = \dfrac{-4M \sec^2 \beta}{1 - 4 \tan \beta}.$

13. $w = \ln \sqrt{a^2 - x^2}.$ *Ans.* $\dfrac{dw}{dx} = \dfrac{-x}{a^2 - x^2}.$

14. $w = \ln (b^2 + x^2)^{\frac{2}{3}}$.

Ans. $\dfrac{dw}{dx} = \dfrac{5x}{b^2 + x^2}$.

15. $x = \ln \dfrac{1 + t^2}{1 - t^2}$.

Ans. $\dfrac{dx}{dt} = \dfrac{4t}{1 - t^4}$.

16. $x = 4 \ln \sqrt{\dfrac{1 - t^3}{1 + t^3}}$.

Ans. $\dfrac{dx}{dt} = \dfrac{-12t^2}{1 - t^6}$.

17. $y = \log_{10} \dfrac{4t - 1}{4t + 1}$.

Ans. $\dfrac{dy}{dt} = \dfrac{8M}{16t^2 - 1}$.

18. $r = \log_{10} \cos^2 4\theta$.

Ans. $\dfrac{dr}{d\theta} = -8M \tan 4\theta$.

19. $y = x^2 \ln x$.   **20.** $y = \ln^3 x$.

21. $u = \dfrac{1}{\ln x}$.   **22.** $u = \dfrac{\ln x}{x^3}$.

23. $v = x \ln (1 - x)$.   **24.** $v = x^2 \ln (1 + x)$.

25. $y = \ln \ln x$.   **26.** $y = \ln \ln (1 - \cos x)$.

27. $y = \sin \ln x$.   **28.** $y = \cot \ln x$.

29. $y = x^3(3 \ln x - 1)$.   *Ans.* $y' = 9x^2 \ln x$.

30. $w = t^2(\cos \ln t - \sin \ln t)$.   *Ans.* $w' = t(\cos \ln t - 3 \sin \ln t)$.

31. $u = t^3(\sin \ln t - \cos \ln t)$.   *Ans.* $u' = 2t^2(2 \sin \ln t - \cos \ln t)$.

32. $y = x \ln (a^2 + x^2) + 2a \operatorname{Arctan} \dfrac{x}{a} - 2x$.   *Ans.* $y' = \ln (a^2 + x^2)$.

33. $y = \ln \sqrt{\dfrac{1 + \sin x}{1 - \sin x}}$.

Ans. $\dfrac{dy}{dx} = \sec x$.

34. $y = \ln \tan \left(\dfrac{\pi}{4} + \dfrac{x}{2} \right)$.

Ans. $\dfrac{dy}{dx} = \sec x$.

35. $y = \ln \dfrac{x^3(x - 1)}{(x + 1)^4}$.   **36.** $y = \ln \dfrac{x(x^2 + 1)}{x^2 - 1}$.

37. $y = \ln \dfrac{(x + 1)(x - 1)^2}{2x - 1}$.   **38.** $y = \ln \dfrac{(x - 1)(2x - 1)}{(x + 1)^3}$.

In Exs. 39–42, find y'.

39. $y \ln x - x \ln y = c$.

Ans. $y' = \dfrac{y(y - x \ln y)}{x(x - y \ln x)}$.

40. $y \ln (x^2 + y^2) = x + c$.   *Ans.* $y' = \dfrac{(x - y)^2}{2y^2 + (x^2 + y^2) \ln (x^2 + y^2)}$.

41. $4 \ln (\sec y + \tan y) - 2x - \sin 2x = c$.   *Ans.* $y' = \cos y \cos^2 x$.

42. $\ln (x^2 + y^2) + 4 \operatorname{Arctan} \dfrac{y}{x} = c$.   *Ans.* $y' = \dfrac{2y - x}{y + 2x}$.

43. For the function $y = x^2 \ln x$, find the first four derivatives.

44. For the function $y = (x^3 - 1) \ln x$, find $\dfrac{d^4y}{dx^4}$.   *Ans.* $\dfrac{d^4y}{dx^4} = \dfrac{6(x^3 + 1)}{x^4}$.

45. For the curve $y = \ln x$, find the equation of a tangent line parallel to the line $3x - y = 5$. *Ans.* $3x - y = 1 + \ln 3$.

46. For the curve $y = x \ln x$, find the equation of a tangent line perpendicular to the line $x + 3y = 4$. *Ans.* $3x - y = e^2$.

47. Find the tangent to the curve $y = \ln x$ at any point (x_1, y_1). By finding the y-intercept of the tangent, derive a ruler-and-compass construction for the tangent at any point of the curve. *Ans.* $x_1 y - x = x_1 y_1 - x_1$.

48. By setting $y = x^n$, taking the logarithm, and differentiating, prove the formula $\dfrac{d}{dx} x^n = nx^{n-1}$ for all values of n.

Sketch carefully each of the curves in Exs. 49–56, locating all maximum, minimum, and inflection points.

49. $y = \ln (x - 1)$.   **50.** $y = \ln (x + 1)$.   **51.** $y = x - \ln x$.
52. $y = x^2 - 2 \ln x$.   **53.** $y = \ln \ln x$.   **54.** $y = \ln \cos x$.
55. $y = 9 \ln (x + 1) - \ln (x - 1)$.

Ans. Min. at $(1.25, 8.68)$; Infl. pt. at $(2, 9.89)$.

56. $y = x^2(\frac{1}{2} - \ln x)$, given (from Chapter 15) that $y \to 0$ as $x \to 0^+$.

Ans. Max. at $(1, \frac{1}{2})$; Infl. pt. at $(0.37, 0.20)$.

79. *Derivative of the Exponential Function*

If

$$y = a^x,$$
$$\ln y = x \ln a.$$

Differentiating by the rule for implicit functions, we find

$$\frac{1}{y} \frac{dy}{dx} = \ln a,$$

$$\frac{dy}{dx} = y \ln a = a^x \ln a;$$

$$\frac{d}{dx} a^x = a^x \ln a.$$

If u is a function of x, this formula becomes

(18) $$\frac{d}{dx} a^u = a^u \ln a \cdot \frac{du}{dx}.$$

For the case $a = e$, we have the important special case*

(19) $$\frac{d}{dx} e^u = e^u \frac{du}{dx}.$$

---

* The number e has a way of appearing in many physical problems (for simple illustrations, see §§ 97, 99), frequently for reasons that are rather obscure. In this it resembles that other remarkable number, π, which turns up in a multitude of situations having no apparent connection with circles.

Example (a). If $y = e^{2x^3}$,

$$y' = e^{2x^3} \cdot 6x^2 = 6x^2 e^{2x^3}.$$

Example (b). If $y = \sin^2 e^{3x}$,

$$y' = 2 \sin e^{3x} \cos e^{3x} \cdot e^{3x} \cdot 3 = 3e^{3x} \sin 2e^{3x}.$$

Example (c). Show that $e^{-x} > 1 - x$ for $x > 0$.
Put

(1) $$y = e^{-x} - 1 + x.$$

We need to show that y is positive for $x > 0$. From (1) it follows that

(2) $$y' = 1 - e^{-x}$$
(3) $$y'' = e^{-x}.$$

At $x = 0$, $y = 0$, and $y' = 0$. Because of (3) the y curve is concave upward for all x. Therefore $y > 0$ for $x > 0$, which yields the desired inequality.

80. *Variable with Variable Exponent*

Let

$$y = u^v, \qquad (u > 0)$$

where both u and v are functions of x.

While it is easy to develop the general formula (Ex. 48 below) for the derivative of this function, it is usually simpler not to use the formula but to *take the logarithm of both members* before differentiating.

Example. Differentiate $\qquad y = x^x$.
We have

$$\ln y = x \ln x,$$
$$\frac{y'}{y} = 1 + \ln x,$$
$$y' = y(1 + \ln x) = x^x(1 + \ln x).$$

EXERCISES

In Exs. 1–28, find the first derivative of the given function.

1. $y = e^{-3x}$.
2. $y = e^{-x^2}$.
3. $x = e^{\sec t}$.
4. $x = e^{-\cos 2t}$.
5. $u = xe^{-2x}$.
6. $u = x^2 e^{-3x}$.
7. $y = \ln(e^{3x} + 2)$.
8. $y = \ln(5 - e^{4x})$.
9. $r = e^{-\theta} \cos 2\theta$.
10. $r = e^{-2\theta} \sin 3\theta$.
11. $x = e^{3t}(\cos t - 3 \sin t)$.
12. $x = e^t(\cos 2t + 2 \sin 2t)$.
13. $y = \cos e^{-4x}$.
14. $y = \text{Arctan } e^{-2x}$.
15. $y = \text{Arcsin } e^{-x}$.
16. $y = 10^{\cos 2x}$.
17. $x = 10^{2t}$.
18. $x = 3^{-4t}$.

19. $y = \sec^2(1 - e^{-x})$.

20. $y = (5 - 2e^{-3x})^{\frac{1}{2}}$.

21. $y = x^{-3}e^{-2x}$.

22. $y = x^3 e^{-\frac{1}{x}}$.

23. $y = \dfrac{e^{2t} + e^{-2t}}{e^{2t} - e^{-2t}}$.

24. $y = \dfrac{e^{3t} - e^{-3t}}{e^{3t} + e^{-3t}}$.

25. $y = x^2 + x^4 e^{-2 \ln x}$.   *Ans.* $y' = 4x$.

26. $y = e^{-2x}(1 + e^{-2x})^{-\frac{1}{2}}$.   *Ans.* $y' = -e^{-2x}(2 + e^{-2x})(1 + e^{-2x})^{-\frac{3}{2}}$.

27. $y = e^{-2x}(e^{3x} - 1)^{-\frac{1}{2}}$.   *Ans.* $y' = -\frac{1}{2}(7e^x - 4e^{-2x})(e^{3x} - 1)^{-\frac{3}{2}}$.

28. $y = (1 + e^{-x})^2(1 - e^{-x})^{\frac{1}{2}}$.

Ans. $y' = -\frac{1}{2}e^{-x}(1 + e^{-x})(3 - 5e^{-x})(1 - e^{-x})^{-\frac{1}{2}}$.

29. Find y' from $x^2 e^{-y} + y^2 e^{-x} = 1$.

30. Find y'' from the equation $y = xe^{-x^2}$.   *Ans.* $y'' = 2xe^{-x^2}(2x^2 - 3)$.

31. Find $\dfrac{d^2x}{dt^2}$ from the equation $x = t^3 e^{-t}$.   *Ans.* $\dfrac{d^2x}{dt^2} = te^{-t}(t^2 - 6t + 6)$.

32. Find $y^{(n)} = \dfrac{d^n y}{dx^n}$ from the equation $y = e^{ax}$.

33. Find $y^{(n)}$ from the equation $y = xe^x$.

34. From $u = e^{-t} \sin t$, show that

$$\frac{d^2u}{dt^2} + 2\frac{du}{dt} + 2u = 0.$$

35. From $y = e^{-3x} \cos 2x$, show that

$$y'' + 6y' + 13y = 0.$$

36. From $x = e^{-\frac{1}{2}t} \cos t$, show that

$$4\frac{d^2x}{dt^2} + 4\frac{dx}{dt} + 5x = 0.$$

In Exs. 37–45, sketch the curve carefully.

37. $y = e^{-3x}$.

38. $y = 1 + e^x$.

39. $y = 4(e^{-x} - 1)$.

40. $y = e^x - x$.

41. $y = e^{-x^2}$.

42. $y = e^{-\frac{1}{x}}$.

43. $y = e^{-x} \sin x$.

44. $y = \operatorname{Arcsin} e^{-x}$.

45. $y = e^{\sin x}$.

46. For the curve $y = e^{-4x}$, find the tangent line parallel to the line $2x + y = 7$.
    Ans. $2x + y = \frac{1}{2}(1 + \ln 2)$.

47. For the curve $y = e^{2x}$, find the tangent line perpendicular to the line

$$x + 18y = 0.$$

    Ans. $18x - y = 9(2 \ln 3 - 1)$.

48. If u and v are functions of x, find the derivative of u^v.

    Ans. $\dfrac{d}{dx} u^v = vu^{v-1}\dfrac{du}{dx} + u^v \ln u \dfrac{dv}{dx}$.

49. Differentiate $y = x^{e^x}$.   *Ans.* $y' = x^{e^x-1}e^x(1 + x \ln x)$.

50. Differentiate $y = x^{x^2}$.   *Ans.* $y' = x^{1+x^2}(1 + 2 \ln x)$.

51. Differentiate $y = e^{x^x}$.   *Ans.* $y' = x^x e^{x^x}(1 + \ln x)$.

52. Differentiate $y = (\ln x)^x$.   *Ans.* $y' = (\ln x)^{x-1}(1 + \ln x \ln \ln x)$.

53. Differentiate $y = x^{\ln x}$.   *Ans.* $y' = 2(\ln x)x^{\ln x-1}$.

54. Show that $e^{-x} > 1 - x + \frac{1}{2}x^2 - \frac{1}{6}x^3$ for $x > 0$.

Fundamental Differentiation Formulas

(1) $\dfrac{dc}{dx} = 0;$

(2) $\dfrac{d}{dx}(u + v) = \dfrac{du}{dx} + \dfrac{dv}{dx};$

(3) $\dfrac{d}{dx}\,uv = u\,\dfrac{dv}{dx} + v\,\dfrac{du}{dx};$ (3′) $\dfrac{d}{dx}\,cv = c\,\dfrac{dv}{dx};$

(4) $\dfrac{d}{dx}\,\dfrac{u}{v} = \dfrac{v\,\dfrac{du}{dx} - u\,\dfrac{dv}{dx}}{v^2};$ (4′) $\dfrac{d}{dx}\,\dfrac{c}{v} = -\,\dfrac{c\,\dfrac{dv}{dx}}{v^2};$

(5) $\dfrac{dy}{dx} = \dfrac{dy}{du}\cdot\dfrac{du}{dx};$ (5′) $\dfrac{dy}{dx} = \dfrac{\dfrac{dy}{du}}{\dfrac{dx}{du}};$ (5″) $\dfrac{dy}{dx} = \dfrac{1}{\dfrac{dx}{dy}};$

(6) $\dfrac{d}{dx}\,u^n = nu^{n-1}\,\dfrac{du}{dx};$ (6′) $\dfrac{d}{dx}\,\sqrt{u} = \dfrac{\dfrac{du}{dx}}{2\,\sqrt{u}};$

(7) $\dfrac{d}{dx}\,\sin u = \cos u\,\dfrac{du}{dx};$

(8) $\dfrac{d}{dx}\,\cos u = -\sin u\,\dfrac{du}{dx};$

(9) $\dfrac{d}{dx}\,\tan u = \sec^2 u\,\dfrac{du}{dx};$

(10) $\dfrac{d}{dx}\,\cot u = -\csc^2 u\,\dfrac{du}{dx};$

(11) $\dfrac{d}{dx}\,\sec u = \sec u \tan u\,\dfrac{du}{dx};$

(12) $\dfrac{d}{dx}\,\csc u = -\csc u \cot u\,\dfrac{du}{dx};$

(13) $\dfrac{d}{dx}\,\text{Arcsin } u = \dfrac{\dfrac{du}{dx}}{\sqrt{1 - u^2}},$ $-\dfrac{\pi}{2} \leqq \text{Arcsin } u \leqq \dfrac{\pi}{2};$

(14) $\dfrac{d}{dx}\,\text{Arccos } u = -\,\dfrac{\dfrac{du}{dx}}{\sqrt{1 - u^2}},$ $0 \leqq \text{Arccos } u \leqq \pi;$

(15) $\dfrac{d}{dx}\,\text{Arctan } u = \dfrac{\dfrac{du}{dx}}{1 + u^2},$ $-\dfrac{\pi}{2} < \text{Arctan } u < \dfrac{\pi}{2};$

(16) $\dfrac{d}{dx}\,\ln u = \dfrac{\dfrac{du}{dx}}{u};$

$$(17) \quad \frac{d}{dx} \log_{10} u = \frac{M \frac{du}{dx}}{u};$$

$$(18) \quad \frac{d}{dx} a^u = a^u \ln a \frac{du}{dx};$$

$$(19) \quad \frac{d}{dx} e^u = e^u \frac{du}{dx}.$$

MISCELLANEOUS EXERCISES

Differentiate the following functions.

1. $y = x \operatorname{Arctan} \frac{1}{2}x.$

2. $y = x(1 - 3x)^{-\frac{1}{2}}.$

3. $x = (t^2 + 2)e^{-2t}.$

4. $x = t^3(3 \ln t - 1).$

5. $u = \sec^3 2t.$

6. $u = \sin 2t \tan 2t.$

7. $r = \ln \sin^2 \theta.$

8. $r = \ln^2 \sin \theta.$

9. $y = \dfrac{x^2}{\sqrt{2ax - x^2}}.$

10. $y = \dfrac{t^3}{(1 - t^2)^2}.$

11. $y = \frac{1}{2}x^2 e^{-2x}.$

12. $y = \log_{10} (4x^2 - 1).$

13. $u = y^3(1 + y^2)^{-\frac{1}{2}}.$

14. $u = e^{-2y} \ln y.$

15. $w = (a^{\frac{2}{3}} - x^{\frac{2}{3}})^{\frac{3}{2}}.$

16. $w = \csc x \cot^2 x.$

17. $\theta = \operatorname{Arcsin} (1 - 2r).$

18. $\theta = \operatorname{Arcsin} e^{-2r}.$

19. $x = t \ln \sqrt{1 - t^2}.$

20. $x = \ln \ln (1 + e^{-t}).$

21. $A = (e^{2x} - 1)^{-\frac{3}{2}}.$

22. $B = (1 - e^{-2x})^{\frac{3}{2}}.$

23. $\alpha = \cos 3\beta \sin^2 \beta.$

24. $\alpha = 5^{-3\beta}.$

25. $\psi = \dfrac{\cos^6 2x}{(1 - \sin 2x)^3}.$

26. $\psi = e^{e^{-x}}.$

27. $r = \sqrt{\dfrac{1 + \cos \theta}{1 - \cos \theta}}.$

28. $r = \ln \dfrac{1 + e^{-2\theta}}{1 - e^{-2\theta}}.$

29. $y = \operatorname{Arctan} \ln x.$

30. $y = \cot^2 (1 - 3x).$

31. $W = (1 - x^2)^{-\frac{1}{2}}(1 + x^2)^{\frac{3}{2}}.$

32. $V = e^x(1 - e^{-2x})^{-\frac{1}{2}}.$

33. $x = \ln \dfrac{t^2}{(1 - t^2)^3}.$

34. $x = \dfrac{t^3}{1 + 3t^2}.$

35. $g = \sin^3 2\theta \cos 2\theta.$

36. $g = \ln (1 + e^{-3\theta})^2.$

37. $u = v(1 - 2 \ln v)^{\frac{1}{2}}.$

38. $u = \operatorname{Arctan} (1 - v^2).$

39. $y = \cos^2 (\frac{1}{4}\pi - 4x).$

40. $y = x^3 e^{-x^3}.$

41. $y = e^{-2x}(1 + e^{2x})^{-\frac{1}{2}}.$

42. $y = \sec^2 2x \tan^3 2x.$

PARAMETRIC EQUATIONS.

MOTION

81. *Parametric Equations*

In both pure and applied mathematics, a curve often arises most naturally as the locus of points whose coordinates are determined by two equations

(1) $$x = f(t), \quad y = g(t),$$

giving x and y in terms of a third variable t. The variable t is then called a *parameter*; the equations (1) are parametric equations of the curve. To obtain the rectangular equation of the curve, we need to eliminate the parameter. As we shall see, such elimination may not be feasible; it may not be wise even when feasible.

A curve may be drawn by plotting points directly from its parametric equations, assigning suitable values to the parameter and computing corresponding values of x and y. The curve may be drawn by eliminating the parameter and then tracing the locus of the rectangular equation by our usual methods. Sometimes it is desirable to combine these two techniques. For the location of maxima, minima, and points of inflection we must develop a technique for obtaining the derivatives of y with respect to x from the parametric equations (1).

Example (a). Find $\dfrac{dy}{dx}$ and $\dfrac{d^2y}{dx^2}$ from

$$x = t^3 + 2t - 4, \quad y = t^3 - t + 2.$$

First we obtain the derivatives of x, and of y, with respect to t:

$$\frac{dx}{dt} = 3t^2 + 2, \quad \frac{dy}{dt} = 3t^2 - 1.$$

Then, by (5′) of § 29, the ratio of these gives the desired first derivative,

$$(2) \qquad \frac{dy}{dx} = \frac{3t^2 - 1}{3t^2 + 2}.$$

Equation (2) exhibits $\frac{dy}{dx}$ in terms of t. We wish to differentiate both members of (2) with respect to x, and t is a function of x. Therefore we need to use the formula for a derivative of a function of a function,

$$(3) \qquad \frac{dF}{dx} = \frac{dF}{dt} \cdot \frac{dt}{dx},$$

which is (5) of § 29, except for changes in notation. Employing the idea in (3) when differentiating the right member of equation (2), we get

$$(4) \qquad \frac{d^2y}{dx^2} = \frac{(3t^2 + 2)(6t) - (3t^2 - 1)(6t)}{(3t^2 + 2)^2} \cdot \frac{dt}{dx}.$$

But $\frac{dt}{dx}$ is the reciprocal of $\frac{dx}{dt}$, as shown in (5″) of § 29. Hence (4) yields

$$\frac{d^2y}{dx^2} = \frac{18t}{(3t^2 + 2)^2} \cdot \frac{1}{3t^2 + 2}$$

$$= \frac{18t}{(3t^2 + 2)^3}.$$

Example (b). Find $\frac{dy}{dx}$ and $\frac{d^2y}{dx^2}$ from

$$(5) \qquad x = t^3 + 1, \quad y = 4t^2 - 4t.$$

As a mild variation of the method used in Example (a), let us employ differentials. From (5) we get

$$(6) \qquad dx = 3t^2\, dt, \quad dy = 4(2t - 1)\, dt.$$

Then

$$(7) \qquad y' = \frac{dy}{dx} = \frac{4(2t - 1)}{3t^2}.$$

The differential of y' may be obtained from (7). It is given by

$$(8) \qquad dy' = \frac{8(1 - t)\, dt}{3t^3}.$$

Now

$$y'' = \frac{d^2y}{dx^2} = \frac{dy'}{dx},$$

so we combine (8) and (6) to obtain

$$(9) \qquad \frac{d^2y}{dx^2} = \frac{8(1 - t)\, dt}{3t^3 \cdot 3t^2\, dt} = \frac{8(1 - t)}{9t^5}.$$

EXERCISES

In Exs. 1–12, find the first and second derivatives of y with respect to x from the parametric equations given.

1. $x = 1 + t^2, y = 4t - 3.$ *Ans.* $y'' = -t^{-3}.$

2. $x = t^3 + 7, y = 6t^2 - 1.$ *Ans.* $y'' = -\frac{4}{3}t^{-4}.$

3. $x = t^3 - 1, y = t^2 + t.$ *Ans.* $y'' = \dfrac{-2(t + 1)}{9t^5}.$

4. $x = 3(t - 2)^2,\ y = 9t^2 + 4.$ *Ans.* $y'' = -(t - 2)^{-3}.$

5. $x = \dfrac{1}{t^2}, y = t^2 - 4t + 1.$ *Ans.* $y'' = t^5(2t - 3).$

6. $x = \dfrac{1}{t^2}, y = t^2 - t.$ *Ans.* $y'' = \frac{1}{4}t^5(8t - 3).$

7. $x = \dfrac{1}{t^3}, y = t^3 + 3t.$ *Ans.* $y'' = \frac{2}{3}t^7(3t^2 + 2).$

8. $x = \dfrac{1}{(t + 1)^2}, y = t^2 + 3.$ *Ans.* $y'' = \frac{1}{2}(t + 1)^5(4t + 1).$

9. $x = \sqrt{1 - t}, y = t^3 - 3t.$ *Ans.* $y'' = 6(1 + 4t - 5t^2).$

10. $x = \sqrt{t + 2}, y = t^2 - 3.$ *Ans.* $y'' = 4(3t + 4).$

11. $x = (t - 2)^{\frac{3}{2}}, y = t^2 - 1.$ *Ans.* $y'' = \dfrac{4(t - 4)}{9(t - 2)^2}.$

12. $x = \dfrac{1}{(t - 1)^2}, y = \dfrac{1}{t + 2}.$ *Ans.* $y'' = \dfrac{-(t - 1)^5(t + 8)}{4(t + 2)^3}.$

From the parametric equations in each of Exs. 13–17, find $y' = \dfrac{dy}{dx}$ from the quotient dy divided by dx.

13. $x = 1 + t^2, \quad y = t^3 - 2.$ *Ans.* $y' = \frac{3}{2}t.$

14. $x = 2 - 3t + t^3, \quad y = 3t^2 - 7.$ *Ans.* $y' = \dfrac{2t}{t^2 - 1}.$

15. $x = (\beta^2 - 1)^2, \quad y = 4\beta^3.$ *Ans.* $y' = \dfrac{3\beta}{\beta^2 - 1}.$

16. $x = \dfrac{1}{u^2}, \quad y = u^4 - 2u^2 + \dfrac{4}{u}.$ *Ans.* $y' = 2u(1 + u^3 - u^5).$

17. $x = \dfrac{1}{t + 1}, \quad y = \dfrac{1}{t - 1}.$ *Ans.* $y' = \left(\dfrac{t + 1}{t - 1}\right)^2.$

In each of Exs. 18–25, find $y'' = \dfrac{d^2y}{dx^2}$ by first obtaining y' and then $\dfrac{dy'}{dx}$.

18. Ex. 13.   *Ans.* $y'' = \dfrac{3}{4t}.$

19. Ex. 14. $Ans.\ y'' = \dfrac{-2(t^2 + 1)}{3(t^2 - 1)^3}.$

20. Ex. 15. $Ans.\ y'' = \dfrac{-3(\beta^2 + 1)}{4\beta(\beta^2 - 1)^3}.$

21. Ex. 16. $Ans.\ y'' = u^3(6u^5 - 4u^3 - 1).$

22. Ex. 17. $Ans.\ y'' = 4\left(\dfrac{t + 1}{t - 1}\right)^3.$

23. $x = t^2 - 3, \quad y = t^3 + t + 1.$ $Ans.\ y'' = \dfrac{3t^2 - 1}{4t^3}.$

24. $x = 1 - \dfrac{1}{t}, \quad y = 6 - \dfrac{7}{t} + \dfrac{2}{t^2}.$ $Ans.\ y'' = 4.$

25. $x = \dfrac{3}{t + 1}, \quad y = t^3.$ $Ans.\ y'' = \tfrac{2}{3}t(t + 1)^3(2t + 1).$

82. *Curve Tracing from Parametric Equations*

Consider the curve of Example (*b*), § 81:

$$(1) \qquad\qquad x = t^3 + 1, \quad y = 4t^2 - 4t.$$

It is possible to eliminate the parameter t from equations (1) and obtain the rectangular equation

$$(2) \qquad\qquad y^3 + 48y(x - 1) - 64(x - 1)(x - 2) = 0.$$

Direct study of (2) is not particularly pleasant if we seek critical points and inflection points. Let us therefore study the curve from its parametric equations (1).

We already know, from Example (*b*), page 159, that

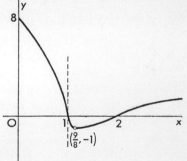

Figure 86

$$(3) \qquad\qquad \frac{dy}{dx} = \frac{4(2t - 1)}{3t^2}$$

and

$$(4) \qquad\qquad \frac{d^2y}{dx^2} = \frac{8(1 - t)}{9t^5}.$$

For a critical point we must have $y' = 0$. Hence, by (3), $t = \tfrac{1}{2}$. For $t = \tfrac{1}{2}$, $x = \tfrac{9}{8}$, $y = -1$, and y'' is positive. Therefore the point $(\tfrac{9}{8}, -1)$ is a minimum point.

Let us set $y'' = 0$. Then $t = 1$, which leads to $x = 2$, $y = 0$, $y' = \tfrac{4}{3}$. It follows that $(2, 0)$ is a point of inflection and that the inflectional tangent has the slope $\tfrac{4}{3}$.

It is useful to note that the slope does not exist at $t = 0$. When $t = 0$, $x = 1$, $y = 0$. There is a vertical tangent line at the point $(1, 0)$.

From the sign of the second derivative in (4) we obtain the direction of concavity of the curve. The results are:

For $t < 0$, $y'' < 0$, curve concave downward;
For $0 < t < 1$, $y'' > 0$, curve concave upward;
For $t > 1$, $y'' < 0$, curve concave downward.

The curve is shown in Fig. 86. Note that there is an inflection point at $(1, 0)$ where the direction of concavity changed because of discontinuity in the derivatives.

EXERCISES

In Exs. 1–13, obtain all maxima, minima, and inflection points without eliminating the parameter. Discuss the direction of concavity and sketch the curve carefully.

1. $x = t^3 - 1$, $y = t^2 + t$. (Ex. 3, page 160.)
2. $x = t^{-2}$, $y = t^2 - 4t + 1$. (Ex. 5, page 160.)
3. $x = t^{-2}$, $y = t^2 - t$. (Ex. 6, page 160.)
4. $x = t^{-3}$, $y = t^3 + 3t$. (Ex. 7, page 160.)
5. $x = (t + 1)^{-2}$, $y = t^2 + 3$. (Ex. 8, page 160.)
6. $x = (1 - t)^{\frac{1}{2}}$, $y = t^3 - 3t$. Ex. 9, page 160.)
7. $x = (t + 2)^{\frac{1}{2}}$, $y = t^2 - 3$. (Ex. 10, page 160.)
8. $x = 1 + t^2$, $y = 4t - 3$. (Ex. 1, page 160.)
9. $x = t^3 + 7$, $y = 6t^2 - 1$. (Ex. 2, page 160.)
10. $x = 1 + t^2$, $y = t^3 - 2$. (Ex. 13, page 160.)
11. $x = (\beta^2 - 1)^2$, $y = 4\beta^3$. (Ex. 15, page 160.)
12. $x = (t + 1)^{-1}$, $y = (t - 1)^{-1}$. (Ex. 17, page 160.)
13. $x = 1 - t^{-1}$, $y = 6 - 7t^{-1} + 2t^{-2}$. (Ex. 24, page 161.)

83. *The Problem of the Moving Point*

As an important application of parametric representation we cite the following problem of mechanics.

When a point moves in a plane curve under the action of a given force* or system of forces, an especially convenient way of studying the motion is to express the rectangular coordinates of the point as functions of the time t. The equations giving x and y in terms of t are *parametric equations of the path*.

To simplify the ideas at the outset, we shall first attack the problem of a point moving in a straight line. After a fairly thorough study of such rectilinear motion we shall move on in § 92 to motion taking place on other plane curves.

---

* The "point" is supposed to be endowed with mass—a "material particle." Further, the argument applies to a body of any size or shape, provided that for present purposes the motion of the entire body is completely characterized by the motion of one of its points. This would be the case, for instance, in computing the range of a projectile, or determining the orbit of a planet.

84. *Rectilinear Motion*

Consider a point P moving in a straight line. Choose as origin any convenient fixed point in the line of motion, and denote the distance OP by x, positive on one side of O, negative on the other. In accordance with the argument of § 24, the *velocity* at any instant is defined as

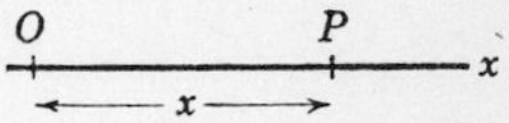

Figure 87

$$(1) \qquad v = \frac{dx}{dt};$$

i.e., *velocity is time-rate of change of distance, measured from a fixed point in the line of motion.*

When the velocity is constant, the motion is said to be *uniform*, and the distance covered in any time is merely proportional to the time. When the velocity changes from instant to instant, the motion is *accelerated*.

Acceleration, denoted in this book by a, is defined by the formula

$$(2) \qquad a = \frac{dv}{dt};$$

i.e., *acceleration is time-rate of change of velocity.*

Since, by the chain rule,

$$\frac{dv}{dt} = \frac{dv}{dx} \cdot \frac{dx}{dt} = v \frac{dv}{dx},$$

an alternative form of (2) is

$$(3) \qquad a = v \frac{dv}{dx}.$$

When a particle of mass m moves with an acceleration a, the motion is said to be due to the action of *force*. Force is defined as the *product of mass by acceleration*:

$$F = ma.$$

If there is no force acting (or if all the forces balance), the particle is *in equilibrium*. A particle in equilibrium is either at rest or moving uniformly in a straight line.

In view of the relation $F = ma$, equations (2) and (3) yield

$$(4) \qquad F = m \frac{dv}{dt} = m \frac{d^2x}{dt^2},$$

and

$$(5) \qquad F = mv \frac{dv}{dx}.$$

When the acceleration (or force) is given as a function of time, the velocity and position can be found by successive integrations. For, by (2),

$$dv = a \, dt,$$

$$v = \int a \, dt + C_1;$$

by (1),

$$dx = v \, dt,$$

$$x = \int v \, dt + C_2.$$

Since two constants of integration are introduced, we must always have given the initial position and velocity, the position at two different times, or some other pair of conditions enabling us to determine the constants. The given data are called *initial conditions*, or *boundary conditions*.

85. *Falling Body*

When the acceleration is constant, the motion is *uniformly accelerated*. An important instance of uniformly accelerated motion arises when a body moves near the earth's surface in a vertical straight line. The attraction of the earth gives it an acceleration, denoted by g, roughly equal to *32 ft. per sec. per sec.

Take the starting point as origin, and the distance x and velocity v as positive downward. If the body starts, at $x = 0$, with an initial velocity v_0,

$$a = \frac{dv}{dt} = g; \qquad \text{when } t = 0, \, x = 0, \, v = v_0.$$

From

$$dv = g \, dt,$$

we get

$$v = gt + C_1.$$

The condition $v = v_0$, $t = 0$ gives $C_1 = v_0$, so that

(1) $$v = gt + v_0.$$

Replacing v by $\frac{dx}{dt}$ and integrating again, we get

$$x = \tfrac{1}{2}gt^2 + v_0 t + C_2;$$

since $x = 0$ when $t = 0$, $C_2 = 0$ and

(2) $$x = \tfrac{1}{2}gt^2 + v_0 t.$$

* A closer approximation is 32.16 ft. per sec. per sec. Since we are interested in methods, rather than in numerical refinement, the value 32 ft. per sec. per sec. will be used.

By eliminating t between equations (1) and (2), we arrive at the useful result:

(3)　　　　$v^2 = v_0{}^2 + 2gx.$

In all motion problems, we shall disregard negative values of t, assuming the motion to start at $t = 0$.

Example (a). A ball is dropped from a balloon at a height of 640 ft. If the balloon is rising 96 ft. per sec., find the highest point reached by the ball, and the time of flight.

By (2), with $g = 32$,

(4)　　　　$x = 16t^2 - 96t.$

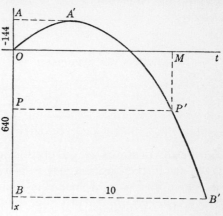

Figure 88

From (4), we obtain

(5)　　　　　　　　　　$v = 32t - 96.$

At the highest point, $v = 0$; hence

$$t = 3, \qquad x = 144 - 288 = -144 \text{ ft.}$$

Thus the height above the starting point is 144 ft.; the distance above the ground is $640 + 144 = 784$ ft. To find the time of flight (time when the ball strikes the ground), put $x = 640$ in (4):

$$640 = 16t^2 - 96t,$$
$$16(t^2 - 6t - 40) = 0,$$
$$t = -4 \quad \text{or} \quad t = 10.$$

Thus the ball is in the air for 10 sec.

The graph of x as a function of t is the parabolic arc $OA'B'$ (Ox positive downward). The actual path of the ball, of course, is from O to A, then down to the ground at B. To find graphically the position at any time, say $t = OM$, erect the ordinate MP' and project P' to P. To find the time corresponding to any position P, draw the abscissa PP' and project P' to M. For $x < 0$ (ball above the starting point), t is two-valued.

Example (b). The velocity 2 ft. below the starting point is 18 ft. per sec. If the start is made from a height of 200 ft., when and with what velocity does the body strike the earth?

With $g = 32$, and the starting point as origin, we have

$$a = v\frac{dv}{dx} = 32; \qquad x = 0 \text{ when } t = 0, \quad v = 18 \text{ when } x = 2.$$

Use the starting point as an origin with x (in ft.) measured positive downward. Then at $x = 2$, $v = 18$ ft. per sec. Equation (3) yields the initial velocity v_0;

$$(18)^2 = v_0{}^2 + 2(32)(2), \; v_0 = \pm 14.$$

For this problem (3) becomes

(6) $$v^2 = 196 + 64x.$$

At $x = 200$ we seek the values of v and t. Since the motion is downward at that time, the velocity is positive. Thus at $x = 200$, the terminal velocity is

$$v_T = \sqrt{196 + 12{,}800} = 114 \text{ ft. per sec.}$$

By (1)

(7) $$v = 32t \pm 14,$$

with the plus sign holding if the initial impetus was downward, the minus sign holding if the initial impetus was upward. With $v = v_T = 114$, equation (7) yields $t = \frac{25}{8}$ sec., or $t = 4$ sec. Thus the body strikes the ground after $\frac{25}{8}$ or 4 sec., with a velocity of 114 ft. per sec.

In this problem it could be foreseen that t must turn out as a two-valued function. For, the given data do not tell whether the initial velocity of 14 ft. per sec. is upward or downward—either one will produce a velocity of 18 ft. per sec. 2 ft. below the starting point; yet the time of reaching the earth will be different in the two cases.

86. *Atwood's Machine*

In the apparatus called *Atwood's machine*, two masses m_1, m_2 are joined by a cord hung over a pulley, as in Fig. 89. Suppose for definiteness that $m_1 > m_2$. The total mass moved (if the masses of the cord and pulley can be neglected) is

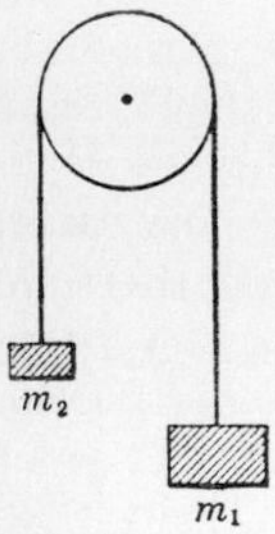

$$m = m_1 + m_2,$$

while the force producing the motion is

$$F = m_1 g - m_2 g.$$

Hence equation (4) of § 84 becomes

m_2

m_1

Figure 89

$$(m_1 + m_2) \frac{dv}{dt} = (m_1 - m_2)g,$$

or

$$\frac{dv}{dt} = \frac{m_1 - m_2}{m_1 + m_2} g.$$

from which the velocity can be determined by integration.

EXERCISES

In Exs. 1–21, a body moves in a vertical line under gravity alone, air resistance, etc. being neglected.

1. If the initial velocity is 24 ft. per sec. upward, how far and for how long a time does the body rise?   *Ans.* 9 ft.; $\frac{3}{4}$ sec.

2. If the initial velocity is 80 ft. per sec. upward, how far and for how long a time does the body rise?   *Ans.* 100 ft.; 2.5 sec.

3. If the velocity after 1 sec. is 24 ft. per sec. downward, find (*a*) the initial velocity and (*b*) the greatest distance above the starting point.

Ans. (*a*) 8 ft. per sec. upward; (*b*) 1 ft.

4. If the velocity after 1 sec. is 24 ft. per sec. upward, find (*a*) the initial velocity and (*b*) the greatest distance above the starting point.

Ans. (*a*) 56 ft. per sec. upward; (*b*) 49 ft.

5. If the body rises 49 ft. before starting to fall, find the initial velocity, and the time required to return to the starting point.

Ans. $v_0 = -56$ ft. per sec.; $t = \frac{7}{4}$ sec.

6. During the third second, the body falls 60 ft. Find the initial velocity.

Ans. −20 ft. per sec.

7. During the third second, the body falls 120 ft. Find the initial velocity.

8. During the third second, the velocity doubles. Find the initial velocity.

Ans. −32 ft. per sec.

9. A ball is thrown upward and rises 9 ft. before starting to fall. Find the total time taken for the ball to return to the starting point.   *Ans.* 1.5 sec.

10. At what times was the ball of Ex. 9 at a distance 8 ft. above its starting point?

Ans. $\frac{1}{2}$ sec., 1 sec.

11. From a point 56 ft. above the ground, with what velocity must a stone be thrown to reach the ground in 1 sec.?   *Ans.* 40 ft. per sec.

12. From a point 56 ft. above the ground, with what velocity must a stone be thrown to take 4 sec. to reach the ground?   *Ans.* 50 ft. per sec. upward.

13. From a point 96 ft. above the ground, a stone is thrown in such a way that it is at the same point, 3 sec. after it was thrown, as it was 2 sec. after it was thrown. How long does it take the stone to reach the ground?   *Ans.* 6 sec.

14. A ball is thrown upward from the ground with a speed of 40 ft. per sec.; at the same instant another ball is dropped (from rest) from a height of 100 ft. Show that they strike the ground at the same time.

15. The velocity 2 ft. below the starting point is 12 ft. per sec. If the starting point is at a height of 56 ft., when and with what velocity does the body strike the earth?   *Ans.* $t = 2$ or 1.75 sec.

16. The velocity 4 ft. above the starting point is 12 ft. per sec. If the starting point is at a height of 176 ft., when and with what velocity does the body reach the earth?   *Ans.* $t = 4$ sec.

17. A stone is thrown vertically upward from the top of a tower. At the end of 2 sec. it is 400 ft. above the ground, and is still rising, with velocity 10 ft. per sec. Find the height of the tower and time of flight.   *Ans.* 316 ft.; 7.3 sec.

18. A stone thrown upward from the top of a tower with a velocity of 100 ft. per sec. reaches the ground with a velocity of 140 ft. per sec. Discuss the motion. Find the height of the tower, and the time of flight.   *Ans.* 150 ft.; 7.5 sec.

19. If a stone dropped from a balloon while ascending at the rate of 20 ft. per sec. reaches the ground in 10 sec., find the initial height and the final velocity.

Ans. 1400 ft.; 300 ft. per sec.

20. A body falls under gravity. Find the distance covered in 6 sec. if at the end of 2 sec. the distance below the starting point is 84 ft.   *Ans.* 636 ft.

21. A stone is thrown upward from the top of a tower. At the end of 2 sec. it is 84 ft., at the end of 3 sec. 36 ft., above the ground. Find the height of the tower.

22. What uniform acceleration will bring an automobile, running at 40 mi. per hr., to rest in 120 ft.? What time will be required?

Ans. -14.3 ft. per sec^2.; 4.1 sec.

23. If a car running at 20 mi. per hr. can be brought to rest in 20 ft. by a constant deceleration, what distance will be required (with the same deceleration) at 40 mi. per hr.?   *Ans.* 80 ft.

24. If a car running at v_0 mi. per hr. can be brought to rest by a constant deceleration in c ft., what distance will be required (with the same deceleration) at v_1 mi. per hr.? Show that doubling the initial velocity quadruples the distance required to bring the car to a stop.

25. The motion of a railroad train is uniformly accelerated. If when the train is 250 ft. past a station the velocity is 30 ft. per sec., when 600 ft. past the station it is 40 ft. per sec., find the acceleration, and the velocity when passing the station.

Ans. $v_0 = 20$ ft. per sec.

26. A cord hangs over a vertical pulley and carries equal weights of 10 lb. at each end. If a 1-lb. weight be added at one end, discuss the motion of the system. Find v when the system has moved 6 ft. (§ 86.)   *Ans.* 4.3 ft. per sec.

27. The weights in Atwood's machine are 8 and 10 lb. If the smaller weight is originally falling 4 ft. per sec., discuss the motion.

28. The weights in Atwood's machine are 4 and 10 lb.; the cord is 3 ft. long. If the weights are initially equidistant from the pulley, what velocity must be given the system to make the heavier weight strike the pulley?   *Ans.* 6.4 ft. per sec.

29. In Atwood's machine, show that the acceleration can be expressed as a function of the ratio $\dfrac{m_1}{m_2}$; hence that the motion depends only on the ratio of the masses, not on their actual values.

30. The weights in Atwood's machine, starting from rest, attain a velocity of 2 ft. per sec. in 1 sec. Find the ratio of the masses.   *Ans.* 17:15.

31. The weights in Atwood's machine, starting from rest, attain a velocity of 4 ft. per sec. in the first 2 ft. Find the ratio of the masses.   *Ans.* 9:7.

32. Find the ratio of the weights, and the initial velocity, if $v = 4$ when $t = 1$, $v = 6$ when $t = 2$.   *Ans.* 17:15; 2 ft. per sec.

33. Find the ratio of the weights, and the initial velocity, if $v = 2$ when $x = 3$, $v = 3$ when $x = 8$.   *Ans.* 65:63; ± 1 ft. per sec.

34. A mass of 12 lb. rests on a smooth horizontal table. A cord attached to this mass runs over a pulley on the edge of the table; from the cord a mass of 4 lb. is suspended. Discuss the motion. If the 12-lb. mass is originally 5 ft. from the edge of the table, find when and with what velocity it reaches the edge.

Ans. 1.1 sec.; 8.9 ft. per sec.

35. In Ex. 34, find the initial velocity if the 12-lb. mass reaches the edge in 1 sec.

Ans. 1 ft. per sec.

87. *Discussion of the Motion*

In studying a motion, the integrations are really only a preliminary step. When x has been found as a function of t, we proceed to develop the character of the motion. A minimum discussion should answer the following questions:

1. *Where, in what direction, and with what velocity does the motion begin?* $(t = 0.)$

2. *When and where does the body come to rest, and in what direction does it start after each stop?* $(v = 0.)$

3. *What happens after a long time?* $(t \to \infty.)$

Example (a). Investigate the motion

$$a = 6t - 18; \qquad x = 0, v = 15 \text{ when } t = 0.$$

The first integration gives

$$v = 3t^2 - 18t + C_1,$$

or, since $v = 15$ when $t = 0$,

$$v = 3t^2 - 18t + 15$$
$$= 3(t - 1)(t - 5).$$

Integrating again, we get

$$x = t^3 - 9t^2 + 15t + C_2,$$

where $x = 0$, $t = 0$ gives $C_2 = 0$:

$$x = t^3 - 9t^2 + 15t.$$

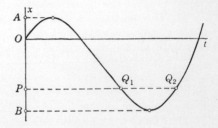

Figure 90

Since x is a polynomial, its graph may be drawn by the method of § 40. The questions above are answered as follows:

1. $t = 0$: $x = 0$, $v = 15$, $a = -18$. The motion starts at O, with a velocity of 15 ft. per sec. in the positive direction (as given); the velocity is diminishing.

2. $v = 0$: when $t = 1$ (the stops must, of course, be taken *in chronological order*), $x = 7$, $a = -12$; since $a < 0$, the body turns back in the negative direction. When $t = 5$, $x = -25$, $a = 12$. Thus the body moves out to A ($OA = 7$), turns back to B ($OB = -25$), then turns in the positive direction.

3. $t \to \infty$: When t increases without bound, both x and v approach infinity.

From Fig. 90 the position at any time, also the time (or times) corresponding to any position, may be read off at once.

When time is not available for drawing the graph of x, the general character of the motion may be exhibited visually by the device shown in Fig.

91. The three "legs" of which this motion consists are shown by directed lines drawn at successively lower levels: from O to A, from A to B, from B to the right.

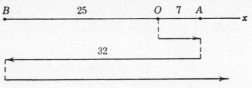

Figure 91

Example (*b*). Study the motion

$$a = 6t - 6; \quad x = 0 \text{ when } t = 0, \quad x = 1 \text{ when } t = 1.$$

Integrating twice, we find

$$v = 3t^2 - 6t + C_1,$$
$$x = t^3 - 3t^2 + C_1t + C_2.$$

Substitution of the (x, t)-pairs gives

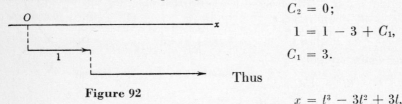

Figure 92

$$C_2 = 0;$$
$$1 = 1 - 3 + C_1,$$
$$C_1 = 3.$$

Thus

$$x = t^3 - 3t^2 + 3t,$$

$$v = 3t^2 - 6t + 3 = 3(t - 1)^2.$$

1. $t = 0:$ $x = 0,$ $v = 3.$
2. $v = 0:$ $t = 1,$ $x = 1,$ $a = 0.$

Since v and a vanish together, the direction of the ensuing motion may be determined by noting that, for $t > 1$, $v > 0$. The same conclusion follows from the fact that

$$\frac{da}{dt} = 6;$$

thus a will become positive, and v will do likewise.

EXERCISES

Discuss fully the rectilinear motions of Exs. 1–16.

1. $a = 2$; when $t = 3$, $x = 3$ and $v = 2$.   *Ans.* $x = t^2 - 4t + 6.$
2. $a = -1$; when $t = 2$, $x = 13$ and $v = 2$.   *Ans.* $x = -\frac{1}{2}t^2 + 4t + 7.$
3. $a = 6(2t - 3)$; when $t = 0$, $x = 2$ and $v = 12$.
                    Ans. $x = 2t^3 - 9t^2 + 12t + 2.$

4. $a = 6(2t - 1)$; when $t = 0$, $x = 13$ and $v = -12$.

$$Ans. \ x = 2t^3 - 3t^2 - 12t + 13.$$

5. $a = 6(t - 2)$; when $t = 1$, $x = 0$ and $v = 3$.

$$Ans. \ x = t^3 - 6t^2 + 12t - 7.$$

6. $a = 6(t - 1)$; when $t = 0$, $x = 0$, and when $t = 4$, $x = 16$.

$$Ans. \ x = t^2(t - 3).$$

7. $a = 12t^2 - 48t + 44$; when $t = 0$, $x = 10$ and $v = -24$.

$$Ans. \ x = t^4 - 8t^3 + 22t^2 - 24t + 10.$$

8. $a = 12t^2 - 8$; when $t = 0$, $x = 25$, and when $t = 1$, $v = -20$.

$$Ans. \ x = t^4 - 4t^2 - 16t + 25.$$

9. $a = 12t^2 - 24t - 16$; when $t = 0$, $v = 48$, and when $t = 1$, $x = -3$.

$$Ans. \ x = t^4 - 4t^3 - 8t^2 + 48t - 40.$$

10. $a = 12(t - 1)(t - 3)$; when $t = 0$, $x = 5$, and when $t = 1$, $x = 0$.

$$Ans. \ x = t^4 - 8t^3 + 18t^2 - 16t + 5.$$

11. $a = 12(t - 1)(3t - 7)$; when $t = 0$, $x = -10$, and when $t = 1$, $x = -21$.

$$Ans. \ x = 3t^4 - 20t^3 + 42t^2 - 36t - 10.$$

12. $a = 3(t - 2)^2$; when $t = 0$, $x = 24$, and when $t = 4$, $x = -8$.

$$Ans. \ x = \tfrac{1}{4}(t - 2)^4 - 8t + 20.$$

13. $a = 12t(t - 2)$; when $t = 1$, $x = 0$ and $v = 8$.

$$Ans. \ x = t^4 - 4t^3 + 16t - 13.$$

14. $a = 12(t - 2)(t - 4)$; when $t = 0$, $x = 15$, and when $t = 1$, $x = -12$.

$$Ans. \ x = t^4 - 12t^3 + 48t^2 - 64t + 15.$$

15. $a = 2(t + 1)^{-3}$; when $t = 0$, $x = 0$ and $v = -1$. $\qquad Ans. \ x = \dfrac{-t}{t + 1}.$

16. $a = 2(t + 1)^{-3}$; when $t = 0$, $x = \tfrac{1}{4}$ and $v = -\tfrac{3}{4}$. $\qquad Ans. \ x = \dfrac{(t - 1)^2}{4(t + 1)}.$

88. *Vectors*

A straight line segment of definite *length*, *direction*, and *sense* is called a *vector*.

Any quantity that is fully characterized when we know its magnitude, direction, and sense may be represented geometrically by a vector (or, as we say for brevity, *is* a vector). The importance of vectors in physics is due to the fact that velocity, acceleration, force, etc., are vector quantities.

Two vectors are said to be *equal* if they have the same magnitude, direction, and sense, even though they do not lie in the same straight line. This agrees with our ordinary ideas. For instance, if two bodies are falling under gravity, they are both subject to the same acceleration, whether or not they happen to be in the same vertical line.

89. *Geometric Addition*

The sum of two vectors V_1, V_2 is called their *resultant*. It is defined as *the diagonal of the parallelogram having* V_1, V_2 *as adjacent sides*. This is the *parallelogram law*. Composition by this law is called *geometric addition*, or *vector addition*. The sum of two vectors is defined in this way for the reason that in any application, the vector V is actually equivalent to the vectors V_1, V_2 combined.

Example. A ship is moving N. at 10 mi. per hr.; a man walks S.E. across the deck at 5 mi. per hr. In what direction and how fast is the man moving, relative to the earth's surface? (Fig. 94.)

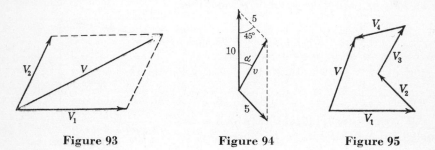

Figure 93   Figure 94   Figure 95

By the cosine law.

$$v = \sqrt{100 + 25 - 2 \times 50 \cos 45°} = \sqrt{54.3}$$
$$= 7.4 \text{ mi. per hr.}$$

By the sine law,

$$\frac{\sin \alpha}{5} = \frac{\sin 45°}{7.4}, \qquad \sin \alpha = 0.48, \qquad \alpha = 29°.$$

Thus the man is actually moving 29° E. of N., at 7.4 mi. per hr.

In Fig. 93, the vectors V_1, V_2 are *components* of V. Frequently, having given a vector V, we wish to resolve it into components. This can be done in an infinite number of ways: if we draw any triangle with V as one side, the other sides, directed as in Fig. 93, are components of V.

By repeated application of the parallelogram law, the resultant of any number of vectors is easily found. Lay off the vectors end to end to form an open polygon; the closing line, directed from the initial to the terminal point, is the resultant. In Fig. 95, V is the resultant of V_1, V_2, V_3, V_4.

90. *Algebraic Addition*

For various reasons, it may happen in a particular problem that geometric addition of vectors is not feasible; we then have recourse to *algebraic addition*.

From the definition of vector sum, it follows at once that two vectors may be added algebraically if and only if they have *the same direction*. (For instance, in the above example, if the man were to walk due north or south, his net velocity would be 15 or 5 mi. per hr., respectively.) Thus, to add a number of vectors having different directions:

1. *Resolve all the vectors into components parallel to Ox and Oy.*

2. *Add (algebraically) all the x-components to form V_x, all the y-components to form V_y.*

3. *Compound V_x and V_y by the parallelogram law: i.e., draw the vector V of magnitude*

$$V = \sqrt{V_x^2 + V_y^2},$$

inclined to Ox at an angle α such that

$$\tan \alpha = \frac{V_y}{V_x}.$$

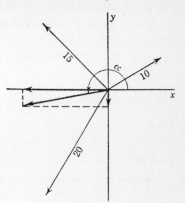

Figure 96

Of course the quadrant in which α lies must be determined as in trigonometry, by examining the signs of V_x and V_y.

Example. Three forces act on a particle: 10 lb. inclined at 30° to Ox, 15 lb. at 135°, 20 lb. at 240°. Find the resultant.

We have (Fig. 96)

$$F_x = 10 \cos 30° + 15 \cos 135° + 20 \cos 240°$$
$$= 10 \cdot \tfrac{1}{2} \sqrt{3} - 15 \cdot \tfrac{1}{2} \sqrt{2} - 20 \cdot \tfrac{1}{2} = -11.9;$$
$$F_y = 10 \sin 30° + 15 \sin 135° + 20 \sin 240°$$
$$= 10 \cdot \tfrac{1}{2} + 15 \cdot \tfrac{1}{2} \sqrt{2} - 20 \cdot \tfrac{1}{2} \sqrt{3} = -1.7.$$

Thus

$$F = \sqrt{(11.9)^2 + (1.7)^2} = 12.0 \text{ lb};$$

$$\tan \alpha = \frac{-1.7}{-11.9} = 0.143, \qquad \alpha = 188°.$$

91. *Inclined Plane*

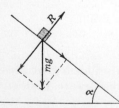

Figure 97

Consider a body of mass m on a smooth plane inclined at an angle α to the horizontal. At any instant the body is subject to two forces: the attraction of gravity, of magnitude mg, and the reaction R of the plane. Resolve the vertical force mg into components $mg \cos \alpha$ and $mg \sin \alpha$ respectively normal and parallel to the plane. The normal component is exactly balanced by the reaction R. Assume that the body is released from rest, or with an initial velocity either directly down or directly up the slope. Then, rectilinear motion occurs, owing to the "effective component" $mg \sin \alpha$:

$$ma = mg \sin \alpha,$$
$$a = g \sin \alpha.$$

Let x be distance measured down the inclined plane from the starting point. At $t = 0$, let $x = 0$ and $v = v_0$.

Then, from $a = g \sin \alpha$, we obtain

$$v = gt \sin \alpha + v_0,$$

$$x = \tfrac{1}{2}gt^2 \sin \alpha + v_0 t.$$

The elimination of t from these two equations yields the useful result

$$v^2 = 2gx \sin \alpha + v_0{}^2.$$

EXERCISES

1. A man can row a boat 5 mi. per hr. He pulls at right angles to the course of a river 2 mi. wide, having a current of 4 mi. per hr. Where and when will he reach the opposite shore? *Ans.* 1.6 mi. downstream; 24 min.

2. In Ex. 1, if the man wishes to land directly opposite his starting point, in what direction must he row, and how long will it take him to cross? *Ans.* 40 min.

3. A steamship is moving at the rate of 12 mi. per hr. A man walks across the deck at right angles to the ship's course, at the rate of 5 mi. per hr. If the deck is 40 ft. wide, how far is he finally from his starting point? In what direction?

4. Across the deck of a vessel going S. at 10 ft. per sec., a man walks S. 30° E. at 6 ft. per sec. If the deck is 15 ft. wide, how long does it take him to cross, and how far does he travel? *Ans.* 5 sec.; 77.4 ft.

5. A river flows S. at 5 mi. per hr. A ferryboat, headed E., is making forward progress at 10 mi. per hr. A man sprints across the deck 30° W. of N. at 20 mi. per hr. How fast and in what direction is he actually moving?

6. A river flows S. at 5 mi. per hr. A boat, headed E., is making forward progress at 20 mi. per hr. On the deck is a man capable of sprinting 100 yd. in 10 sec. Can he hold himself motionless, relative to the earth's surface? *Ans.* No.

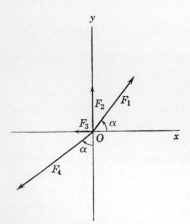

Figure 98

it travel before starting to fall?

7. Find the resultant of a plane system of forces, $F_1 = 10$ lb., $F_2 = 7$ lb., $F_3 = 3$ lb., $F_4 = 15$ lb., acting as in Fig. 98, where $\tan \alpha = \tfrac{4}{3}$. *Ans.* $F = 10.8$ lb.; angle with $Ox = 146° 19'$.

8. Six forces, of 1, 2, 3, 4, 5, 6 lb., respectively, act at the same point, making angles of 60° with each other. Find their resultant. *Ans.* 6 lb., along the line of the 5-lb. force.

In Exs. 9–11, a body moves on a plane inclined 30° to the horizontal. All distances and velocities are measured along the inclined plane.

9. If the body rises 18 ft. before starting to fall, what was its initial velocity? *Ans.* −24 ft. per sec.

10. A body is given an initial velocity of 20 ft. per sec. upward. How far, and for how long, does *Ans.* 12.5 ft.; $\tfrac{5}{4}$ sec.

11. A body is given an initial velocity of 16 ft. per sec. upward. How long does it take the body to reach a point 4.5 ft. below its starting point?   *Ans.* $\frac{9}{4}$ sec.

12. A body moves on an inclined plane. After 1 sec., the body is 3 ft. below its starting point and has a velocity of 7 ft. per sec., distance and velocity being measured along the plane. Find the angle of inclination of the plane.

Ans. About 14° 30′.

13. If the initial velocity is 16 ft. per sec. upward along an inclined plane and the body moves 12 ft. before starting to return, find the angle of inclination of the plane.

Ans. About 19° 30′.

14. It is known that the gravitational attraction of the moon at its surface is approximately 0.165g, in terms of the gravitational attraction of the earth at its surface. Find the angle of inclination of a plane near the earth's surface which will yield the same equations of motion, along that plane, as the equations of motion of a freely falling body near the surface of the moon.   *Ans.* About 9° 30′.

15. Solve Ex. 14 for Mars (surface gravity 0.38g) and Venus (surface gravity 0.85g).   *Ans.* Mars: 22° 20′; Venus: 58° 13′.

16. A bead is strung on a smooth straight wire inclined at 45° to the horizontal. What initial velocity must the bead be given to raise it to a vertical height of 10 ft.?

Ans. 25.3 ft. per sec.

17. Show that it takes a body twice as long to slide down a plane of 30° inclination as it would take to fall through the "height" of the plane.

18. A hillside slopes gently on one face, steeply on another. Toboggans start at the same time down the two faces. If friction is negligible, find (*a*) which will reach level ground first, and (*b*) which will acquire the greater velocity.

19. A car, starting with a velocity of 10 mi. per hr., coasts for 20 sec. down a 2% grade, and then ascends a 3% grade. Neglecting friction, find how far it will go up the grade.   *Ans.* 393 ft.

20. A car, starting from rest, coasts 200 ft. down a 2% grade and then ascends a 10% grade under an acceleration, due to its own power, of 2 ft. per sec. per sec. How far up can it go?   *Ans.* 107 ft.

92. *Velocity and Acceleration in Curvilinear Motion*

If a point moves in a plane curve, its coordinates are functions of time:

$$(1) \qquad\qquad x = \varphi(t), \qquad y = \psi(t).$$

Equations (1) may be regarded as *parametric equations of the path* in terms of the parameter t. The distance s described along the curve is also a function of time.

The *velocity* at any point P is defined as the *vector, laid off from P on the tangent to the path*, of magnitude

$$v = \operatorname*{Lim}_{\Delta t \to 0} \frac{\Delta s}{\Delta t} = \frac{ds}{dt}.$$

The components of velocity parallel to the axes are

$$v_x = v \cos \alpha, \qquad v_y = v \sin \alpha,$$

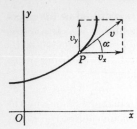

Figure 99

where α is the angle between Ox and the tangent at P. By § 46,

$$v \cos \alpha = \frac{ds}{dt} \cdot \frac{dx}{ds} = \frac{dx}{dt},$$

$$v \sin \alpha = \frac{ds}{dt} \cdot \frac{dy}{ds} = \frac{dy}{dt},$$

so that

$$v_x = \frac{dx}{dt}, \qquad v_y = \frac{dy}{dt}.$$

Thus the total velocity is the vector sum of the velocities parallel to the axes (or in any two perpendicular directions—see Ex. 22 below).

By § 90, the magnitude of the velocity is

$$v = \sqrt{v_x{}^2 + v_y{}^2} = \sqrt{\left(\frac{dx}{dt}\right)^2 + \left(\frac{dy}{dt}\right)^2},$$

inclined to the x-axis at an angle α such that

$$\tan \alpha = \frac{v_y}{v_x}.$$

The *acceleration* is the vector a whose components, parallel to the axes, are

(2) $$a_x = \frac{dv_x}{dt} = \frac{d^2x}{dt^2}, \qquad a_y = \frac{dv_y}{dt} = \frac{d^2y}{dt^2}.$$

The total acceleration is

$$a = \sqrt{a_x{}^2 + a_y{}^2},$$

inclined to the x-axis at an angle β such that

$$\tan \beta = \frac{a_y}{a_x}.$$

When each member is multiplied by m, equations (2) yield the components of force:

$$F_x = m \frac{dv_x}{dt}, \qquad F_y = m \frac{dv_y}{dt}.$$

93. *Projectiles*

A simple example of curvilinear motion is furnished by a projectile moving under gravity alone—i.e., in a medium whose resistance can be neglected. This is only a first approximation to actual fact, since in the majority of practical cases the resistance of the medium affects the results materially. (See § 273.)

Let a particle be projected with an initial velocity v_0 inclined at an angle α to the horizontal. With the starting point as origin and the y-axis *positive upward*, the initial conditions are

$$x = 0, \quad y = 0, \quad v_x = v_0 \cos \alpha, \quad v_y = v_0 \sin \alpha \qquad \text{when } t = 0.$$

The force of gravity acts vertically downward; there is no horizontal force. Hence the equations of motion are

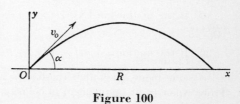

$$\frac{d^2x}{dt^2} = 0, \qquad \frac{d^2y}{dt^2} = -g.$$

Figure 100

These equations may be integrated and the constants determined precisely as in our earlier work; the results are as follows:

(1) $$v_x = v_0 \cos \alpha, \qquad v_y = -gt + v_0 \sin \alpha;$$

(2) $$x = v_0 t \cos \alpha, \qquad y = -\tfrac{1}{2}gt^2 + v_0 t \sin \alpha.$$

EXERCISES

1. Obtain equations (1) and (2), § 93.

2. By eliminating t from (2), show that the path is a parabola opening downward.

3. Show that a projectile whose initial velocity is horizontal will strike the ground in the same time as a body let fall from rest from the same height.

4. The *time of flight* is the time from the starting point until the projectile strikes the ground. Show that on a horizontal plane the time of flight is

$$T = \frac{2v_0}{g} \sin \alpha.$$

5. The *range* of a projectile is the distance from the starting point to the point where it strikes the ground. Show that the range on a horizontal plane is

$$R = \frac{v_0^2}{g} \sin 2\alpha.$$

6. What elevation gives the greatest range on a horizontal plane? (Ex. 5.)

In Exs. 7–18, a point moves in a plane curve, its coordinates being determined by the given formulas. Discuss the motion, for $t \geqq 0$, and draw the path of the point.

7. $x = 3t, y = 9t(2 - t)$.
8. $x = 3(t^2 - 2t + 2), y = 3(t - 2)$.
9. $x = 2(1 - t), y = -4(1 - t)(2 - t)$.
  Ans. Parabolic arc: $(x + 1)^2 = -(y - 1)$ for $x \leqq 2$.
10. $x = 3(t^2 + 1), y = 3(1 + t)$.
  Ans. Parabolic arc: $(y - 3)^2 = 3(x - 3)$ for $y \geqq 3$.

11. $x = \dfrac{4(t + 3)}{t + 2}, y = \dfrac{1}{t + 3}.$ **12.** $x = 1 - t, y = 2t(1 - t)(2 - t).$

13. $x = 3 - t, y = \sqrt{t(6 - t)}.$ **14.** $x = 3 \sin 2t, y = 3 \cos 2t.$

15. $x = \sqrt{t(4 - t)}, y = 2(t - 2).$ **16.** $x = 2 \sin t, y = 4 \cos t.$

17. $x = e^{-2t} - e^{-t}, y = 1 - e^{-t}.$ **18.** $x = 1 - 2 \ln t, y = 1 + t^2.$

19. If the motions in Exs. 7 and 8 take place in the same plane, will the bodies collide? *Ans.* At $(6, 0)$.

20. If the motions $x_1 = t - 2$, $y_1 = t^2$, and $x_2 = t^2 - 8$, $y_2 = \dfrac{4t^2}{t + 1}$, take place in the same plane, show that the bodies will collide, and determine which has the greater velocity at the moment of collision. *Ans.* At $(1, 9)$; $v_2 > v_1$.

21. If the motions $x_1 = t^2$, $y_1 = t^3$, and $x_2 = 3t - 2$, $y_2 = t^2 + 4$, take place in the same plane, will the bodies collide? *Ans.* At $(4, 8)$.

22. A point moves in a plane curve, the rectangular coordinates x, y, being functions of the time t. If the axes are rotated to a new system x_1, y_1, by the usual formulas,

$$x = x_1 \cos \varphi - y_1 \sin \varphi, \qquad y = x_1 \sin \varphi + y_1 \cos \varphi,$$

prove that

$$\sqrt{\left(\frac{dx}{dt}\right)^2 + \left(\frac{dy}{dt}\right)^2} = \sqrt{\left(\frac{dx_1}{dt}\right)^2 + \left(\frac{dy_1}{dt}\right)^2},$$

and interpret the result physically.

23. A point describes the parabola $y^2 = 4x + 1$, with a constant vertical velocity, $v_y = 4$. Find v_x, a_x, a_y, at $(2, 3)$. *Ans.* $v_x = 6$; $a_x = 8$.

24. A point describes the parabola $y^2 = 4x + 1$, with a constant horizontal velocity, $v_x = 3$. Find v_y, a_y, a_x, at $(2, 3)$. *Ans.* $v_y = 2$; $a_y = -\frac{4}{3}$.

25. A particle moves on the circle $x^2 + y^2 = 25$, with a constant horizontal velocity $v_x = -2$. Find v_y, a_y, a_x, at $(3, 4)$. *Ans.* $v_y = \frac{3}{2}$; $a_y = -\frac{25}{16}$.

26. A particle starts at the point $(0, -4)$ and moves along the parabola

$$y = x^2 - 4,$$

with a variable horizontal velocity given by $v_x = 2t - 1$. At time $t = 2$, find the position of the particle, and its various components of velocity and accleration. *Ans.* $(2, 0)$; $v_x = 3$; $v_y = 12$; $a_x = 2$; $a_y = 26$.

27. In Ex. 26, let the particle start at the point $(-2, 0)$, but leave the rest of the problem unchanged. *Ans.* $(0, -4)$; $v_x = 3$; $v_y = 0$; $a_x = 2$; $a_y = 18$.

28. The motion of a certain body is determined by its components of acceleration, $a_x = 2$ and $a_y = -6t$, together with the initial conditions that, when $t = 0$, then $x = 0$, $y = 0$, $v_x = 0$, and $v_y = 1$. Find the equation of the path of the motion. *Ans.* $y = (1 - x) \sqrt{x}$.

29. The motion of a certain body is determined by its components of acceleration, $a_x = 1 - t$ and $a_y = 0$, together with the initial conditions that, when $t = 0$, then $x = 1$, $y = 0$, $v_x = 0$, and $v_y = -\frac{1}{2}$. Find the equation of the path of the motion. *Ans.* $3(x - 1) = 2y^2(3 + 2y)$.

30. Starting at the origin, initially at rest $(v = 0)$, a particle is subjected to a constant horizontal acceleration b, and a constant vertical acceleration c. Find the equation of the path of motion. *Ans.* $by = cx$.

31. In Ex. 30, let the particle have an initial velocity $v_0 \neq 0$, but leave the remainder of the problem unchanged. Show that the path of motion is, in general, a parabola.

32. Prove that when a point traverses a curve with constant velocity $v = k$, the acceleration is always directed along the normal to the path. (Differentiate both members of the equation $v_x{}^2 + v_y{}^2 = k^2$.)

33. A pitcher throws a ball with a speed of 120 ft. per sec., the ball leaving his hand horizontally at a height of 5 ft. If the distance from pitcher to batter is 60 ft., at what height will the ball pass the batter?

34. A stone is thrown horizontally from the top of a tower 400 ft. high, with a velocity of 20 ft. per sec. (*a*) When, (*b*) where, and (*c*) with what velocity does it strike the ground?

Ans. (*a*) 5 sec.; (*c*) 161.2 ft. per sec., at 7° 8′ to the vertical.

35. A man on a cliff 160 ft. high throws a stone, with velocity 100 ft. per sec., directly toward a point 120 ft. out from the foot of the cliff. By what distance does the stone miss the mark?   *Ans.* 28.1 ft.

HYPERBOLIC FUNCTIONS

94. *The Hyperbolic Sine and Cosine*

Two particular combinations of exponential functions appear with such frequency in both pure and applied mathematics that it has been worth while to use special symbols for those combinations. The hyperbolic sine of x, written sinh x, is defined by

$$(1) \qquad \sinh x = \frac{e^x - e^{-x}}{2};$$

the hyperbolic cosine of x, written cosh x, is defined by

$$(2) \qquad \cosh x = \frac{e^x + e^{-x}}{2}.$$

The use of symbols and names so similar to those of trigonometry may seem unwise. Some justification will appear in § 96 where the basic formulas for these new functions are shown to bear a striking resemblance to those of ordinary trigonometry. It will be shown also that the hyperbolic sine and cosine are related to the equilateral hyperbola in much the same way that the ordinary (circular) sine and cosine are related to the circle.

95. *Other Hyperbolic Functions*

Four more hyperbolic functions are defined in a manner to be expected:

$$\tanh x = \frac{\sinh x}{\cosh x}, \qquad \text{sech } x = \frac{1}{\cosh x},$$
$$\text{csch } x = \frac{1}{\sinh x}, \qquad \coth x = \frac{1}{\tanh x}.$$

96. *Basic Formulas of Hyperbolic Trigonometry*

From the definition of sinh x and cosh x, it follows that

$$\sinh^2 x = \tfrac{1}{4}(e^{2x} - 2 + e^{-2x})$$

and

$$\cosh^2 x = \tfrac{1}{4}(e^{2x} + 2 + e^{-2x}),$$

so that

$$(1) \qquad \cosh^2 x - \sinh^2 x = 1,$$

180

an identity similar to the identity $\cos^2 x + \sin^2 x = 1$ in circular trigonometry. Many other such relations will be found in the exercises below.

Directly from the definition we find that

$$y = \sinh u$$

is equivalent to

$$y = \tfrac{1}{2}(e^u - e^{-u}).$$

Hence, if u is a function of x, then

$$\frac{dy}{dx} = \tfrac{1}{2}(e^u + e^{-u})\frac{du}{dx};$$

that is,

(2) $\quad \dfrac{d}{dx}\sinh u = \cosh u\,\dfrac{du}{dx}.$

The same method yields the result

(3) $\quad \dfrac{d}{dx}\cosh u = \sinh u\,\dfrac{du}{dx}.$

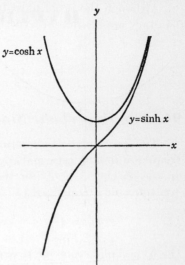

Figure 101

The derivations of the corresponding formulas for the derivatives of the other hyperbolic functions are left as exercises.

The curves $y = \cosh x$ and $y = \sinh x$ are exhibited in Fig. 101. Note the
important properties:

(a) $\cosh x \geqq 1$, for all real x,
(b) the only real value of x for which $\sinh x = 0$ is $x = 0$,
(c) $\cosh(-x) = \cosh x$; i.e., $\cosh x$ is an even function of x,
(d) $\sinh(-x) = -\sinh x$; $\sinh x$ is an odd function of x.

The hyperbolic functions have no real period. Corresponding to the
period 2π possessed by the circular functions, there is a period $2\pi i$ for the
six hyperbolic functions.

With regard to the word "hyperbolic" in the name of the functions being
treated here, consider the parametric equations

(4) $\qquad\qquad x = a\cosh t, \qquad y = a\sinh t,$

with t as a parameter. From the identity (1) above, it follows that

$$x^2 - y^2 = a^2,$$

so that the equations (4) are seen to be parametric equations of an equilateral hyperbola. This is analogous to the result that

$$x = a\cos t, \qquad y = a\sin t,$$

are parametric equations of the circle

$$x^2 + y^2 = a^2.$$

97. *The Catenary*

Although the proof must be deferred to § 257, we now mention one elementary application of hyperbolic functions.

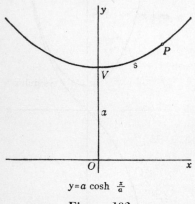

$y = a \cosh \frac{x}{a}$

Figure 102

When a flexible, homogeneous cord or wire hangs from two of its points under its own weight (suspended cable, telephone wire, clothesline), it falls in a curve called the *catenary*. With the origin at distance a below the lowest point, the equation is

$$(1) \qquad y = a \cosh \frac{x}{a}.$$

We know by observation, of course, that the curve has the general form shown in Fig. 102. Using the table, pp. 560–565, the student may easily plot the curve.

We shall see in § 257 that the constant in equation (1) is the ratio of the tension exerted at the vertex V divided by the weight per unit length of the cable.

In Fig. 102 let s be the length of arc VP from the vertex to any point of the curve. We shall show in Ex. 16, page 313, that

$$(2) \qquad s = a \sinh \frac{x}{a}.$$

Suppose a catenary has been formed, as in Fig. 103, by suspending a given length of wire or cable between two points A, B at the same height* in a vertical plane. We seek a relation between the length of the cable L, the depth of the dip d, and the constant a. It is assumed that the axes have been chosen so that the equation of the catenary is (1) above. At the point A, $y = a + d$ and $s = \frac{1}{2}L$. Then, by (1) and (2), we have

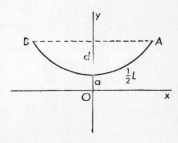

Figure 103

$$(3) \qquad a + d = a \cosh \frac{x}{a}. \qquad \tfrac{1}{2}L = a \sinh \frac{x}{a}.$$

Since $\cosh^2 z - \sinh^2 z = 1$, equations (3) yield

$$(a + d)^2 - \tfrac{1}{4}L^2 = a^2,$$

$$(4) \qquad L^2 = 4d(2a + d).$$

---

* Of course the wire will hang in a catenary whether or not the points of suspension are at the same height.

EXERCISES

In Exs. 1–17, prove the stated property of the hyperbolic functions. Use the definitions, the results in the text, or the properties obtained in any previous exercise.

1. $\sinh 0 = 0$; $\cosh 0 = 1$; $\tanh 0 = 0$.
2. $\sinh(-x) = -\sinh x$; $\cosh(-x) = \cosh x$; $\tanh(-x) = -\tanh x$.
3. $\operatorname{sech}^2 x = 1 - \tanh^2 x$.   4. $\operatorname{csch}^2 x = \coth^2 x - 1$.
5. $e^x = \cosh x + \sinh x$; $e^{-x} = \cosh x - \sinh x$.
6. $\sinh^2 y = \frac{1}{2}(\cosh 2y - 1)$.   7. $\cosh^2 y = \frac{1}{2}(\cosh 2y + 1)$.
8. $\cosh 2A = \cosh^2 A + \sinh^2 A = 2\cosh^2 A - 1 = 2\sinh^2 A + 1$.
9. $\sinh 2y = 2\sinh y \cosh y$.
10. $\sinh(x + y) = \sinh x \cosh y + \cosh x \sinh y$;
    $\sinh(x - y) = \sinh x \cosh y - \cosh x \sinh y$.
11. $\cosh(x + y) = \cosh x \cosh y + \sinh x \sinh y$;
    $\cosh(x - y) = \cosh x \cosh y - \sinh x \sinh y$.
12. $\tanh(x + y) = \dfrac{\tanh x + \tanh y}{1 + \tanh x \tanh y}$;

    $\tanh(x - y) = \dfrac{\tanh x - \tanh y}{1 - \tanh x \tanh y}$.
13. $\dfrac{d}{dx}\cosh u = \sinh u \dfrac{du}{dx}$.
14. $\dfrac{d}{dx}\tanh u = \operatorname{sech}^2 u \dfrac{du}{dx}$.
15. $\dfrac{d}{dx}\operatorname{csch} u = -\operatorname{csch} u \coth u \dfrac{du}{dx}$.
16. $\dfrac{d}{dx}\operatorname{sech} u = -\operatorname{sech} u \tanh u \dfrac{du}{dx}$.
17. $\dfrac{d}{dx}\coth u = -\operatorname{csch}^2 u \dfrac{du}{dx}$.
18. Let c_1, c_2, and k be constants. Show that from

$$y = c_1 \sinh(kx) + c_2 \cosh(kx)$$

it follows that $y'' - k^2 y = 0$.

In Exs. 19–32, find the first derivative.

19. $y = \sinh 4x$.   20. $y = \cosh(2x - 1)$.   21. $y = \tanh(1 - 3x)$.
22. $y = \operatorname{sech} 4x$.   23. $x = \cosh^2 3t$.   24. $x = \sinh^2(1 - t)$.
25. $y = (1 - x)^2 \sinh 2x$.   26. $y = (2x - 1)^3 \cosh 4x$.
27. $y = e^{-x} \cosh x$.   28. $y = e^{-x} \sinh x$.
29. $y = \operatorname{Arctan} \sinh x$.   *Ans.* $y' = \operatorname{sech} x$.
30. $y = \operatorname{Arcsin} \tanh x$.   *Ans.* $y' = \operatorname{sech} x$.
31. $y = \ln \sinh 3x$.   *Ans.* $y' = 3 \coth 3x$.
32. $y = \ln \tanh^2 3x$.   *Ans.* $y' = 12 \operatorname{csch} 6x$.
33. Sketch the curve which has the parametric equations

$$x = 4\cosh t, \qquad y = 3\sinh t.$$

34. Trace the curve $y = a \sinh \dfrac{x}{a}$. [Reflect the curve $y = ae^{\frac{x}{a}}$ in the origin to obtain $y = -ae^{-\frac{x}{a}}$; average the ordinates.]

35. Trace the curve $y = a \sinh \dfrac{x}{a}$ by the method of § 40. Also use the table, pp. 560–565.

36. Trace the curve $y = a \tanh \dfrac{x}{a}$.   **37.** Trace the curve $y = a \operatorname{sech} \dfrac{x}{a}$.

38. Prove that $\operatorname{Arcsin} \tanh x = \operatorname{Arctan} \sinh x$.

39. Prove that $\operatorname{Arcsin} \tanh x = \operatorname{Arccos} \operatorname{sech} x \ (x \geqq 0)$.

98. *Inverse Hyperbolic Functions*

The *inverse hyperbolic sine*, also called *antihyperbolic sine*, is defined and denoted as follows:

$$y = \sinh^{-1} x \quad if \quad x = \sinh y.$$

Similarly for the other inverse functions.

Since the hyperbolic functions are exponential, the inverse functions must be logarithmic. The explicit formulas are as follows:

(1) $\qquad \sinh^{-1} x = \ln (x + \sqrt{x^2 + 1});$

(2) $\qquad \cosh^{-1} x = \ln (x + \sqrt{x^2 - 1}), \qquad x \geqq 1;$

(3) $\qquad \tanh^{-1} x = \dfrac{1}{2} \ln \dfrac{1 + x}{1 - x}, \qquad |x| < 1;$

(4) $\qquad \coth^{-1} x = \dfrac{1}{2} \ln \dfrac{x + 1}{x - 1}, \qquad |x| > 1;$

(5) $\qquad \operatorname{sech}^{-1} x = \ln \dfrac{1 + \sqrt{1 - x^2}}{x}, \qquad 0 < x \leqq 1;$

(6) $\qquad \operatorname{csch}^{-1} x = \begin{cases} \ln \dfrac{1 + \sqrt{1 + x^2}}{x}, & x > 0; \\[2ex] -\ln \dfrac{1 + \sqrt{1 + x^2}}{-x}, & x < 0. \end{cases}$

The problem of deriving these formulas is similar to Example *(a)*, § 77. The equation

$$y = \cosh^{-1} x$$

means that

$$\cosh y = x,$$

$$\frac{e^y + e^{-y}}{2} = x, \qquad e^y + e^{-y} - 2x = 0,$$

$$e^{2y} - 2xe^y + 1 = 0.$$

Solving this quadratic in e^y, we get

$$e^y = x \pm \sqrt{x^2 - 1},$$

which gives two values of y:

$$y = \ln (x + \sqrt{x^2 - 1}),$$
$$y = \ln (x - \sqrt{x^2 - 1}).$$

By Ex. 51, page 147, with $a = 1$,

$$\ln (x - \sqrt{x^2 - 1}) = - \ln (x + \sqrt{x^2 - 1}),$$

so that the two values of y are

$$y = \pm \ln (x + \sqrt{x^2 - 1}), \qquad x \geqq 1.$$

It is easily seen that y is imaginary if $x < 1$. Thus it turns out that $\cosh^{-1} x$ is two-valued: to make it one-valued, we agree to retain only the positive value.

The other formulas above may be verified by the student. The derivatives may be found either by differentiation of (1)–(6) or by the indirect method used in § 79.

99. *The Tractrix*

To illustrate the fact that inverse hyperbolic functions appear in comparatively elementary physical problems, we cite an example.

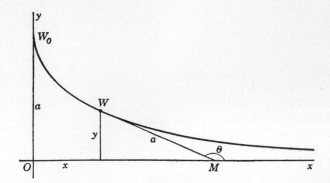

Figure 104

A man, standing at O, holds a rope of length a to which a weight is attached, initially at W_0. The man walks to the right, dragging the weight after him: when the man is at M, the weight is at W. The path of the weight (the tractrix) will at least resemble the curve of Fig. 104. In § 258 it will be shown that the equation is

$$x = a \operatorname{sech}^{-1} \frac{y}{a} - \sqrt{a^2 - y^2};$$

from this we can trace the curve accurately (Ex. 23 below).

EXERCISES

1. Trace the curve $y = \sinh^{-1} x$ by reflecting, in the 45°-line, the curve

$$y = \sinh x.$$

2. Trace the curve $y = \cosh^{-1} x$ by reflecting, in the 45°-line, the positive half of the curve $y = \cosh x$.

3. Trace the curve $y = \tanh^{-1} x$.　　　　**4.** Obtain formula (1), § 98.

5. Obtain formula (3), § 98.　　　　　　**6.** Obtain formula (4), § 98.

7. Obtain formula (5), § 98. (Of the two values that appear, only the positive is retained, by agreement.)

8. Obtain formula (6), § 98. (Of the two values that appear, one is imaginary when $x < 0$, the other when $x > 0$, so that the function is automatically one-valued.)

In Exs. 9–14, verify the given formula, if u is a function of x.

9. $\dfrac{d}{dx} \sinh^{-1} u = \dfrac{\dfrac{du}{dx}}{\sqrt{1 + u^2}}.$　　　　**10.** $\dfrac{d}{dx} \tanh^{-1} u = \dfrac{\dfrac{du}{dx}}{1 - u^2}.$

11. $\dfrac{d}{dx} \cosh^{-1} u = \dfrac{\dfrac{du}{dx}}{\sqrt{u^2 - 1}}.$　　　　**12.** $\dfrac{d}{dx} \coth^{-1} u = \dfrac{\dfrac{du}{dx}}{1 - u^2}.$

13. $\dfrac{d}{dx} \operatorname{sech}^{-1} u = - \dfrac{\dfrac{du}{dx}}{u \sqrt{1 - u^2}}.$

14. $\dfrac{d}{dx} \operatorname{csch}^{-1} u = - \dfrac{\dfrac{du}{dx}}{u \sqrt{1 + u^2}}, u > 0;$　　$\dfrac{d}{dx} \operatorname{csch}^{-1} u = \dfrac{\dfrac{du}{dx}}{u \sqrt{1 + u^2}}, u < 0.$

15. Show that $\tanh^{-1} (-x) = - \tanh^{-1} x$.

16. Show that $\sinh^{-1} (-x) = - \sinh^{-1} x$.

17. Show that $\operatorname{csch}^{-1} (-x) = - \operatorname{csch}^{-1} x$.

18. Show that $\sinh^{-1} \tan \varphi = \ln (\sec \varphi + \tan \varphi)$, $\sec \varphi \geq 1$.

19. Find y' from $y = (1 + x^2)^{\frac{1}{2}} \sinh^{-1} x - x$.

20. Find y' from $y = (x^2 - 1)^{\frac{1}{2}} \cosh^{-1} x - x$.

21. Find the slope of the tractrix at any point. (Read off $\tan \theta$ directly from Fig. 104.) Hence show that the curve starts at W_0 tangent to the y-axis.

$$Ans. \frac{dy}{dx} = - \frac{y}{\sqrt{a^2 - y^2}}.$$

22. Solve Ex. 21 by finding y' from the equation of the curve. [Formula (5″), page 156.]

23. Trace the tractrix by subtracting abscissas of the circular arc $x = \sqrt{a^2 - y^2}$ from those of the curve $y = a \operatorname{sech} \dfrac{x}{a}$. (Ex. 37, page 184.)

CURVATURE

100. *Curvature; Radius of Curvature*

We say in ordinary language that a curve whose direction changes rapidly has great *curvature*, or is sharply curved. Thus a circular arc is said to have greater curvature when the radius is small than when it is large. This somewhat vague idea may be made precise as follows:

Consider, first, two points P, P' on a circle, and denote the arc PP' by Δs, the angle between the tangents at P, P' by $\Delta\alpha$.

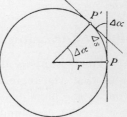

Figure 105

The quotient $\dfrac{\Delta\alpha}{\Delta s}$ is the *change in direction* of the curve, per unit of arc. The central angle subtended by Δs is equal to $\Delta\alpha$; hence, by the formula

$$arc = radius \times angle,$$

derived in trigonometry, we obtain a relation between Δs and $\Delta\alpha$:

$$\Delta s = r\,\Delta\alpha,$$

so that the change in direction per unit of arc is

$$\frac{\Delta\alpha}{\Delta s} = \frac{1}{r}.$$

That is, in the case of the circle the quotient $\dfrac{\Delta\alpha}{\Delta s}$ is constant; it is called the *curvature* of the circle.

If now the curve in question is not a circle, the direction of the curve no longer changes uniformly, and the quotient $\dfrac{\Delta\alpha}{\Delta s}$ represents the *average curvature* of the arc Δs. But as P' (Fig. 106) approaches P along the curve, so

187

that Δs and $\Delta \alpha$ approach zero, the quantity $\dfrac{\Delta \alpha}{\Delta s}$ in general approaches a limit $\dfrac{d\alpha}{ds}$, which is called the *curvature at the point P*:

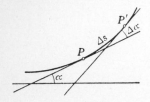

Figure 106

(1) $$\kappa = \operatorname*{Lim}_{\Delta s \to 0} \frac{\Delta \alpha}{\Delta s} = \frac{d\alpha}{ds}.$$

The reciprocal of the curvature is called the *radius of curvature*, and is denoted by ρ:

(2) $$\rho = \frac{1}{\kappa} = \frac{ds}{d\alpha}.$$

However, it is customary to consider κ and ρ as essentially positive (just as, for a circle, the radius of the circle—equal to the radius of curvature—is always positive); and, of course, if s decreases as α increases, the derivative $\dfrac{ds}{d\alpha}$ is a negative quantity. Thus, as our defining formulas, we shall replace (1) and (2) by

(3) $$\kappa = \left| \frac{d\alpha}{ds} \right|,$$

(4) $$\rho = \left| \frac{ds}{d\alpha} \right|.$$

101. *Expression in Rectangular Coordinates*

The definitions above are independent of the particular coordinate system used; the angle α is the angle made by the tangent at P with any fixed line in the plane of the curve. When the equation of the curve is given in rectangular coordinates, it is convenient to take α as the slope-angle of the tangent—i.e., the angle between the tangent and the x-axis. The curvature κ is then easily expressed in terms of the coordinates. For,

$$\tan \alpha = \frac{dy}{dx} = y',$$

$$\alpha = \operatorname{Arctan} y',$$

(1) $$d\alpha = \frac{dy'}{1 + (y')^2} = \frac{y'' \, dx}{1 + (y')^2}.$$

Also, by § 46,

(2) $$ds = \pm \sqrt{1 + (y')^2} \, dx.$$

Substituting (1) and (2) in the defining formulas above, we find

$$\kappa = \frac{|y''|}{[1 + (y')^2]^{\frac{3}{2}}},$$

$$\rho = \frac{[1 + (y')^2]^{\frac{3}{2}}}{|y''|}.$$

Example (*a*). Find the radius of curvature of the equilateral hyperbola

$$x^2 - y^2 = a^2 \tag{3}$$

at any point (x, y) on the curve.

We have, directly or by Example (*c*), § 33,

$$y' = \frac{x}{y}, \qquad y'' = -\frac{a^2}{y^3}.$$

Thus

$$\rho = \frac{\left(1 + \dfrac{x^2}{y^2}\right)^{\frac{3}{2}}}{\dfrac{a^2}{|y^3|}} = \frac{|y^3|\left(1 + \dfrac{x^2}{y^2}\right)^{\frac{3}{2}}}{a^2} = \frac{(x^2 + y^2)^{\frac{3}{2}}}{a^2}. \tag{4}$$

Example (*b*). In Example (*a*), find the points of maximum curvature.*

The differentiation is somewhat simpler if instead of making κ a maximum, we make ρ a minimum. It will be convenient to express ρ in terms of y by means of (3):

$$\rho = \frac{(a^2 + 2y^2)^{\frac{3}{2}}}{a^2},$$

$$\frac{d\rho}{dy} = \frac{6y(a^2 + 2y^2)^{\frac{1}{2}}}{a^2},$$

so that

$$\frac{d\rho}{dy} = 0 \quad \text{when } y = 0.$$

Thus the curvature is greatest at the vertices. We actually have maximum κ, rather than minimum or neither, for we know that far out in the first quadrant, and again in the fourth quadrant, the curve is nearly straight.

We might just as easily have happened to express ρ in terms of x. If so, an interesting situation arises:

$$\rho = \frac{(2x^2 - a^2)^{\frac{3}{2}}}{a^2},$$

$$\frac{d\rho}{dx} = \frac{6x(2x^2 - a^2)^{\frac{1}{2}}}{a^2},$$

so that

$$\frac{d\rho}{dx} = 0 \quad \text{when } x = 0 \quad \text{or} \quad x = \pm\tfrac{1}{2}\sqrt{2}\,a.$$

Now all these critical values are barred, since the hyperbola does not reach so far. We are not yet fully equipped to trace the curve

$$\rho^2 = \frac{(2x^2 - a^2)^3}{a^4},$$

---

* This particular problem can be solved by inspection. A glance at (4) shows that ρ is least when the quantity $x^2 + y^2$ is least—i.e., at that point of the curve that is nearest the origin.

but it has the form shown in Fig. 122, page 222. Since we are limited to $|x| \geqq a,\ \rho > 0$, only the portions drawn full have a meaning. Hence ρ, as a function of x, has *endpoint minima* at $x = \pm a$.

102. *Circle of Curvature*

At any point on a curve $y = f(x)$, where y' and y'' exist and $y'' \neq 0$, there is associated with the curve a circle, which is called the *circle of curvature*. In a sense, the circle of curvature is the circle which comes nearest (of all circles) to fitting the curve in the immediate vicinity of the point under consideration.

At a point (x, y) on $y = f(x)$, let y' and y'' exist with $y'' \neq 0$. Let a circle, with unspecified radius r and center at (a, b), pass through the point (x, y) and have, at that point, the same y' and y'' as those of the curve $y = f(x)$. The circle has the equation

(1) $$(x - a)^2 + (y - b)^2 = r^2.$$

From (1), by differentiating each member twice, we obtain

(2) $$x - a + y'(y - b) = 0,$$
(3) $$1 + y''(y - b) + (y')^2 = 0.$$

It is a simple matter to obtain the coordinates a and b, of the center of the circle (1), from equations (2) and (3). The results are

(4) $$a = x - \frac{y'[1 + (y')^2]}{y''},$$

(5) $$b = y + \frac{1 + (y')^2}{y''}.$$

Next we form the expression $(x - a)^2 + (y - b)^2$ to find the radius of the circle. From (4) and (5), we get

$$(x - a)^2 + (y - b)^2 = \frac{(y')^2[1 + (y')^2]^2}{(y'')^2} + \frac{[1 + (y')^2]^2}{(y'')^2}$$

$$= \frac{[1 + (y')^2]^3}{(y'')^2}.$$

Hence

$$r^2 = \frac{[1 + (y')^2]^3}{(y'')^2},$$

so that $r = \rho$, the radius of curvature of $y = f(x)$.

We have shown that the circle of curvature, at a point (x, y) on a curve, is the circle with *center at* (a, b) given by equations (4) and (5), and with *radius equal to the radius of curvature of the curve* at the point under consideration.

Example. Find the circle of curvature of the parabola $y^2 = 2x$ at the point $(\frac{1}{2}, 1)$, at one end of the latus rectum.

From $y = \sqrt{2}\, x^{\frac{3}{2}}$, we obtain

$$y' = \tfrac{1}{2}\sqrt{2}\, x^{-\frac{1}{2}},$$
$$y'' = -\tfrac{1}{4}\sqrt{2}\, x^{-\frac{3}{2}}.$$

Thus at the point $(\tfrac{1}{2}, 1)$ we have

$$y' = \tfrac{1}{2}\sqrt{2}\cdot\sqrt{2} = 1,$$
$$y'' = -\tfrac{1}{4}\sqrt{2}\cdot(\sqrt{2})^3 = -1.$$

Hence the circle of curvature has for coordinates of its center, from equations (4) and (5),

$$a = \frac{1}{2} - \frac{1(1+1)}{-1} = \frac{5}{2},$$
$$b = 1 + \frac{1+1}{-1} = -1.$$

The radius of the circle of curvature is

$$\rho = \frac{[1+1]^{\frac{3}{2}}}{|-1|} = +2\sqrt{2}.$$

The circle of curvature, then, is

(6) $$(x - \tfrac{5}{2})^2 + (y + 1)^2 = 8.$$

Note the check which is obtained by showing that the circle (6) passes through the given point $(\tfrac{1}{2}, 1)$.

EXERCISES

In Exs. 1–12, find the radius of curvature at the given point.

1. $y = x - \tfrac{1}{4}x^2$, at $(\tfrac{1}{2}, \tfrac{3}{16})$. *Ans.* $\tfrac{125}{32}$.

2. $y = x^2 - 3x + 1$, at $(1, -1)$. *Ans.* $\sqrt{2}$.

3. $y = 6x - x^3$, at $(1, 5)$. *Ans.* $\tfrac{5}{3}\sqrt{10}$.

4. $y = x(x - a)^2$, at $(0, 0)$. *Ans.* $\dfrac{(1 + a^4)^{\frac{3}{2}}}{4|a|}$.

5. $y = x(x - a)^2$, at $(a, 0)$. *Ans.* $\dfrac{1}{2|a|}$.

6. $y = x^3(x - a)$, at $(a, 0)$. *Ans.* $\dfrac{(1 + a^6)^{\frac{3}{2}}}{6a^2}$.

7. $y^2 = 4(x - 3)$, at $(4, 2)$. *Ans.* $4\sqrt{2}$.

8. $y^2 = 4(x - 3)$, at $(7, 4)$. *Ans.* $10\sqrt{5}$.

9. $y = 2\ln\sin\tfrac{1}{2}x$, at $x = \tfrac{1}{3}\pi$. *Ans.* 4.

10. $y = \cos x$, at $(\pi, -1)$. *Ans.* 1.

11. $y = a \sec \dfrac{x}{a}$, at $x = \dfrac{\pi a}{4}$.   *Ans.* $a \sqrt{\dfrac{3}{2}}$.

12. $y = \ln \tan \dfrac{x}{2}$, at $x = \dfrac{\pi}{4}$.   *Ans.* $2(\tfrac{3}{2})^{\frac{3}{2}}$.

In Exs. 13–26, find the radius of curvature at any point of the curve. In exercises involving parametric equations, reference may be made to § 81.

13. $y = \tan x$.   *Ans.* $\dfrac{(1 + \sec^4 x)^{\frac{3}{2}}}{2 \sec^2 x |\tan x|}$.

14. $y = \cos x$.   **15.** $y = \ln \sin x$.   *Ans.* $|\csc x|$.

16. $y = \ln \sec x$.   *Ans.* $|\sec x|$.

17. The parabola $y^2 = 4ax$.   *Ans.* $\dfrac{2(a + x)^{\frac{3}{2}}}{a^{\frac{1}{2}}}$.

18. The hyperbola $2xy = a^2$.   *Ans.* $\dfrac{(4x^4 + a^4)^{\frac{3}{2}}}{8a^2 |x^3|}$.

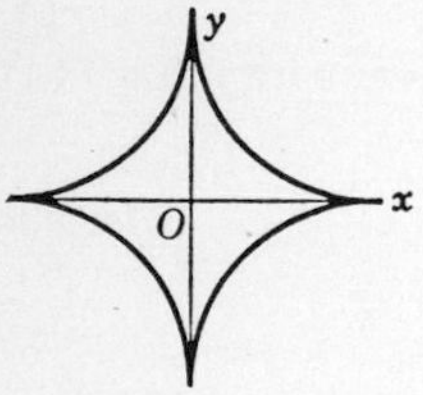

19. The *four-cusped hypocycloid* $x^{\frac{2}{3}} + y^{\frac{2}{3}} = a^{\frac{2}{3}}$. (Fig. 107.)
          Ans. $3|axy|^{\frac{1}{3}}$.

Figure 107

20. $x = 2t + 1$, $y = t^2 + 1$, with t as a parameter.
          Ans. $2(1 + t^2)^{\frac{3}{2}}$.

21. $x = 1 - 3t$, $y = t^2 + 4$.   *Ans.* $\tfrac{1}{6}(9 + 4t^2)^{\frac{3}{2}}$.

22. $x = a \sin^3 t$, $y = a \cos^3 t$, the four-cusped hypocycloid of Ex. 19.   *Ans.* $3|a \sin t \cos t|$.

23. The ellipse $x = a \cos \varphi$, $y = b \sin \varphi$.
          Ans. $|ab|^{-1}(a^2 \sin^2 \varphi + b^2 \cos^2 \varphi)^{\frac{3}{2}}$.

24. The parabola $x = a \tan^2 \varphi$, $y = 2a \tan \varphi$.
          Ans. $2|a \sec^3 \varphi|$.

25. $x = a \tan \varphi$, $y = a \cot \varphi$.   *Ans.* $\tfrac{1}{2}|a \tan^3 \varphi|(1 + \cot^4 \varphi)^{\frac{3}{2}}$.

26. $x = a \cos^4 \theta$, $y = a \sin^4 \theta$.   *Ans.* $2a(\sin^4 \theta + \cos^4 \theta)^{\frac{3}{2}}$.

In Exs. 27–37, find the points of maximum curvature.

27. $3y = x^3$.   *Ans.* $x = \pm (\tfrac{1}{5})^{\frac{1}{4}}$.   **28.** $4y = x^4$.   *Ans.* $x = \pm (\tfrac{2}{7})^{\frac{1}{6}}$.

29. $21y = x^{14}$.   *Ans.* $x = \pm 1$.   **30.** $x^2 y = a^3$.   *Ans.* $x = \pm (5)^{\frac{1}{6}} a$.

31. $y = \sin x$.   **32.** $y = \ln \sin x$.   *Ans.* $x = \tfrac{1}{2}\pi$.

33. $y = a \cosh \dfrac{x}{a}$.

34. A parabola. (Ex. 17.)   *Ans.* The vertex.

35. $y = e^x$.   *Ans.* $(-\tfrac{1}{2} \ln 2, \tfrac{1}{2} \sqrt{2})$.

36. $y = \ln x$. (Cf. Ex. 35.)

37. $y = \sinh x$.   *Ans.* $x = \pm \ln (1 + \sqrt{2})$.

38. If x is given as a function of y, derive the formula (see § 29)

$$\rho = \frac{\left[\left(\dfrac{dx}{dy}\right)^2 + 1 \right]^{\frac{3}{2}}}{\left|\dfrac{d^2x}{dy^2}\right|}.$$

39. Find the radius of curvature of the tractrix

$$x = a \operatorname{sech}^{-1} \frac{y}{a} - \sqrt{a^2 - y^2}.$$

Ans. (See Ex. 21, p. 186.) $-\dfrac{a}{y'}$.

40. Show that when a weight is drawn along the ground as in Fig. 104, page 185, the path of the weight continually tends to straighten out. (Ex. 39.)

41. In Example (*b*), § 101, verify in two ways (§§ 37, 38) that ρ is a minimum.

42. Find the point of minimum curvature for the four-cusped hypocycloid.

Ans. Midway between the cusps.

In Exs. 43–47, find the equation of the circle of curvature at the given point. Draw the figure.

43. $y = x^2$ at $(0, 0)$.   *Ans.* $x^2 + y^2 = y$.
44. $y = x^2$ at $(1, 1)$.   *Ans.* $x^2 + y^2 + 8x - 7y = 3$.
45. $y = x^3 - x^2$ at $(0, 0)$.   *Ans.* $x^2 + y^2 + y = 0$.
46. $y = x^3 - x^2$ at $(1, 0)$.   *Ans.* $x^2 + y^2 = x + y$.

47. The four-cusped hypocycloid $x^{\frac{2}{3}} + y^{\frac{2}{3}} = 2$, at the point of minimum curvature in the first quadrant. See Ex. 42.   *Ans.* $x^2 + y^2 = 8x + 8y - 14$.

48. Let x and y be functions of a parameter t. Denote derivatives with respect to t by primes. Show that the formula for curvature κ becomes

$$\kappa = \frac{|x'y'' - x''y'|}{[(x')^2 + (y')^2]^{\frac{3}{2}}}.$$

INDETERMINATE FORMS

103. *Rolle's Theorem*

Consider a curve

$$(1) \qquad\qquad\qquad y = f(x)$$

which cuts the x-axis at $x = a$ and $x = b$. That is, $f(a) = 0$ and $f(b) = 0$. If $f(x)$ is continuous over the closed interval $a \leqq x \leqq b$, we know from Theorem 9, page 28, that $f(x)$ takes on a maximum and a minimum value some-

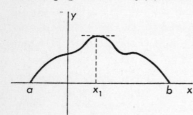

Figure 108

where in the interval. If $f(x)$ is not identically zero, the maximum and minimum values cannot both be zero. Suppose the maximum is not zero and that the maximum occurs at x_1. Since $f(x_1) \neq 0$, x_1 must lie in the open interval $a < x_1 < b$.

Let us add the condition that the derivative $f'(x)$ exists throughout the open interval $a < x < b$. Then $f'(x_1)$ must exist and (by the definition of a derivative)

$$(2) \qquad\qquad \operatorname*{Lim}_{\Delta x \to 0} \frac{f(x_1 + \Delta x) - f(x_1)}{\Delta x} = f'(x_1).$$

Now $f(x_1) \geqq f(x_1 + \Delta x)$, since a maximum occurs at x_1. Then

$$(3) \qquad\qquad \frac{f(x_1 + \Delta x) - f(x_1)}{\Delta x} \leqq 0, \qquad \text{for } \Delta x > 0$$

and

$$(4) \qquad\qquad \frac{f(x_1 + \Delta x) - f(x_1)}{\Delta x} \geqq 0, \qquad \text{for } \Delta x < 0.$$

The limit in (2) exists. It cannot be positive because of (3), and it cannot be negative because of (4). Hence the limit is zero, so $f'(x_1) = 0$. The proof is easily adjusted to the situation in which the maximum of $f(x)$ is zero but the minimum is not zero.

We have proved the following theorem, which is used frequently in more advanced mathematics as well as in our study of calculus.

ROLLE'S THEOREM

THEOREM 21. *If $f(x)$ is continuous over the closed interval $a \leqq x \leqq b$, if $f'(x)$ exists over the open interval $a < x < b$, if $f(a) = 0$ and $f(b) = 0$, then there exists an x_1 in the open interval $a < x_1 < b$ such that $f'(x_1) = 0$.*

For a function $f(x)$ which satisfies the conditions imposed in Rolle's theorem, the theorem states that the curve $y = f(x)$ must have a horizontal tangent line at some point between $x = a$ and $x = b$. There may be many such intermediate points. Note also that the function $f(x) \equiv 0$ yields $f'(x) \equiv 0$, so that such a function fits into Rolle's theorem without its being amenable to the proof used here.

104. *The First Law of the Mean*

Examination of Fig. 108 suggests that Rolle's theorem may contain (for sufficiently well-behaved curves) a property essentially independent of the coordinate system. On an arc of the curve in Fig. 108 there is a tangent line parallel to the chord which joins the ends of the arc. We wish to obtain the explicit extension of Rolle's theorem suggested by the above discussion.

In Fig. 109, suppose there exists between S and Q the point P at which the tangent line is parallel to the chord SQ. The slope of the chord is

$$\frac{RQ}{SR} = \frac{f(b) - f(a)}{b - a};$$

the slope of the tangent at P is $f'(x_1)$, where x_1 is the abscissa of P. Hence

$$\frac{f(b) - f(a)}{b - a} = f'(x_1).$$

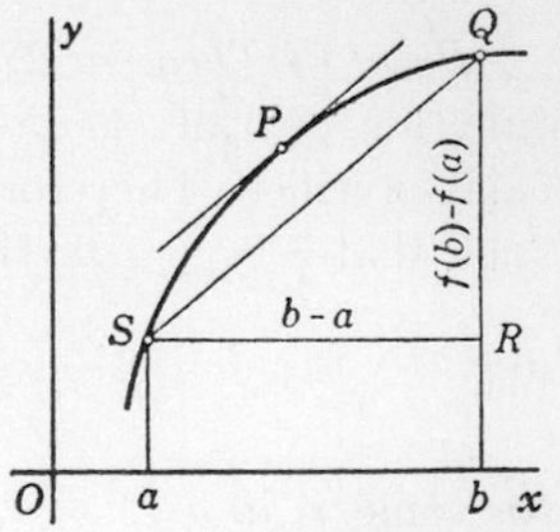

The precise result will now be expressed as a theorem. The formula in the theorem is called the *first law of the mean*.

Figure 109

THEOREM 22. *If $f(x)$ is continuous over the closed interval $a \leqq x \leqq b$, and if the derivative $f'(x)$ exists throughout the open interval $a < x < b$, there exists an x_1 in the open interval such that*

(1) $$f(b) - f(a) = (b - a)f'(x_1), \qquad a < x_1 < b.$$

Theorem 22 differs from Rolle's theorem only in the form of the conclusion and in that the function is not required to vanish at the endpoints of the interval. It is natural to try to use Rolle's theorem in the proof of

Theorem 22. We therefore attempt to set up a function $\varphi(x)$ which retains the continuity and differentiability properties of $f(x)$ and which is such that $\varphi(a) = 0$ and $\varphi(b) = 0$. The continuity and differentiability properties of $f(x)$ will surely be retained if we add to $f(x)$ any polynomial in x. Since we need to satisfy the two conditions

(2) $$\varphi(a) = 0, \qquad \varphi(b) = 0,$$

two constants should suffice, so we add to $f(x)$ a linear polynomial in x.

The determination of $\varphi(x)$ is made simpler by starting with a function which already satisfies one of the conditions (2). Therefore let us set

(3) $$\varphi(x) = f(x) - f(a) + c(x - a)$$

so that $\varphi(x)$ vanishes at $x = a$. We determine the constant c by requiring that $\varphi(b) = 0$. Thus

$$0 = f(b) - f(a) + c(b - a),$$

from which

$$c = -\frac{f(b) - f(a)}{b - a}.$$

Employing the above expression for c in equation (3) yields the desired function

(4) $$\varphi(x) = f(x) - f(a) - \frac{f(b) - f(a)}{b - a}(x - a).$$

Proof of Theorem 22. If $f(x)$ satisfies the conditions of Theorem 22, the function $\varphi(x)$ of (4) satisfies all the requirements of Rolle's theorem, as is easily verified. Therefore there exists an x_1, in the open interval $a < x_1 < b$, such that $\varphi'(x_1) = 0$. Hence, by (4),

(5) $$0 = f'(x_1) - \frac{f(b) - f(a)}{b - a}$$

for some x_1 in $a < x_1 < b$. Since (5) is a rearrangement of (1), the proof of Theorem 22 is now complete.

An interesting application of Theorem 22 is obtained by choosing

(6) $$f(x) = \int_a^x g(y)\, dy.$$

If $g(y)$ is continuous in $a \leq y \leq b$, then $f(x)$ satisfies the conditions of Theorem 22. Now from (6)

$$f'(x) = g(x),$$

so that we may conclude from the theorem that

(7) $$\int_a^b g(y)\, dy - \int_a^a g(y)\, dy = (b - a)g(x_1), \qquad a < x_1 < b.$$

The second integral in (7) is zero. Hence

(8) $$\int_a^b g(y)\, dy = (b - a)g(x_1), \qquad a < x_1 < b,$$

which is a law of the mean for integrals.

105. *The Indeterminate Forms* $\dfrac{0}{0}$ *and* $\dfrac{\infty}{\infty}$

Theorem 22 of the preceding section furnishes us with a tool which frequently aids in the evaluation of a limit of a quotient,

(1) $$\operatorname*{Lim}_{x \to a} \frac{f(x)}{F(x)},$$

in which both $f(a) = 0$ and $F(a) = 0$. The quotient $\dfrac{f(x)}{F(x)}$ is said to* *assume the "indeterminate form"* $\dfrac{0}{0}$ at $x = a$, and is undefined at that point. Nevertheless the *limit* of the quotient may exist. This fact is illustrated in the derivation of the fundamental differentiation formulas, where in each case both numerator and denominator of the difference-quotient $\dfrac{\Delta y}{\Delta x}$ approach zero, yet the derivative, which is the limit of that quotient, exists. See also Example (b), § 9, and formula (1), § 12.

If the function $\dfrac{f(x)}{F(x)}$ does approach a limit, it may be possible to evaluate the limit by means of simple transformations of $\dfrac{f(x)}{F(x)}$, as was done in deriving the differentiation formulas. In many cases the limit may be obtained by a method that will now be developed.

THEOREM 23. *If* $f(a) = F(a) = 0$ *and if both* $f'(x)$ *and* $F'(x)$ *exist in some interval including the point* $x = a$,

(2) $$\operatorname*{Lim}_{x \to a} \frac{f(x)}{F(x)} = \operatorname*{Lim}_{x \to a} \frac{f'(x)}{F'(x)}$$

in the sense that if the right member of (2) exists, the left member also exists and their values are equal.

---

* It should be clearly understood that the symbols $\dfrac{0}{0}$, $\dfrac{\infty}{\infty}$, etc., are never to be taken literally, since, so taken, they have no meaning whatever. In fact, the term "indeterminate form" is something of a misnomer, since the function is simply not defined at the point in question. No confusion will arise if we always remember that these symbols are nothing more than convenient shorthand to designate the various situations described.

Proof. Under the assumptions of Theorem 23 we may choose x close enough to a so that the functions $f(y)$ and $F(y)$ are both continuous in the closed interval $a \leqq y \leqq x$ and their derivatives $f'(y)$ and $F'(y)$ exist in the open interval $a < y < x$.

Now consider the function $\varphi(y)$ defined by

$$(3) \qquad \varphi(y) = f(y)F(x) - f(x)F(y).$$

In the interval $a \leqq y \leqq x$, $\varphi(y)$ satisfies the conditions of Rolle's theorem, page 195. Note that $f(a) = F(a) = 0$ results in $\varphi(a) = 0$ and the form of $\varphi(y)$ leads to $\varphi(x) = 0$. Then there exists an x_1 in the open interval such that $\varphi'(x_1) = 0$. That is,

$$(4) \qquad f'(x_1)F(x) - f(x)F'(x_1) = 0, \qquad a < x_1 < x.$$

Since neither F nor F' can be identically zero (or the problem is trivial), we may choose x close enough to a so that neither $F(x)$ nor $F'(x_1)$ is zero. Hence (4) leads to the result that there exists an x_1 in $a < x_1 < x$ such that

$$(5) \qquad \frac{f(x)}{F(x)} = \frac{f'(x_1)}{F'(x_1)}, \qquad a < x_1 < x.$$

When $x \to a$, $x_1 \to a$ and the conclusion stated in Theorem 23 follows from (5).

Example (a). Evaluate

$$\operatorname*{Lim}_{\theta \to \frac{1}{2}\pi} \frac{1 - \sin \theta}{(\pi - 2\theta)^2}.$$

Since $1 - \sin \frac{1}{2}\pi = 0$ and $(\pi - \pi)^2 = 0$, the fraction involved does assume the indeterminate form $\dfrac{0}{0}$ at $\theta = \frac{1}{2}\pi$. Both the functions $(1 - \sin \theta)$ and $(\pi - 2\theta)^2$ are continuous and differentiable for all finite θ. Hence we may apply Theorem 23; i.e., we may differentiate the numerator and denominator separately and replace the old problem by a new one:

$$(6) \qquad \operatorname*{Lim}_{\theta \to \frac{1}{2}\pi} \frac{1 - \sin \theta}{(\pi - 2\theta)^2} = \operatorname*{Lim}_{\theta \to \frac{1}{2}\pi} \frac{-\cos \theta}{-4(\pi - 2\theta)} = \frac{1}{4} \operatorname*{Lim}_{\theta \to \frac{1}{2}\pi} \frac{\cos \theta}{\pi - 2\theta}.$$

Again the fraction involved, $\dfrac{\cos \theta}{\pi - 2\theta}$, assumes the form $\dfrac{0}{0}$ at $\theta = \frac{1}{2}\pi$. But the functions $\cos \theta$ and $(\pi - 2\theta)$ satisfy the conditions of Theorem 23. Hence we apply the process again:

$$(7) \qquad \frac{1}{4} \operatorname*{Lim}_{\theta \to \frac{1}{2}\pi} \frac{\cos \theta}{\pi - 2\theta} = \frac{1}{4} \operatorname*{Lim}_{\theta \to \frac{1}{2}\pi} \frac{-\sin \theta}{-2} = \frac{1}{4} \cdot \frac{-1}{-2} = \frac{1}{8}.$$

From (6) and (7) we obtain the desired evaluation

$$(8) \qquad \operatorname*{Lim}_{\theta \to \frac{1}{2}\pi} \frac{1 - \sin \theta}{(\pi - 2\theta)^2} = \frac{1}{8}.$$

Theorem 23 applies also when x approaches a from one side only, $x \to a^+$ or $x \to a^-$. By using the substitution $x = \frac{1}{z}$, it is easy to show that Theorem 23 may be extended to the situation in which $x \to \infty$ or $x \to -\infty$.

If $f(x)$ and $F(x)$ both increase without bound (in either direction) as x approaches a, the quotient $\frac{f(x)}{F(x)}$ is said to *assume the indeterminate form* $\frac{\infty}{\infty}$ at $x = a$. Here again it may happen that $\underset{x \to a}{\mathrm{Lim}}\, \frac{f(x)}{F(x)}$ exists, and it can be shown that, subject to certain broad conditions that are satisfied in all ordinary cases, the same method may be applied in this case as in the one just treated.

Thus in all these cases we may differentiate the numerator and the denominator *separately*, and take the limit of the new quantity thus formed. It must be borne clearly in mind, however, that the theorem applies only to *quotients* in which the numerator and the denominator *both approach zero or both increase without bound*.

Example (b). Evaluate $\underset{x \to 0^+}{\mathrm{Lim}}\, \dfrac{e^{-\frac{1}{x}}}{x}$.

Proceeding directly, we find

$$\underset{x \to 0^+}{\mathrm{Lim}}\, \frac{e^{-\frac{1}{x}}}{x} = \underset{x \to 0^+}{\mathrm{Lim}}\, \frac{\frac{1}{x^2} e^{-\frac{1}{x}}}{1} = \underset{x \to 0^+}{\mathrm{Lim}}\, \frac{e^{-\frac{1}{x}}}{x^2}$$

$$= \underset{x \to 0^+}{\mathrm{Lim}}\, \frac{\frac{1}{x^2} e^{-\frac{1}{x}}}{2x} = \underset{x \to 0^+}{\mathrm{Lim}}\, \frac{e^{-\frac{1}{x}}}{2x^3}.$$

Evidently nothing is being accomplished. But, prominence of $\frac{1}{x}$ in the original expression suggests the substitution $z = \frac{1}{x}$:

$$\underset{x \to 0^+}{\mathrm{Lim}}\, \frac{e^{-\frac{1}{x}}}{x} = \underset{z \to \infty}{\mathrm{Lim}}\, ze^{-z} = \underset{z \to \infty}{\mathrm{Lim}}\, \frac{z}{e^z} = \underset{z \to \infty}{\mathrm{Lim}}\, \frac{1}{e^z} = 0.$$

Any factor (of the *whole expression*) which approaches a limit different from zero may be replaced by its limit as soon as it makes its appearance.

Example (c). $\underset{\alpha \to 0}{\mathrm{Lim}}\, \dfrac{\sin \alpha - \alpha}{\tan^3 \alpha} = \underset{\alpha \to 0}{\mathrm{Lim}}\, \dfrac{\cos \alpha - 1}{3 \tan^2 \alpha \sec^2 \alpha}$

$$= \underset{\alpha \to 0}{\mathrm{Lim}}\, \frac{\cos \alpha - 1}{3 \tan^2 \alpha} = \underset{\alpha \to 0}{\mathrm{Lim}}\, \frac{-\sin \alpha}{6 \tan \alpha \sec^2 \alpha}$$

$$= \underset{\alpha \to 0}{\mathrm{Lim}}\, \frac{-\sin \alpha}{6 \tan \alpha} = \underset{\alpha \to 0}{\mathrm{Lim}}\, \frac{-\cos \alpha}{6 \sec^2 \alpha} = -\frac{1}{6}.$$

Finally, to see that our method, even when applicable, does not always succeed, consider the next example.

Example (*d*). Evaluate $\underset{x \to \infty}{\text{Lim}} \dfrac{3^x}{2^{x^2}}$.

This is of the type $\dfrac{\infty}{\infty}$:

$$\underset{x \to \infty}{\text{Lim}} \frac{3^x}{2^{x^2}} = \underset{x \to \infty}{\text{Lim}} \frac{3^x \ln 3}{2^{x^2} \cdot 2x \ln 2}; \text{ etc.}$$

Evidently differentiation will never affect the exponential factors. But we may write

$$\underset{x \to \infty}{\text{Lim}} \frac{3^x}{2^{x^2}} = \underset{x \to \infty}{\text{Lim}} \frac{3^x}{2^{2x}} \cdot \frac{1}{2^{x^2-2x}}$$

$$= \underset{x \to \infty}{\text{Lim}} \left[\left(\frac{3}{4} \right)^x \cdot \frac{1}{2^{x^2-2x}} \right] = 0,$$

since each factor approaches zero. See also Exs. 40 and 53 below.

106. *The Indeterminate Form* 0 · ∞

Consider the product of two functions $f(x) \cdot F(x)$ such that, as x approaches a, one function approaches zero while the other increases indefinitely. The product is then said to *take the indeterminate form* 0 · ∞.

If we write

$$f(x) \cdot F(x) = \frac{f(x)}{\dfrac{1}{F(x)}},$$

it follows that the quotient last written assumes the form $\dfrac{0}{0}$ or $\dfrac{\infty}{\infty}$, and the methods of § 105 may be applied.

Example. Evaluate $\underset{x \to 0^+}{\text{Lim}} \; x^2 \ln x$.

This takes the form 0 · ∞. We write

$$\underset{x \to 0^+}{\text{Lim}} \; x^2 \ln x = \underset{x \to 0^+}{\text{Lim}} \frac{\ln x}{\dfrac{1}{x^2}} = \underset{x \to 0^+}{\text{Lim}} \frac{\dfrac{1}{x}}{\dfrac{-2}{x^3}} = \underset{x \to 0^+}{\text{Lim}} \left(-\frac{x^2}{2} \right) = 0.$$

EXERCISES

In Exs. 1–20, evaluate the limit by employing Theorem 23.

1. $\underset{x \to 0}{\text{Lim}} \dfrac{x + \tan x}{\sin 4x}$.   *Ans.* $\frac{1}{2}$.   2. $\underset{x \to \frac{1}{2}\pi}{\text{Lim}} \dfrac{1 - \sin x}{\cos 5x}$.   *Ans.* 0.

3. $\underset{\beta \to 0}{\text{Lim}} \dfrac{\beta}{\text{Arcsin } \beta}$.   *Ans.* 1.   4. $\underset{\beta \to 0}{\text{Lim}} \dfrac{\text{Arctan } \beta}{\beta}$.   *Ans.* 1.

5. $\underset{y\to 0}{\text{Lim}} \dfrac{y^2}{\ln \cos y}.$ *Ans.* $-2.$ **6.** $\underset{y\to \frac{1}{2}}{\text{Lim}} \dfrac{1 + \cos 2\pi y}{(2y - 1)^2}.$ *Ans.* $\frac{1}{2}\pi^2.$

7. $\underset{z\to \infty}{\text{Lim}} \dfrac{\ln z}{z}.$ *Ans.* $0.$ **8.** $\underset{x\to \infty}{\text{Lim}} (x^2 e^{-x}).$ *Ans.* $0.$

9. $\underset{y\to \infty}{\text{Lim}} \dfrac{e^{2y}}{y^3}.$ **10.** $\underset{x\to \infty}{\text{Lim}} \dfrac{\ln^2 x}{x}.$

11. $\underset{x\to \pi}{\text{Lim}} \dfrac{\ln x - \ln \pi}{\sin 2x}.$ **12.** $\underset{x\to 1}{\text{Lim}} \dfrac{\ln x}{x^2 - 4x + 3}.$

13. $\underset{x\to 0^+}{\text{Lim}} (\text{Arcsin } x) \ln x.$ **14.** $\underset{y\to 0^+}{\text{Lim}} y e^{\frac{1}{y}}.$

15. $\underset{x\to 0}{\text{Lim}} \dfrac{\ln (1 + 4x)}{x}.$ **16.** $\underset{x\to 0^+}{\text{Lim}} (\text{Arctan } x) \ln x.$

17. $\underset{x\to 0}{\text{Lim}} \dfrac{x - \tan x}{x(1 - \cos x)}.$ *Ans.* $-\frac{2}{3}.$ **18.** $\underset{y\to 0}{\text{Lim}} \dfrac{y - \tan y}{y \sin^2 y}.$ *Ans.* $-\frac{1}{3}.$

19. $\underset{x\to 0}{\text{Lim}} \dfrac{x^2 \sin x}{x - \sin x}.$ *Ans.* $6.$ **20.** $\underset{x\to 0}{\text{Lim}} \dfrac{x e^x - \sin x}{\sin^2 x}.$ *Ans.* $1.$

In Exs. 21–30, evaluate each limit by two methods.

21. $\underset{x\to 1}{\text{Lim}} \dfrac{x^2 - 4x + 3}{2x^2 - x - 1}.$ **22.** $\underset{x\to -2}{\text{Lim}} \dfrac{2x^2 + 3x - 2}{x^2 + 3x + 2}.$

23. $\underset{x\to 3}{\text{Lim}} \dfrac{x^3 - x^2 - 7x + 3}{x^3 - 8x - 3}.$ **24.** $\underset{x\to \infty}{\text{Lim}} \dfrac{3x^4 - x + 1}{2x^4 + x^3 - 6}.$

25. $\underset{\theta\to 0}{\text{Lim}} \dfrac{\sin^2 \theta}{1 - \cos \theta}.$ **26.** $\underset{\alpha\to 0}{\text{Lim}} \dfrac{1 - \cos^4 \alpha}{\alpha \sin \alpha}.$

27. $\underset{x\to 0}{\text{Lim}} \dfrac{x - \tan x}{\sin x}.$ **28.** $\underset{y\to 0}{\text{Lim}} \dfrac{\sqrt{y + 4} - 2}{y}.$

29. $\underset{x\to 0}{\text{Lim}} \dfrac{x}{\sqrt{1 + x} - \sqrt{1 - x}}.$ **30.** $\underset{x\to 0}{\text{Lim}} \dfrac{x^2}{1 - \cos x}.$

In Exs. 31–46, evaluate the limits by any available method.

31. $\underset{x\to 1}{\text{Lim}} \dfrac{x^3 - 7x + 6}{2x^3 + 3x^2 - 4x - 1}.$ *Ans.* $-\frac{1}{2}.$

32. $\underset{x\to 1}{\text{Lim}} \dfrac{x^3 - 7x + 6}{2x^3 - 3x^2 + 1}.$ *Ans.* No limit.

33. $\underset{\alpha\to 0}{\text{Lim}} \dfrac{\sec \alpha - 1}{\alpha \sin \alpha}.$ *Ans.* $\frac{1}{2}.$ **34.** $\underset{x\to 0}{\text{Lim}} \dfrac{2 \tan x - \sin 2x}{x^3}.$ *Ans.* $2.$

35. $\underset{x\to 0}{\text{Lim}} \dfrac{\tan 2x - 2 \sin x}{x^3}.$ *Ans.* $3.$ **36.** $\underset{y\to 0}{\text{Lim}} \dfrac{\tan^2 y - \sin^2 y}{y^3 \sin y}.$ *Ans.* $1.$

37. $\underset{x\to \infty}{\text{Lim}} \dfrac{\cos x}{x}.$ *Ans.* $0.$ **38.** $\underset{x\to \infty}{\text{Lim}} \dfrac{\tan x}{x}.$ *Ans.* No limit.

39. $\displaystyle \lim_{x \to \infty} \frac{x - \sin x}{x}$.   *Ans.* 1.   **40.** $\displaystyle \lim_{n \to \infty} \frac{e^n}{\pi^n}$.   *Ans.* 0.

41. $\displaystyle \lim_{x \to 0} \frac{\text{Arcsin } x - \text{Arctan } x}{\tan x \sin^2 x}$.   *Ans.* $\frac{1}{2}$.

42. $\displaystyle \lim_{y \to 0} \frac{\sin 2y(1 - \cos 2y)}{\text{Arcsin } y - \sin y}$.   *Ans.* 12.

43. $\displaystyle \lim_{x \to 0} \frac{2 - 2 \cos x - x \ln (1 + x)}{x \sin^2 x}$.   *Ans.* $\frac{1}{2}$.

44. $\displaystyle \lim_{x \to 0} \frac{e^{-x} + \cos x + \sin x - 2}{x \sin^2 x}$.   *Ans.* $-\frac{1}{3}$.

45. $\displaystyle \lim_{x \to \infty} (x \sin e^{-x})$.   *Ans.* 0.   **46.** $\displaystyle \lim_{x \to \infty} \left(\sin \frac{1}{x} \csc e^{-x}\right)$.   *Ans.* ∞.

Prove the theorems of Exs. 47–52, k being any positive number.

47. $\displaystyle \lim_{x \to \infty} \frac{x^k}{e^x} = 0$.   **48.** $\displaystyle \lim_{x \to \infty} \frac{\ln x}{x^k} = 0$.   **49.** $\displaystyle \lim_{x \to 0^+} x^k \ln x = 0$.

50. $\displaystyle \lim_{x \to \infty} \frac{e^x}{x^k} = \infty$.   **51.** $\displaystyle \lim_{x \to \infty} \frac{x^k}{\ln x} = \infty$.   **52.** $\displaystyle \lim_{x \to 0^+} \frac{\ln x}{x^k} = -\infty$.

53. Solve Example (d), § 105, by a second method. (Note that $3 = 2^{\log_2 3}$.)

54. If $b > 1$, $k > 1$, prove that $\displaystyle \lim_{x \to \infty} \frac{a^x}{b^{x^k}} = 0$, regardless of the magnitude of the ratio $\dfrac{a}{b}$. (Cf. Ex. 53.)

107. *The Indeterminate Form* $\infty - \infty$

When two functions $f(x)$ and $F(x)$ both approach infinity, with the same signs, as x approaches a, the *difference* $f(x) - F(x)$ is said to *assume the indeterminate form* $\infty - \infty$. While no general rules can be laid down for evaluating the limit (if any) of this difference, we try to find some transformation that will render the expression amenable to Theorem 23.

Example. Evaluate $\displaystyle \lim_{x \to \frac{\pi}{2}^+} (\sec^3 x - \tan^3 x)$.

This takes the form $-\infty + \infty$. The transformations required are simple:

$$\lim_{x \to \frac{\pi}{2}^+} (\sec^3 x - \tan^3 x) = \lim_{x \to \frac{\pi}{2}^+} \left(\frac{1}{\cos^3 x} - \frac{\sin^3 x}{\cos^3 x}\right) = \lim_{x \to \frac{\pi}{2}^+} \frac{1 - \sin^3 x}{\cos^3 x}$$

$$= \lim_{x \to \frac{\pi}{2}^+} \frac{-3 \sin^2 x \cos x}{-3 \cos^2 x \sin x} = \lim_{x \to \frac{\pi}{2}^+} \tan x = -\infty.$$

That is, the given quantity increases without bound in the negative direction.

108. *The Indeterminate Forms* 0^0, ∞^0, 1^∞

Consider the function

(1) $$y = [f(x)]^{F(x)}.$$

If

$$\operatorname{Lim}_{x \to a} f(x) = 0, \qquad \operatorname{Lim}_{x \to a} F(x) = 0,$$

or if

$$\operatorname{Lim}_{x \to a} f(x) = \infty, \qquad \operatorname{Lim}_{x \to a} F(x) = 0,$$

or if

$$\operatorname{Lim}_{x \to a} f(x) = 1, \qquad \operatorname{Lim}_{x \to a} F(x) = \infty,$$

the function (1) is said, in the respective cases, to *assume the indeterminate form* 0^0, or ∞^0, or 1^∞. To investigate any one of these limits, take the logarithm:

$$\ln y = F(x) \ln f(x),$$

and in each case the right-hand member is of the type discussed in § 106.

If $\ln y$ approaches a limit k, then y itself approaches the limit e^k.

Example. Evaluate $\operatorname{Lim}_{x \to 0^+} (1 - \cos x)^{\frac{1}{\ln x}}$.

Put $y = (1 - \cos x)^{\frac{1}{\ln x}}$. Then

$$\ln y = \frac{\ln (1 - \cos x)}{\ln x}.$$

Therefore,

$$\operatorname{Lim}_{x \to 0^+} \ln y = \operatorname{Lim}_{x \to 0^+} \frac{\ln (1 - \cos x)}{\ln x}$$

$$= \operatorname{Lim}_{x \to 0^+} \frac{\dfrac{\sin x}{1 - \cos x}}{\dfrac{1}{x}}$$

$$= \operatorname{Lim}_{x \to 0^+} \frac{x \sin x}{1 - \cos x}$$

$$= \operatorname{Lim}_{x \to 0^+} \frac{\sin x + x \cos x}{\sin x}$$

$$= 1 + 1 = 2.$$

From $\ln y \to 2$ it follows that $y \to e^2$.

Hence

$$\operatorname{Lim}_{x \to 0^+} (1 - \cos x)^{\frac{1}{\ln x}} = e^2.$$

EXERCISES

In Exs. 1–24, evaluate the limits by first converting the problem to a proper form to enable you to use Theorem 23.

1. $\lim\limits_{\alpha \to 0} \left(\dfrac{1}{\sin^2 \alpha} - \dfrac{1}{\alpha^2} \right).$ *Ans.* $\frac{1}{3}$.   **2.** $\lim\limits_{x \to 0} \left(\dfrac{1}{\sin x} - \dfrac{1}{\sinh x} \right).$ *Ans.* 0.

3. $\lim\limits_{x \to 0} \left(\cot x - \dfrac{1}{e^x - 1} \right).$ *Ans.* $\frac{1}{2}$.

4. $\lim\limits_{x \to 1} \left(\dfrac{x}{x - 1} - \dfrac{1}{\ln x} \right).$ *Ans.* $\frac{1}{2}$.   **5.** $\lim\limits_{y \to 0} \left(\dfrac{e^{-y^2}}{y^2} - \dfrac{\sec y}{y^2} \right).$ *Ans.* $-\frac{3}{2}$.

6. $\lim\limits_{x \to 0} \left(\dfrac{1}{\sin^2 x} - \dfrac{\sin x}{x^3} \right).$ *Ans.* $\frac{1}{2}$.

7. $\lim\limits_{x \to 0} \left[\dfrac{1}{\ln (1 + x)} - \dfrac{1}{\operatorname{Arctan} x} \right].$ *Ans.* $\frac{1}{2}$.

8. $\lim\limits_{\theta \to \frac{1}{2}\pi} (\sec \theta - \tan \theta).$ *Ans.* 0.

9. $\lim\limits_{x \to 0} \left[\dfrac{1}{(\operatorname{Arctan} x)^2} - \dfrac{1}{x^2} \right].$ *Ans.* $\frac{2}{3}$.

10. $\lim\limits_{y \to 0} \left[\dfrac{1}{\ln (1 + y)} - \dfrac{1}{\sin y} \right].$ *Ans.* $\frac{1}{2}$.

11. $\lim\limits_{x \to 0^+} x^x.$ *Ans.* 1.   **12.** $\lim\limits_{x \to 0} (1 + x^2)^{\csc^2 x}.$ *Ans.* e.

13. $\lim\limits_{x \to 1} x^{\csc \pi x}.$ *Ans.* $e^{\frac{-1}{\pi}}$.   **14.** $\lim\limits_{y \to 0} (y + 1)^{\cot 2y}.$ *Ans.* $e^{\frac{1}{2}}$.

15. $\lim\limits_{x \to 0} (1 + x^2)^{\frac{1}{x}}.$ *Ans.* 1.   **16.** $\lim\limits_{\alpha \to 0^+} (\sin \alpha)^{\tan \alpha}.$ *Ans.* 1.

17. $\lim\limits_{x \to 0} (1 + \sin^2 x)^{\frac{1}{x^2}}.$ *Ans.* e.   **18.** $\lim\limits_{x \to 0} (e^x + 3x)^{\frac{1}{x}}.$ *Ans.* e^4.

19. $\lim\limits_{\alpha \to 0^+} (\csc \alpha)^{\sin \alpha}.$ *Ans.* 1.   **20.** $\lim\limits_{x \to \frac{\pi}{2}^-} (\tan x)^{\cos x}.$ *Ans.* 1.

21. $\lim\limits_{\alpha \to 0} (\cos \alpha - \sin \alpha)^{\frac{1}{\alpha}}.$ *Ans.* e^{-1}.

22. $\lim\limits_{\alpha \to 0} (\sec \alpha + \tan \alpha)^{\csc \alpha}.$ *Ans.* e.

23. $\lim\limits_{x \to 0} (\cos x)^{\frac{1}{x^2}}.$ *Ans.* $e^{-\frac{1}{2}}$.   **24.** $\lim\limits_{x \to 0} \left(\dfrac{\sin x}{x} \right)^{\frac{1}{x^2}}.$ *Ans.* $e^{-\frac{1}{6}}$.

In Exs. 25–38, evaluate the limit by any available method.

25. $\lim\limits_{x \to \infty} (e^x - x).$ *Ans.* $+\infty$.   **26.** $\lim\limits_{x \to 0^+} (x + \ln x).$ *Ans.* $-\infty$.

27. $\lim\limits_{x \to \infty} (x - \ln x).$ *Ans.* $+\infty$.

28. $\lim\limits_{\alpha \to \pi^+} (\csc^3 \alpha - \cot^3 \alpha).$ *Ans.* $-\infty$.

29. $\lim\limits_{\alpha \to \pi^-} (\csc^3 \alpha - \cot^3 \alpha).$ *Ans.* $+\infty$.

30. $\lim\limits_{\alpha \to \pi} (\csc^3 \alpha - \cot^3 \alpha)$.   *Ans.* No limit.

31. $\lim\limits_{x \to 0} (\csc^3 x - \cot^3 x)$.   *Ans.* No limit.

32. $\lim\limits_{x \to 0} (x \csc^3 x - x \cot^3 x)$.   *Ans.* $\frac{3}{2}$.

33. $\lim\limits_{x \to \infty} (1 + x^2 e^x)^{\frac{1}{x}}$.   *Ans.* e.   **34.** $\lim\limits_{x \to \infty} (1 + e^{2x})^{\frac{1}{\ln(1+e^x)}}$.   *Ans.* e^2.

35. $\lim\limits_{x \to 0^+} (1 + e^{\frac{4}{x}})^x$.   *Ans.* e^4.   **36.** $\lim\limits_{x \to 0^-} (1 + e^{\frac{4}{x}})^x$.   *Ans.* 1.

37. $\lim\limits_{x \to \infty} (1 + x e^{3x^2})^{\frac{1}{x^2}}$.   *Ans.* e^3.   **38.** $\lim\limits_{\beta \to \infty} (1 + \beta \ln \beta)^{\frac{1}{\ln(1+\beta)}}$.   *Ans.* e.

39. Evaluate $\lim\limits_{x \to 0} \left(\dfrac{\pi x - 1}{2x^2} + \dfrac{\pi}{x(e^{2\pi x} - 1)} \right)$.   *Ans.* $\dfrac{\pi^2}{6}$.

In Exs. 40–44, evaluate the limit without resorting to differentiation.

40. $\lim\limits_{x \to 0^+} (1 + \tan x)^{\cot x}$. Put $\cot x = v$.

41. $\lim\limits_{x \to 0} (\sec x)^{2\cot^2 x}$.   *Ans.* e.

42. $\lim\limits_{x \to \frac{\pi}{2}} (\sec^2 x - \tan^2 x)^{\sec x}$.   *Ans.* 1.

43. $\lim\limits_{x \to 0^+} (\cot x)^{x^3 - e^3 \ln x}$.   *Ans.* 1.   **44.** $\lim\limits_{x \to 1} x^{\frac{1}{\ln x}}$.   *Ans.* e.

45. What limiting form is approached, in the first quadrant, by the curve $x^n + y^n = a^n$ as n increases through positive integral values? [Consider intersections with lines through O. Putting $y = mx$, find $x = \dfrac{a}{(1 + m^n)^{\frac{1}{n}}}$; investigate $\lim\limits_{n \to \infty} x$ for $m < 1$ and $m > 1$.]   *Ans.* One quadrant of the square $x = \pm a$, $y = \pm a$; if n is even, the entire curve approaches the entire square.

46. Find the points of intersection of the curves $x^{100} + y^{100} = 1$, $y = x$. (Cf. Ex. 45.)   *Ans.* $(\pm 0.993, \pm 0.993)$.

47. From the fact (Ex. 45) that $\lim\limits_{n \to \infty} (1 + m^n)^{\frac{1}{n}} = 1$, $m < 1$, deduce without differentiation the fact that $\lim\limits_{n \to \infty} (1 + m^n)^{\frac{1}{n}} = m$, $m > 1$. Note first that

$$ (1 + m^n)^{\frac{1}{n}} = m(1 + m^{-n})^{\frac{1}{n}}. $$

48. Draw the curve $y = \lim\limits_{n \to \infty} (1 + x^n)^{\frac{1}{n}}$, $x > 0$. (Ex. 47.)

CURVE TRACING

109. *Introduction*

In this chapter we shall make a systematic attack upon the problem of curve tracing. Factorable equations (so-called degenerate curves) are excluded.

In §§ 109–119 only algebraic curves are under consideration. We shall for simplicity confine our attention chiefly to cases in which either y or y^2 is a rational function of x:

$$(1) \qquad y = \frac{P(x)}{Q(x)},$$

or

$$(2) \qquad y^2 = \frac{P(x)}{Q(x)},$$

where $P(x)$, $Q(x)$ are polynomials. Since *cubics* (curves of third degree) and *quarlics* (curves of fourth degree) are the curves most commonly occurring, most of our work will be with these types.

It will be assumed that $P(x)$ and $Q(x)$ contain no common factor. Hence the only kind of discontinuity that can occur is the infinite discontinuity.

110. *Asymptotes*

As the point of contact of a tangent to a curve recedes indefinitely from the origin, the tangent may or may not approach a limiting position. If it does, the line approached is called an *asymplote*.* Thus an asymptote is sometimes said to be "a tangent whose point of contact lies at infinity"; but of course it is not a tangent in the strict sense.

---

* According to some writers, an asymptote is a line that is approached more and more closely by the *curve*, even though the tangent does not approach a limiting position. For algebraic curves, the two definitions are equivalent. But see Exs. 34–35, page 225.

For example, the hyperbola

$$\frac{x^2}{a^2} - \frac{y^2}{b^2} = 1$$

has the lines

$$y = \pm \frac{b}{a} x$$

as asymptotes. On the other hand, the parabola has no asymptotes, since as the point of tangency recedes, the tangent does not approach any limiting position. Many higher plane curves have one or more asymptotes, and they play an important part in the study of those curves.

For algebraic curves, the discussion in §§ 16–17 leads to the following rule for the determination of asymptotes parallel to the axes.

RULE. *If y becomes infinite as x approaches a, the line x = a is an asymptote; if y approaches b as x becomes infinite, the line y = b is an asymptote.*

Example (a). Examine the curve

$$y = \frac{ax^2}{(x - a)(x - 3a)}$$

for horizontal and vertical asymptotes.

Equating the denominator to zero, we find the vertical asymptotes $x = a$, $x = 3a$. As x increases (in either direction), y approaches a (by § 105, or by direct inspection); thus the line $y = a$ is a horizontal asymptote. See Fig. 110, page 209.

We know from analytic geometry that a curve of nth degree may intersect a straight line in not more than n points. Since a tangent is the limiting position of a secant when two points of intersection come to coincidence, the point of tangency counts as two intersections, so that a tangent may intersect the curve in not more than $(n - 2)$ other points. An asymptote is not a tangent, but it is the limiting position of a tangent. It can be shown (proof is omitted here) that a curve of the nth degree may intersect an asymptote in at most $(n - 2)$ points.

No curve of types (1)–(2) of § 109 can intersect a vertical asymptote; if $Q(x) = 0$, y does not exist. These curves may, however, intersect a horizontal asymptote, and such intersections should always be looked for.

Example (b). In the equation of Example (a),

$$y = \frac{ax^2}{(x - a)(x - 3a)},$$

put $y = a$;

$$a(x^2 - 4ax + 3a^2) = ax^2, \qquad x = \tfrac{3}{4}a;$$

thus the curve crosses its horizontal asymptote at $(\tfrac{3}{4}a, a)$. (Fig. 110, page 209.)

111. *Restriction to Definite Regions*

It is frequently possible to show that the curve is confined to certain definite portions of the plane, and a result of this kind is of great value in tracing the curve. Although no general directions can be given, in case the equation is, or can be, *solved for y* (or some power of *y*), it is highly instructive to note the *changes of sign* of the right member. The process will be explained by examples as need arises.

112. *Summary*

The method of curve tracing outlined in § 40 may now be greatly strengthened, as follows:

1. *Test for symmetry with respect to axes and origin.*
2. *Find the points of intersection with the axes.*
3. *Determine the behavior of y for large values of x. Find the horizontal asymptotes.*
4. *Find the vertical asymptotes.*
5. *Determine as closely as possible those regions of the plane in which the curve lies.*
6. *Find and classify the critical points.*

The above is only a general outline of the process to be followed; other steps will often suggest themselves. In some cases the points of inflection may be found and the inflectional tangents drawn, but this is not worth while if the second derivative is complicated. In fact, any step that leads to serious algebraic difficulty should be omitted if adequate information is obtainable otherwise. The elementary method of point plotting is not usually worth using extensively, but it is often advisable to plot a few points as a check on the analysis.

113. *Rational Fractions*

Consider the function

$$(1) \qquad\qquad y = \frac{P(x)}{Q(x)},$$

where

$$P(x) = a_0 x^p + a_1 x^{p-1} + \cdots + a_p,$$

$$Q(x) = b_0 x^q + b_1 x^{q-1} + \cdots + b_q, \qquad q \geqq 1.$$

If $q = 0$ (denominator a constant), y is a polynomial; little can be added at this time to the discussion of § 40. If $q = 1$, $p \leqq 2$, the curve is a hyperbola. These cases will therefore be excluded.

Before considering special examples, it will be well to apply our analysis to the rational fraction in general, thus deducing certain results applicable to all curves of this class. The proofs are left to the student.

1. There is no symmetry with respect to Ox.
2. The x-intercepts are the real zeros of P.
3. As x increases in either direction:

(a) If P is of higher degree than $Q(p > q)$, y becomes large, though not necessarily of the same sign as x.

(b) If P and Q are of the same degree, y approaches $\dfrac{a_0}{b_0}$; the line $y = \dfrac{a_0}{b_0}$ is an asymptote.

(c) If P is of lower degree than Q, the x-axis is an asymptote.

4. y increases without bound as Q approaches zero. Thus we find the real zeros (if any) of the denominator, say $r_1, r_2, \cdots$; the lines $x = r_1$, $x = r_2, \cdots$ are asymptotes.

5. The fraction *changes sign* when either P or Q does so. Thus we list the zeros of P and Q (already found in steps 2 and 4), *casting out those of even order*, and note for each of the others a change of sign of y and a passage of the curve across the x-axis: by intersection where $P = 0$, by jumping where $Q = 0$.

6. There may be as many as $p + q - 1$ critical points.

Example. Trace the curve (Examples, § 110)

$$y = \frac{ax^2}{(x - a)(x - 3a)}.$$

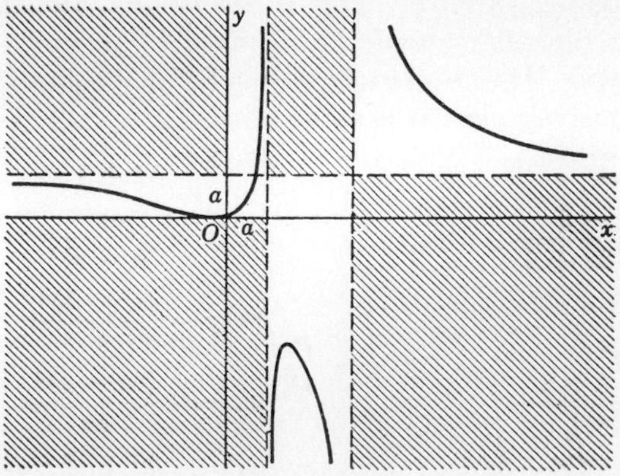

Figure 110

1. No symmetry.
2. $(0, 0)$.
3. The line $y = a$ is an asymptote, intersecting the curve at $(\tfrac{3}{4}a, a)$.
4. The lines $x = a$, $x = 3a$ are asymptotes.

5. The numerator vanishes at $x = 0$ but does not change sign because of the even exponent; the denominator, and hence the fraction, changes sign as x goes through a, $3a$. For large positive x, $x^2 > (x - a)(x - 3a)$ and $y > a$; for large negative x, $y < a$. This limits the curve to the unshaded regions.

6. $y' = \dfrac{2a^2x(3a - 2x)}{(x - a)^2(x - 3a)^2}$. Thus the critical points are $(0, 0)$, $(\frac{3}{2}a, -3a)$.

Figure 110 shows the curve, necessarily somewhat distorted because of the small space available.

EXERCISES

In Exs. 1–34, trace the curve.

1. $y = \dfrac{x - 4}{x^2 - 9}$.

2. $y = \dfrac{x - 2}{x^2 - 9}$.

3. $y = \dfrac{a^2(x - a)}{x^2 + a^2}$.

4. $y = \dfrac{a^3}{x^2 + a^2}$.

5. $y = \dfrac{2x}{1 - x^2}$.

6. $y = \dfrac{2x}{x^2 + 1}$.

7. $y = \dfrac{1 - x^2}{1 + x^2}$.

8. $y = \dfrac{1 + x^2}{1 - x^2}$.

9. $y = \dfrac{x}{(x - 2)(x + 1)}$.

10. $y = \dfrac{1}{x^3 - x^2 - 12x}$.

11. $y = \dfrac{x}{x^3 - 13x + 12}$.

12. $y = \dfrac{x - 2}{x^3 - 7x - 6}$.

13. $y = \dfrac{x^3}{1 - x^2}$.

14. $y = \dfrac{x^3}{1 - x^4}$.

15. $y = \dfrac{x^3}{1 - x^3}$.

16. $y = \dfrac{x}{x^4 + 1}$.

17. $y = \dfrac{2x - 2}{x^2 - 2x + 5}$.

18. $y = \dfrac{ax^3}{(a - x)^3}$.

19. $y = \dfrac{a^2x}{(x - a)^2}$.

20. $y = \dfrac{(x^2 - 1)^2}{x}$.

21. $y = \dfrac{x^2 + x + 1}{x^2 - 1}$.

22. $y = \dfrac{(2a - x)^3}{ax}$.

23. $y = \dfrac{(x - a)(x - 3a)^2}{ax}$.

24. $y = \dfrac{x^3 + x^2 - 2}{x^3}$.

25. $y = \dfrac{x^2 - 4}{(x - 1)(x + 4)}$.

26. $y = \dfrac{x^2 + 5}{(x - 1)(x + 4)}$.

27. $y = \dfrac{x^2 - 6}{x(x^2 - 4)}$.

28. $y = \dfrac{(x^2 - 2)^2}{x^2(x + 3)^2}$.

29. $y = \dfrac{(x^2 - 4)^2}{x - 4}$.

30. $y = \dfrac{2x^3 - 10}{x^3 - 3x^2 + 2x}$.

31. $y^3 = \dfrac{x}{x^2 - 1}$.

32. $y^3 = \dfrac{x}{x^2 + 1}$.

33. $y = \dfrac{2(x^2 - 4x + 3)}{x^2}$.

34. $y = \dfrac{x + 1}{x^2(x + 9)}$.

In Exs. 35–38, draw a curve from which the given function may be read if $\tan \theta$ is given.

35. $\tan 2\theta$. (Ex. 5.)

36. $\sin 2\theta$. (Ex. 6.)

37. $\cos 2\theta$. (Ex. 7.)

38. $\sec 2\theta$. (Ex. 8.)

39. Draw a curve from which $\sec 2\theta$ may be read if $\cos \theta$ is given.

40. A circular cone is circumscribed about a sphere of radius a. Express the volume of the cone as a function of its radius. Draw the graph, taking $a = 1$.

$$Ans. \ V = \frac{2}{3} \pi a \cdot \frac{r^4}{r^2 - a^2}.$$

41. In Ex. 40, graph the altitude as a function of the radius.

$$Ans. \ h = \frac{2ar^2}{r^2 - a^2}.$$

114. *Two-valued Functions*

Consider now the curve

(1)
$$y^2 = \frac{P(x)}{Q(x)},$$

where

$$P(x) = a_0 x^p + a_1 x^{p-1} + \cdots + a_p,$$
$$Q(x) = b_0 x^q + b_1 x^{q-1} + \cdots + b_q.$$

We exclude the case $q = 0$, $p \leqq 2$, since then the curve is a conic.

By way of general analysis, the following remarks may be made.

1. All curves of this class are symmetric with respect to Ox.
2. The x-intercepts are the real zeros of $P(x)$.
3. For large x (in either direction), y may be imaginary. If not:
(a) If $p < q$, the x-axis is an asymptote.
(b) If $p = q$, there are two horizontal asymptotes.
4. A vertical asymptote falling in a region where y is imaginary may be disregarded.
5. y^2 changes from positive to negative, y from real (positive and negative) to imaginary, or vice versa, as x passes through a zero *of odd order* of either $P(x)$ or $Q(x)$.
6. Critical points where y is imaginary are disregarded.

Example. Trace the curve $y^2 = \dfrac{(x+1)(x+2)}{x}$.

1. Symmetric with respect to Ox.
2. $y = 0$ at $x = -1$ and $x = -2$.
3. For large positive x, y is real; for large negative x, y is imaginary.
4. Vertical asymptote: $x = 0$.
5. The fraction changes sign as x goes through -2, -1, 0. At the extreme left $y^2 < 0$; thus the curve is absent when $x < -2$, present when $-2 < x < -1$, absent when $-1 < x < 0$, present when $x > 0$.
6. $2yy' = \dfrac{x^2 - 2}{x^2}$, $y' = \dfrac{x^2 - 2}{2x^2 y}$.

Thus the critical points are at $x = \sqrt{2}$, $y = \pm(\sqrt{2} + 1)$ and $x = -\sqrt{2}$, $y = \pm(\sqrt{2} - 1)$. The tangent is vertical at $(-2, 0)$, $(-1, 0)$.

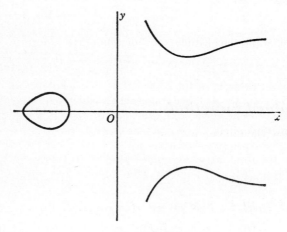

Figure 111

The curve is shown in Fig. 111. In the figure, the y-scale is twice the x-scale. The inflection points on the right have been pulled toward the y-axis in order to exhibit, in the small space available, the fact that the direction of concavity does change at a point to the right of the extremes. By the methods of Chapter 17, it can be shown that those inflection points occur at $x = 4.27$; see Ex. 25, page 232.

EXERCISES

In Exs. 1–24, trace the curve.

1. $y^2 = x(x^2 - 4)$.
2. $y^2 = x(9 - x^2)$.
3. $y^2 = x^2(3 - x)$.
4. $y^2 = (x - 2)^2(x - 3)$.
5. $y^2 = x^4 - 5x^2 + 4$.
6. $y^2 = x^4(5 - x)$.

7. $y^2 = \dfrac{x}{1+x}.$

8. $y^2 = \dfrac{x}{1-x}.$

9. $y^2 = \dfrac{1-x}{x^2+8}.$

10. $y^2 = \dfrac{x-1}{x^2+8}.$

11. $y^2 = \dfrac{x-5}{x^2-16}.$

12. $y^2 = \dfrac{5-x}{x^2-16}.$

13. $y^2 = \dfrac{x^2-4x}{x^2-25}.$

14. $y^2 = \dfrac{x^2-3x}{x^2-25}.$

15. $y^2 = \dfrac{x^3}{1-x^2}.$

16. $y^2 = \dfrac{a^3x}{x^2-a^2}.$

17. $y^2 = \dfrac{x+1}{2x-x^2}.$

18. $y^2 = \dfrac{x}{(x+1)(x-2)}.$

19. $y^2 = \dfrac{(x^2-1)(x^2-9)}{x(x^2-4)}.$

20. $y^2 = \dfrac{(x^2-1)(x^2-4)}{x^2(x^2-9)}.$

21. $y^2 = \dfrac{x^2(x-3)}{(x-1)(x+4)^4}.$

22. $y^2 = \dfrac{x(x-1)(x-4)}{(x-2)^3}.$

23. $y^2 = \dfrac{x(x+1)}{(x-1)^2(x-2)}.$

24. $y^2 = \dfrac{(x-1)^2(x-2)}{x(x+1)}.$

25. Graph the eccentricity of the conic $cx^2 + y^2 = c$ in terms of c.

26. In Ex. 25, graph the distance from focus to directrix.

27. Draw a curve from which $\cos \theta$ can be measured if $\tan \theta$ is given.

28. Draw the graph of $\sin \theta$ as a function of $\sec \theta$.

29. Draw on the same axes the curves $y^2 = 1 - x^n$ for $n = 1, 2, 3, 4, 5$.

30. Draw on the same axes the curves $x^n + y^n = 1$ for $n = 1, 2, 3, 4, 100$. (Cf. Exs. 45–46, page 205.)

115. *Oblique and Curvilinear Asymptotes*

Asymptotes parallel to the axes are not the only ones which enter the study of simple algebraic curves. On this topic we confine our attention to an illustrative example and a few exercises.

Example. Sketch the curve

(1) $$y = \frac{x^3}{x-2}.$$

First, proceed as in the earlier portions of this chapter, thus determining that the curve (1) has the following properties:

(a) $y = 0$ only at $x = 0$;

(b) Minimum point at $(3, 27)$;

(c) Inflection point with horizontal tangent at $(0, 0)$;

(d) Vertical asymptote $x = 2$;

(e) As $x \to \infty$, $y \to \infty$, and as $x \to -\infty$, $y \to \infty$.

The one new tool to be introduced now is based upon carrying out the division of x^3 by $(x - 2)$ on the right in equation (1). That procedure shows that (1) can be rewritten in the form

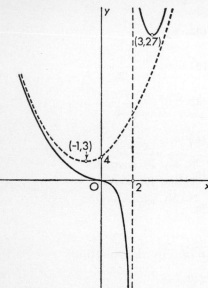

(2) $\quad y = x^2 + 2x + 4 + \dfrac{8}{x - 2}.$

As $|x| \to \infty$, equation (2) is well approximated by

(3) $\qquad y = x^2 + 2x + 4,$

because $\dfrac{8}{x - 2} \to 0$, as $|x| \to \infty$.

Let the y of the cubic (2) be denoted by y_1, the y of the parabola (3) by y_2. Then, from

$$y_1 = x^2 + 2x + 4 + \frac{8}{x - 2}$$

and

$$y_2 = x^2 + 2x + 4,$$

Figure 112

we obtain

(4) $\qquad\qquad y_1 - y_2 = \dfrac{8}{x - 2}.$

Differentiation of equation (4) yields

$$y_1' - y_2' = -\frac{8}{(x - 2)^2}.$$

It is now easy to see that, as $|x| \to \infty$, $(y_1 - y_2) \to 0$ and also $(y_1' - y_2') \to 0$. Then we call the parabola (3) a *curvilinear asymptote* to the cubic (1).

EXERCISES

In each exercise find and sketch the curvilinear or rectilinear asymptote, and trace the curve whose equation is given.

1. $y = \dfrac{x^2}{x - 2}.$
2. $y = \dfrac{x^2}{x + 2}.$

3. $y = \dfrac{x^3 - 2}{x}.$
4. $y = \dfrac{x^3}{x - 1}.$

5. $y = \dfrac{x^3}{1 + x^2}.$
6. $y = \dfrac{x^3}{1 - x^2}.$

7. $y = \dfrac{x^4}{x^2 - 1}.$
8. $y = \dfrac{x^4}{x^2 + 1}.$

9. $y = \dfrac{x^2 - 9}{x - 4}.$

10. $y = \dfrac{x^2 - 9}{x - 2}.$

11. $y = \dfrac{x^3 - 9}{x^2 - 1}.$

12. $y = \dfrac{x^3 - 3x^2 + 4}{x}.$

13. $y^2 = \dfrac{x^2}{x - 2}.$

14. $y^2 = \dfrac{x^2}{x + 2}.$

15. $y^2 = \dfrac{x^2 - 9}{x - 4}.$

16. $y^2 = \dfrac{x^2 - 9}{x - 2}.$

17. $y^2 = \dfrac{x^2(x^2 - 8)}{(x + 2)^2}.$

18. $y^2 = \dfrac{x^6}{x^3 - 1}.$

19. Ex. 13, page 210.

20. Ex. 20, page 210.

21. Ex. 29, page 211.

22. Ex. 40, page 211.

23. Ex. 15, page 213.

24. Ex. 24, page 213.

116. *Singular Points*

If y is defined implicitly as a function of x by the equation

$$F(x, y) = 0,$$

the derivative in general takes the form of a fraction whose numerator and denominator are functions of x and y; say,

$$y' = \frac{N(x, y)}{D(x, y)}.$$

(See, for instance, the examples and exercises under § 33.)

If $N(x, y)$ and $D(x, y)$ both vanish at a point (x, y) on the curve, the slope at that point assumes the indeterminate form $\frac{0}{0}$. A point at which the derivative takes this form is called a *singular point*.

To find the singular points of a curve, we must therefore find the values of x and y that satisfy the three equations

(1) $\qquad F(x, y) = 0, \qquad N(x, y) = 0, \qquad D(x, y) = 0.$

As we have but two unknowns x and y to satisfy three equations, it follows that a curve will have singular points only if these three equations happen to have one or more common solutions.

For the moment, we consider only curves having a singular point at the origin. Singularities occurring elsewhere will be discussed in § 119.

117. *Determination of Tangents by Inspection*

Let the equation of the curve be written in the form

(1) $\quad a_0 + b_0x + b_1y + c_0x^2 + c_1xy + c_2y^2 + d_0x^3 + \cdots + g_ny^n = 0;$

i.e., we arrange the left member in ascending powers of x and y.

Differentiating, we find

$$b_0 + b_1y' + 2c_0x + c_1xy' + c_1y + 2c_2yy' + \cdots = 0,$$

$$y' = -\frac{b_0 + 2c_0x + c_1y + \cdots}{b_1 + c_1x + 2c_2y + \cdots}.$$

The origin is on the curve only if $a_0 = 0$. In that case the equation of the tangent at $(0, 0)$ is found by the usual methods to be

$$b_0x + b_1y = 0,$$

provided b_0 and b_1 are not both zero; i.e., the equation of the tangent at the origin may be found by equating to zero the group of terms of the first degree.

If a_0, b_0, and b_1 are all zero, the origin is on the curve and the derivative is indeterminate at that point; hence the origin is a singular point. In this case, since the method of § 34 fails, we proceed as follows.

For convenience let us put

$$c_0x^2 + c_1xy + c_2y^2 \equiv c_2(y - m_1x)(y - m_2x).$$

(The argument needs only slight modification when $c_2 = 0$.) Equation (1) becomes

$$c_2(y - m_1x)(y - m_2x) + d_0x^3 + \cdots = 0.$$

The abscissas of the points of intersection of the line

$$y = mx$$

with this curve are given by the equation

(2) $$c_2x^2(m - m_1)(m - m_2) + x^3(d_0 + \cdots) + \cdots = 0.$$

Two roots of this equation are zero; every line $y = mx$ intersects the curve in two coincident points at the origin. But (2) also shows that if we let m approach either m_1 or m_2, the coefficient of x^2 approaches zero; i.e., a third point of intersection of the curve with the line $y = mx$ approaches the origin, and the lines

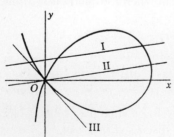

Figure 113

$$y = m_1x, \qquad y = m_2x.$$

are both tangent to the curve at the singular point. These lines may, of course, be real and distinct, real and coincident, or imaginary.

To interpret all this geometrically, let us examine Fig. 113, which exhibits a typical situation—that in which the curve crosses itself. The random line I intersects the curve in three distinct points. As it moves toward position II, two points approach each other and finally coincide—every line through the singular point intersects the curve twice there. Now as the line rotates to position III, the third point approaches, and ultimately, in the position of tangency, attains coincidence with the other two. Evidently in this figure there are two positions of tangency.

Since

$$c_2(y - m_1x)(y - m_2x) \equiv c_0x^2 + c_1xy + c_2y^2,$$

we see that the equations of the two tangents are obtained by *equating the group of terms of second degree to zero*, and factoring the left member of the resulting equation.

The argument we have used can be extended to show that if $F(x, y)$ has no terms of degree lower than the kth, any line through the origin meets the curve there in k points, and the k tangents to the curve at the origin are obtained by *equating the group of terms of lowest degree to zero*.

A point at which there are two tangents (whether distinct, coincident, or imaginary) is called a *double point*; one at which there are three tangents is a *triple point*; etc. In most cases that arise in practice, a curve having only one singular point, and that a triple or higher-ordered singularity, is much more easily traced from its polar than from its rectangular equation. Partly for this reason, and partly because they occur much more often, we shall study chiefly curves whose only singularities are double points.

THEOREM 24. *If the equation $F(x, y) = 0$ contains terms of the second, but none of lower degree, the origin is a double point; the tangents at that point are found by equating to zero, and factoring, the group of terms of second degree.*

As noted above, every line through a double point has at that point two coincident intersections with the curve. Hence a (nondegenerate) cubic cannot have more than one double point; for, if there were two, the straight line through those points would have four intersections with the curve. By similar argument, it follows that no cubic can have a triple point.

118. *Classification of Double Points*

If the tangents at a double point are real and different, the point is called a *node*: Two branches of the curve cross each other, as in Fig. 114.

If the tangents are imaginary, the point is an *isolated point*, or *conjugate point*: There is no other portion of the curve in its vicinity. Such a point is P in Fig. 115.

Figure 114

Figure 115

If the tangents are real and coincident, the point is either a *cusp* (Figs. 116–117) or a *double cusp* (Fig. 118), or in some instances an isolated point.

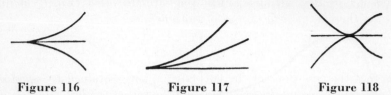

| Figure 116 | Figure 117 | Figure 118 |

If the two branches of a cusp lie on opposite sides of the cuspidal tangent, as in Fig. 116, the point is a *cusp of the first kind*; if on the same side, as in Fig. 117, a *cusp of the second kind*.

Example (a). Trace the curve $y^2 = 4x^2(1 - x)$.

1. The curve is symmetric with respect to Ox.
2. The curve intersects the axes at $(0, 0)$, $(1, 0)$.
3. When x is large positive, y is imaginary; x large negative, y large positive and negative.
4. No vertical asymptotes.
5. y is imaginary when $x > 1$.
6. $2yy' = 4(2x - 3x^2)$, $y' = \dfrac{2(2x - 3x^2)}{y}$. Equating the numerator to

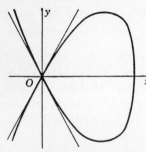

zero, we appear to find the critical values $x = 0$, $x = \frac{2}{3}$. But by the equation of the curve, when $x = 0$, $y = 0$, so that y' takes the form $\frac{0}{0}$, and the origin is a singular point. The only critical points are $(\frac{2}{3}, \pm\frac{4}{9}\sqrt{3})$.

7. Since the equation contains no terms of degree lower than the second, the origin is a singular point (as also discovered above). Equating to zero the terms of lowest degree, i.e., $y^2 - 4x^2 = 0$, we find the two real distinct tangents $y = \pm 2x$; thus the origin is a node. See Fig. 119.

Figure 119

Example (b). Trace the curve $y^2 = x^4(1 - x^2)$.

1. The curve is symmetric with respect to both axes.
2. The curve crosses the axes at $(0, 0)$, $(\pm 1, 0)$.
3. When x is large, y is imaginary.
4. There are no vertical asymptotes.
5. y is imaginary outside the interval $-1 < x < 1$.
6. $2yy' = 4x^3 - 6x^5$, $y' = \dfrac{x^3(2 - 3x^2)}{y}$. At $(0, 0)$ the derivative is indeterminate, so that the origin is a singular point; the only critical values are $x = \pm\sqrt{\frac{2}{3}}$.

7. The tangents at the origin are the coincident lines $y^2 = 0$ (the x-axis counted twice). Thus the point is either a cusp or a double cusp; by symmetry, it must be the latter. See Fig. 120.

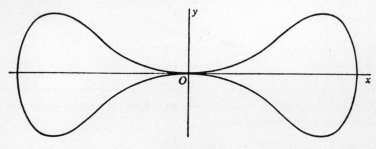

Figure 120

Example (c). Trace the curve $y^3 = x^2(3a - x)$.

1. There is no symmetry.
2. $(0, 0)$, $(3a, 0)$.
3. When x is large positive or negative, y is large negative or positive.
4. No vertical asymptotes.
5. When $x < 3a$, $y > 0$; when $x > 3a$, $y < 0$.
6. $3y^2y' = 3x(2a - x)$, $y' = \dfrac{x(2a - x)}{y^2}$. The slope is indeterminate at $(0, 0)$; the point $(2a, 4^{\frac{1}{3}}a)$ is a maximum.

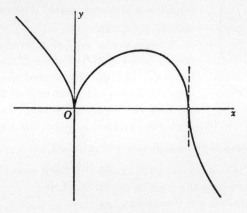

Figure 121

7. The tangents at $(0, 0)$ are given by $3ax^2 = 0$: the y-axis counted twice. By the result of step 5, the origin is a cusp.

The slope is infinite—tangent vertical—at $(3a, 0)$; this is also a point of inflection. See Fig. 121.

EXERCISES

In Exs. 1–32, trace the curve.

1. $y^2 = 10x^2 - 7x^3 + x^4$.

2. $a^3y^2 = x^5$.

3. $y^2 = 4x^3 - 3x^4$.

4. $y^2 = 35x^2 + 2x^3 - x^4$.

5. $a^2y^2 = x^2(a^2 - x^2)$.

6. $a^2y^2 = x^2(x^2 - a^2)$.

7. $y^2 = x^2(x + 3)$.

8. $y^2 = x^3(x + 3)$.

9. $y^2 = \dfrac{a^2x^2}{x^2 + a^2}$.

10. $y^2 = \dfrac{a^2x^2}{x^2 - a^2}$.

11. $y^2 = \dfrac{x^4}{1 - x^2}$.

12. $y^2 = \dfrac{x^3}{1 - x^2}$.

13. $y^2 = \dfrac{x^2}{x - 1}$.

14. $y^2 = \dfrac{x^2}{(1 - x)^3}$.

15. $y^2 = \dfrac{x^2}{x^2 + 3x - 4}$.

16. $y^2 = \dfrac{x^2}{(x - 1)^2(x + 4)}$.

17. $y^2 = \dfrac{x^2}{(x - 1)(x - 2)}$.

18. $y^2 = \dfrac{x^2}{(x - 1)^2(x - 2)}$.

19. $y^2 = x^6 - 4x^4 + 3x^2$.

20. $y^2 = 20x^2 - x^5$.

21. $y^2 = \dfrac{x^3}{a - x}$, the cissoid.

22. $y^2 = \dfrac{x^2(3a - x)}{a + x}$, the trisectrix of Maclaurin.

23. $y^2 = \dfrac{x^2(x - 1)}{x - 2}$.

24. $y^2 = \dfrac{x^2(1 - x)}{x - 2}$.

25. $y^2 = \dfrac{x^2(x + 1)}{x - 2}$.

26. $y^2 = \dfrac{x^2(x + 1)}{2 - x}$.

27. $y^3 = x^2(8 - x^2)$.

28. $y^3 = 4x^5 - 5x^4$.

29. $y^3 = \dfrac{a^3x^2}{(x - a)^2}$.

30. $y^3 = \dfrac{x^2}{1 - x^2}$.

31. $y^4 = \dfrac{x^4}{x^2 - 7x + 10}$.

32. $y^2 = \dfrac{x^2(x^2 + 4ax + 3a^2)}{(x - a)^2}$.

In Exs. 33–40, solve for y and analyze the two branches separately.

33. $(3x - y)^2 = x^3$.

34. $y^2 - 2xy = -x^4$.

35. $y^2 - 2xy = x^3$.

36. $(y - x^2)^2 = x^5$.

37. $(y + x)^2 = \dfrac{x^3}{1 - x}$.

38. $(y - x)^2 = \dfrac{(x - 1)^2}{x}$.

39. $y^2 - 2x^3y = -x^8$.

40. $(y - x^2)^2 = x^5(2 - x)$.

In Exs. 41–50, transform the equation to one in polar coordinates. Sketch the curve.

41. $(x^2 + y^2)^2 = 2a^2xy$.   *Ans.* $r^2 = a^2 \sin 2\theta$.

42. $(x^2 + y^2)^3 = 4a^2x^2y^2$.   *Ans.* $r = a \sin 2\theta$.

43. $(x^2 + y^2)^3 = a^4x^2$. *Ans.* $r^2 = a^2 \cos \theta$.
44. $(x^2 + y^2 + ax)^2 = a^2(x^2 + y^2)$. *Ans.* $r = a(1 - \cos \theta)$.
45. $(x^2 + y^2)(x^2 + y^2 - a^2)^2 = a^4y^2$. *Ans.* $r^2 = a^2(1 + \sin \theta)$.
46. $(x^2 + y^2 - 2ax)^2 = a^2(x^2 + y^2)$. *Ans.* $r = a(1 + 2 \cos \theta)$.
47. $(x^2 + y^2)^3 = 4a^2xy(x^2 - y^2)$. *Ans.* $r^2 = a^2 \sin 4\theta$.
48. $(x^2 + y^2)^5 = 16a^2x^2y^2(x^2 - y^2)^2$. *Ans.* $r = a \sin 4\theta$.
49. $y^4 - 2axy^2 = x^4$. *Ans.* $r = a \sin \theta \tan 2\theta$.
50. $y^4 + 2a^2xy = x^4$. *Ans.* $r^2 = a^2 \tan 2\theta$.

Prove the theorems in Exs. 51–55.

51. The graph of a one-valued algebraic function $y = f(x)$ cannot have a singular point.

52. A line tangent to a cubic at a double point cannot intersect the curve elsewhere.

53. If a quartic curve has a triple point, it can have no other singularity.

54. A quartic cannot have more than three double points. (Assume four; then consider the conic through these four points and a fifth point of the curve.)

55. A straight line through two double points of a quartic cannot intersect the curve elsewhere.

119. *Singular Points Not at the Origin*

To locate singular points not at the origin, we must look for values of x and y satisfying the three equations (1) of § 116. Of course no rules can be given; we try to solve the simplest-looking pair, then substitute the coordinates of the points thus found in the other equation. The algebra may conceivably be very difficult. But when a curve has only one singularity, if that point is not taken as origin, it is at least, in most cases, placed on a coordinate axis; if there are two, the line joining them is likely to be taken as one of the axes. Thus as a rule the problem of finding singular points is actually rather simple.

THEOREM 25. *Given the curve*

(1) $$y^k = \frac{P(x)}{Q(x)}, \qquad k \geqq 2,$$

where $P(x)$, $Q(x)$ are polynomials, if $(x - c)^r (r \geqq 2)$ is a factor of $P(x)$, the point $(c, 0)$ is a singular point of the curve.

Further, if $k = 2$, $r = 2$, the point is a node or isolated point; if $k = 2$, $r \geqq 3$, or if $k \geqq 3$, $r = 2$, the point is a cusp with horizontal or vertical tangent respectively, or an isolated point.

To prove the theorem, merely write $P(x)$ in the form

$$P(x) = (x - c)^r R(x),$$

and find y' from (1). Translation of the origin to $(c, 0)$ easily proves the succeeding statements.

Example. Graph the radius of curvature of the hyperbola

(2) $$x^2 - y^2 = a^2$$

as a function of x.

In Example (*b*), § 101 (page 189), we found

(3) $$\rho = \frac{(2x^2 - a^2)^{\frac{3}{2}}}{a^2}.$$

First rationalize the equation:

$$a^4\rho^2 = (2x^2 - a^2)^3.$$

1. Symmetric with respect to both axes.
2. $\rho = 0$, $x = \pm\frac{1}{2}\sqrt{2}\,a$.
3. x large positive or negative, ρ large positive and negative.
4. No vertical asymptotes.
5. ρ is imaginary for $|x| < \frac{1}{2}\sqrt{2}\,a$.
6. $2a^4\rho\rho' = 12x(2x^2 - a^2)^2$, $\rho' = \dfrac{6x(2x^2 - a^2)^2}{a^4\rho}$. There are no critical

points, since ρ' is indeterminate for $x = \pm\frac{1}{2}\sqrt{2}\,a$, and ρ is imaginary for $x = 0$.

7. By Theorem 25, and remarks following, the points $(\pm\frac{1}{2}\sqrt{2}\,a,\ 0)$ are cusps with the x-axis as cuspidal tangent.

Since we must have $|x| \geqq a$, by (2), and ρ is limited to positive values, the graph of (3) is the part of the curve drawn full.

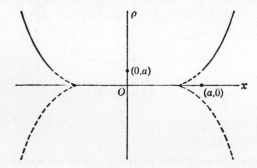

Figure 122

EXERCISES

In Exs. 1–16, trace the curve.

1. $y^2 = x(x - 4)^2$.
2. $y^2 = x(x + 2)^2$.
3. $y^2 = x^3(x - 1)^2$.
4. $y^2 = x^3(x + 2)^2$.

5. $y^2 = x(x-1)^3$.

6. $a^3y^2 = x(a^2 - x^2)^2$.

7. $ay^4 = x(a^2 - x^2)^2$.

8. $ay^3 = (x^2 - a^2)^2$.

9. $y^2 = \dfrac{(x-4)^2}{x}$.

10. $y^2 = \dfrac{(x-4)^2}{x^3}$.

11. $y^2 = \dfrac{(x^2 - 4a^2)^2}{x^2 - a^2}$.

12. $y^2 = \dfrac{a^4(x^2 - 4a^2)^2}{(x^2 - a^2)^3}$.

13. $y^2 = \dfrac{a^3(x^2 - a^2)^2}{x^5}$.

14. $y^2 = \dfrac{x(x+1)^2}{(x^2 + 1)^2}$.

15. $y^2 = \dfrac{x^3(x-1)^2}{(x^2 + 1)^4}$.

16. $y^2 = \dfrac{a^4(x^2 - a^2)}{(x^2 - 4a^2)^2}$.

17. Graph the curvature of the parabola $y^2 = 4ax$ as a function of x.

18. Rationalize the equation $x^{\frac{2}{3}} + y^{\frac{2}{3}} = a^{\frac{2}{3}}$, and trace the curve.

Ans. $(x^2 + y^2 - a^2)^3 + 27a^2x^2y^2 = 0$.

120. *Transcendental Curves*

We have already had from time to time considerable practice in tracing the graphs of transcendental functions; but many curves were excluded by the fact that, at one or more points, the function or its derivative takes an "indeterminate" form. A few simple cases of this sort will now be studied.

Example (a). Trace the curve $y = xe^x$. The curve is shown in Fig. 123 below.

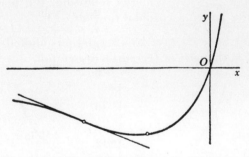

Figure 123

1. There is no symmetry.

2. The curve crosses the axes at $(0, 0)$.

3. As x becomes large and negative, y approaches zero (§ 106); hence the negative x-axis is an asymptote. When x is large and positive, y is large and positive.

4. There are no vertical asymptotes.

5. Since e^x is always positive, y has the same sign as x: The curve lies in the first and third quadrants.

6. Since $y' = xe^x + e^x$, the only critical point is $(-1, -e^{-1})$. This is a minimum point.

7. Putting $y'' = xe^x + 2e^x = 0$, we find the point of inflection $x = -2$, $y = -2e^{-2}$, with $y' = -e^{-2}$.

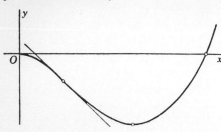

Figure 124

In Fig. 123, the y-scale is three times as large as the x-scale.

Example (*b*). Trace the curve $y = x^2 \ln x$.

1. No symmetry.
2. As $x \to 0^+$, $y \to 0^-$. When $y = 0$, $x = 1$.
3. As $x \to \infty$, $y \to \infty$.
4. There are no asymptotes.

5. For $x > 1$, $y > 0$; for $0 < x < 1$, $y < 0$; for $x < 0$, y is imaginary.

6. $y' = 2x \ln x + x = x(1 + 2 \ln x)$. Because y does not exist for $x = 0$, the only critical value is $x = e^{-\frac{1}{2}}$. Since $x < 0$ leads to imaginary y, the curve exists only to the right of the origin. But, $\underset{x \to 0^+}{\text{Lim }} y' = 0$, so the slope is small for small positive x. The curve drops to a minimum at $(e^{-\frac{1}{2}}, -\frac{1}{2}e^{-1})$, then rises as shown in Fig. 124. The y-scale in the figure is twice the x-scale.

EXERCISES

In Exs. 1–33, trace the curve.

1. $y = xe^{-x}$.

2. $y = x \ln x$.

3. $y = e^{-x^2}$.

4. $y = x^2 e^{-x}$.

5. $y = x \ln^2 x$.

6. $y = xe^{-x^2}$.

7. $y = \dfrac{e^x}{x}$.

8. $y = \dfrac{\ln x}{x}$.

9. $y = \dfrac{\ln x}{x^2}$.

10. $y = \dfrac{e^{-x}}{x}$.

11. $y = \dfrac{1 - \ln x}{x}$.

12. $y = \dfrac{1 + \ln x}{x}$.

13. $y = \dfrac{e^{-x}}{x^2}$.

14. $y = \dfrac{x}{\ln x}$.

15. $y = \dfrac{\ln x}{x^3}$.

16. $y = \dfrac{\ln^2 x}{x^2}$.

17. $y = \dfrac{x}{\ln^2 x}$.

18. $y = \dfrac{e^x}{x^2 - 3}$.

19. $y = \dfrac{1 - \sin x}{\cos x}$.

20. $y = \dfrac{1 - \tan x}{\cos 2x}$.

21. $y = \dfrac{\cos x}{e^x}$.

22. $y^2 = \ln x$.

23. $y^2 = xe^{-x}$.

24. $y^2 = -xe^{-x}$.

25. $y^2 = e^{-x}(8 - x^2)$.

26. $y^2 = x \ln x$.

27. $y^2 = -x \ln x$.

28. $y = e^{-\frac{1}{x}}$.

29. $y = e^{\frac{1}{4-x^2}}$.

30. $y = e^{\frac{1}{x^2-4}}$.

31. $y = \dfrac{1}{1 + e^{-\frac{1}{x}}}$.

32. $y = \dfrac{1}{4 - e^{\frac{1}{x}}}$.

33. $y = \dfrac{1}{1 + e^{\frac{1}{x^2-1}}}$.

34. For the curve $y = \dfrac{\sin x^2}{x}$, show that $\lim\limits_{x \to \infty} y = 0$, but that $\lim\limits_{x \to \infty} y'$ does not exist; hence that the x-axis is not an asymptote.

35. For the curve $y = e^{-x} \sin e^x$, investigate $\lim\limits_{x \to \infty} y$, $\lim\limits_{x \to \infty} y'$.

36. Sketch $y^2 = - \ln x$.

SOLUTION OF EQUATIONS:

NEWTON'S METHOD

121. *Newton's Method*

A problem of first importance in engineering, physics, and the other mathematical sciences is to find, to any desired degree of approximation, the root or roots of an equation which cannot be solved by elementary methods. This problem can be solved by *Newton's method*, which we shall now develop.

Newton's method is essentially one for improving an approximation already obtained. With skilled application, it can be made to yield a root to any desired degree of accuracy. It is useful in obtaining approximations to imaginary roots, as well as real roots, of equations. Only approximations to real roots are treated here.

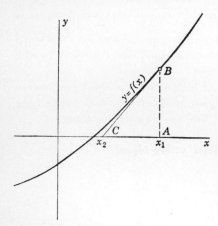

Figure 125

Let the equation whose root is desired be

$$(1) \qquad f(x) = 0.$$

Consider the curve

$$(2) \qquad y = f(x).$$

A root of equation (1) is the x-coordinate of a point at which the curve (2) crosses the x-axis

Let the first approximation to the root be $x = x_1$, as shown in Fig. 125. The point B, where the ordinate AB intersects the curve, has the coordinates $x = x_1,\ y = f(x_1)$. The tangent line at B will intersect the x-axis at C, whose coordinate x_2 may be a better approximation to the desired root than is x_1.

To find x_2, knowing x_1, note that $\overline{BA} = f(x_1)$, $\overline{CA} = x_1 - x_2$, and $\dfrac{\overline{BA}}{\overline{CA}} = f'(x_1)$. Thus

$$\frac{f(x_1)}{x_1 - x_2} = f'(x_1),$$

which yields

(3)
$$x_2 = x_1 - \frac{f(x_1)}{f'(x_1)}.$$

If we have one approximation x_1, to a root of $f(x) = 0$, equation (3) gives us another approximation, x_2, to that root. From x_2 still another approximation, x_3, is obtained in the same way by using

$$x_3 = x_2 - \frac{f(x_2)}{f'(x_2)},$$

and the process can be repeated as many times as we wish.

In following the discussion, it is helpful to carry out the details for an equation whose solution is known. The equation

$$f(x) = x^2 - 2x - 1 = 0$$

has roots $x = 1 \pm \sqrt{2}$. Therefore, the parabola

$$y = x^2 - 2x - 1$$

crosses Ox near $x = 2.4$ and $x = -0.4$. For this equation choose as the first approximation $x_1 = 2.4$, compute $f(x_1), f'(x_1)$, and the second approximation x_2 by employing equation (3).

The term $\left[-\dfrac{f(x_1)}{f'(x_1)} \right]$ in equation (3) may be called the correction; it is the difference between the successive approximations x_1 and x_2. Newton's method is to iterate this process until the correction has vanished to the number of decimal places required in the root.

Examples of the use of the method will follow after a short discussion of the difficulties to be avoided and of some common procedures for obtaining a first approximation to get the wheels of Newton's method rolling.

122. *Difficulties Present in Newton's Method*

In the basic formula

$$x_2 = x_1 - \frac{f(x_1)}{f'(x_1)}$$

of Newton's method, the correction term will usually be large if its denominator $f'(x_1)$ is small. Since $f'(x)$ will vanish at a critical point of $y = f(x)$, it is highly desirable to avoid such a point in using Newton's method. Figure

126 emphasizes that if x_1 is unwisely chosen, then the slope of the tangent line is small, and the next approximation, x_2, is distressingly far from the desired root.

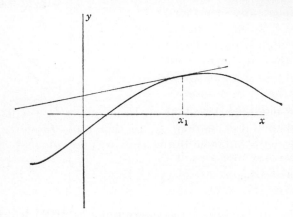

Figure 126

When two roots of the equation $f(x) = 0$ are close together, it can become a serious problem to avoid the nearby critical point. When the root is a repeated root, both $f(x)$ and $f'(x)$ vanish there. In theory, no difficulty arises because $\dfrac{f(x)}{f'(x)} \to 0$ as x approaches the desired root; in practice, considerable difficulty arises because we lose significant figures rapidly in computing the small values of $f(x)$ and $f'(x)$ near the root. The cure is usually effected by solving $f'(x) = 0$ for a double root of the original equation, or $f''(x) = 0$ for a triple root, etc.

Since the solution of equations is a minor, not a major, portion of this course, the difficulties discussed here will be avoided by careful selection of problems to be solved.

123. *The First Approximation*

Three simple methods for obtaining a first approximation will now be explained.

FIRST METHOD. Plot points on the curve $y = f(x)$ until the root is pinned in between two values of x, one yielding a positive y, the other a negative y. Then approximate the root by interpolation, call that approximation x_1, and proceed with Newton's method. See Example (a) in the next section.

SECOND METHOD. If the equation $f(x) = 0$ can be written, by transferring terms from one side to the other, as $g(x) = h(x)$, where $g(x)$ and $h(x)$ are simple functions, then plot $y_1 = g(x)$ and $y_2 = h(x)$. The x-coordinate of a point of intersection of these curves is a root of the equation $f(x) = 0$.

Example. The equation $x^2 - \sin x = 0$ can be written $x^2 = \sin x$. By sketching $y_1 = x^2$ and $y_2 = \sin x$ on the same figure (Fig. 127), we obtain a first rough approximation, $x_1 = 0.9$.

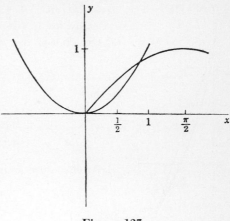

Figure 127

THIRD METHOD. If the equation is so simple that its component parts can be obtained readily from a single table, then a first approximation may be obtained from that table by inspection. For example, to start on the solution of the equation $e^{-x} = x$, we may well consult a table of exponentials, pp. 560–565, and look down the appropriate columns until we find where e^{-x} and x are about equal. Thus we soon find that $x_1 = 0.57$ is a good first approximation.

In summary, any of the three methods may be employed or combinations of them can be particularly useful. The first method has many advantages in that the more we know about the curve $y = f(x)$, the more effective will be our use of Newton's method.

124. *Solution of Equations*

In applying the technique described in this chapter, it should be kept in mind that any approximation x_n is considered exact, once chosen, and that $f(x_n)$ and $f'(x_n)$ are computed on that basis. If tables are used, the precision of the result is restrained by the limited accuracy of the tables. The root can then be approximated more closely only by computing the functions $f(x_n)$ and $f'(x_n)$ to a greater degree of accuracy than that present in the tables.

For a smooth curve, Newton's method yields the root as closely as desired; it "converges" to the correct value of x. In practice, once we get fairly close to the root, the method converges quite rapidly. Often two or three additional significant figures are picked up in a single step.

Example (*a*). Find to four decimal places the smaller positive root of the equation

$$(1) \qquad\qquad x^3 - 4x + 2 = 0.$$

Here
$$f(x) = x^3 - 4x + 2,$$
$$f'(x) = 3x^2 - 4.$$

Put
$$y = x^3 - 4x + 2.$$

When $x = 0$, $y = 2$; when $x = 1$, $y = -1$. A root lies between $x = 0$ and $x = 1$, Fig. 128. The chord joining $(0, 2)$ and $(1, -1)$ crosses Ox at $x = \frac{2}{3}$; but since $y'' = 6x$, the curve is concave upward in this interval and will cross Ox to the left of the chord; try $x_1 = 0.5$. By direct substitution, we find

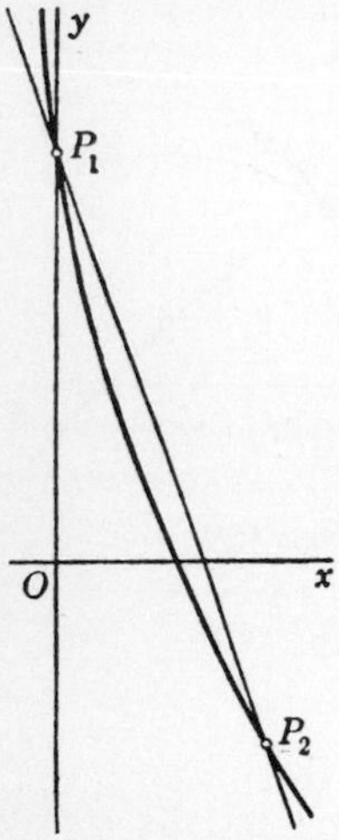

$$f(x_1) = 0.125, \qquad f'(x_1) = -3.25,$$

so that

$$x_2 = 0.5 - \frac{0.125}{-3.25} = 0.5 + 0.04,$$

$$x_2 = 0.54.$$

Next we use x_2 in a similar manner to find

$$f(x_2) = -0.0025, \qquad f'(x_2) = -3.13,$$

and

$$x_3 = 0.54 - \frac{-0.0025}{-3.13} = 0.54 - 0.0008$$

$$= 0.5392.$$

Figure 128

Finally, from x_3 we obtain

$$x_4 = 0.5392 - \frac{-0.00003}{-3.13} = 0.5392 - 0.00001$$

$$= 0.5392,$$

so that the desired root, to four decimal places, is $x = 0.5392$.

The work is conveniently arranged in tabular form. Let $y_n = f(x_n)$, $y'_n = f'(x_n)$.

n	x_n	y_n	y'_n	$-y_n/y'_n$
1	0.5	0.125	-3.25	0.04
2	0.54	-0.0025	-3.13	-0.0008
3	0.5392	-0.00003	-3.13	-0.00001

Example (b). Solve the equation $\cos x = x$.

A rough sketch (Fig. 129) of the curve $y = \cos x$ and the line $y = x$ shows that they intersect at only one point, somewhere near $x = \frac{1}{4}\pi$. Until we learn (in Chapter 31) how to compute the cosine function to any desired degree of accuracy, we are forced to use trigonometric tables in this problem. The number of significant figures in our answer is therefore dictated by the table used.

Let us turn to the table on page 571 and hunt for the place where "radian" and "cosine" are nearly equal. We thus obtain, as a first approximation, $x_1 = 0.74$.

Put

$$f(x) = x - \cos x.$$

Then

$$f'(x) = 1 + \sin x.$$

For $x_1 = 0.74$ we find that

$$\cos x_1 = 0.738\ 47,$$
$$\sin x_1 = 0.674\ 29.$$

Then $f(x_1) = +0.001\ 53$, $f'(x_1) = +1.67$, so that

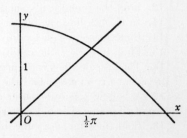

Figure 129

$$x_2 = 0.74 - \frac{0.001\ 53}{1.67} = 0.74 - 0.001 = 0.739.$$

We use interpolation in the table to obtain

$$\cos x_2 = 0.739\ 14,$$
$$\sin x_2 = 0.673\ 55.$$

Then

$$f(x_2) = -0.000\ 14,$$
$$f'(x_2) = 1.67.$$

Hence

$$x_3 = 0.739 - \frac{-0.000\ 14}{1.67} = 0.739.$$

Since we dare not interpolate to a hundredth of the interval in the table, the root we sought is $x = 0.739$ as accurately as it can be obtained without a more extensive trigonometric table.

EXERCISES

1. Find, to three decimal places, the cube root of 4. (Solve $x^3 = 4$.) Do not use a table of cube roots. *Ans.* 1.587.

2. Find, to three decimal places, the cube root of 2. *Ans.* 1.260.

3. Find, to two decimal places, the cube root of 98. *Ans.* 4.61.

4. Find, to two decimal places, the positive root of $x^4 + x - 3 = 0$. *Ans.* 1.16.

5. Find the other real root of the equation of Ex. 4. *Ans.* −1.45.

6. Find, to two decimal places, the positive root of $x^3 + 3x^2 - 1 = 0$. *Ans.* 0.53.

7. Find the other roots of the equation of Ex. 6. *Ans.* −2.88, −0.65.

8. Find, to three decimal places, the real root of $x^3 + 3x - 2 = 0$. *Ans.* 0.596.

9. In Example (a), § 124, find the larger positive root. *Ans.* 1.675.

10. In Example (*a*), § 124, find the negative root. Add the answers to Example (*a*), Ex. 9, and Ex. 10. What should be the sum, and why?   *Ans.* $x = -2.214$.

11. Find the smaller positive root of $x^3 - x^2 - 2x + 1 = 0$.   *Ans.* 0.445.

12. Find the numerically smallest root of $x^3 + 9x^2 + 23x + 14 = 0$.

13. In Ex. 12, find the intermediate root.

14. Find, in inches, the radius of a sphere of volume $\frac{1}{8}$ cu. ft.   *Ans.* 3.72.

15. Find, in inches, the radius of a sphere of volume 1 cu. ft.   *Ans.* 7.44.

16. The base of a box is a square; the height is 1 ft. less than the side of the base. If the volume is 6 cu. ft., find the dimensions.   *Ans.* One side = 2.22 ft.

17. A hollow sphere of outer radius 10 in. weighs one-fifth as much as a solid sphere of the same size and material. Find the inner radius.   *Ans.* 9.28 in.

18. Find the edge of a cube, if the volume is tripled when the edge is increased 1 in.   *Ans.* 2.26 in.

19. Find the radius of a sphere, if the volume is halved when the radius is decreased by 2 in.

20. A metal sphere of radius 2 in. is recast in the form of a cone of height 2 in. surmounted by a hemisphere of the same radius as the cone. Find the radius of the cone.   *Ans.* 2.23 in.

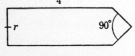

Figure 130

21. A torpedo has the longitudinal section shown. When submerged it displaces a volume of water equal to a sphere of radius 1 ft. Find *r* in feet.

22. A cylinder is inscribed in a sphere of radius *a*. Find the half-altitude of the cylinder, if the volume of the cylinder is half that of the sphere.   *Ans.* $0.395a$, $0.742a$.

23. A cylinder is inscribed in a cone whose diameter and height are equal. Find the radius of the cylinder, if its volume is three-twentieths that of the cone. (Two answers.)

24. A metal hemisphere of radius 2 is recast as a circular cylinder of base radius *r* and height 8, surmounted by a hemisphere of radius *r*. Find *r*.   *Ans.* 0.791.

25. The curve $y^2 = x^{-1}(x + 1)(x + 2)$ was discussed in the example of § 114. Solve the equation for *y* and derive the formula

$$4y'' = \pm x^{-\frac{5}{2}}(x^2 + 3x + 2)^{-\frac{3}{2}}(-x^4 + 12x^2 + 24x + 12).$$

Obtain the *x*-coordinates of all inflection points of the curve.   *Ans.* 4.27.

In Exs. 26–43, find all roots of the given equation unless otherwise directed.

26. $\sin \alpha = \alpha^3$.   *Ans.* 0, ± 0.929.

27. $e^{-x} = 1 - x^3$.   *Ans.* $x_1 = 0$, $x_2 = 0.825$.

28. $x = 3 \ln x$.   *Ans.* $x_1 = 1.86$, $x_2 = 4.53$.

29. $x^2 e^x = 1$.   **30.** $\sin \theta = 1 - \theta$.

31. $\tan x = e^x$, $0 \leq x \leq \frac{1}{2}\pi$.   **32.** $x + \ln x = 0$.

33. $e^x \cos x = 1$, $0 \leq x \leq \frac{1}{2}\pi$.   **34.** $\tan \theta = 2\theta$, $0 \leq \theta \leq \frac{1}{2}\pi$.

35. $x + e^x = 0$.   **36.** $e^x = 3x$.

37. $e^x \sin x = 1$, $0 \leq x \leq \frac{1}{2}\pi$.   **38.** $(x + 2)e^{-x} = 1$.

39. $\cosh x = 3x$.   **40.** $\sinh x = 2x$.

41. $\cos \alpha = \alpha^2$.   **42.** $\sinh x = \cos x$.

43. $\theta = 2 \tan \theta$, the smallest positive root.

44. A piece of wire 18 in. long is bent in the form of a circular arc, with the ends 1 ft. apart. Find the angle subtended at the center.   *Ans.* 171.5°.

45. Solve Ex. 28 by first passing to the exponential form.

46. Solve Ex. 29 by first passing to the logarithmic form.

47. Solve Ex. 32 by first passing to the exponential form.

48. Solve Ex. 38 by first passing to the logarithmic form.

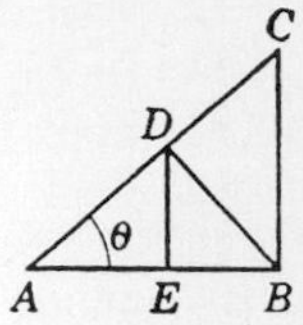

49. The triangular frame *ABC* in Fig. 131 is to be strengthened by braces *BD* perpendicular to *AC* and *DE* perpendicular to *AB*. If *AE* must equal *DC*, find θ.   *Ans.* 40° 59′.

Figure 131

50. Solve Ex. 49 if *AE* is to equal *BC*.   *Ans.* 34° 18.5′.

51. From the corners of a piece of tin 16 in. by 10 in. equal squares are cut out and the flaps bent up to form an open box, as in Example (*a*), § 41. If the box is to contain 100 cu. in., find the size of the squares. (Two answers.)

52. Find the eccentricity of an ellipse if the latus rectum is one-fourth the distance between the directrices. (Two answers.)

53. A circular cone is inscribed in a sphere in such a manner that the volume of the cone is one-eighth the volume of the sphere. Find the altitude of the cone.

54. A top, consisting of a cone of radius *a* and height *a* surmounted by a hemisphere of the same radius, is whittled down to a cylinder with axis coinciding with that of the top. How much of the material can be saved?   *Ans.* 51.5%.

55. A rope 22 ft. long is tied at the same height to posts 20 ft. apart. Find the "dip". (§ 97.)

56. A rope, tied at the same height to posts 20 ft. apart, sags 2 ft. in the middle. Find the length of the rope. Note that $d = a \left(\cosh \dfrac{10}{a} - 1 \right)$. (§ 97.)

FUNDAMENTAL

INTEGRATION FORMULAS

125. *Standard Formulas*

In this chapter we shall learn how to apply the following basic formulas:

(1) $\displaystyle\int u^n \, du = \frac{u^{n+1}}{n+1} + C, \qquad n \neq -1,$

(2) $\displaystyle\int \frac{du}{u} = \ln u + C, \qquad u > 0,$

(2') $\displaystyle\int \frac{du}{u} = \ln(-u) + C_1, \qquad u < 0,$

(2'') $\displaystyle\int \frac{du}{u} = \ln|u| + C_2, \qquad u \neq 0,$

(3) $\displaystyle\int e^u \, du = e^u + C,$

(3') $\displaystyle\int a^u \, du = \frac{a^u}{\ln a} + C, \qquad a > 0,$

(4) $\displaystyle\int \cos u \, du = \sin u + C,$

(5) $\displaystyle\int \sin u \, du = -\cos u + C,$

(6) $\displaystyle\int \sec^2 u \, du = \tan u + C,$

(7) $\displaystyle\int \csc^2 u \, du = -\cot u + C,$

(8) $\displaystyle\int \sec u \tan u \, du = \sec u + C,$

(9) $\displaystyle\int \csc u \cot u \, du = -\csc u + C,$

(10) $\displaystyle\int \frac{du}{\sqrt{a^2 - u^2}} = \operatorname{Arcsin} \frac{u}{a} + C, \qquad a > 0$

(11) $\int \dfrac{du}{a^2 + u^2} = \dfrac{1}{a} \operatorname{Arctan} \dfrac{u}{a} + C,$

(12) $\int u\,dv = uv - \int v\,du.$

The test of the correctness of an integral is that its derivative must be the given integrand. The above formulas are easily verified by differentiation.

126. *Formula* (1): *Powers*

Although the power formula was studied in § 50 (which should be thoroughly reviewed), our attention there was necessarily confined to algebraic integrands, so that further work with this formula is needed. The power formula is

(1) $$\int u^n\,du = \dfrac{u^{n+1}}{n+1} + C, \qquad n \neq -1.$$

Example (a). Evaluate $\int \sqrt{\cos 2\theta}\, \sin 2\theta\, d\theta.$

Since
$$d(\cos 2\theta) = -2 \sin 2\theta\, d\theta,$$

we insert the factor -2 and apply (1) with $u = \cos 2\theta$:

$$\int \sqrt{\cos 2\theta}\, \sin 2\theta\, d\theta = -\tfrac{1}{2} \int (\cos 2\theta)^{\frac{1}{2}}(-2 \sin 2\theta)\, d\theta$$

$$= -\frac{1}{2} \cdot \frac{(\cos 2\theta)^{\frac{3}{2}}}{\frac{3}{2}} + C$$

$$= -\tfrac{1}{3}(\cos 2\theta)^{\frac{3}{2}} + C.$$

Example (b). Evaluate $\int \dfrac{u \ln^2 (1 + u^2)\, du}{1 + u^2}.$

An integral such as the one above should be evaluated by inspection. Note that, essentially, the integral contains only a power of $\ln (1 + u^2)$ and the differential,

$$d \ln (1 + u^2) = \frac{2u\, du}{1 + u^2},$$

of that quantity. Therefore the integral is basically one of the power-formula type. The result should contain the quantity $\ln (1 + u^2)$ to an exponent higher by unity than the exponent in the integrand. Hence we perform the differentiation

$$d \ln^3 (1 + u^2) = 3 \ln^2 (1 + u^2) \frac{2u\, du}{1 + u^2}$$

$$= \frac{6u \ln^2 (1 + u^2)\, du}{1 + u^2}.$$

The above differential agrees with the integrand except for a *constant* factor 6, which we know (§ 49) can be adjusted. We are thus able to write

$$\int \frac{u \ln^2 (1 + u^2) \, du}{1 + u^2} = \frac{1}{6} \ln^3 (1 + u^2) + C.$$

EXERCISES

Evaluate the following integrals; check by differentiation.

1. $\int \sin^3 y \cos y \, dy.$

2. $\int \cos^4 x \sin x \, dx.$

3. $\int \frac{\cos x \, dx}{\sin^4 x}.$

4. $\int \frac{\sin y \, dy}{\cos^2 y}.$

5. $\int \sin 4x \cos 4x \, dx.$ (Two ways.)

6. $\int \sin \frac{v}{3} \cos \frac{v}{3} \, dv.$ (Two ways.)

7. $\int (4 - 3 \sin 2\beta)^4 \cos 2\beta \, d\beta.$

8. $\int (2 \cos 4\varphi - 1)^{\frac{1}{2}} \sin 4\varphi \, d\varphi.$

9. $\int \frac{\cos 2t \, dt}{(1 + \sin 2t)^4}.$

Ans. $-\frac{1}{6}(1 + \sin 2t)^{-3} + C.$

10. $\int \frac{\sin t \, dt}{(4 + \cos t)^{\frac{3}{2}}}.$

Ans. $2(4 + \cos t)^{-\frac{1}{2}} + C.$

11. $\int \tan \beta \sec^2 \beta \, d\beta.$ (Two ways.)

12. $\int \cot \alpha \csc^2 \alpha \, d\alpha.$ (Two ways.)

13. $\int \sec^5 x \tan x \, dx.$

14. $\int \cot z \csc^3 z \, dz.$

15. $\int \frac{\ln y \, dy}{y}.$

16. $\int \frac{d\beta}{\beta \ln^4 \beta}.$

17. $\int \frac{(1 + 2 \ln x)^4 \, dx}{x}.$

18. $\int \frac{x^2 \ln^3 (1 + x^3)}{1 + x^3} \, dx.$

19. $\int e^x (4 - e^x)^{\frac{3}{2}} \, dx.$

20. $\int (1 + e^{-2y})^{\frac{1}{2}} e^{-2y} \, dy.$

21. $\int \frac{e^t \, dt}{\sqrt{1 + 5e^t}}.$

22. $\int \frac{e^{4v} \, dv}{(1 + 3e^{4v})^2}.$

23. $\int \tan^2 (3x - 1) \sec^2 (3x - 1) \, dx.$

24. $\int \sin^4 (e^{2x}) \cos (e^{2x}) e^{2x} \, dx.$

25. $\int v^3 \cos^2 (v^4) \sin (v^4) \, dv.$

26. $\int \csc^2 \psi \sqrt{1 + 3 \cot \psi} \, d\psi.$

27. $\int \frac{\sec^2 \varphi \, d\varphi}{(1 - 4 \tan \varphi)^{\frac{5}{2}}}.$

28. $\displaystyle\int \frac{\sec x \tan x \, dx}{(3 + 4 \sec x)^{\frac{1}{2}}}.$

29. $\displaystyle\int \tan \alpha \ln \sec \alpha \, d\alpha.$

30. $\displaystyle\int \cot \beta \ln \sin \beta \, d\beta.$

31. $\displaystyle\int \frac{\sec^3 x \tan x \, dx}{(1 + \sec^3 x)^2}.$ *Ans.* $\dfrac{-1}{3(1 + \sec^3 x)} + C.$

32. $\displaystyle\int \frac{(2x + 1) \, dx}{(x + 2)^4 (x - 1)^4}.$ *Ans.* $\dfrac{-1}{3(x^2 + x - 2)^3} + C.$

33. $\displaystyle\int \frac{(x + 1)^{\frac{3}{2}} \, dx}{x^{\frac{7}{2}}}.$ *Ans.* $-\dfrac{2}{5}\left(1 + \dfrac{1}{x}\right)^{\frac{5}{2}} + C.$

34. $\displaystyle\int \frac{\tan \varphi \, d\varphi}{(1 + \ln \cos \varphi)^{\frac{3}{2}}}.$ *Ans.* $2(1 + \ln \cos \varphi)^{-\frac{1}{2}} + C.$

35. $\displaystyle\int (6 \cos^2 \varphi + \sin^2 \varphi)^{\frac{1}{2}} \cos \varphi \sin \varphi \, d\varphi.$

36. $\displaystyle\int (3 \sin^2 \varphi - \cos^2 \varphi)^{-\frac{1}{2}} \sin \varphi \cos \varphi \, d\varphi.$

37. $\displaystyle\int \cosh^2 y \sinh y \, dy.$ **38.** $\displaystyle\int \sinh^3 2x \cosh 2x \, dx.$

39. $\displaystyle\int \frac{\sinh 3w \, dw}{(1 + 4 \cosh 3w)^2}.$ **40.** $\displaystyle\int \frac{\cosh 3z \, dz}{(1 + 2 \sinh 3z)^5}.$

127. *Formula* (2): *Logarithms*

Next we shall apply

$$(2) \qquad\qquad \int \frac{du}{u} = \ln u + C, \qquad u > 0,$$

together with its associated forms

$$(2') \qquad\qquad \int \frac{du}{u} = \ln (-u) + C_1, \qquad u < 0,$$

$$(2'') \qquad\qquad \int \frac{du}{u} = \ln |u| + C_2, \qquad u \neq 0.$$

Example (a). Evaluate $\displaystyle\int \frac{x \, dx}{1 - x^2}.$

Formula (2) says, in words: The integral of any quotient *whose numerator is the differential of the denominator* is the logarithm of the denominator. Therefore we insert the factor -2:

$$\int \frac{x \, dx}{1 - x^2} = -\frac{1}{2} \int \frac{-2x \, dx}{1 - x^2} = -\frac{1}{2} \ln (1 - x^2) + C.$$

The integral in this example can equally well be evaluated in the following manner:

$$\int \frac{x\,dx}{1-x^2} = -\int \frac{x\,dx}{x^2-1} = -\frac{1}{2}\int \frac{2x\,dx}{x^2-1}$$

$$= -\tfrac{1}{2}\ln(x^2-1) + C_1, \qquad |x| > 1,$$

a result which can also be obtained by employing (2′) directly.

Application of (2″) yields

$$\int \frac{x\,dx}{1-x^2} = -\frac{1}{2}\ln|1-x^2| + C_2, \qquad x \neq 1, \;\; x \neq -1.$$

Each of the above three evaluations of the integral in this example has its own restrictions, its own range of validity. In practice, specific problems usually dictate the form to be used because the variables involved range over known intervals.

In this book we shall ordinarily leave answers in the form to which (2) leads us. It is assumed that the reader can convert the result to the form given by (2′) or (2″) whenever such conversion is necessary.

Example (b). Evaluate $\int \dfrac{x^2 - x}{x + 1}\, dx$.

By division we find

$$\frac{x^2 - x}{x + 1} = x - 2 + \frac{2}{x + 1}.$$

Therefore

$$\int \frac{x^2 - x}{x + 1}\, dx = \int \left(x - 2 + \frac{2}{x + 1} \right) dx$$

$$= \tfrac{1}{2}x^2 - 2x + 2\ln(x + 1) + C.$$

RULE. *As the first step toward integrating a rational fraction, carry out the indicated division until the numerator is of lower degree than the denominator.*

EXERCISES

Evaluate each integral; check by differentiation.

1. $\displaystyle\int \frac{2dy}{3y - 4}$.

2. $\displaystyle\int \frac{4dt}{5t + 2}$.

3. $\displaystyle\int \frac{x^2\,dx}{x^3 + 4}$.

4. $\displaystyle\int \frac{v\,dv}{6v^2 - 1}$.

5. $\displaystyle\int \frac{(2x - 5)\,dx}{x^2 - 5x + 3}$.

6. $\displaystyle\int \frac{(y - 3)\,dy}{y^2 - 6y + 1}$.

7. $\displaystyle\int \frac{(1 - 2x)^2\,dx}{x}$.

8. $\displaystyle\int \frac{(u^2 + 1)^2\,du}{u^3}$.

9. $\displaystyle\int \frac{y\,dy}{(1 + y^2)^4}$.

10. $\displaystyle\int \frac{x^3\,dx}{(x^4 + 16)^2}$.

11. $\displaystyle\int \frac{v + 3}{v - 1}\,dv$.

12. $\displaystyle\int \frac{v(v^2 - 1)}{v^2 + 1}\,dv$.

13. $\displaystyle\int \tan x\,dx.$

14. $\displaystyle\int \cot y\,dy.$

15. $\displaystyle\int \frac{\cos\beta\,d\beta}{2 + 3\sin\beta}.$

16. $\displaystyle\int \frac{\sin 2t\,dt}{4 - 3\cos 2t}.$

17. $\displaystyle\int \frac{\csc^2 x\,dx}{1 + \cot x}.$

18. $\displaystyle\int \frac{\sec^2 y\,dy}{1 + \tan y}.$

19. $\displaystyle\int \frac{dz}{(2 + z)^{\frac{1}{2}}}.$

20. $\displaystyle\int \frac{(x^2 - 2)\,dx}{x^3 - 6x + 2}.$

21. $\displaystyle\int \frac{x^3\,dx}{x - 1}.$

22. $\displaystyle\int \frac{x^3 - 2x^2 + 2}{x - 1}\,dx.$

23. $\displaystyle\int \frac{\sec\theta\tan\theta\,d\theta}{2\sec\theta + 3}.$

24. $\displaystyle\int \frac{\csc\theta\cot\theta\,d\theta}{1 - \csc\theta}.$

25. $\displaystyle\int \frac{e^y\,dy}{e^y - 1}.$

26. $\displaystyle\int \frac{e^{3x}\,dx}{4 + e^{3x}}.$

27. $\displaystyle\int \frac{e^{2y}\,dy}{e^y - 1}.$

28. $\displaystyle\int \frac{e^{2t} + e^{-2t}}{e^{2t} - e^{-2t}}\,dt.$

29. $\displaystyle\int \frac{dx}{x\ln x}.$

30. $\displaystyle\int \frac{dy}{y(1 + 2\ln y)}.$

31. $\displaystyle\int \frac{\sin 2\theta\,d\theta}{1 + \sin^2\theta}.$

32. $\displaystyle\int \frac{\sec^2 x\tan x\,dx}{4 + \tan^2 x}.$

33. $\displaystyle\int \frac{(x + 6)\,dx}{(x + 2)^2}.$

$Hint\!:\ \dfrac{x + 6}{(x + 2)^2} = \dfrac{(x + 2) + 4}{(x + 2)^2}.$

34. $\displaystyle\int \frac{dx}{\sqrt{x}\,(1 + \sqrt{x})}.$

$Ans.\ 2\ln(1 + \sqrt{x}) + C.$

35. $\displaystyle\int \frac{dx}{x(1 + x^2)}.$ $\left[\dfrac{1}{x(1 + x^2)} = \dfrac{(1 + x^2) - x^2}{x(1 + x^2)}.\right]$ $Ans.\ \dfrac{1}{2}\ln\dfrac{x^2}{1 + x^2} + C.$

36. $\displaystyle\int \sec\theta\,d\theta.$ (Multiply and divide by $\sec\theta + \tan\theta$.)

$Ans.\ \textbf{ln}\,(\textbf{sec}\,\boldsymbol{\theta} + \textbf{tan}\,\boldsymbol{\theta}) + \textbf{C}.$

37. Ex. 36 by a second method. (Multiply and divide by $\sec\theta - \tan\theta$.)

38. $\displaystyle\int \csc\theta\,d\theta$ by two methods. (Cf. Exs. 36–37.)

$Ans.\ \textbf{ln}\,(\textbf{csc}\,\boldsymbol{\theta} - \textbf{cot}\,\boldsymbol{\theta}) + \textbf{C}.$

39. $\displaystyle\int \frac{d\theta}{\sin 2\theta}.$

40. $\displaystyle\int \frac{d\varphi}{\cos 3\varphi}.$

41. $\displaystyle\int \frac{3 + \sin 4x}{\sin 4x}\,dx.$

42. $\displaystyle\int \frac{1 + \cos t}{\cos t}\,dt.$

43. $\int \dfrac{\cos x - \tan x}{\cos^2 x}\, dx.$ **44.** $\int \dfrac{\sin y + \cot y}{\sin^2 y}\, dy.$

45. $\int \tanh 2x\, dx.$ **46.** $\int \coth \tfrac{1}{2}y\, dy.$

47. $\int \dfrac{dx}{\sin x \cos x}.$ Solve in two ways: (a) by using $\sin x \cos x = \tfrac{1}{2} \sin 2x$; and (b) by first dividing numerator and denominator by $\sin^2 x$.

128. *Formulas* (3)–(3′): *Exponential Functions*

There are two basic formulas for the integration of exponential functions:

$$(3) \qquad\qquad \int e^u\, du = e^u + C,$$

$$(3') \qquad\qquad \int a^u\, du = \frac{a^u}{\ln a} + C, \qquad a > 0.$$

Equation (3′) includes (3) as a special case but (3) is used much more frequently than the general (3′).

Example (a). Evaluate $\int \sin 2x\; e^{\cos 2x}\, dx.$

If we insert the factor -2, this can be evaluated by (3), with $u = \cos 2x$, $du = -2 \sin 2x\, dx$:

$$\int \sin 2x\; e^{\cos 2x}\, dx = -\tfrac{1}{2} \int e^{\cos 2x}\, (-2 \sin 2x)\, dx = -\tfrac{1}{2} e^{\cos 2x} + C.$$

Example (b). Evaluate $\int \dfrac{dx}{3^{2x}}.$
Since

$$\frac{d}{dx}\, a^u = a^u (\ln a)\, \frac{du}{dx},$$

we proceed as follows:

$$\int \frac{dx}{3^{2x}} = \int 3^{-2x}\, dx = -\frac{1}{2} \frac{3^{-2x}}{\ln 3} + C.$$

EXERCISES

Evaluate the following integrals.

1. $\int e^{-3x}\, dx.$ **2.** $\int e^{2x}\, dx.$

3. $\int \dfrac{dv}{e^v}.$ **4.** $\int y e^{-y^2}\, dy.$

5. $\int 2^{-x}\, dx.$ **6.** $\int 10^{-3x}\, dx.$

7. $\int (e^t - e^{-t})^2\, dt.$ **8.** $\int e^{2x}(1 + e^{2x})^3\, dx.$

9. $\displaystyle\int ze^{4z^2}\,dz.$

10. $\displaystyle\int ve^{3v^2-1}\,dv.$

11. $\displaystyle\int \frac{e^\theta\,d\theta}{(6e^\theta+1)^{\frac{3}{2}}}.$

12. $\displaystyle\int e^{3y}(1-e^{3y})^{\frac{1}{2}}\,dy.$

13. $\displaystyle\int \frac{(e^x+1)^2}{e^x}\,dx.$

14. $\displaystyle\int \frac{e^{2t}\,dt}{1+6e^{2t}+9e^{4t}}.$

15. $\displaystyle\int \frac{e^{2\theta}\,d\theta}{1+3e^{2\theta}}.$

16. $\displaystyle\int \frac{e^{\tan\theta}\,d\theta}{\cos^2\theta}.$

17. $\displaystyle\int \frac{e^{\frac{1}{x}}\,dx}{x^2}.$

18. $\displaystyle\int (1-2e^{\tan x})\sec^2 x\,dx.$

19. $\displaystyle\int 4e^{3\,\ln x}\,dx.$ *Ans.* $x^4 + C.$

20. $\displaystyle\int \ln e^{2x}\,dx.$ *Ans.* $x^2 + C.$

21. $\displaystyle\int \sinh u\,du = \cosh u + C.$

22. $\displaystyle\int \cosh u\,du = \sinh u + C.$

23. $\displaystyle\int \sinh 2x\,dx.$

24. $\displaystyle\int \cosh 3t\,dt.$

25. $\displaystyle\int \tanh u\,du.$

26. $\displaystyle\int \coth u\,du.$

27. $\displaystyle\int x\coth x^2\,dx.$

28. $\displaystyle\int e^{-y}\sinh y\,dy.$

129. *Formulas* (4)–(9): *Trigonometric Functions*

The basic formulas for integrations involving trigonometric functions are

(4) $$\int \cos u\,du = \sin u + C,$$

(5) $$\int \sin u\,du = -\cos u + C,$$

(6) $$\int \sec^2 u\,du = \tan u + C,$$

(7) $$\int \csc^2 u\,du = -\cot u + C,$$

(8) $$\int \sec u\tan u\,du = \sec u + C,$$

(9) $$\int \csc u\cot u\,du = -\csc u + C.$$

Notice the way in which the functions pair off for purposes of integration. The pairs $\sin u$ and $\cos u$, $\sec u$ and $\tan u$, $\csc u$ and $\cot u$ fit well together. An integral involving, for instance, $\sin x$ and $\tan x$ is not in appropriate form for application of simple integration formulas. Upon meeting such an integral we first put the integrand entirely in terms of $\sin x$ and $\cos x$ or in terms of $\tan x$ and $\sec x$.

Example (a). Evaluate $\int \sin x \tan x \, dx$.

We proceed as follows:

$$\int \sin x \tan x \, dx = \int \frac{\sin^2 x \, dx}{\cos x} = \int \frac{1 - \cos^2 x}{\cos x} \, dx$$

$$= \int \sec x \, dx - \int \cos x \, dx$$

$$= \ln (\sec x + \tan x) - \sin x + C,$$

in which we have used the result in Ex. 36, page 239.

Because of the situation described above, the exercises are usually stated in terms of appropriate pairs of functions. Such pairing permits the student to do more exercises (and thus acquire more skill) in a specified time than would otherwise be possible. There is, of course, no guarantee of corresponding simplicity in the integrals encountered in the normal course of events in engineering or other scientific work.

Example (b). $\int x \sin x^2 \, dx = \tfrac{1}{2} \int \sin x^2 \cdot 2x \, dx$

$$= -\tfrac{1}{2} \cos x^2 + C.$$

Example (c). $\int \tan^2 \theta \, d\theta = \int (\sec^2 \theta - 1) \, d\theta = \tan \theta - \theta + C.$

EXERCISES

Evaluate the integrals below.

1. $\int \sin 3\theta \, d\theta.$

2. $\int \sec^2 4x \, dx.$

3. $\int \cos \tfrac{1}{2}y \, dy.$

4. $\int \csc^2 2t \, dy.$

5. $\int \csc 5t \cot 5t \, dt.$

6. $\int \sec \tfrac{1}{2}z \tan \tfrac{1}{2}z \, dz$

7. $\int \dfrac{\sec^2 3x \, dx}{1 + 4 \tan 3x}.$

8. $\int \dfrac{\sin 2t \cos 2t \, dt}{1 + 3 \cos 4t}$

9. $\int \dfrac{\cos \ln x \, dx}{x}.$

10. $\int \dfrac{dy}{e^y \sin^2 (e^{-y})}.$

11. $\int \cot^2 y \, dy.$

12. $\int \tan^2 by \, dy.$

13. $\int \dfrac{\sin \varphi \, d\varphi}{\cos^4 \varphi}.$

14. $\int \dfrac{\cos^2 \varphi \, d\varphi}{\sin^4 \varphi}.$

15. $\int (\tan \theta - 1)^2 \, d\theta.$

16. $\int (1 + \cot 2\theta)^2 \, d\theta.$

17. $\int \dfrac{\cos^2 y \, dy}{1 - \sin y}.$

18. $\int \dfrac{\sin^3 y \, dy}{1 + \cos y}.$

19. $\displaystyle\int \frac{\cos^3 \theta \, d\theta}{1 - \sin \theta}.$

20. $\displaystyle\int \frac{\sin^2 \theta \, d\theta}{1 + \cos \theta}.$

21. $\displaystyle\int \sin^2 x \csc^2 2x \, dx.$

22. $\displaystyle\int \tan\left(y - \tfrac{1}{4}\pi\right) dy.$

23. $\displaystyle\int (\cos^4 x - \sin^4 x) \, dx.$

24. $\displaystyle\int \sin 3x \sin 6x \, dx.$

25. $\displaystyle\int \frac{(\cos x + 2 \sin x)^2 \, dx}{\cos x}.$

26. $\displaystyle\int \frac{(2 \cos x - \sin x)^2 \, dx}{\sin x}.$

27. $\displaystyle\int (\cos C + 1) \, dC.$ 　　　　　　　　　 *Ans.* $\sin C + C + x.$

28. $\displaystyle\int \cot\left(C - \tfrac{1}{4}\pi\right) dC.$ 　　　　　 *Ans.* $\ln \sin\left(C - \tfrac{1}{4}\pi\right) + y.$

Use the "double angle" formulas of trigonometry in Exs. 29–32.

29. $\displaystyle\int \frac{1 - \cos 2y}{1 + \cos 2y} \, dy.$

30. $\displaystyle\int \frac{1 + \cos 4y}{1 - \cos 4y} \, dy.$

31. $\displaystyle\int \frac{\tan w \, dw}{1 - \tan^2 w}.$

32. $\displaystyle\int \cos \beta \, (1 - \cos 2\beta)^3 \, d\beta.$

130. *Transformation by Trigonometric Formulas*

Many trigonometric integrals can be evaluated after transformations of the integrand, requiring only the most familiar trigonometric formulas. If, instead of memorizing the types listed below, the student will observe the character of the transformations employed, he can easily pick the requisite method in any given case.

Type I. $\displaystyle\int \sin^m x \cos^n x \, dx,$ *where either m or n is a positive odd integer.*

For definiteness, let n be a positive odd integer. Writing the integral in the form $\displaystyle\int \sin^m x \cos^{n-1} x \cdot \cos x \, dx,$ and putting

$$\cos^2 x = 1 - \sin^2 x,$$

we obtain a series of powers of $\sin x$ each multiplied by $\cos x \, dx$. We proceed in a similar manner when m is odd and positive.

Example (a).

$$\int \sin^2 x \cos^3 x \, dx = \int \sin^2 x \cos^2 x \cdot \cos x \, dx$$

$$= \int \sin^2 x (1 - \sin^2 x) \cos x \, dx$$

$$= \int \sin^2 x \cos x \, dx - \int \sin^4 x \cos x \, dx$$

$$= \tfrac{1}{3} \sin^3 x - \tfrac{1}{5} \sin^5 x + C.$$

Type II. $\int \tan^n x \, dx$, or $\int \cot^n x \, dx$, *where n is an integer.*

By use of the formulas

$$\tan^2 x = \sec^2 x - 1, \qquad \cot^2 x = \csc^2 x - 1,$$

these integrals reduce to forms that can be evaluated.

Example (b).

$$\int \tan^4 x \, dx = \int \tan^2 x (\sec^2 x - 1) \, dx$$

$$= \int \tan^2 x \sec^2 x \, dx - \int \tan^2 x \, dx$$

$$= \tfrac{1}{3} \tan^3 x - \int (\sec^2 x - 1) \, dx$$

$$= \tfrac{1}{3} \tan^3 x - \tan x + x + C.$$

Type III. $\int \tan^m x \sec^n x \, dx$, or $\int \cot^m x \csc^n x \, dx$, *where n is a positive even integer.*

Example (c).

$$\int \tan^2 x \sec^4 x \, dx = \int \tan^2 x \sec^2 x (1 + \tan^2 x) \, dx$$

$$= \int \tan^2 x \sec^2 x \, dx + \int \tan^4 x \sec^2 x \, dx$$

$$= \tfrac{1}{3} \tan^3 x + \tfrac{1}{5} \tan^5 x + C.$$

Type IV. $\int \sin^m x \cos^n x \, dx$, *where both m and n are positive even integers.*

When *m* and *n* are *both even*, it is easily seen that the method used for Type I is useless. Instead, we use the formulas

$$\sin^2 x = \tfrac{1}{2}(1 - \cos 2x), \qquad \cos^2 x = \tfrac{1}{2}(1 + \cos 2x),$$
$$\sin x \cos x = \tfrac{1}{2} \sin 2x,$$

repeatedly if necessary.

Example (d).

$$\int \sin^4 \theta \cos^2 \theta \, d\theta = \int (\sin^2 \theta \cos^2 \theta) \sin^2 \theta \, d\theta$$

$$= \tfrac{1}{8} \int \sin^2 2\theta (1 - \cos 2\theta) \, d\theta$$

$$= \tfrac{1}{8} \int \sin^2 2\theta \, d\theta - \tfrac{1}{8} \int \sin^2 2\theta \cos 2\theta \, d\theta$$

$$= \tfrac{1}{16} \int (1 - \cos 4\theta) \, d\theta - \tfrac{1}{48} \sin^3 2\theta$$

$$= \tfrac{1}{16}\theta - \tfrac{1}{64} \sin 4\theta - \tfrac{1}{48} \sin^3 2\theta + C.$$

EXERCISES

Evaluate each of the following integrals.

1. $\displaystyle\int \sin^3 x \, dx.$ *Ans.* $\frac{1}{3} \cos^3 x - \cos x + C.$

2. $\displaystyle\int \cos^3 x \, dx.$ *Ans.* $\sin x - \frac{1}{3} \sin^3 x + C.$

3. $\displaystyle\int \cos^3 y \sin^3 y \, dy.$ *Ans.* $\frac{1}{4} \sin^4 y - \frac{1}{6} \sin^6 y + C_1,$

   or $\frac{1}{6} \cos^6 y - \frac{1}{4} \cos^4 y + C_2.$

4. **Do Ex. 3 with the aid of the formula:** $\sin y \cos y = \frac{1}{2} \sin 2y.$

   Ans. $\frac{1}{48} \cos^3 2y - \frac{1}{16} \cos 2y + C_3.$

5. $\displaystyle\int \cos^2 2\theta \sin^3 2\theta \, d\theta.$ *Ans.* $-\frac{1}{6} \cos^3 2\theta + \frac{1}{10} \cos^5 2\theta + C.$

6. $\displaystyle\int \cos^2 t \sin^5 t \, dt.$ *Ans.* $-\frac{1}{3} \cos^3 t + \frac{2}{5} \cos^5 t - \frac{1}{7} \cos^7 t + C.$

7. $\displaystyle\int \sin^2 u \cos^5 u \, du.$ *Ans.* $\frac{1}{3} \sin^3 u - \frac{2}{5} \sin^5 u + \frac{1}{7} \sin^7 u + C.$

8. $\displaystyle\int \cos^5 3y \, dy.$ *Ans.* $\frac{1}{3} \sin 3y - \frac{2}{9} \sin^3 3y + \frac{1}{15} \sin^5 3y + C.$

9. $\displaystyle\int \frac{\sin^3 x \, dx}{\cos^6 x}.$ 10. $\displaystyle\int \frac{\cos^3 x \, dx}{\sin^4 x}.$

11. $\displaystyle\int \sin^2 x \tan x \, dx.$ 12. $\displaystyle\int \cos^2 y \cot y \, dy.$

13. $\displaystyle\int \sin^3 x (2 - 3 \cos x)^2 \, dx.$ 14. $\displaystyle\int \sin x (2 - 3 \cos x)^2 \, dx.$

15. $\displaystyle\int \frac{\sin^5 t \, dt}{\cos^2 t}.$ 16. $\displaystyle\int \frac{\cos^5 3z \, dz}{\sin^2 3z}.$

17. $\displaystyle\int \cos^7 \theta \, d\theta.$ 18. $\displaystyle\int \sin^5 x \cos^5 x \, dx.$

19. $\displaystyle\int \sin^2 x \, dx.$ *Ans.* $\frac{1}{2}x - \frac{1}{4} \sin 2x + C.$

20. $\displaystyle\int \cos^2 y \, dy.$ *Ans.* $\frac{1}{2}y + \frac{1}{4} \sin 2y + C.$

21. $\displaystyle\int \sin^2 \beta \cos^2 \beta \, d\beta.$ (See Ex. 4.)   *Ans.* $\frac{1}{8}\beta - \frac{1}{32} \sin 4\beta + C.$

22. $\displaystyle\int \sin^4 3\theta \, d\theta.$ *Ans.* $\frac{3}{8}\theta - \frac{1}{12} \sin 6\theta + \frac{1}{96} \sin 12\theta + C.$

23. $\displaystyle\int \sin^3 x \sin^3 2x \, dx.$ 24. $\displaystyle\int \cos^2 x \sin^3 2x \, dx.$

25. $\displaystyle\int \sin^2 y \cos^4 y \, dy.$

26. $\displaystyle\int \sin^4 t \cos^4 t \, dt.$

27. $\displaystyle\int \cos^4 x \sin^3 x \, dx.$

28. $\displaystyle\int \sin^4 y \cos^5 y \, dy.$

29. $\displaystyle\int \cos^6 \tfrac{1}{2} t \, dt.$

30. $\displaystyle\int \sin^6 x \cos^6 x \, dx.$

31. $\displaystyle\int \tan^3 \theta \, d\theta.$

Ans. $\frac{1}{2} \sec^2 \theta - \ln \sec \theta + C_1$

$= \frac{1}{2} \tan^2 \theta - \ln \sec \theta + C_2$

$= \frac{1}{2} \sec^2 \theta + \ln \cos \theta + C_3,$ etc.

32. $\displaystyle\int \cot^4 y \, dy.$

Ans. $-\frac{1}{3} \cot^3 y + \cot y + y + C.$

33. $\displaystyle\int \cot^6 \theta \, d\theta.$

34. $\displaystyle\int \cot^5 2y \, dy.$

35. $\displaystyle\int \sec^4 \beta \, d\beta.$

36. $\displaystyle\int \csc^4 \alpha \, d\alpha.$

37. $\displaystyle\int \sec^2 x \tan^3 x \, dx.$

38. $\displaystyle\int \sec^4 y \tan^3 y \, dy.$

39. $\displaystyle\int \tan^5 x \, dx.$

Ans. $\frac{1}{4} \tan^4 x - \frac{1}{2} \tan^2 x - \ln \cos x + C.$

40. $\displaystyle\int \tan^6 x \, dx.$

Ans. $\frac{1}{5} \tan^5 x - \frac{1}{3} \tan^3 x + \tan x - x + C.$

41. $\displaystyle\int \sec^6 \theta \tan \theta \, d\theta.$

42. $\displaystyle\int \sec^6 \theta \tan^2 \theta \, d\theta.$

43. $\displaystyle\int \sec^4 y \tan^4 y \, dy.$

44. $\displaystyle\int \csc^6 u \, du.$

131. *Formulas* (10)–(11): *Inverse Trigonometric Functions*

Consider next the two formulas:

(10) $$\int \frac{du}{\sqrt{a^2 - u^2}} = \text{Arcsin} \, \frac{u}{a} + C, \qquad a > 0,$$

(11) $$\int \frac{du}{a^2 + u^2} = \frac{1}{a} \text{Arctan} \, \frac{u}{a} + C.$$

In applying (10), it is important to note that the numerator du is the differential of the variable quantity u which appears squared inside the square root symbol.

Example (a). Evaluate $\displaystyle\int \frac{dx}{\sqrt{9 - 4x^2}}.$

The presence of a constant minus the square of a variable under the square root sign is what suggests the use of formula (10). Therefore we mentally put the quantity under the radical into the form of the square of a constant minus the square of a variable. That is, we think of $\sqrt{9 - 4x^2}$ as $\sqrt{3^2 - (2x)^2}$. This shows that the u in formula (10) is to be $2x$. Hence $du = 2dx$ and we need to insert the constant 2 into the numerator before we can employ (10). To insert the constant legitimately, we must compensate for it by putting its reciprocal as a factor outside the integral. Therefore we write

$$\int \frac{dx}{\sqrt{9 - 4x^2}} = \frac{1}{2} \int \frac{2dx}{\sqrt{9 - (2x)^2}}$$

$$= \frac{1}{2} \operatorname{Arcsin} \frac{2x}{3} + C.$$

Example (b).

$$\int \frac{dy}{9y^2 + 6y + 5} = \int \frac{dy}{(3y + 1)^2 + 4}$$

$$= \frac{1}{3} \int \frac{3dy}{(3y + 1)^2 + 4}$$

$$= \frac{1}{3} \cdot \frac{1}{2} \operatorname{Arctan} \frac{3y + 1}{2} + C$$

$$= \frac{1}{6} \operatorname{Arctan} \frac{3y + 1}{2} + C.$$

Example (c). $\displaystyle\int \frac{dx}{x\sqrt{1 - 4\ln^2 x}} = \int \frac{\dfrac{dx}{x}}{\sqrt{1 - 4\ln^2 x}}$

$$= \frac{1}{2} \int \frac{2\dfrac{dx}{x}}{\sqrt{1 - 4\ln^2 x}}$$

$$= \frac{1}{2} \operatorname{Arcsin} (2\ln x) + C.$$

EXERCISES

Perform the indicated integrations.

1. $\displaystyle\int \frac{dx}{16 + x^2}.$

2. $\displaystyle\int \frac{dy}{\sqrt{9 - y^2}}.$

3. $\displaystyle\int \frac{dv}{9 + 4v^2}.$

4. $\displaystyle\int \frac{dt}{\sqrt{5 - 16t^2}}.$

5. $\displaystyle\int \frac{y\,dy}{\sqrt{25 - 16y^2}}.$

6. $\displaystyle\int \frac{x\,dx}{9 + x^2}.$

7. $\displaystyle\int \frac{y\,dy}{\sqrt{25 - 16y^4}}.$

8. $\displaystyle\int \frac{x\,dx}{9 + x^4}.$

9. $\displaystyle\int \frac{dz}{z^2 + 6z + 10}.$

10. $\displaystyle\int \frac{d\varphi}{4\varphi^2 - 4\varphi + 5}.$

11. $\displaystyle\int \frac{e^{2x}\,dx}{\sqrt{9 - 4e^{4x}}}.$

12. $\displaystyle\int \frac{e^{4x}\,dx}{\sqrt{9 - 4e^{4x}}}.$

13. $\displaystyle\int \frac{\sin\varphi \cos\varphi\,d\varphi}{5 + \cos^2\varphi}.$

14. $\displaystyle\int \frac{\sin\varphi\,d\varphi}{5 + \cos^2\varphi}.$

15. $\displaystyle\int \frac{dQ}{\sqrt{15 + 4Q - 4Q^2}}.$

16. $\displaystyle\int \frac{dw}{6w - 2 - 9w^2}.$

17. $\displaystyle\int \frac{(y + 4)\,dy}{y^2 + 16}.$

18. $\displaystyle\int \frac{(y^2 + 1)\,dy}{y^2 + 4}.$

19. $\displaystyle\int \frac{e^{3x}\,dx}{9 + 4e^{6x}}.$

20. $\displaystyle\int \frac{e^{6x}\,dx}{9 + 4e^{6x}}.$

21. $\displaystyle\int \frac{x^3\,dx}{x^2 + 1}.$

22. $\displaystyle\int \frac{x^4\,dx}{x^2 + 1}.$

23. $\displaystyle\int \frac{\sec^2\theta\,d\theta}{\sqrt{5 - \sec^2\theta}}.$ *Ans.* Arcsin $(\tfrac{1}{2}\tan\theta) + C.$

24. $\displaystyle\int \frac{du}{\sqrt{9e^{-2u} - 1}}.$ *Ans.* Arcsin $(\tfrac{1}{3}e^u) + C.$

25. $\displaystyle\int \frac{(3x - 2)\,dx}{x^2 + 2x + 17}.$ Write as $\displaystyle\int \frac{3(x + 1) - 5}{(x + 1)^2 + 16}\,dx.$

   Ans. $\dfrac{3}{2}\ln (x^2 + 2x + 17) - \dfrac{5}{4}\text{Arctan}\,\dfrac{x + 1}{4} + C.$

26. $\displaystyle\int \frac{(4x - 7)\,dx}{x^2 - 6x + 13}.$ See Ex. 25.

27. $\displaystyle\int \frac{(10y + 11)\,dy}{4y^2 - 4y + 5}.$

28. $\displaystyle\int \frac{x\,dx}{\sqrt{-7 - 8x - x^2}}.$

29. $\displaystyle\int \frac{u(u^2 + 4)\,du}{u^4 + 9}.$

30. $\displaystyle\int \frac{\sin\theta\,(\cos\theta + 4)\,d\theta}{1 + \cos^2\theta}.$

31. $\displaystyle\int \frac{dx}{\sqrt{2ax - x^2}}.$

32. $\displaystyle\int \frac{x\,dx}{\sqrt{2ax - x^2}}.$

33. $\displaystyle\int \frac{(3\sin\theta - 7)\cos\theta\,d\theta}{4\sin^2\theta + 9}.$

34. $\displaystyle\int \frac{(1 + \tan x)\,dx}{\cos^2 x\,\sqrt{5 - 3\tan^2 x}}.$

35. $\displaystyle\int \frac{dt}{t\,\sqrt{t^2 - a^2}}.$ *Ans.* $-\dfrac{1}{a}\text{Arcsin}\,\dfrac{a}{t} + C.$

36. $\displaystyle\int \frac{\tan\theta\, d\theta}{\sec\theta + 4\cos\theta}.$
     37. $\displaystyle\int \frac{\cot\theta\, d\theta}{\csc\theta + 4\sin\theta}.$

132. *Formula* (12): *Integration by Parts*

From the formula for the differential of a product,

$$d(uv) = u\, dv + v\, du,$$

we find, integrating both sides,

$$uv = \int u\, dv + \int v\, du.$$

Transposing, we obtain the formula

(12) $$\int u\, dv = uv - \int v\, du.$$

Integration by this formula is called *integration by parts*.

Example (a). Evaluate $\displaystyle\int x \sin 2x\, dx.$

Let

$$u = x, \qquad dv = \sin 2x\, dx,$$
$$du = dx, \qquad v = \int \sin 2x\, dx = -\tfrac{1}{2}\cos 2x.$$

(It is a fact, which should be verified by the student, that in evaluating $\displaystyle\int dv = v$, the constant of integration may be omitted, since the final result is the same with or without it.) Hence

$$\int x \sin 2x\, dx = -\tfrac{1}{2}x \cos 2x + \tfrac{1}{2} \int \cos 2x\, dx$$

$$= -\tfrac{1}{2}x \cos 2x + \tfrac{1}{4}\sin 2x + C.$$

Only by experience and practice can one develop skill in telling when integration by parts is indicated. Further, when it has been decided to try the method, no rules can be laid down telling how to choose u and dv except that dv must be chosen so that $\displaystyle\int dv$ can be evaluated. However, in integrating a product, this method gives us a chance to differentiate one of the factors. In Example (a), differentiating x, we replace it by 1; differentiating $\sin x$, we replace it by $\cos x$. The former change, being more drastic, seems more promising. By looking ahead a bit in this way, we can usually make the right choice in the first instance.

Example (b). Evaluate $\int \sec^3 \theta \, d\theta$.

Take

$$u = \sec \theta, \qquad\qquad dv = \sec^2 \theta \, d\theta,$$
$$du = \sec \theta \tan \theta \, d\theta, \qquad v = \tan \theta;$$

$$\int \sec^3 \theta \, d\theta = \sec \theta \tan \theta - \int \sec \theta \tan^2 \theta \, d\theta$$

$$= \sec \theta \tan \theta - \int \sec^3 \theta \, d\theta + \int \sec \theta \, d\theta.$$

Evaluate the last integral (Ex. 36, page 239) and transpose the next-to-last to the other side:

$$2 \int \sec^3 \theta \, d\theta = \sec \theta \tan \theta + \ln (\sec \theta + \tan \theta) + C,$$

$$\int \sec^3 \theta \, d\theta = \tfrac{1}{2} \sec \theta \tan \theta + \tfrac{1}{2} \ln (\sec \theta + \tan \theta) + C_1.$$

Example (c). Evaluate $\int e^x \sin 2x \, dx$.

Take

$$u = e^x, \qquad\qquad dv = \sin 2x \, dx,$$
$$du = e^x \, dx, \qquad v = -\tfrac{1}{2} \cos 2x;$$

(1) $$\int e^x \sin 2x \, dx = -\tfrac{1}{2}e^x \cos 2x + \tfrac{1}{2} \int e^x \cos 2x \, dx.$$

Since this new integral is no simpler than the original, let us return to the given integral and take

$$u = \sin 2x, \qquad\qquad dv = e^x \, dx,$$
$$du = 2 \cos 2x \, dx, \qquad v = e^x;$$

(2) $$\int e^x \sin 2x \, dx = e^x \sin 2x - 2 \int e^x \cos 2x \, dx.$$

Here again we have failed temporarily, but since the troublesome integral is exactly the same one that appeared in (1), it may be *eliminated from the two equations*; multiplying each member of (1) by 4 and adding it to the corresponding member of (2), we find that

$$5 \int e^x \sin 2x \, dx = -2e^x \cos 2x + e^x \sin 2x + C,$$

$$\int e^x \sin 2x \, dx = -\tfrac{2}{5}e^x \cos 2x + \tfrac{1}{5}e^x \sin 2x + C_1.$$

Before considering himself skilled in the use of integration by parts, the student should learn to disassociate the technique from the letters employed in formula (12). The original integrand is always split into two factors, one of which involves a differential. Let us place those factors beside one another. Then beneath the factor with the differential put its integral; beneath the factor with no differential put its differential. Thus, in attacking the integral

$$\int \text{Arcsin } u \; du$$

we form the array shown below.

Arcsin u	du
$\dfrac{du}{\sqrt{1 - u^2}}$	u

The components of the lower line are the factors in the new integrand. The integrated portion in formula (12) is the product of the two components which contain no differential. Therefore we write

$$\int \text{Arcsin } u \; du = u \, \text{Arcsin } u - \int \frac{u \, du}{\sqrt{1 - u^2}}$$
$$= u \, \text{Arcsin } u + (1 - u^2)^{\frac{1}{2}} + C.$$

EXERCISES

In Exs. 1–30, perform the integrations.

1. $\displaystyle\int xe^x \, dx.$

2. $\displaystyle\int ye^{-2y} \, dy.$

3. $\displaystyle\int y \cos 4y \, dy.$

4. $\displaystyle\int u^2 \sin 2u \, du.$

5. $\displaystyle\int t^2 \cos t \, dt.$

6. $\displaystyle\int t^2 \cos (t^3) \, dt.$

7. $\displaystyle\int \ln x \, dx.$

8. $\displaystyle\int y \ln y \, dy.$

9. $\displaystyle\int x^2 e^{-x} \, dx.$

10. $\displaystyle\int y^2 e^{2y} \, dy.$

11. $\displaystyle\int \text{Arctan } u \, du.$

12. $\displaystyle\int u \, \text{Arctan } u \, du.$

13. $\displaystyle\int x \sin (x^2) \, dx.$

14. $\displaystyle\int x^3 \sin (x^2) \, dx.$

15. $\displaystyle\int x(2x - 1)^7 \, dx$, by parts.

16. $\displaystyle\int x(2x - 1)^7 \, dx$, by using $x = \frac{1}{2}(2x - 1) + \frac{1}{2}.$

17. $\displaystyle\int \frac{y \, dy}{(y - 1)^4}$, in two ways. See Exs. 15, 16.

18. $\displaystyle\int x \sqrt{x + 3} \, dx$, in two ways. See Exs. 15, 16.

19. $\int x^3(a^2 + x^2)^{\frac{1}{2}}\, dx.$ **20.** $\int y^3(a^2 - y^2)^{\frac{1}{2}}\, dy.$

21. $\int xe^{-x^2}\, dx.$ **22.** $\int x^3 e^{-x^2}\, dx.$

23. $\int v \sin^2 v\, dv.$ **24.** $\int \beta \sin 4\beta \cos 4\beta\, d\beta.$

25. $\int y \sec^2 y\, dy.$ **26.** $\int y \csc^2 y \cot y\, dy.$

27. $\int x \cosh \dfrac{x}{a}\, dx.$ **28.** $\int y \sinh \dfrac{y}{a}\, dy.$

29. $\int y \cos y \sin^2 y\, dy.$ *Ans.* $\frac{1}{3}y \sin^3 y + \frac{1}{3} \cos y - \frac{1}{9} \cos^3 y + C.$

30. $\int x \cos^3 x\, dx.$ *Ans.* $x \sin x - \frac{1}{3}x \sin^3 x + \frac{2}{3} \cos x + \frac{1}{9} \cos^3 x + C.$

In Exs. 31–36, employ integration by parts twice to evaluate the indicated integral.

31. $\int \sin x \sin 4x\, dx.$ *Ans.* $\frac{1}{15}(\cos x \sin 4x - 4 \sin x \cos 4x) + C.$

32. $\int \cos 2x \sin 3x\, dx.$ *Ans.* $-\frac{1}{5}(3 \cos 2x \cos 3x + 2 \sin 2x \sin 3x) + C.$

33. $\int e^{ax} \cos mx\, dx.$ *Ans.* $\dfrac{e^{ax}(a \cos mx + m \sin mx)}{a^2 + m^2} + C.$

34. $\int e^{ax} \sin mx\, dx.$ *Ans.* $\dfrac{e^{ax}(a \sin mx - m \cos mx)}{a^2 + m^2} + C.$

35. $\int \ln^2 x\, dx.$ *Ans.* $x \ln^2 x - 2x \ln x + 2x + C.$

36. $\int \sin (\ln x)\, dx.$ *Ans.* $\frac{1}{2}x[\sin (\ln x) - \cos (\ln x)] + C.$

37. $\int x^3 e^{-x}\, dx.$ **38.** $\int y^3 e^{-2y}\, dy.$

39. $\int x^3 \sin x\, dx.$ **40.** $\int y^3 \cos 2y\, dy.$

In Exs. 41–46, combine integration by parts with other appropriate devices, as in Example (b) above, to evaluate the indicated integral.

41. $\int \csc^3 y\, dy.$ *Ans.* $-\frac{1}{2} \csc y \cot y + \frac{1}{2} \ln(\csc y - \cot y) + C.$

42. $\int \sqrt{a^2 - x^2}\, dx.$ *Ans.* $\frac{1}{2}x \sqrt{a^2 - x^2} + \frac{1}{2}a^2 \text{Arcsin} \dfrac{x}{a} + C.$

43. $\int \sec x \tan^2 x \, dx.$ *Ans.* $\frac{1}{2} \sec x \tan x - \frac{1}{2} \ln(\sec x + \tan x) + C.$

44. $\int \sec^5 x \, dx.$ *Ans.* $\frac{1}{4} \sec^3 x \tan x + \frac{3}{8} \sec x \tan x + \frac{3}{8} \ln(\sec x + \tan x) + C.$

45. $\int \csc x \cot^2 x \, dx.$ **46.** $\int \csc^5 x \, dx.$

MISCELLANEOUS EXERCISES

1. $\int \cot^3 y \, dy.$ **2.** $\int \cos^3 x \sin^4 x \, dx.$

3. $\int x \cos 3x \, dx.$ **4.** $\int 10^{-2x} \, dx.$

5. $\int \dfrac{1 + \cos 2y}{1 - \cos 2y} \, dy.$ **6.** $\int \dfrac{e^{3t} \, dt}{(1 + e^{3t})^2}.$

7. $\int \cos^3 y \sin^3 2y \, dy.$ **8.** $\int e^{2x} \sqrt{1 - e^{2x}} \, dx.$

9. $\int \dfrac{d\varphi}{\cos 5\varphi}.$ **10.** $\int \dfrac{\sec^2 3u \, du}{1 - \tan 3u}.$

11. $\int \dfrac{x^3 + x - 4}{x - 1} \, dx.$ **12.** $\int \dfrac{\theta \, d\theta}{(\theta + 1)^3}.$

13. $\int \sin^5 2\theta \, d\theta.$ **14.** $\int (e^x + e^{-x})^2 \, dx.$

15. $\int x^2 \operatorname{Arctan} x \, dx.$ **16.** $\int \cot x \ln \sin x \, dx.$

17. $\int \csc^4 y \cot^3 y \, dy.$ **18.** $\int 2^x \, dx.$

19. $\int x \sqrt{x - 2} \, dx.$ **20.** $\int y^4 e^{-y} \, dy.$

21. $\int \dfrac{x^2 - 3}{x^2 + 1} \, dx.$ **22.** $\int \dfrac{\cos 2t \, dt}{4 - 3 \sin 2t}.$

23. $\int \dfrac{\cos y + \tan y}{\cos^2 y} \, dy.$ **24.** $\int \dfrac{(2\beta - 1) \, d\beta}{16\beta^2 + 8\beta + 37}.$

25. $\int \dfrac{u + 2}{u - 1} \, du.$ **26.** $\int \dfrac{dt}{4t^2 + 4t + 5}.$

27. $\int \dfrac{\cos^2 \alpha}{1 + \sin \alpha} \, d\alpha.$ **28.** $\int \dfrac{\cos^3 \theta \, d\theta}{\sin \theta}.$

29. $\int \dfrac{x \, dx}{\sqrt{16 - 25x^4}}.$ **30.** $\int \dfrac{e^{2t} \, dt}{1 + 4e^{2t} + 4e^{4t}}.$

31. $\int \dfrac{(1 - \cos 4x) \, dx}{(1 + \cos 4x)^2}.$ **32.** $\int \dfrac{e^{2x} \, dx}{1 + e^x}.$

33. $\displaystyle\int \sin^7 x \, dx.$

34. $\displaystyle\int y e^{3y} \, dy.$

35. $\displaystyle\int \frac{\sin^3 x \, dx}{\cos^5 x}.$

36. $\displaystyle\int \frac{y \, dy}{(1 + y^2)^3}.$

37. $\displaystyle\int \frac{(t^2 - 1)^2}{t^3} \, dt.$

38. $\displaystyle\int \frac{dy}{\sqrt{16 - y^2}}.$

39. $\displaystyle\int \cos^5 t \, \sin^4 t \, dt.$

40. $\displaystyle\int x(3x + 1)^7 \, dx.$

41. $\displaystyle\int \frac{t \sin^3 (t^2) \, dt}{\cos (t^2)}.$

42. $\displaystyle\int \frac{du}{u \ln^3 u}.$

43. $\displaystyle\int \frac{x + 4}{x^2 + 9} \, dx.$

44. $\displaystyle\int \frac{e^{-\frac{1}{x}}}{x^2} \, dx.$

45. $\displaystyle\int \frac{\cos^3 \theta}{1 - \sin \theta} \, d\theta.$

46. $\displaystyle\int \frac{e^{2x} \, dx}{\sqrt{7 - e^{4x}}}.$

47. $\displaystyle\int \frac{dy}{\sqrt{3 + 4y - 4y^2}}.$

48. $\displaystyle\int \frac{dx}{\sin 3x}.$

49. $\displaystyle\int t^2 \sin t \, dt.$

50. $\displaystyle\int (1 + \cot x)^2 \, dx.$

51. $\displaystyle\int \frac{x^2 \, dx}{(x^3 + 8)^2}.$

52. $\displaystyle\int \frac{y \, dy}{4 + y^4}.$

53. $\displaystyle\int \frac{(3y^2 + 2) \, dy}{y^3 + 2y - 7}.$

54. $\displaystyle\int \frac{dy}{4y - 25 - 4y^2}.$

55. $\displaystyle\int \cos^4 2\theta \, d\theta.$

56. $\displaystyle\int \cos (\ln x) \, dx.$

57. $\displaystyle\int \frac{dt}{\sqrt{3 - 4t^2}}.$

58. $\displaystyle\int \frac{\cos^2 x \, dx}{\sin^4 x}.$

59. $\displaystyle\int \frac{dx}{x^2 + 2x + 10}.$

60. $\displaystyle\int \frac{\sin^2 x \, dx}{1 - \cos x}.$

61. $\displaystyle\int \sec^2 \beta \, \tan^2 \beta \, d\beta.$

62. $\displaystyle\int x^2 e^{3x} \, dx.$

63. $\displaystyle\int \frac{(e^y - 1)^2 \, dy}{e^y}.$

64. $\displaystyle\int \frac{\sin^3 u}{1 - \cos u} \, du.$

65. $\displaystyle\int \tan^4 2x \, \sec^2 2x \, dx.$

66. $\displaystyle\int \sin x \, \sqrt{1 + 4 \cos x} \, dx.$

67. $\displaystyle\int \frac{(4x - 15) \, dx}{x^2 - 4x + 13}.$

63. $\displaystyle\int \frac{dt}{t(1 + \ln t)}.$

69. $\displaystyle\int \frac{e^{2t} \, dt}{e^{2t} - 4}.$

70. $\displaystyle\int \frac{\cos \varphi \, d\varphi}{\sin^4 \varphi}.$

71. $\displaystyle\int \sin\,(\text{Arctan }x)\,dx.$ **72.** $\displaystyle\int xe^{-x}\,dx.$

73. $\displaystyle\int \sin\beta(1 + \cos 2\beta)^3\,d\beta.$ **74.** $\displaystyle\int \sin^2 z \sin^3 2z\,dz.$

75. $\displaystyle\int \frac{y\,\cos\,(y^2)\,dy}{\sin\,(y^2)}.$ **76.** $\displaystyle\int \frac{\sqrt{x+1}}{x^{\frac{3}{2}}}\,dx.$

INTEGRATION BY

SUBSTITUTION

133. *Change of Variable of Integration*

Many integrals may be evaluated by introducing a new variable of integration, say z, in place of the original variable x, the two variables being connected by some suitable formula. The change of variable is usually brought about by means of an explicit substitution

$$x = \varphi(z), \qquad dx = \varphi'(z) \, dz.$$

This process, called *integration by substitution*, is highly important. It is to be remembered that *not merely x, but dx as well*, must be replaced by the proper expression in terms of the new variable.

The substitution to be made must be determined by inspection of the integrand. No general rules can be given; skill in the choice of substitutions comes only with practice. There is, however, one rather crude rule of thumb which succeeds often enough to make it worth consideration. Determine, if possible, what quantity seems to be causing the trouble (keeping you from performing the integration by the simple devices of Chapter 18) and then introduce a new variable for that quantity. In many cases, several different substitutions may be found, any one of which will succeed.

Example (a). Evaluate $\displaystyle\int \frac{\sqrt{x} \, dx}{1 + x}$.

Put $\sqrt{x} = z$. Then $x = z^2$ and $dx = 2z \, dz$. Hence

$$\int \frac{\sqrt{x} \, dx}{1 + x} = 2 \int \frac{z^2 \, dz}{1 + z^2} = 2 \int \left(1 - \frac{1}{1 + z^2}\right) dz$$

$$= 2z - 2 \operatorname{Arctan} z + C$$

$$= 2\sqrt{x} - 2 \operatorname{Arctan} \sqrt{x} + C.$$

Example (*b*). Evaluate $\int \dfrac{z^3\,dz}{\sqrt{z^2 - a^2}}$.

Put $\sqrt{z^2 - a^2} = v$. Then $z^2 = v^2 + a^2$ and $z\,dz = v\,dv$. Since $z\,dz$ is expressed simply (as $v\,dv$) in terms of the new variable, it is wise to exhibit $z\,dz$ explicitly before proceeding with the substitution. Therefore we write

$$\int \frac{z^3\,dz}{\sqrt{z^2 - a^2}} = \int \frac{z^2 \cdot z\,dz}{\sqrt{z^2 - a^2}} = \int \frac{(v^2 + a^2)v\,dv}{v}$$

$$= \tfrac{1}{3}v^3 + a^2 v + C$$

$$= \tfrac{1}{3}(z^2 - a^2)^{\frac{3}{2}} + a^2(z^2 - a^2)^{\frac{1}{2}} + C.$$

At times it is desirable to put the result in other forms. From the above we obtain

$$\int \frac{z^3\,dz}{\sqrt{z^2 - a^2}} = \frac{1}{3}(z^2 - a^2)^{\frac{1}{2}}[z^2 - a^2 + 3a^2] + C$$

$$= \tfrac{1}{3}(z^2 + 2a^2)(z^2 - a^2)^{\frac{1}{2}} + C.$$

Integrals involving $\sqrt{a^2 - x^2}$, $\sqrt{a^2 + x^2}$, $\sqrt{x^2 - a^2}$ occur very often. It should be noted that substitution of a new variable for the radical, as in Example (*b*), is indicated whenever the integrand contains, as a factor, an *odd* positive or negative integral power of x; but if not, the radical will reappear after the substitution.

It will be found that some of the integrals in this chapter can be solved directly by the methods of Chapter 18. Although substitutions are frequently necessary, the student should be alert for opportunities to avoid them by exercise of a little ingenuity. For instance, the integral in Example (*b*) above is easily evaluated without recourse to a substitution. Write

$$\int \frac{z^3\,dz}{\sqrt{z^2 - a^2}} = \int \frac{(z^2 - a^2 + a^2)z\,dz}{\sqrt{z^2 - a^2}}$$

$$= \int (z^2 - a^2)^{\frac{1}{2}}z\,dz + a^2 \int (z^2 - a^2)^{-\frac{1}{2}}z\,dz, \text{ etc.}$$

134. *A Dimensional Check*

In Example (*b*) of the preceding section, let z and a each represent a length. Then dz is also a length and the integral

$$(1) \qquad \int \frac{z^3\,dz}{\sqrt{z^2 - a^2}}$$

has the dimension (length)^3. In every step of the work in evaluating (1), each term must have the dimension (length)^3. This dimensional property should be used to check the work. Any term not having the proper dimension is incorrect, a fact which can be proved with the aid of the concept of homogeneity (defined in Ex. 49, p. 363 and in § 250).

EXERCISES

Evaluate the integrals in Exs. 1–38.

1. $\int \dfrac{(12x + 1)\, dx}{\sqrt{4x - 3}}$.

    Ans. $\frac{1}{2}(4x - 3)^{\frac{3}{2}} + 5(4x - 3)^{\frac{1}{2}} + C$

    $= \frac{1}{2}(4x + 7)(4x - 3)^{\frac{1}{2}} + C.$

2. $\int \dfrac{dx}{1 + \sqrt{x}}$.

    Ans. $2\sqrt{x} - 2\ln(1 + \sqrt{x}) + C.$

3. $\int \dfrac{(4x - 1)\, dx}{(2x + 1)^{\frac{3}{2}}}$.

    Ans. $(5 + 4x)(2x + 1)^{-\frac{1}{2}} + C.$

4. $\int \sin\sqrt{t}\, dt.$

    Ans. $2(\sin\sqrt{t} - \sqrt{t}\cos\sqrt{t}) + C.$

5. $\int \dfrac{(5y + 4)\, dy}{\sqrt{5y - 1}}$.

    Ans. $\frac{2}{15}(5y + 14)(5y - 1)^{\frac{1}{2}} + C.$

6. $\int \sqrt{1 + \sqrt{z}}\, dz.$

    Ans. $\frac{4}{15}(3\sqrt{z} - 2)(1 + \sqrt{z})^{\frac{3}{2}} + C.$

7. $\int \dfrac{(1 + \ln x)\, dx}{x^3}$.

    Ans. $-\frac{1}{4}x^{-2}(3 + 2\ln x) + C.$

8. $\int v^3(a^2 - v^2)^{\frac{1}{2}}\, dv.$

    Ans. $\frac{1}{5}(a^2 - v^2)^{\frac{5}{2}} - \frac{1}{3}a^2(a^2 - v^2)^{\frac{3}{2}} + C$

    $= -\frac{1}{15}(3v^2 + 2a^2)(a^2 - v^2)^{\frac{3}{2}} + C.$

9. $\int \dfrac{x^3\, dx}{(x^2 + a^2)^3}$.

    Ans. $\dfrac{x^4}{4a^2(x^2 + a^2)^2} + C.$

10. $\int \dfrac{\sqrt{y^5 - 1}}{y}\, dy.$

    Ans. $\frac{2}{5}\sqrt{y^5 - 1} - \frac{2}{5}\operatorname{Arctan}\sqrt{y^5 - 1} + C.$

11. $\int \dfrac{dx}{x^2(a^2 + x^2)}$.

    Ans. $-\dfrac{1}{a^2 x} + \dfrac{1}{a^3}\operatorname{Arctan}\dfrac{a}{x} + C.$

12. $\int \dfrac{\sqrt{x^2 - a^2}}{x}\, dx.$

    Ans. $\sqrt{x^2 - a^2} + a\operatorname{Arcsin}\dfrac{a}{x} + C.$

13. $\int \dfrac{x^3\, dx}{(x^2 - a^2)^3}$.

14. $\int x^3\sqrt{a^2 + x^2}\, dx.$

15. $\int \dfrac{dx}{x(x^2 - a^2)}$.

16. $\int \dfrac{z^5\, dz}{(z^2 - a^2)^2}$.

17. $\int \dfrac{x\, dx}{(x^2 + a^2)^3}$.

18. $\int \dfrac{x\, dx}{(x^2 - a^2)^{\frac{2}{3}}}$.

19. $\int \sqrt{e^x - 9}\, dx.$

20. $\int \cos\sqrt{t}\, dt.$

21. $\int (1 + \sqrt{\theta})^{-\frac{3}{2}}\, d\theta.$

22. $\int e^{2z}\sqrt{1 - e^z}\, dz.$

23. $\int (5z - 1)\sqrt{z + 2}\, dz.$

24. $\int \ln(\sqrt{y} + 3)\, dy.$

25. $\int \dfrac{x^3\,dx}{(a^2 - x^2)^2}.$

26. $\int \dfrac{dt}{1 - t^{\frac14}}.$

27. $\int \dfrac{\sqrt{x^3 - 1}\,dx}{x}.$

23. $\int \dfrac{y\,dy}{1 + \sqrt{y}}.$

29. $\int \dfrac{(x^3 + 4x)\,dx}{\sqrt{1 - x^4}}.$

30. $\int \dfrac{e^{3v}\,dv}{\sqrt{e^v - 1}}.$

31. $\int \dfrac{dy}{y^{\frac12} + y^{\frac13}}.$

32. $\int \dfrac{\cos\theta \sin^2\theta\,d\theta}{\sqrt{1 + \sin\theta}}.$

33. $\int \dfrac{dy}{\sqrt{y + 4} - 2}.$

34. $\int \dfrac{dt}{\sqrt{1 + t^{\frac13}}}.$

35. $\int \dfrac{(x^2 - a^2)^{\frac32}\,dx}{x}.$

36. $\int \dfrac{(x^2 - a^2)^{\frac34}\,dx}{x}.$

37. $\int \sec^2\theta \tan\theta\,(1 + 3\tan\theta)^{\frac12}\,d\theta.$

38. $\int x^3(x^2 + a^2)^k\,dx.$ Note the special treatment necessary for $k = -1$ and $k = -2$.

In Exs. 39–46, use the reciprocal substitution $x = \dfrac{a^2}{v}.$

39. $\int \dfrac{dx}{x^2\sqrt{a^2 - x^2}}.$ $\qquad$ Ans. $-\dfrac{\sqrt{a^2 - x^2}}{a^2 x} + C.$

40. $\int \dfrac{\sqrt{a^2 + x^2}\,dx}{x^4}.$ $\qquad$ Ans. $\dfrac{-(a^2 + x^2)^{\frac32}}{3a^2 x^3} + C.$

41. $\int \dfrac{dx}{(a^2 + x^2)^{\frac32}}.$

42. $\int \dfrac{dx}{(a^2 - x^2)^{\frac12}}.$

43. Ex. 9. $\qquad\qquad\qquad\qquad$ **44.** Ex. 11.

45. Ex. 13. $\qquad\qquad\qquad\qquad$ **46.** Ex. 15.

135. *Trigonometric Substitutions*

Many integrals can be evaluated by substituting a trigonometric function for x. The following substitutions are especially promising:

(1) *When the integrand involves* $a^2 - x^2$, *try* $x = a \sin\theta$.

(2) *When the integrand involves* $a^2 + x^2$, *try* $x = a \tan\theta$.

(3) *When the integrand involves* $x^2 - a^2$, *try* $x = a \sec\theta$.

However, it will be found that these combinations by no means exhaust the usefulness of trigonometric substitutions.

Let us examine the reasons underlying the choice (1) above. We know that

$$1 - \sin^2 \theta = \cos^2 \theta.$$

Therefore, if x is chosen to be $a \sin \theta$,

$$a^2 - x^2 = a^2 - a^2 \sin^2 \theta = a^2 \cos^2 \theta.$$

We thus replace $(a^2 - x^2)$ by a single term $a^2 \cos^2 \theta$. Furthermore, that single term is a perfect square, which is particularly effective when the quantity $(a^2 - x^2)$ appears under a square root symbol. Corresponding analyses of the choices (2) and (3) above should be made by the student.

Example (a). Evaluate $\displaystyle\int \frac{dx}{(a^2 - x^2)^{\frac{3}{2}}}$.

Putting $x = a \sin \theta$, $dx = a \cos \theta \, d\theta$, we get

$$\int \frac{a \cos \theta \, d\theta}{(a^2 - a^2 \sin^2 \theta)^{\frac{3}{2}}} = \frac{1}{a^2} \int \frac{\cos \theta \, d\theta}{(1 - \sin^2 \theta)^{\frac{3}{2}}} = \frac{1}{a^2} \int \frac{\cos \theta \, d\theta}{\cos^3 \theta}$$

$$= \frac{1}{a^2} \int \sec^2 \theta \, d\theta = \frac{1}{a^2} \tan \theta + C.$$

Figure 132

From the triangle,

$$\tan \theta = \frac{x}{\sqrt{a^2 - x^2}},$$

whence

$$\int \frac{dx}{(a^2 - x^2)^{\frac{3}{2}}} = \frac{x}{a^2 \sqrt{a^2 - x^2}} + C.$$

The triangle in Fig. 132 was constructed, of course, to permit easy return to the original variable x. Note that the quantity $\sqrt{a^2 - x^2}$, which originally suggested the substitution used, appears in the triangle. This brings in a mild check on the work. Unless the quantity which suggests a trigonometric substitution appears in the associated triangle relating new and old variables, there is probably an error in the work.

Example (b). Evaluate $\displaystyle\int \frac{\sqrt{x - a}}{x^{\frac{5}{2}}} \, dx$.

Here there are two troublesome elements; both $(x - a)$ and x appear with fractional exponents. If we put $x = u^2$, the disturbing element $(u^2 - a)$ would appear under a square root sign. The choice $x - a = v^2$ would introduce $(v^2 + a)$ for x, which is undesirable in the same way.

Now $(x - a)$ may be thought of as $(\sqrt{x})^2 - (\sqrt{a})^2$, thus suggesting the substitution in (3) above. Hence we try

$$\sqrt{x} = \sqrt{a} \sec \theta$$

from which

$$x = a \sec^2 \theta, \qquad dx = 2a \sec^2 \theta \tan \theta \, d\theta.$$

Then

$$\int \frac{\sqrt{x-a}}{x^{\frac{5}{2}}}\, dx = \int \frac{\sqrt{a\sec^2\theta - a}\cdot 2a\sec^2\theta\tan\theta\, d\theta}{a^{\frac{5}{2}}\sec^5\theta}$$

$$= \frac{2}{a}\int \frac{\sqrt{\sec^2\theta - 1}\cdot\tan\theta\, d\theta}{\sec^3\theta}$$

$$= \frac{2}{a}\int \tan^2\theta\cos^3\theta\, d\theta$$

$$= \frac{2}{a}\int \sin^2\theta\cos\theta\, d\theta$$

$$= \frac{2}{3a}\sin^3\theta + C = \frac{2}{3a}\frac{(x-a)^{\frac{3}{2}}}{x^{\frac{3}{2}}} + C.$$

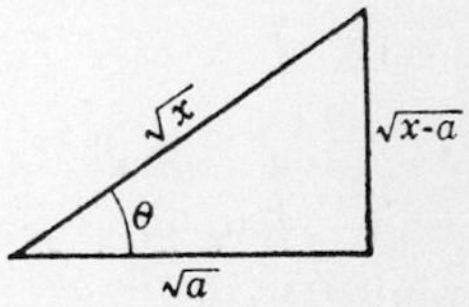

Figure 133

EXERCISES

Evaluate the integrals in Exs. 1–60, making use of trigonometric substitutions.

1. $\displaystyle\int \frac{dx}{(a^2 + x^2)^{\frac{3}{2}}}.$ *Ans.* $\displaystyle\frac{x}{a^2\sqrt{a^2 + x^2}} + C.$

2. $\displaystyle\int \frac{dx}{(a^2 + x^2)^{\frac{5}{2}}}.$ *Ans.* $\displaystyle\frac{x(3a^2 + 2x^2)}{3a^4(a^2 + x^2)^{\frac{3}{2}}} + C.$

3. $\displaystyle\int \frac{dx}{x^2\sqrt{a^2 - x^2}}.$ *Ans.* $\displaystyle\frac{-\sqrt{a^2 - x^2}}{a^2 x} + C.$

4. $\displaystyle\int \sqrt{a^2 - x^2}\, dx.$ *Ans.* $\frac{1}{2}x\sqrt{a^2 - x^2} + \frac{1}{2}a^2\,\text{Arcsin}\,\frac{x}{a} + C.$

5. $\displaystyle\int \frac{\sqrt{a^2 - x^2}}{x^2}\, dx.$ *Ans.* $\displaystyle\frac{-\sqrt{a^2 - x^2}}{x} - \text{Arcsin}\,\frac{x}{a} + C.$

6. $\displaystyle\int \frac{dx}{(x^2 - a^2)^{\frac{3}{2}}}.$ *Ans.* $\displaystyle\frac{-x}{a^2\sqrt{x^2 - a^2}} + C.$

7. $\displaystyle\int \frac{v^2\, dv}{(a^2 - v^2)^{\frac{3}{2}}}.$ *Ans.* $\displaystyle\frac{v}{\sqrt{a^2 - v^2}} - \text{Arcsin}\,\frac{v}{a} + C.$

8. $\displaystyle\int \frac{dw}{w^2\sqrt{w^2 + a^2}}.$ *Ans.* $\displaystyle\frac{-\sqrt{w^2 + a^2}}{a^2 w} + C.$

9. $\displaystyle\int \frac{dy}{\sqrt{y^2 + a^2}}.$ *Ans.* $\ln(y + \sqrt{y^2 + a^2}) + C.$

10. $\displaystyle\int \frac{du}{(u^2 + a^2)^2}.$ *Ans.* $\displaystyle\frac{1}{2a^3}\left(\frac{au}{u^2 + a^2} + \text{Arctan}\,\frac{u}{a}\right) + C.$

11. $\displaystyle\int \frac{dx}{x\sqrt{a^2 - x^2}}.$ 12. $\displaystyle\int \frac{y^3\, dy}{(a^2 - y^2)^{\frac{5}{2}}}.$

13. $\displaystyle\int z^3(a^2 - z^2)^{\frac{3}{2}}\, dz.$ 14. $\displaystyle\int x^3(a^2 - x^2)^{\frac{1}{2}}\, dx.$

15. $\displaystyle\int \frac{(z^2 + v^2)^{\frac{3}{2}}\, dv}{v^4}.$

16. $\displaystyle\int \frac{(y^2 + x^2)^{\frac{3}{2}}\, dx}{x^6}.$

17. $\displaystyle\int \frac{dx}{(a^2 - x^2)^{\frac{5}{2}}}.$ $\qquad\qquad\qquad$ *Ans.* $\dfrac{x(3a^2 - 2x^2)}{3a^4(a^2 - x^2)^{\frac{3}{2}}} + C.$

18. $\displaystyle\int \sqrt{a^2 + x^2}\, dx.$ $\qquad$ *Ans.* $\dfrac{x}{2} \sqrt{a^2 + x^2} + \dfrac{a^2}{2} \ln (x + \sqrt{a^2 + x^2}) + C.$

19. $\displaystyle\int \frac{x^2\, dx}{\sqrt{a^2 + x^2}}.$ $\qquad$ *Ans.* $\dfrac{x}{2} \sqrt{a^2 + x^2} - \dfrac{a^2}{2} \ln (x + \sqrt{a^2 + x^2}) + C.$

20. $\displaystyle\int (a^2 - x^2)^{\frac{3}{2}}\, dx.$ $\quad$ *Ans.* $\dfrac{x}{4} (a^2 - x^2)^{\frac{3}{2}} + \dfrac{3a^2x}{8} (a^2 - x^2)^{\frac{1}{2}} + \dfrac{3a^4}{8} \text{Arcsin} \dfrac{x}{a} + C.$

21. $\displaystyle\int \frac{x^3\, dx}{(a^2 + x^2)^2}.$

22. $\displaystyle\int \frac{dy}{y(a^2 + y^2)^2}.$

23. $\displaystyle\int \frac{du}{u^2(c^2 + u^2)}.$

24. $\displaystyle\int \frac{w^2\, dw}{(c^2 + w^2)^{\frac{3}{2}}}.$

25. $\displaystyle\int \frac{\alpha^3\, d\alpha}{\sqrt{\beta^2 - \alpha^2}}.$

26. $\displaystyle\int \frac{\alpha^3\, d\alpha}{(\beta^2 + \alpha^2)^{\frac{3}{2}}}.$

27. $\displaystyle\int \frac{x^3\, dx}{(a^2 - x^2)^{\frac{3}{2}}}.$

28. $\displaystyle\int \frac{dx}{x(a^2 + x^2)^{\frac{3}{2}}}.$

29. $\displaystyle\int \frac{dx}{x^2(x^2 - a^2)^{\frac{3}{2}}}.$

30. $\displaystyle\int \frac{x^2\, dx}{(x^2 - a^2)^{\frac{3}{2}}}.$

31. $\displaystyle\int \frac{\theta^3\, d\theta}{(16 + 9\theta^2)^{\frac{3}{2}}}.$

32. $\displaystyle\int \frac{\theta^4\, d\theta}{(16 + 9\theta^2)^{\frac{5}{2}}}.$

33. $\displaystyle\int \frac{z^4\, dz}{(16 + z^2)^2}.$

34. $\displaystyle\int \frac{dz}{z(4 + z^2)^3}.$

35. $\displaystyle\int \frac{dx}{x^2(9 + x^2)^{\frac{3}{2}}}.$

36. $\displaystyle\int \frac{dx}{x(x^2 - 4)^{\frac{3}{2}}}.$

37. $\displaystyle\int \frac{\sqrt{9x^2 - 4}}{x}\, dx.$

38. $\displaystyle\int \frac{\sqrt{16 - x^2}}{x}\, dx.$

39. $\displaystyle\int \frac{dy}{y(y^2 + 1)}.$

40. $\displaystyle\int \frac{dy}{y^3(y^2 + 1)}.$

41. $\displaystyle\int \frac{du}{u^2 \sqrt{4u^2 - 1}}.$

42. $\displaystyle\int \frac{du}{u^4 \sqrt{4u^2 - 1}}.$

43. $\displaystyle\int \frac{dx}{x^4 \sqrt{9 - x^2}}.$

44. $\displaystyle\int \frac{y^2\, dy}{(16y^2 + 9)^{\frac{3}{2}}}.$

45. $\displaystyle\int \frac{\sqrt{x}\, dx}{(1 + x)^2}.$

46. $\displaystyle\int \frac{\sqrt{x}\, dx}{(1 + x)^3}.$

47. $\displaystyle\int \frac{dx}{\sqrt{x^2 - a^2}}.$

43. $\displaystyle\int \frac{dx}{(x^2 - a^2)^{\frac{5}{2}}}.$

49. $\int \dfrac{dx}{x(a^2 + x^2)^{\frac{1}{2}}}.$

50. $\int \dfrac{dx}{x^2(x^2 - a^2)^{\frac{1}{2}}}.$

51. $\int \dfrac{\sqrt{a - y}}{\sqrt{y}}\, dy.$

52. $\int \dfrac{\sqrt{y}}{\sqrt{a - y}}\, dy.$

53. $\int \dfrac{dx}{\sqrt{1 + \sqrt{x}}}.$

54. $\int \sqrt{1 - \sqrt{x}}\; dx.$

55. $\int \dfrac{\cos \varphi \sin \varphi\, d\varphi}{(1 - \cos \varphi)^2}.$

56. $\int \dfrac{\cos \beta\, d\beta}{(1 + \sin^2 \beta)^{\frac{1}{2}}}.$

57. $\int \dfrac{dx}{x\sqrt{2ax - x^2}}.$ (Put $x = 2a \sin^2 \theta.$)   *Ans.* $\;-\dfrac{\sqrt{2ax - x^2}}{ax} + C.$

58. $\int \dfrac{dx}{x\sqrt{2ax + x^2}}.$ (Put $x = 2a \tan^2 \theta.$)   *Ans.* $\;-\dfrac{\sqrt{2ax + x^2}}{ax} + C.$

59. $\int \dfrac{dx}{x\sqrt{x^2 - 2ax}}.$ (Put $x = 2a \sec^2 \theta.$)   *Ans.* $\;\dfrac{\sqrt{x^2 - 2ax}}{ax} + C.$

60. Solve Ex. 57 by a second method. Put $x - a = a \sin \theta.$

61. Solve Ex. 58 by a second method.

62. Solve Ex. 59 by a second method.

63. Evaluate $\displaystyle\int \dfrac{dx}{x(x^4 - 1)}$ in several ways.

64. Evaluate $\displaystyle\int \dfrac{dy}{y(y^4 + 1)}$ in at least three ways.

In Exs. 65–82, evaluate the integral with, or without, the aid of trigonometric substitutions, using whatever method seems best adapted to the problem.

65. $\int \dfrac{dy}{1 - e^y}.$

66. $\int \dfrac{du}{e^{2u} + 1}.$

67. $\int \dfrac{dx}{\sqrt{4 - 9x^2}}.$

68. $\int \dfrac{d\varphi}{9\varphi^2 + 1}.$

69. $\int \dfrac{dx}{x(x + k)^2}.$

70. $\int \dfrac{dx}{\sqrt{4e^{2x} - 9}}.$

71. $\int \dfrac{dy}{y(y - 4)^2}.$

72. $\int \dfrac{x^2\, dx}{(x^2 + a^2)^2}.$

73. $\int \dfrac{y^3\, dy}{(y^2 + a^2)^3}.$

74. $\int \dfrac{x^5\, dx}{(a^2 + x^2)^{\frac{5}{2}}}.$

75. $\int \dfrac{y^3\, dy}{\sqrt{a^2 + y^2}}.$

76. $\int \dfrac{y^5\, dy}{\sqrt{a^2 + y^2}}.$

77. $\int \dfrac{d\beta}{\beta(\beta^2 - \alpha^2)^{\frac{1}{2}}}.$

78. $\int \dfrac{\theta^3\, d\theta}{(\theta^2 - x^2)^{\frac{3}{2}}}.$

79. $\int \dfrac{d\theta}{\theta(\theta^2 - x^2)^{\frac{3}{2}}}.$

80. $\int \dfrac{c^5\, dc}{(c^2 + y^2)^3}.$

81. $\int \dfrac{c^3\, dc}{(c^2 - x^2)^{\frac{1}{2}}}.$

82. $\int \dfrac{dx}{x(a^2 + x^2)^{\frac{3}{2}}}.$

INTEGRATION OF

RATIONAL FRACTIONS

136. *Introduction*

We take up next the problem of integrating a *rational algebraic fraction*—i.e., the quotient of two polynomials.

As noted in § 127, the first step in dealing with an integral of this type is to *carry out the indicated division until the numerator is of lower degree than the denominator*. In developing our theory, we shall suppose always that this preliminary step has been taken.

In this chapter, whenever the quantity $ax^2 + bx + c$ occurs, it will be assumed that $b^2 - 4ac < 0$. If $b^2 - 4ac \geqq 0$, the quantity $ax^2 + bx + c$ can be factored into real linear factors.

By methods already familiar, we can immediately integrate fractions of the forms

$$\frac{A}{(ax + b)^n}, \qquad \frac{A(2ax + b)}{(ax^2 + bx + c)^n}, \qquad \frac{A}{ax^2 + bx + c}.$$

The first two lead to powers, if $n > 1$, to logarithms, if $n = 1$; the third leads to an arctangent. We can also integrate

$$\frac{A}{(ax^2 + bx + c)^n}, \qquad n > 1,$$

by a trigonometric substitution.

137. *Partial Fractions*

It is shown in algebra that every rational fraction whose numerator is of lower degree than the denominator can be broken up into so-called *partial fractions* of the exact forms listed above. It follows that *every rational fraction can be integrated* in elementary terms. In the next few pages we show how to effect the breakup into partial fractions.

264

In order to apply the results, it is necessary that the operator actually be able to find the linear and quadratic factors of the denominator—conceivably a formidable task. Fortunately, most cases that arise are relatively simple.

138. *Distinct Linear Factors*

The simplest case is that in which the denominator can be broken up into real linear factors, none of which is repeated. In this case we may always rewrite the given fraction (provided the numerator is of lower degree than the denominator) as a sum of fractions whose numerators are constants and whose respective denominators are the factors of the original denominator.

Example (a). Evaluate $\int \dfrac{x^3 + 2}{x^3 - x}\, dx$.

By division,

$$\frac{x^3 + 2}{x^3 - x} = 1 + \frac{x + 2}{x^3 - x}.$$

The factors of the denominator are x, $x + 1$, $x - 1$. Assume

$$\frac{x + 2}{x^3 - x} = \frac{A}{x} + \frac{B}{x + 1} + \frac{C}{x - 1},$$

where A, B, C are constants to be determined. Clearing of fractions, we find

$$x + 2 = A(x^2 - 1) + Bx(x - 1) + Cx(x + 1).$$

This relation must hold for *all values* of x. Hence, assigning to x any three values whatever, we must obtain three simultaneous equations to determine A, B, C. But the most convenient values to use are $0, -1, 1$ (the zeros of the original denominator), for each of these causes two terms to drop out:

$$x = 0, \qquad A = -2;$$
$$x = -1, \qquad B = \tfrac{1}{2};$$
$$x = 1, \qquad C = \tfrac{3}{2}.$$

Thus

$$\int \frac{x^3 + 2}{x(x^2 - 1)}\, dx = \int \left(1 - \frac{2}{x} + \frac{1}{2}\cdot\frac{1}{x + 1} + \frac{3}{2}\cdot\frac{1}{x - 1}\right) dx$$
$$= x - 2\ln x + \tfrac{1}{2}\ln(x + 1) + \tfrac{3}{2}\ln(x - 1) + C.$$

The student is urgently warned not to forget the preliminary division (when necessary). Without that, the above process will determine values of A, B, C; but the sum of partial fractions thus found will be equal to the given fraction for no values of x except the three that were assigned.

Careful scrutiny of the method used in Example (a) shows that the expansion is easily obtained mentally. Let us develop the idea in detail.

Consider any rational fraction with numerator of lower degree than the denominator, and with denominator consisting of distinct linear factors only. Let $(x - a)$ be a representative factor of the denominator. Then the fraction may be written $\dfrac{f(x)}{(x - a)g(x)}$, where $g(a) \neq 0$. The theory of rational fractions shows that

(1) $$\frac{f(x)}{(x - a)g(x)} = \frac{A}{x - a} + \varphi(x),$$

where $\varphi(x)$ is the sum of the other terms in the desired expansion.

Multiply each term of (1) by $(x - a)$, thus getting

$$\frac{f(x)}{g(x)} = A + (x - a)\varphi(x),$$

from which

$$A = \frac{f(a)}{g(a)}.$$

Thus the numerator of the representative term $\dfrac{A}{x - a}$ can be obtained from the original fraction by (mentally) removing the factor $(x - a)$ and evaluating what remains at $x = a$.

Example (b). Expand $\dfrac{x^2 + 1}{(x - 2)(x - 1)(2x + 1)}$ into partial fractions.

We know that

$$\frac{x^2 + 1}{(x - 2)(x - 1)(2x + 1)} = \frac{A}{x - 2} + \frac{B}{x - 1} + \frac{C}{2x + 1},$$

from which

$$A = \left[\frac{x^2 + 1}{(x - 1)(2x + 1)}\right]_{x=2} = \frac{5}{(1)(5)} = 1,$$

$$B = \left[\frac{x^2 + 1}{(x - 2)(2x + 1)}\right]_{x=1} = \frac{2}{(-1)(3)} = -\frac{2}{3},$$

$$C = \left[\frac{x^2 + 1}{(x - 2)(x - 1)}\right]_{x=-\frac{1}{2}} = \frac{\frac{5}{4}}{(-\frac{5}{2})(-\frac{3}{2})} = \frac{1}{3}.$$

Therefore,

$$\frac{x^2 + 1}{(x - 2)(x - 1)(2x + 1)} = \frac{1}{x - 2} + \frac{-\frac{2}{3}}{x - 1} + \frac{\frac{1}{3}}{2x + 1},$$

all of which should be accomplished mentally.

139. *An Important Logarithmic Formula*

Under the heading of § 138, one particular integral occurs so often that it is worth listing for reference.

To evaluate $\int \dfrac{dx}{a^2 - x^2}$, use the method of Example (*b*), page 266, to get

$$\int \frac{dx}{a^2 - x^2} = \frac{1}{2a} \int \frac{dx}{a + x} + \frac{1}{2a} \int \frac{dx}{a - x}$$

$$= \frac{1}{2a} \ln (a + x) - \frac{1}{2a} \ln (a - x) + C,$$

or

$$\int \frac{dx}{a^2 - x^2} = \frac{1}{2a} \ln \frac{a + x}{a - x} + C = \frac{1}{2a} \ln \frac{x + a}{x - a} + C'.$$

As a corollary, by changing signs we get

$$\int \frac{dx}{x^2 - a^2} = \frac{1}{2a} \ln \frac{a - x}{a + x} + C_1 = \frac{1}{2a} \ln \frac{x - a}{x + a} + C_1'.$$

EXERCISES

Evaluate each of the following integrals.

1. $\displaystyle\int \frac{(2x + 11)\, dx}{x^2 + x - 6}.$ *Ans.* $3 \ln (x - 2) - \ln (x + 3) + C.$

2. $\displaystyle\int \frac{(x - 1)\, dx}{x^2 + 5x + 6}.$ *Ans.* $4 \ln (x + 3) - 3 \ln (x + 2) + C.$

3. $\displaystyle\int \frac{dx}{x^2 + ax}.$ *Ans.* $\dfrac{1}{a} \ln \dfrac{x}{x + a} + C.$

4. Do Ex. 3 by using the reciprocal substitution, $x = \dfrac{a^2}{v}.$

5. $\displaystyle\int \frac{(3x^2 + 8x - 12)\, dx}{x^3 + 7x^2 + 12x}.$ *Ans.* $3 \ln (x + 3) - \ln x + \ln (x + 4) + C.$

6. $\displaystyle\int \frac{(x^2 - 5x + 3)\, dx}{x^3 - 4x^2 + 3x}.$ *Ans.* $\ln x + \frac{1}{2} \ln (x - 1) - \frac{1}{2} \ln (x - 3) + C.$

7. $\displaystyle\int \frac{(17x - 6)\, dx}{x^3 - x^2 - 6x}.$ 8. $\displaystyle\int \frac{(5x - 12)\, dx}{x^3 - 6x^2 + 8x}.$

9. $\displaystyle\int \frac{(3x^2 - 4x - 1)\, dx}{x^2 - x - 2}.$ 10. $\displaystyle\int \frac{(x^2 - 8)\, dx}{x^2 + 5x + 6}.$

11. $\displaystyle\int \frac{(y^3 + 4)\, dy}{y(y + 1)}.$ 12. $\displaystyle\int \frac{(y^3 + 1)\, dy}{y(y + 2)}.$

13. $\displaystyle\int \frac{(y + 13)\, dy}{(y + 1)(y + 3)(y - 2)}.$ 14. $\displaystyle\int \frac{(y^2 - 14y + 5)\, dy}{y(y - 1)(y - 5)}.$

15. $\displaystyle\int \frac{21\, dv}{(v - 1)(v + 3)(v - 4)}.$ 16. $\displaystyle\int \frac{v^2\, dv}{(v + 1)(v + 2)(v + 3)}.$

17. $\displaystyle\int \frac{6y^2\, dy}{y^6 + 4y^3 + 3}.$ 18. $\displaystyle\int \frac{5 \sin \theta \cos \theta\, d\theta}{\sin^2 \theta + 3 \sin \theta - 4}.$

19. $\int \dfrac{x^3\,dx}{x^2 - 9}$.

20. $\int \dfrac{y^3\,dy}{y^4 - 16}$.

21. $\int \dfrac{3t^2\,dt}{t^4 + 5t^2 + 4}$.

22. $\int \dfrac{8t^2\,dt}{9t^4 + 10t^2 + 1}$.

23. $\int \dfrac{(2v^3 - 3v)\,dv}{v^4 + 16}$.

24. $\int \dfrac{(5v^3 + 2v)\,dv}{v^4 + 1}$.

25. $\int \dfrac{dx}{(9 - x)\sqrt{x}}$.

26. $\int \dfrac{e^{3x}\,dx}{e^{2x} - 9}$.

27. $\int \dfrac{6dx}{x(1 - x^6)}$.

28. $\int \dfrac{8dx}{x(x^4 + 4)}$.

29. $\int \dfrac{dy}{\sqrt{1 - 4e^{2y}}}$.

30. $\int \dfrac{dy}{\sqrt{e^{2y} + 4}}$.

31. $\int \dfrac{9dx}{e^x + 9}$. Use the substitution $e^x + 9 = v$.

32. $\int \dfrac{9dx}{e^x + 9}$. Use the substitution $e^x = 9 \tan^2 \varphi$.

33. $\int \dfrac{9dx}{e^x + 9}$. Use the fact that $\dfrac{9}{e^x + 9} = \dfrac{9e^{-x}}{1 + 9e^{-x}}$.

34. $\int \dfrac{9dx}{e^x + 9}$. Use the fact that $\dfrac{9}{e^x + 9} = 1 - \dfrac{e^x}{e^x + 9}$.

35. $\int \dfrac{4dx}{e^x + 4}$. See the suggestions in Exs. 31–34.

36. $\int \dfrac{4dx}{e^{2x} + 4}$. Adapt the suggestions in Exs. 31–34.

37. $\int \dfrac{dx}{x\sqrt{a^2 + x^2}}$. (Put $a^2 + x^2 = v^2$.)   *Ans.* $-\dfrac{1}{a}\ln\dfrac{a + \sqrt{a^2 + x^2}}{x} + C$.

38. $\int \dfrac{dx}{x\sqrt{a^2 - x^2}}$. (Put $a^2 - x^2 = y^2$.)   *Ans.* $-\dfrac{1}{a}\ln\dfrac{a + \sqrt{a^2 - x^2}}{x} + C$.

39. $\int \dfrac{\sqrt{a^2 - x^2}}{x}\,dx$. (Put $a^2 - x^2 = y^2$.)

140. *Repeated Linear Factors*

If the denominator contains a factor $(x - \alpha)^r$, the above method fails, since there would be r partial fractions with denominator $x - \alpha$, and these could be combined into a single fraction with denominator $x - \alpha$. In this case, corresponding to the factor $(x - \alpha)^r$, we *assume r partial fractions of the form*

$$\frac{A}{x - \alpha} + \frac{B}{(x - \alpha)^2} + \cdots + \frac{D}{(x - \alpha)^r}.$$

Example. Evaluate $\displaystyle\int \frac{x^3 - 1}{x(x + 1)^3}\, dx$.

Assume

(1) $$\frac{x^3 - 1}{x(x + 1)^3} = \frac{A}{x} + \frac{B}{x + 1} + \frac{C}{(x + 1)^2} + \frac{D}{(x + 1)^3},$$

(2) $$x^3 - 1 = A(x + 1)^3 + Bx(x + 1)^2 + Cx(x + 1) + Dx.$$

To get the necessary four equations for the determination of A, B, C, D, two methods are at once available. Specific values of x can be used in the identity (2), or the coefficients of like powers of x in the two members of (2) can be equated.

We naturally employ whatever combination of these methods yields simple equations to be solved for the unknowns A, B, etc.

From (2) we obtain equations as follows:

$$x = 0:\qquad -1 = A,$$
$$x = -1:\quad -2 = -D,$$
$$\text{Coefficients of } x^3:\quad 1 = A + B,$$
$$\text{Coefficients of } x^2:\quad 0 = 3A + 2B + C.$$

These equations yield $A = -1$, $B = 2$, $C = -1$, $D = 2$, whence

$$\int \frac{(x^3 - 1)\, dx}{x(x + 1)^3} = \int \left(-\frac{1}{x} + \frac{2}{x + 1} - \frac{1}{(x + 1)^2} + \frac{2}{(x + 1)^3} \right) dx$$

$$= -\ln x + 2 \ln (x + 1) + \frac{1}{x + 1} - \frac{1}{(x + 1)^2} + C.$$

The algebra may be checked by obtaining an additional equation from the identity (2). For instance,

$$x = 1:\quad 0 = 8A + 4B + 2C + D,$$

which must also be satisfied by the A, B, C, D, if they are correct.

EXERCISES

Evaluate each of the following integrals.

1. $\displaystyle\int \frac{dx}{x(x + 2)^2}$.   *Ans.* $\frac{1}{4} \ln x - \frac{1}{4} \ln (x + 2) + \frac{1}{2}(x + 2)^{-1} + C.$

2. $\displaystyle\int \frac{(x + 1)\, dx}{x^2(x - 1)}$.   *Ans.* $x^{-1} - 2 \ln x + 2 \ln (x - 1) + C.$

3. $\displaystyle\int \frac{(5y - 4)\, dy}{y^3 + 4y^2}$.   *Ans.* $y^{-1} + \frac{3}{2} \ln y - \frac{3}{2} \ln (y + 4) + C.$

4. $\displaystyle\int \frac{dy}{y^3 - 2y^2}$.   *Ans.* $\frac{1}{2}y^{-1} - \frac{1}{4} \ln y + \frac{1}{4} \ln (y - 2) + C.$

5. $\int \dfrac{(2x^2 + 1)\, dx}{x^3 - 3x + 2}.$ *Ans.* $\ln (x - 1) - (x - 1)^{-1} + \ln (x + 2) + C.$

6. $\int \dfrac{(x^2 - 7)\, dx}{x^3 - 12x + 16}.$ *Ans.* $\frac{3}{4} \ln (x - 2) + \frac{1}{2}(x - 2)^{-1} + \frac{1}{4} \ln (x + 4) + C.$

7. $\int \dfrac{(x^4 + 1)\, dx}{x^2(x + 1)^2}.$ *Ans.* $x - 2 \ln x - x^{-1} - 2(x + 1)^{-1} + C.$

8. $\int \dfrac{(x - 1)(2x^3 + 2x^2 + 3x + 2)\, dx}{x^3(x + 1)}.$

  Ans. $2x - x^{-1} + x^{-2} - 2 \ln (x + 1) + C.$

9. $\int \dfrac{(5v + 3)\, dv}{v^2(v + 1)(v - 3)}.$ **10.** $\int \dfrac{(3v^3 - 2v^2 - 4)\, dv}{v^2(v - 1)(v + 2)}.$

11. $\int \dfrac{(2\theta^2 - 11)\, d\theta}{\theta^3 + 3\theta^2 - 4}.$ **12.** $\int \dfrac{(4\beta^2 - 3\beta + 6)\, d\beta}{\beta^4(\beta - 2)}.$

13. $\int \dfrac{9(x - 1)\, dx}{x^2(x^2 - 9)}.$ **14.** $\int \dfrac{(x^3 - 12x + 4)\, dx}{(x^2 - 3x + 2)^2}.$

15. $\int \dfrac{(x^2 + 1)\, dx}{x^3(x - 1)^2}.$ **16.** $\int \dfrac{dx}{x^2(x - 2)^2}.$

17. $\int \dfrac{y\, dy}{(y^2 - 4)^3}.$ **18.** $\int \dfrac{dx}{(x + 2)^3}.$

19. $\int \dfrac{x\, dx}{(x + 2)^3}.$ **20.** $\int \dfrac{y\, dy}{(y - 3)^4}.$

21. $\int \dfrac{d\theta}{\sin \theta \cos^2 \theta}.$ Introduce a new variable, $\alpha = \cos \theta.$

22. $\int \dfrac{dx}{(a^2 - x^2)^2}.$ *Ans.* $\dfrac{x}{2a^2(a^2 - x^2)} + \dfrac{1}{4a^3} \ln \dfrac{a + x}{a - x} + C.$

23. $\int \sec^3 \theta\, d\theta. \left[\sec^3 \theta = \dfrac{1}{\cos^3 \theta} = \dfrac{\cos \theta}{\cos^4 \theta} = \dfrac{\cos \theta}{(1 - \sin^2 \theta)^2}; \text{Ex. 22.} \right]$

24. $\int \csc^3 \theta\, d\theta.$ (Cf. Ex. 23.)   *Ans.* $- \dfrac{\cos \theta}{2 \sin^2 \theta} + \dfrac{1}{4} \ln \dfrac{1 - \cos \theta}{1 + \cos \theta} + C.$

25. $\int \dfrac{dx}{x(x^2 - 1)^2}.$ *Ans.* $\dfrac{1}{2(1 - x^2)} + \dfrac{1}{2} \ln \dfrac{x^2}{x^2 - 1} + C.$

26. Do Ex. 25 in another way.

27. $\int \dfrac{dx}{e^x(e^x - 1)}.$ Use $v = e^x.$ *Ans.* $\ln (e^x - 1) - x + e^{-x} + C.$

28. Do Ex. 27 in two other ways.

29. $\int \dfrac{dx}{e^x(e^x + 1)}.$ See Exs. 27–28.   **30.** $\int \dfrac{dx}{(1 - e^x)^2}.$ Use $e^x = \beta.$

31. Do Ex. 30, using $e^{-x} = v.$

32. Do Ex. 30, using $e^x = \sin^2 \varphi.$

33. $\int \dfrac{dx}{x(1 - \sqrt{x})^2}.$ *Ans.* $\dfrac{2}{1 - \sqrt{x}} + \ln \dfrac{x}{(1 - \sqrt{x})^2} + C.$

34. $\int \dfrac{dx}{x(1 + \sqrt{x})^2}.$

141. *Quadratic Factors*

Corresponding to a factor in the denominator of the form $ax^2 + bx + c$ with $b^2 - 4ac < 0$, we assume the partial fraction* $\dfrac{A(2ax + b) + B}{ax^2 + bx + c}$, where A and B are to be determined.

Example (a). Evaluate $\displaystyle\int \frac{x^2 + 4x + 10}{x^3 + 2x^2 + 5x}\, dx$.

Assume

$$\frac{x^2 + 4x + 10}{x^3 + 2x^2 + 5x} = \frac{A}{x} + \frac{B(2x + 2)}{x^2 + 2x + 5} + \frac{C}{x^2 + 2x + 5},$$

$$x^2 + 4x + 10 = A(x^2 + 2x + 5) + Bx(2x + 2) + Cx.$$

Put $x = 0$: $5A = 10$, $A = 2$.

Equate coefficients of x^2: $A + 2B = 1$, $B = -\frac{1}{2}$.

Equate coefficients of x: $2A + 2B + C = 4$, $C = 1$.

Therefore

$$\int \frac{x^2 + 4x + 10}{x^3 + 2x^2 + 5x}\, dx = \int \left(\frac{2}{x} - \frac{1}{2} \cdot \frac{2x + 2}{x^2 + 2x + 5} + \frac{1}{x^2 + 2x + 5} \right) dx$$

$$= 2 \ln x - \frac{1}{2} \ln (x^2 + 2x + 5) + \frac{1}{2} \operatorname{Arctan} \frac{x + 1}{2} + C.$$

The case of repeated quadratic factors occurs less often. Corresponding to a factor $(ax^2 + bx + c)^r$, we assume r partial fractions with linear numerators as above, and successive denominators building up step-by-step just as in § 140.

Example (b). Evaluate $\displaystyle\int \frac{x^2\, dx}{(x^2 + 4x + 5)^2}$.

Assume

$$\frac{x^2}{(x^2 + 4x + 5)^2} = \frac{A(2x + 4) + B}{(x^2 + 4x + 5)} + \frac{C(2x + 4) + D}{(x^2 + 4x + 5)^2};$$

etc. The last integral may be evaluated as suggested in § 136.

EXERCISES

Evaluate the following integrals.

1. $\displaystyle\int \frac{x\, dx}{x^2 + 6x + 13}$.   *Ans.* $\dfrac{1}{2} \ln (x^2 + 6x + 13) - \dfrac{3}{2} \operatorname{Arctan} \dfrac{x + 3}{2} + C.$

2. $\displaystyle\int \frac{(4x + 5)\, dx}{x^2 + 4x + 20}$.   *Ans.* $2 \ln (x^2 + 4x + 20) - \dfrac{3}{2} \operatorname{Arctan} \dfrac{x + 2}{4} + C.$

3. $\displaystyle\int \frac{4dx}{x^3 - 4x^2 + 8x}$.

$\qquad\qquad$ *Ans.* $\frac{1}{2} \ln x - \frac{1}{4} \ln (x^2 - 4x + 8) + \frac{1}{2} \operatorname{Arctan} (\frac{1}{2}x - 1) + C.$

---

* This form rather than the equivalent form $\dfrac{Ax + B}{ax^2 + bx + c}$, in order that the new integrals will be in form to evaluate at once.

4. $\int \dfrac{10dx}{4x^3 - 4x^2 + 5x}.$

$\quad Ans.\ 2 \ln x - \ln (4x^2 - 4x + 5) + \text{Arctan} (x - \tfrac{1}{2}) + C.$

5. $\int \dfrac{dy}{(y - 1)(y^2 + 1)}.$
6. $\int \dfrac{(9y + 14)\, dy}{(y - 2)(y^2 + 4)}.$

7. $\int \dfrac{y\, dy}{(4 + y^2)^3}.$
8. $\int \dfrac{y\, dy}{4y^4 + 1}.$

9. $\int \dfrac{du}{u(1 + u^2)^2}.$
10. $\int \dfrac{du}{u^3(1 + u^2)}.$

11. $\int \dfrac{\cos \theta\, d\theta}{\sin \theta + \sin^3 \theta}.$
12. $\int \dfrac{\sec^2 \varphi\, d\varphi}{\tan^3 \varphi + 4 \tan \varphi}.$

13. $\int \dfrac{5x\, dx}{x^3 + x^2 + 4x + 4}.$
14. $\int \dfrac{dx}{x^2 \sqrt{1 - x}}.$

15. $\int \dfrac{(x^3 - 4)\, dx}{x^3 + 2x^2 + 2x}.$
$\quad Ans.\ x - 2 \ln x + 2 \text{ Arctan} (x + 1) + C.$

16. $\int \dfrac{(x^3 + 10)\, dx}{x^3 - 2x^2 + 5x}.$
$\quad Ans.\ x + 2 \ln x - \dfrac{1}{2} \text{ Arctan} \dfrac{x - 1}{2} + C.$

17. $\int \dfrac{v \ln v\, dv}{(1 + v^2)^2}.$
$\quad Ans.\ \dfrac{1}{2} \ln v - \dfrac{1}{4} \ln (1 + v^2) - \dfrac{1}{2} \dfrac{\ln v}{1 + v^2} + C.$

18. $\int \dfrac{\text{Arctan } y\, dy}{y^3}.$
$\quad Ans.\ -\dfrac{1}{2y} - \dfrac{1 + y^2}{2y^2} \text{ Arctan } y + C.$

19. $\int \dfrac{dx}{x^3 - 2x^2 + 9x - 18}.$
20. $\int \dfrac{(2x + 7)\, dx}{x^3 + x^2 + 4x + 4}.$

21. $\int \dfrac{(\theta + 65)\, d\theta}{\theta^3 + \theta^2 + \theta - 39}.$

$\quad Ans.\ 2 \ln (\theta - 3) - \ln (\theta^2 + 4\theta + 13) - 3 \text{ Arctan} \dfrac{\theta + 2}{3} + C.$

22. $\int \dfrac{(y - 1)(y - 5)\, dy}{y^3 - y^2 + 3y - 5}.$

$\quad Ans.\ \dfrac{3}{2} \ln (y + 1) - \dfrac{1}{4} \ln (y^2 - 2y + 5) - \dfrac{3}{2} \text{ Arctan} \dfrac{y - 1}{2} + C.$

23. $\int \dfrac{dx}{(x^2 + 2x + 10)^2}.$
$\quad Ans.\ \dfrac{x + 1}{18(x^2 + 2x + 10)} + \dfrac{1}{54} \text{ Arctan} \dfrac{x + 1}{3} + C.$

24. $\int \dfrac{(x^3 - 2x^2 + 1)\, dx}{(x^2 - 2x + 5)^2}.$

$\quad Ans.\ \dfrac{1}{2} \ln (x^2 - 2x + 5) + \dfrac{1}{4} \text{ Arctan} \dfrac{x - 1}{2} - \dfrac{x - 6}{2(x^2 - 2x + 5)} + C.$

25. $\int \dfrac{4dx}{(x^2 - 2x + 5)^2}.$
26. $\int \dfrac{(x^3 - x^2 + 1)\, dx}{(x^2 + 2x + 2)^2}.$

DEFINITE INTEGRALS.

WALLIS' FORMULA

142. *Definite Integrals*

Now that we have acquired some facility in integration, it is feasible to start seriously on the many applications of the definite integral. Before taking up the applications, let us review the technique of definite integration and, in § 145, add one more tool to our kit.

Example. Evaluate $\int_0^{\frac{\pi}{3}} x \sin x \, dx$.

We employ integration by parts to obtain

$$\int_0^{\frac{\pi}{3}} x \sin x \, dx = \left[-x \cos x \right]_0^{\frac{\pi}{3}} + \int_0^{\frac{\pi}{3}} \cos x \, dx$$

$$= -\frac{\pi}{3} \cos \frac{\pi}{3} + 0 + \left[\sin x \right]_0^{\frac{\pi}{3}}$$

$$= -\frac{\pi}{6} + \sin \frac{\pi}{3} - 0$$

$$= \frac{\sqrt{3}}{2} - \frac{\pi}{6} = 0.342.$$

143. *Change of Limits with Change of Variable*

In the definite integral $\int_a^b f(x) \, dx$ it is always implied that a and b are *the limiting values of the variable of integration* x. If we change the variable by a substitution

(1) $$x = \varphi(z),$$

we must either return to the original variable before substituting the limits, or *change the limits to correspond with the change of variable.* The latter method

273

is usually preferable. The new limits are found, of course, from the equation of substitution (1).

Example. Evaluate $\displaystyle\int_0^a \frac{x^3\,dx}{(a^2+x^2)^{\frac{3}{2}}}$.

Put $x = a\tan\varphi$. Then $dx = a\sec^2\varphi\,d\varphi$; when $x = 0$, $\varphi = 0$, and when $x = a$, $\varphi = \frac{1}{4}\pi$. Thus we proceed as follows:

$$\int_0^a \frac{x^3\,dx}{(a^2+x^2)^{\frac{3}{2}}} = \int_0^{\frac{\pi}{4}} \frac{a^3\tan^3\varphi\, a\sec^2\varphi\,d\varphi}{(a^2\sec^2\varphi)^{\frac{3}{2}}}$$

$$= \frac{1}{a}\int_0^{\frac{\pi}{4}} \frac{\tan^3\varphi\,d\varphi}{\sec^3\varphi} = \frac{1}{a}\int_0^{\frac{\pi}{4}} \sin^3\varphi\,d\varphi$$

$$= \frac{1}{a}\int_0^{\frac{\pi}{4}} \sin\varphi(1 - \cos^2\varphi)\,d\varphi$$

$$= \frac{1}{a}\left[-\cos\varphi + \frac{\cos^3\varphi}{3}\right]_0^{\frac{\pi}{4}}$$

$$= \frac{1}{a}\left[-\frac{1}{\sqrt{2}} + \frac{1}{6\sqrt{2}} - \left(-1 + \frac{1}{3}\right)\right]$$

$$= \frac{1}{a}\left[\frac{2}{3} - \frac{5}{6\sqrt{2}}\right] = \frac{4\sqrt{2} - 5}{6a\sqrt{2}}.$$

144. *Limitations on Certain Formulas*

To verify (10), page 234, the work is as follows:

$$\frac{d}{du}\operatorname{Arcsin}\frac{u}{a} = \frac{\dfrac{1}{a}}{\sqrt{1 - \dfrac{u^2}{a^2}}} = \frac{1}{a}\cdot\frac{1}{\sqrt{\dfrac{a^2 - u^2}{a^2}}} = \frac{1}{a}\cdot\frac{\sqrt{a^2}}{\sqrt{a^2 - u^2}}.$$

This proves the formula for the case $a > 0$; but if $a < 0$, then $\sqrt{a^2} = -a$, and *the formula must be changed* to read

$$(1) \qquad \int \frac{du}{\sqrt{a^2 - u^2}} = -\operatorname{Arcsin}\frac{u}{a} + C \qquad a < 0.$$

The above is typical of a phenomenon that occurs many times in integration. A formula, valid within certain ranges, is incorrect in other ranges, even though all the functions occurring are well defined there. The commonest region of failure is for negative values of the variable of integration x, or of some constant.

With the limitation $a > 0$ on (10), the standard formulas (page 234) are valid wherever the functions are defined.

Example. Find the area in the second quadrant bounded by the curve $y^2 = \dfrac{x^2 - 1}{x^2}$, the x-axis, and the line $x = -2$.

In the second quadrant

$$y = -\frac{\sqrt{x^2 - 1}}{x},$$

(2) $$A = \int_{-2}^{-1} y\,dx = -\int_{-2}^{-1} \frac{\sqrt{x^2 - 1}\,dx}{x}.$$

An attempt to evaluate the above integral by using the result of Ex. 12, page 258,

(3) $$\int \frac{\sqrt{x^2 - a^2}}{x}\,dx = \sqrt{x^2 - a^2} + a \operatorname{Arcsin}\frac{a}{x} + C,$$

is doomed to failure, because (3) is based on the assumption that x is positive. [In the derivation of (3), $\sqrt{x^2}$ is replaced by x.] Indeed,

$$-\left[\sqrt{x^2 - 1} + \operatorname{Arcsin}\frac{1}{x}\right]_{-2}^{-1}$$

$$= -\operatorname{Arcsin}(-1) - \left[-\sqrt{3} - \operatorname{Arcsin}\left(-\tfrac{1}{2}\right)\right]$$

$$= \sqrt{3} + \frac{\pi}{3} = 1.73 + 1.05 = 2.78.$$

But the area A, shaded in Fig. 134, is less than $\tfrac{1}{2}\sqrt{3} = 0.87$.

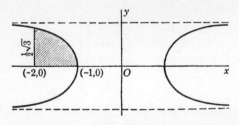

Figure 134

Evaluation of the integral in (3) for negative x, replacing $\sqrt{x^2}$ by $(-x)$ in the derivation, yields

(4) $$\int \frac{\sqrt{x^2 - a^2}}{x}\,dx = \sqrt{x^2 - a^2} - a \operatorname{Arcsin}\frac{a}{x} + C; \quad x \leqq -a < 0.$$

The integral in (2) may now be evaluated with the aid of (4), which produces the correct answer,

$$A = \sqrt{3} - \frac{\pi}{3} = 0.68.$$

Although, of course, such situations are not the most usual thing, they occur far too often to be considered freakish. But it would be wearisome and time-consuming to keep constant track of such matters in our daily work; thus we have perforce ignored them and must continue to do so. We leave the subject with the following injunction (applying not so much to the work of this course, where these difficulties will be largely avoided, as to activities in applied mathematics in which the student may now or subsequently be interested):

In an integration involving a square root or other many-valued function, particularly when some of the quantities are negative, watch every detail closely to make sure that in each transformation the right branch is taken.

145. *Wallis' Formula*

The integral

(1)
$$\int_0^{\frac{\pi}{2}} \sin^m x \cos^n x \, dx,$$

in which m and n are integers $\geqq 0$, arises over and over again in elementary applications. Fortunately, the integral (1) can be evaluated simply, with a formula which is easy to remember in words, though bulky looking in symbols.

We shall prove in § 146 that if m and n are integers >1,

(2)
$$\int_0^{\frac{\pi}{2}} \sin^m x \cos^n x \, dx$$

$$= \frac{\left[(m-1)(m-3) \cdots \begin{matrix} \text{or} \\ 1 \end{matrix} ^{2}\right]\left[(n-1)(n-3) \cdots \begin{matrix} \text{or} \\ 1 \end{matrix} ^{2}\right]}{(m+n)(m+n-2) \cdots \begin{matrix} \text{or} \\ 1 \end{matrix} ^{2}} \cdot \alpha,$$

in which

$$\alpha = \frac{\pi}{2}, \quad \text{if } m \text{ and } n \text{ are both even,}$$

$$\alpha = 1, \quad \text{otherwise.}$$

In words, the value of the integral (1) is $\dfrac{A \cdot B}{C} \cdot \alpha$, in which

$A =$ the product, starting with one less than the exponent m, going down 2 at a time, until 2 or 1 is reached;

$B =$ a similar product, starting with one less than the other exponent;

$C =$ a similar product, starting with the sum of the exponents.

If either m or n is unity, the integral (1) can be evaluated at once by the power formula. If either m or n is zero, the result is not so simple, but one added device permits us to include that result in the formula (2).

RULE. *If the first factor in any of the products to be formed in applying Wallis' formula, for m, $n \geq 0$, is less than one, replace that product by unity.*

The validity of the above rule will be established in § 146.

Example (a). Evaluate $\displaystyle\int_0^{\frac{\pi}{2}} \sin^8 x \cos^4 x \, dx$.

By Wallis' formula, we obtain

$$\int_0^{\frac{\pi}{2}} \sin^8 x \cos^4 x \, dx = \frac{(7 \cdot 5 \cdot 3 \cdot 1)(3 \cdot 1)}{12 \cdot 10 \cdot 8 \cdot 6 \cdot 4 \cdot 2} \cdot \frac{\pi}{2} = \frac{7\pi}{2^{11}} = \frac{7\pi}{2048}.$$

Example (b). Evaluate $\displaystyle\int_0^{\frac{\pi}{2}} \sin^5 \beta \cos^6 \beta \, d\beta$.

By Wallis' formula,

$$\int_0^{\frac{\pi}{2}} \sin^5 \beta \cos^6 \beta \, d\beta = \frac{(4 \cdot 2)(5 \cdot 3 \cdot 1)}{11 \cdot 9 \cdot 7 \cdot 5 \cdot 3 \cdot 1} \cdot 1 = \frac{2^3}{11 \cdot 9 \cdot 7} = \frac{8}{693}.$$

Example (c). Evaluate $\displaystyle\int_0^{\frac{\pi}{2}} \cos^3 \varphi \sin^5 \varphi \, d\varphi$.

At once,

$$\int_0^{\frac{\pi}{2}} \cos^3 \varphi \sin^5 \varphi \, d\varphi = \frac{(2)(4 \cdot 2)}{8 \cdot 6 \cdot 4 \cdot 2} \cdot 1 = \frac{1}{8 \cdot 3} = \frac{1}{24}.$$

Example (d). Evaluate $\displaystyle\int_0^{\frac{\pi}{2}} \cos^7 \varphi \sin \varphi \, d\varphi$.

Here, in forming the product associated with the exponent of the sine, we would normally start with one less than one, namely, with zero. Hence, by the rule above, we replace that product by unity and write

$$\int_0^{\frac{\pi}{2}} \cos^7 \varphi \sin \varphi \, d\varphi = \frac{(6 \cdot 4 \cdot 2)(1)}{8 \cdot 6 \cdot 4 \cdot 2} = \frac{1}{8},$$

a result readily verified by direct integration. Since this integration is so easily performed by the power formula of § 126, the student should realize that the example is included only because it permits such simple verification. In practice we do not use Wallis' formula when one of the exponents is unity; such a procedure would be somewhat like using an atom bomb to remove a tree stump.

Example (e). Evaluate $\displaystyle\int_0^{\frac{\pi}{2}} \sin^6 y \, dy$.

Here one exponent is zero. Now $6 + 0 = 6$, to start the denominator product. Also, 6 and 0 are both even. Hence,

$$\int_0^{\frac{\pi}{2}} \sin^6 y \, dy = \frac{(5 \cdot 3 \cdot 1)(1)}{6 \cdot 4 \cdot 2} \cdot \frac{\pi}{2} = \frac{5\pi}{2^5} = \frac{5\pi}{32}.$$

146. *Derivation of Wallis' Formula*

First, consider the integral

(1) $$T = \int_0^{\frac{\pi}{2}} \cos^n x \, dx.$$

Use integration by parts, with $u = \cos^{n-1} x$, $dv = \cos x \, dx$, to obtain

$$T = \left[\cos^{n-1} x \sin x \right]_0^{\frac{\pi}{2}} + (n - 1) \int_0^{\frac{\pi}{2}} \cos^{n-2} x \sin^2 x \, dx$$

$$= 0 + (n - 1) \int_0^{\frac{\pi}{2}} \cos^{n-2} x (1 - \cos^2 x) \, dx$$

$$= (n - 1) \int_0^{\frac{\pi}{2}} \cos^{n-2} x \, dx - (n - 1) T,$$

from which

(2) $$T = \frac{n - 1}{n} \int_0^{\frac{\pi}{2}} \cos^{n-2} x \, dx.$$

In a like manner, replacing n by $(n - 2)$ in (2), we find that

$$\int_0^{\frac{\pi}{2}} \cos^{n-2} x \, dx = \frac{n - 3}{n - 2} \int_0^{\frac{\pi}{2}} \cos^{n-4} x \, dx,$$

and the process can be iterated, beating down the exponent of the cosine two at a time, until the exponent is one or zero.

Thus, if n is even,

$$T = \frac{n - 1}{n} \cdot \frac{n - 3}{n - 2} \cdots \frac{3}{4} \cdot \frac{1}{2} \int_0^{\frac{\pi}{2}} \cos^0 x \, dx$$

$$= \frac{(n - 1)(n - 3) \cdots 3 \cdot 1}{n(n - 2) \cdots 4 \cdot 2} \cdot \frac{\pi}{2},$$

as described in the rule of the preceding section.

If n is odd, iteration of (2) yields

$$T = \frac{n-1}{n} \cdot \frac{n-3}{n-2} \cdots \frac{4}{5} \cdot \frac{2}{3} \int_0^{\frac{\pi}{2}} \cos x \, dx$$

$$= \frac{(n-1)(n-3) \cdots 4 \cdot 2}{n(n-2) \cdots 5 \cdot 3} \cdot 1,$$

also as described in the rule of the preceding section.

In order to evaluate $\int_0^{\frac{\pi}{2}} \sin^n x \, dx$, put $x = \frac{1}{2}\pi - y$, and thus obtain

$$\int_0^{\frac{\pi}{2}} \sin^n x \, dx = - \int_{\frac{\pi}{2}}^0 \cos^n y \, dy = \int_0^{\frac{\pi}{2}} \cos^n y \, dy,$$

the integral already treated above.

Finally, consider

(3)
$$W = \int_0^{\frac{\pi}{2}} \sin^m x \cos^n x \, dx.$$

Use integration by parts, with $u = \sin^{m-1} x$, $dv = \cos^n x \sin x \, dx$, to find that

$$W = \frac{-1}{n+1} \left[\sin^{m-1} x \cos^{n+1} x \right]_0^{\frac{\pi}{2}} + \frac{m-1}{n+1} \int_0^{\frac{\pi}{2}} \sin^{m-2} x \cos^{n+2} x \, dx$$

$$= 0 + \frac{m-1}{n+1} \int_0^{\frac{\pi}{2}} \sin^{m-2} x \cos^n x (1 - \sin^2 x) \, dx,$$

or

$$W = \frac{m-1}{n+1} \int_0^{\frac{\pi}{2}} \sin^{m-2} x \cos^n x \, dx - \frac{m-1}{n+1} W.$$

This last equation is easily solved for W, yielding

(4)
$$W = \frac{m-1}{m+n} \int_0^{\frac{\pi}{2}} \sin^{m-2} x \cos^n x \, dx.$$

Formula (4) can be used to reduce the exponent on the sine two at a time, until that exponent is one or zero.

If m is odd in (3), then iteration of (4) gives

$$W = \frac{(m-1)(m-3) \cdots 4 \cdot 2}{(m+n)(m+n-2) \cdots (n+5)(n+3)} \int_0^{\frac{\pi}{2}} \sin x \cos^n x \, dx$$

$$= \frac{(m-1)(m-3) \cdots 4 \cdot 2}{(m+n)(m+n-2) \cdots (n+5)(n+3)(n+1)},$$

from which the result stated in Wallis' formula follows by inserting the

factors $\left[(n-1)(n-3) \cdots \begin{matrix} 2 \\ \text{or} \\ 1 \end{matrix} \right]$ in numerator and denominator.

If m is even in (3), then iteration of (4) gives

$$W = \frac{(m-1)(m-3) \cdots 3 \cdot 1}{(m+n)(m+n-2) \cdots (n+4)(n+2)} \int_0^{\frac{\pi}{2}} \cos^n x \, dx.$$

As the last step in obtaining the desired expression for W, we insert the value of the integral T, of equation (1), as determined at the beginning of this section, and we thus arrive at Wallis' formula.

EXERCISES

In Exs. 1–28, use Wallis' formula.

1. $\int_0^{\frac{\pi}{2}} \sin^2 x \, dx.$ *Ans.* $\frac{\pi}{4}$.

2. $\int_0^{\frac{\pi}{2}} \cos^2 x \, dx.$ *Ans.* $\frac{\pi}{4}$.

3. $\int_0^{\frac{\pi}{2}} \cos^5 y \, dy.$ *Ans.* $\frac{8}{15}$.

4. $\int_0^{\frac{\pi}{2}} \sin^7 y \, dy.$ *Ans.* $\frac{16}{35}$.

5. $\int_0^{\frac{\pi}{2}} \sin^4 \beta \, d\beta.$ *Ans.* $\frac{3\pi}{16}$.

6. $\int_0^{\frac{\pi}{2}} \cos^8 \beta \, d\beta.$ *Ans.* $\frac{35\pi}{256}$.

7. $\int_0^{\frac{\pi}{2}} \sin^4 \varphi \cos^3 \varphi \, d\varphi.$ *Ans.* $\frac{2}{35}$.

8. $\int_0^{\frac{\pi}{2}} \sin^2 \varphi \cos^6 \varphi \, d\varphi.$ *Ans.* $\frac{5\pi}{256}$.

9. $\int_0^{\frac{\pi}{2}} \sin^2 \alpha \cos^2 \alpha \, d\alpha.$

10. $\int_0^{\frac{\pi}{2}} \sin^4 x \cos^5 x \, dx.$

11. $\int_0^{\frac{\pi}{2}} \sin^3 x \cos^3 x \, dx.$

12. $\int_0^{\frac{\pi}{2}} \sin^4 x \cos^4 x \, dx.$

13. $\int_0^{\frac{\pi}{2}} \cos^6 \theta \sin^7 \theta \, d\theta.$

14. $\int_0^{\frac{\pi}{2}} \cos^5 \theta \sin^5 \theta \, d\theta.$

15. $\int_0^{\frac{\pi}{2}} \sin^3 x \cos^6 x \, dx.$

16. $\int_0^{\frac{\pi}{2}} \sin^2 x \cos^4 x \, dx.$

17. $\int_0^{\frac{\pi}{2}} \sin^6 y \cos^6 y \, dy.$

18. $\int_0^{\frac{\pi}{2}} \sin^4 y \cos^7 y \, dy.$

19. $\int_0^1 (1 - x^2)^{\frac{3}{2}} \, dx.$ Put $x = \sin \varphi.$ *Ans.* $\frac{5\pi}{32}$.

20. $\int_0^a x^2(a^2 - x^2)^{\frac{1}{2}} \, dx.$ Put $x = a \sin \varphi.$ *Ans.* $\frac{\pi a^6}{32}$.

21. $\int_0^a x^5(a^2 - x^2)^6 \, dx.$

22. $\int_0^1 x^4 \sqrt{1 - x^2} \, dx.$

23. $\int_0^a (a^2 - x^2)^{\frac{3}{2}} \, dx.$

24. $\int_0^a x^4(a^2 - x^2)^{\frac{5}{2}} \, dx.$

25. $\int_0^{\frac{\pi}{6}} \cos^8 3\theta \, d\theta.$ Put $3\theta = x.$ *Ans.* $\dfrac{35\pi}{768}.$

26. $\int_0^\pi \sin^5 \tfrac{1}{2}y \, \cos^7 \tfrac{1}{2}y \, dy.$ *Ans.* $\tfrac{1}{60}.$

27. $\int_0^{\frac{\pi}{4}} \sin^2 4y \, \cos^2 2y \, dy.$ *Ans.* $\dfrac{\pi}{16}.$

28. $\int_0^1 \sqrt{1 - \sqrt{u}} \, du.$ Put $u = \sin^4 x.$ *Ans.* $\tfrac{8}{15}.$

In Exs. 29–60, evaluate the given definite integral by any available device.

29. $\int_0^1 \dfrac{dx}{\sqrt{1 + 8x}}.$ *Ans.* $\tfrac{1}{2}.$

30. $\int_{-1}^0 \dfrac{x^2 \, dx}{(1 - x^3)^{\frac{2}{3}}}.$ *Ans.* $\dfrac{2 - \sqrt{2}}{3}.$

31. $\int_0^{\frac{\pi}{3}} \sin^3 y \, dy.$ *Ans.* $\tfrac{5}{24}.$

32. $\int_0^{\frac{\pi}{2}} \sin^3 y \, dy.$ *Ans.* $\tfrac{2}{3}.$

33. $\int_1^4 \sqrt{\sqrt{x} - 1} \, dx.$ *Ans.* $\tfrac{32}{15}.$

34. $\int_0^\pi \cos^3 \theta \, d\theta.$ *Ans.* $0.$

35. $\int_0^1 \dfrac{x^2 \, dx}{(x + 1)^4}.$ *Ans.* $\tfrac{1}{24}.$

36. $\int_0^{\ln 2} \dfrac{e^{2x} \, dx}{\sqrt{1 + e^x}}.$ *Ans.* $\dfrac{2 \sqrt{2}}{3}.$

37. $\int_0^1 \text{Arcsin } y \, dy.$ *Ans.* $\tfrac{1}{2}\pi - 1.$

38. $\int_0^{\frac{\pi}{2}} x \cos 2x \, dx.$ *Ans.* $-\tfrac{1}{2}.$

39. $\int_1^{\sqrt{2}} \dfrac{dx}{x^2 \sqrt{4 - x^2}}.$ *Ans.* $\dfrac{\sqrt{3} - 1}{4}.$

40. $\int_0^{\frac{\pi}{3}} \sin^2 x \, dx.$ *Ans.* $\dfrac{4\pi - 3\sqrt{3}}{24}.$

41. $\int_0^{\ln 2} xe^{-x} \, dx.$ *Ans.* $\tfrac{1}{2}(1 - \ln 2).$

42. $\int_1^2 \dfrac{x \, dx}{x + 1}.$ *Ans.* $1 - \ln \tfrac{3}{2}.$

43. $\int_0^{\frac{1}{2}} \dfrac{(5 - x) \, dx}{4x^2 + 1}.$ *Ans.* $\dfrac{5\pi - \ln 2}{8}.$

44. $\int_1^{\sqrt{3}} \text{Arctan } x \, dx.$ *Ans.* $-\dfrac{1}{2}\ln 2 + \dfrac{\pi}{12}(4\sqrt{3} - 3).$

45. $\int_0^1 \dfrac{y \, dy}{(1 + y)^4}.$ *Ans.* $\tfrac{1}{12}.$

46. $\displaystyle\int_0^1 x \sin (2x^2)\, dx.$ *Ans.* $\frac{1}{4}(1 - \cos 2).$

47. $\displaystyle\int_2^3 \frac{x^3 - 2x}{x - 1}\, dx.$ *Ans.* $\frac{47}{6} - \ln 2.$

48. $\displaystyle\int_3^4 \frac{dv}{(2 - v)^3}.$ *Ans.* $-\frac{3}{8}.$ **49.** $\displaystyle\int_{-2}^2 \frac{dv}{v^2 + 4}.$ *Ans.* $\frac{\pi}{4}.$

50. $\displaystyle\int_{\frac{\pi}{3}}^{\frac{2\pi}{3}} \csc x \cot x\, dx.$ *Ans.* 0.   **51.** $\displaystyle\int_0^a \frac{x^2\, dx}{(a^2 + x^2)^2}.$ *Ans.* $\frac{\pi - 2}{8a}.$

52. $\displaystyle\int_0^1 \frac{x^3\, dx}{(1 + x^2)^3}.$ *Ans.* $\frac{1}{16}.$ **53.** $\displaystyle\int_{-1}^1 \frac{dz}{\sqrt{4 - z^2}}.$ *Ans.* $\frac{\pi}{3}.$

54. $\displaystyle\int_0^{\frac{\pi}{6}} \tan 2\theta\, d\theta.$ *Ans.* 0.347.   **55.** $\displaystyle\int_0^{\ln 2} \frac{e^x\, dx}{2e^x - 1}.$ *Ans.* 0.549.

56. $\displaystyle\int_2^3 \frac{dx}{x^2 - 6x + 10}.$ *Ans.* $\frac{\pi}{4}.$ **57.** $\displaystyle\int_0^{\frac{\pi}{2}} \alpha \sin 3\alpha\, d\alpha.$ *Ans.* $-\frac{1}{9}.$

58. $\displaystyle\int_1^2 \frac{\ln x}{x}\, dx.$ *Ans.* 0.240.   **59.** $\displaystyle\int_0^1 ye^{-y^2}\, dy.$ *Ans.* $\frac{1}{2}(1 - e^{-1}).$

60. $\displaystyle\int_0^2 \frac{u\, du}{u^4 + 1}.$ *Ans.* 0.663.

PLANE AREAS.

IMPROPER INTEGRALS

147. *Plane Areas*

In our first attack on the problem of plane area, we were greatly handicapped by limited facility in integration. We therefore return briefly to this topic.

Example. Find the area of the loop of the curve

$$y^2 = 4x^2(1 - x).$$

We have

$$A = 2 \int_0^1 y \, dx = 4 \int_0^1 x \sqrt{1 - x} \, dx.$$

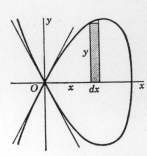

Integrate by parts, with $u = x$:

$$A = -\tfrac{8}{3} \left[x(1 - x)^{\frac{3}{2}} \right]_0^1 + \tfrac{8}{3} \int_0^1 (1 - x)^{\frac{3}{2}} \, dx$$

$$= 0 - \tfrac{16}{15} \left[(1 - x)^{\frac{5}{2}} \right]_0^1 = \tfrac{16}{15}.$$

Figure 135

Let us obtain a check by evaluating the integral in another way. Put $\sqrt{1 - x} = v$. Then

$$x = 1 - v^2, \qquad dx = -2v \, dv.$$

When $x = 0$, $v = 1$, and when $x = 1$, $v = 0$. Therefore

$$A = 4 \int_1^0 (1 - v^2)v(-2v \, dv) = 8 \int_0^1 v^2(1 - v^2) \, dv$$

$$= 8 \left[\frac{v^3}{3} - \frac{v^5}{5} \right]_0^1$$

$$= 8 \left(\frac{1}{3} - \frac{1}{5} \right) = \frac{16}{15}.$$

148. *Substitution Suggested by the Problem*

In Chapter 8, when finding plane areas by the formula

(1) $$A = \int_a^b y\, dx,$$

we invariably substituted for y. But it is equally proper, and frequently more convenient, to *substitute for dx and change to y-limits*. That is, we take, as the substitution formula, *the equation of the curve itself.*

Of course similar remarks will apply in all the other applications that we shall take up.

Example (a). Find, in two ways, the area in the first quadrant bounded by the cubic $y = 3x - x^3$, and the lines $x = 0$, $y = 2$. The curve is shown in Fig. 136.

First Method. Using a vertical element (not shown) and the technique of Chapter 8, we find that

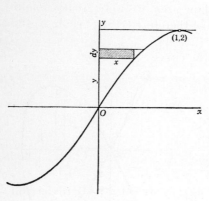

$$A = \int_0^1 (2 - y)\, dx$$

$$= \int_0^1 (2 - 3x + x^3)\, dx$$

$$= \left[2x - \frac{3x^2}{2} + \frac{x^4}{4} \right]_0^1$$

$$= 2 - \frac{3}{2} + \frac{1}{4} = \frac{3}{4}.$$

Second Method. As a check, we find the same area, using the horizontal element shown in Fig. 136:

Figure 136

$$A = \int_0^2 x\, dy.$$

It is not feasible to substitute for x, but we may easily substitute for dy and change limits:

$$dy = (3 - 3x^2)\, dx; \qquad x = 0 \text{ when } y = 0, \ x = 1 \text{ when } y = 2;$$

$$A = \int_0^2 x\, dy = 3 \int_0^1 (x - x^3)\, dx$$

$$= \left[\tfrac{3}{2}x^2 - \tfrac{3}{4}x^4 \right]_0^1 = \tfrac{3}{4}.$$

To evaluate an integral such as (1) when x and y are given in terms of a parameter, we *substitute for both y and dx*, taking as new limits the values of the parameter corresponding to the given limits.

Example (*b*). Find the area of the ellipse (Fig. 137)

$$x = a \cos \varphi, \qquad y = b \sin \varphi.$$

At once

$$A = 4 \int_0^a y \, dx.$$

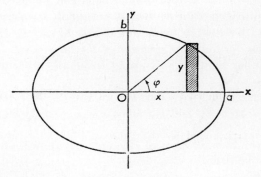

Figure 137

When $x = 0$, $\varphi = \frac{1}{2}\pi$, and when $x = a$, $\varphi = 0$. Therefore

$$A = 4 \int_{\frac{1}{2}\pi}^0 (b \sin \varphi)(-a \sin \varphi \, d\varphi)$$

$$= 4ab \int_0^{\frac{1}{2}\pi} \sin^2 \varphi \, d\varphi$$

$$= 4ab \cdot \frac{1}{2} \cdot \frac{\pi}{2} = \pi ab.$$

The transformations suggested in this section are intuitively reasonable. Rigorous justification of them belongs to a course in advanced calculus.

EXERCISES

1. Find the area under one arch of the curve $y = \cos \frac{1}{4}x$.   *Ans.* 8.

2. Find the area under one arch of the curve $y = a \sin \dfrac{x}{a}$·   *Ans.* $2a^2$.

In Exs. 3–12, find the area bounded by the given curves and lines.

3. $y^2 = \dfrac{1}{(2 - x)^3}$, $x = -2$, $x = 0$.   *Ans.* 0.828.

4. $y = \ln x$, $y = 0$, $x = e$. Solve in two ways.   *Ans.* 1.

5. $y = \ln x$, $y = 0$, $x = e$, $x = 2e$.   *Ans.* 3.77.

6. $xy = a^2$, $y = 0$, $x = a$, $x = 2a$.   *Ans.* $a^2 \ln 2$.

7. Solve Ex. 6, using the parametric equations $x = a \sec \varphi$, $y = a \cos \varphi$.

8. $y = (1 - x^2)^2$, $y = 0$.   *Ans.* $\frac{16}{15}$.

9. Solve Ex. 8, using the horizontal element. Evaluate the integral in two ways.

10. $a^2y^2 = x^2(a^2 - x^2)$. *Ans.* $\frac{4}{3}a^2$.

11. $y = \dfrac{x}{1 - x}$, $x = 0$, $y = e - 1$, $y = 2e - 1$. *Ans.* $e - \ln 2$.

12. $y = \frac{1}{4}x^3 - 3x$, $y = -4$. *Ans.* 27.

13. Find the area in the first quadrant bounded by the x-axis, the line $x = a$, and the curve with parametric equations $x = a \sin^2 \varphi$, $y = 2a \sin \varphi$. Check your answer with that of Example (*a*), page 112.

14. Find the area under the catenary $y = a \cosh \dfrac{x}{a}$ from $x = -a$ to $x = a$.

Ans. $2.35a^2$.

15. Find the area bounded by the curve $y = xe^{-x^2}$, the x-axis, and the maximum ordinate. *Ans.* $\frac{1}{2}(1 - e^{-\frac{1}{2}})$.

16. Find the area bounded by the curve $y = \dfrac{x}{(x^2 + 3)^2}$, the x-axis, and the extreme ordinates. *Ans.* $\frac{1}{12}$.

17. Find the area bounded by the curve $y = \dfrac{\ln x}{x}$, the x-axis, and the maximum ordinate. *Ans.* $\frac{1}{2}$.

18. Find the area bounded by the curve $y = \dfrac{\ln x - 1}{x}$, the x-axis, and the maximum ordinate. *Ans.* $\frac{1}{2}$.

19. Show that the area bounded by the curve $y = \dfrac{\ln x - c}{x}$, the x-axis, and the maximum ordinate is independent of the constant c.

20. Find the area under the first arch of the curve $y = x \sin x$. *Ans.* π.

21. Find the area of the first arch of the curve $y = x \cos x$.

22. Find the area of the first arch of the curve $y = e^{-x} \sin x$. *Ans.* $\frac{1}{2}(1 + e^{-\pi})$.

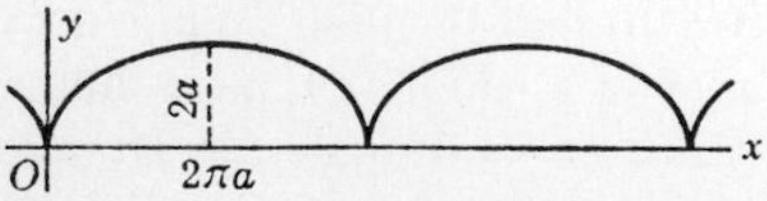

23. Find the area of one arch of the cycloid (Fig. 138)

$$x = a(\theta - \sin \theta), \quad y = a(1 - \cos \theta).$$

Ans. $3\pi a^2$.

Figure 138

24. Find the area of a circular sector of radius r and angle α. *Ans.* $\frac{1}{2}r^2\alpha$.

25. Find the area of the four-cusped hypocycloid $x^{\frac{2}{3}} + y^{\frac{2}{3}} = a^{\frac{2}{3}}$. (Fig. 107, page 192.) *Ans.* $\frac{3}{8}\pi a^2$.

26. Solve Ex. 25, using the parametric equations $x = a \cos^3 t$, $y = a \sin^3 t$.

27. Find the area bounded by the curve $y = \dfrac{1 + x^2}{2x^2}$ and the lines $y = 0$, $y = x$, $x = 2$. *Ans.* $\frac{5}{4}$.

28. Find the area bounded by the curve $y^3 = x^3 + x^4$ and the x-axis. *Ans.* $\frac{9}{28}$.

29. Find the area bounded by the curve $y = \dfrac{2x - 3}{x^2 + 4}$, the axes, and the minimum ordinate. *Ans.* 0.92.

30. Find the area in the first quadrant under the curve $y^2 = \dfrac{x^2}{x-1}$ between the minimum ordinate and the line $x = 3$.   *Ans.* 2.05.

31. Find the area bounded by the curve $2y^2 + 2y - x - 2 = 0$ and the line $x = 2y$.   *Ans.* $\frac{8}{3}$.

32. Find the area bounded by the parabolas $y^2 = 4x$ and $y^2 + 12x = 36$.
                                                                    Ans. 12.

In Exs. 33–36, find the area of the loop of the given curve.

33. $y^2 = x(1 - x^2)^2$.   *Ans.* $\frac{16}{21}$.   **34.** $y^2 = x^3(1 - x^2)^2$.   *Ans.* $\frac{16}{45}$.
35. $y^2 = x^3(1 - x)^2$.   *Ans.* $\frac{8}{35}$.   **36.** $a^7y^2 = x^5(a^2 - x^2)^2$.   *Ans.* $\frac{16}{77}a^2$.

In Exs. 37–42, find the area enclosed by the given curve. It will be found that Wallis' formula is particularly useful in doing these exercises.

37. $y^2 = x^4(1 - x^2)$.   *Ans.* $\frac{1}{4}\pi$.   **38.** $y^2 = x^6(1 - x^2)^3$.   *Ans.* $\frac{8}{35}$.
39. $y^2 = x^3(1 - x)$.   *Ans.* $\frac{1}{8}\pi$.   **40.** $y^2 = x(1 - x)^5$.   *Ans.* $\frac{5}{64}\pi$.
41. $a^6y^2 = x^5(a - x)^3$.   *Ans.* $\frac{3}{128}\pi a^2$.
42. $y^2 = (1 - x^2)^9$.   *Ans.* $\frac{63}{128}\pi$.

In Exs. 43–48, find the area of the loop of the given curve. You may find Wallis' formula useful in these exercises.

43. $y^2 = x^4(1 - x)^3$.   *Ans.* $\frac{32}{315}$.   **44.** $y^2 = x^4(1 - x)^5$.   *Ans.* $\frac{32}{693}$.
45. $y^2 = x(1 - x)^6$.   *Ans.* $\frac{64}{315}$.   **46.** $y^2 = x^3(1 - x)^6$.   *Ans.* $\frac{64}{1155}$.
47. $a^3y^2 = x^2(a - x)^3$.   *Ans.* $\frac{8}{35}a^2$.   **48.** $a^9y^2 = x^6(a - x)^5$.   *Ans.* $\frac{64}{3003}a^2$.
49. Find the area enclosed by the curve $y^2 = (x + 1)^2(4 - x^2)$.

                                                            Ans. $6\sqrt{3} + \frac{4}{3}\pi$.

149. *Plane Areas in Polar Coordinates*

Given the equation

$$r = f(\theta)$$

of a plane curve in polar coordinates, let us try to find the area bounded by the curve and two fixed radius vectors $\theta = \alpha$, $\theta = \beta$. (Fig. 139, page 288.)

Inscribe in the area n *circular sectors* of radius r_i and angle $\Delta\theta$. By elementary geometry (or Ex. 24, page 286), the area of each sector is $\frac{1}{2}r_i^2\,\Delta\theta$.

Now add up the areas of all the sectors: $\displaystyle\sum_{i=1}^{n} \frac{1}{2}r_i^2\,\Delta\theta$. As n increases and the sectors become narrower and narrower, this sum *approaches as its limit the area under the curve.* Hence, by Theorem 19, page 107,

$$A = \operatorname*{Lim}_{n\to\infty} \sum_{i=1}^{n} \tfrac{1}{2}r_i^2\,\Delta\theta = \tfrac{1}{2}\int_{\alpha}^{\beta} r^2\,d\theta.$$

For the present, we must rely upon geometric intuition to assure us that the limit of this sum (i.e., the area) is the same as the one appearing in the definition (§ 55). From a formulation to be set up in § 196, this fact will appear clearly.

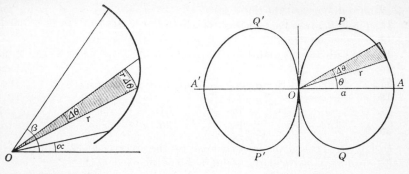

Figure 139　　　　　　　　　　**Figure 140**

Example. Find the area within the curve $r^2 = a^2 \cos \theta$. (Fig. 140.)

As θ varies from 0 to $\frac{1}{2}\pi$, we get positive and negative values of r, giving rise to the arcs APO, $A'P'O$. For $\frac{1}{2}\pi < \theta < \frac{3}{2}\pi$, r is imaginary. For $\frac{3}{2}\pi < \theta < 2\pi$, we get the arcs OQA, $OQ'A'$. Integrate through the first quadrant and multiply by 4:

$$A = 4 \cdot \frac{1}{2} \int_0^{\frac{1}{2}\pi} r^2 \, d\theta = 2a^2 \int_0^{\frac{1}{2}\pi} \cos \theta \, d\theta = 2a^2 \left[\sin \theta \right]_0^{\frac{1}{2}\pi} = 2a^2.$$

In this example, since the curve is symmetric in all four quadrants, it might seem that we could equally well have integrated from 0 to 2π. Trying this, we find

$$\frac{1}{2} \int_0^{2\pi} r^2 \, d\theta = \frac{1}{2}a^2 \int_0^{2\pi} \cos \theta \, d\theta = \frac{1}{2}a^2 \left[\sin \theta \right]_0^{2\pi} = 0.$$

This result, puzzling at first, is due to a peculiarity of the polar coordinate system. Although the curve appears in the second and third quadrants, these arcs, as noted above, correspond not to values of θ in those quadrants but to values of θ in the first and fourth quadrants with negative r; when $\frac{1}{2}\pi < \theta < \frac{3}{2}\pi$, r^2 becomes negative and r imaginary. When we integrate across a region in which this occurs, each of the elements $\frac{1}{2}r^2 \, d\theta$ is negative, and the same is true of the limit of their sum. This illustrates the fact that in polar coordinates *it is not safe to choose the limits merely from the appearance of the curve.* Here even more than in rectangular coordinates, it is best to *keep the limits of integration as narrow as possible* by using considerations of symmetry to the fullest extent.

EXERCISES

In Exs. 1–22, find the area enclosed by the given curve.

1. $r = 2a \cos \theta$.　　　*Ans.* πa^2.　　　2. $r = 2a \cos^2 \theta$.　　　*Ans.* $\frac{3}{2}\pi a^2$.
3. $r = 2a \sin^2 \theta$.　　　　　　　　　　4. $r = 2a \sin \theta$.

5. $r = a \cos 2\theta$.   *Ans.* $\frac{1}{2}\pi a^2$.   **6.** $r = a \sin 2\theta$.   *Ans.* $\frac{1}{2}\pi a^2$.

7. $r = a \cos 3\theta$.   *Ans.* $\frac{1}{4}\pi a^2$.   **8.** $r = a \sin 3\theta$.   *Ans.* $\frac{1}{4}\pi a^2$.

9. $r = a(1 - \cos \theta)$.   *Ans.* $\frac{3}{2}\pi a^2$.   **10.** $r = a(1 + \sin \theta)$.   *Ans.* $\frac{3}{2}\pi a^2$.

11. $r = a(2 - \sin \theta)$.   *Ans.* $\frac{9}{2}\pi a^2$.   **12.** $r = a(3 - 2 \cos \theta)$.   *Ans.* $11\pi a^2$.

13. $r^2 = a^2 \sin 2\theta$.   *Ans.* a^2.   **14.** $r^2 = a^2 \cos 2\theta$.   *Ans.* a^2.

15. $r^2 = a^2(2 \cos \theta - 1)$.   *Ans.* $1.37a^2$.

16. $r^2 = a^2 \cos \theta(1 - \cos \theta)$.   *Ans.* $0.43a^2$.

17. $r^2 = a^2 \sin \theta(1 + \sin \theta)$.   *Ans.* $3.57a^2$.

18. $r^2 = a^2 \sin \theta(1 - 2 \sin \theta)$.   *Ans.* $0.09a^2$.

19. $r^2 = a^2(\sin \theta + \cos \theta)$.   *Ans.* $2\sqrt{2a^2}$.

20. $r^2 = a^2 \sin \theta(1 - \cos \theta)$.   *Ans.* $2a^2$.

21. $r^2 = a^2 \cos \theta(2 - \cos^2 \theta)$.   *Ans.* $\dfrac{8a^2}{3}$.

22. $r^2 = a^2 \cos \theta \cos 2\theta$.   *Ans.* $\frac{1}{3}(4\sqrt{2} - 2)a^2 = 1.22a^2$.

23. Find the area of the inner loop of the curve $r = a(1 + 2 \cos \theta)$.

Ans. $0.54a^2$.

24. Find the area between the inner and outer ovals of the curve $r^2 = a^2(1 + \sin \theta)$.

Ans. $4a^2$.

25. Find the area between the ovals of the curve $r^2 = a^2(2 - \cos \theta)$.   *Ans.* $4a^2$.

26. Find the area inside the *spiral of Archimedes* $r = a\theta$, from $\theta = 0$ to $\theta = 2\pi$.

Ans. $\frac{4}{3}\pi^3 a^2$.

27. Find the area inside the *logarithmic spiral* $r = ae^{k\theta}$, from $\theta = 0$ to $\theta = 2\pi$.

Ans. $\dfrac{a^2}{4k}(e^{4k\pi} - 1)$.

Solve Exs. 28–33 in polar coordinates.

28. Find the area cut off from the parabola $y^2 = 4ax$ by a chord through the vertex making an angle α with the axis.   *Ans.* $\frac{8}{3}a^2 \cot^3 \alpha$.

29. A chord of a circle makes an angle α with the tangents at its ends. Find the area of the segment cut off.   *Ans.* $(\alpha - \sin \alpha \cos \alpha)a^2$.

30. Find the area in the first quadrant bounded by the curves $y = x^3$, $y = 2x$.

31. Find the area bounded by the curves $y^2 = 4ax$, $y = 2x$, $y = 4x$.   *Ans.* $\frac{7}{24}a^2$.

32. Find the area of the loop of the folium $x^3 + y^3 = 3axy$.   *Ans.* $\frac{3}{2}a^2$.

33. Find the area in the first quadrant bounded by the straight line $y = x$ and the curve $(x^2 + a^2)y^2 = 4a^2x^2$.   *Ans.* $\frac{1}{2}a^2$.

34. Solve Ex. 33 in rectangular coordinates.

150. *Integrable Functions*

A function $f(x)$ is said to be *integrable* in the interval $a \leqq x \leqq b$ if the definite integral

$$A = \int_a^b f(x) \, dx$$

exists.

We know (§ 55) that the area "under" any continuous curve exists; hence *every continuous function is integrable*. Whether or not we can express

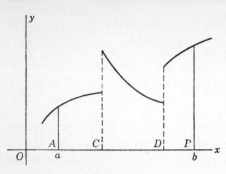

Figure 141

the integral in elementary terms is immaterial: if not, it will still be possible by more advanced methods to evaluate it in the strict sense of the term—*i.e.*, to find its value, to any degree of approximation, for given values of a and b.

Furthermore, if the function is continuous except for a finite number of finite discontinuities in the interval, as in Fig. 141, the area still exists, and the function is integrable.

DEFINITION. *If $f(x)$ is continuous in the interval $a \leqq x < b$, then*

$$\int_a^b f(x) \, dx = \operatorname*{Lim}_{c \to b^-} \int_a^c f(x) \, dx;$$

if $f(x)$ is continuous in the interval $a < x \leqq b$, then

$$\int_a^b f(x) \, dx = \operatorname*{Lim}_{c \to a^+} \int_c^b f(x) \, dx.$$

Applying this definition, repeatedly if necessary, we integrate over the separate segments and add the results. In this connection, missing point discontinuities (§ 14) may be ignored, since the value of the function, or lack of any value, at a single point cannot affect the value of the area.

Example (*a*). Find the area in the first quadrant under the curve

$$y = 1 + x^2, \qquad x \leqq 1,$$
$$= 2 - x^2, \qquad x > 1.$$

With the aid of Fig. 142 we write

$$A = \int_0^{\sqrt{2}} y \, dx$$

$$= \int_0^1 (1 + x^2) \, dx$$

$$+ \operatorname*{Lim}_{c \to 1^+} \int_c^{\sqrt{2}} (2 - x^2) \, dx.$$

Since $(2 - x^2)$ is continuous at $x = 1$, we have at once

$$A = \int_0^1 (1 + x^2) \, dx + \int_1^{\sqrt{2}} (2 - x^2) \, dx.$$

Simple integrations lead quickly to the evaluation $A = \frac{1}{3}(4\sqrt{2} - 1) = 1.55$.

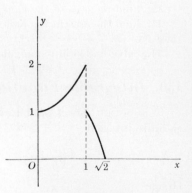

Figure 142

Example (b). In Ex. 24, page 84, there occurs the function

$$f(x) = \sqrt{x + \sqrt{x - \tfrac{1}{4}}} + \sqrt{x - \sqrt{x - \tfrac{1}{4}}}.$$

Let $y = \dfrac{d}{dx}[xf(x)]$. Find the area under the y-curve from $x = \tfrac{1}{4}$ to $x = 1$. See Fig. 143.

In this example the function $y(x)$ is chosen as the derivative of a known function in order to make available a simple check on our answer.

It can be shown (by doing Ex. 24, page 84) that $f(x)$ is imaginary for $x < \tfrac{1}{4}$ and

$$f(x) = 1, \qquad \tfrac{1}{4} \leqq x \leqq \tfrac{1}{2},$$
$$= \sqrt{4x - 1}, \qquad x > \tfrac{1}{2}.$$

Therefore, since $y = \dfrac{d}{dx}[xf(x)]$,

$$y = 1, \qquad \tfrac{1}{4} < x < \tfrac{1}{2},$$
$$= \frac{6x - 1}{\sqrt{4x - 1}}, \qquad x > \tfrac{1}{2}.$$

The desired area may now be obtained from

$$A = \int_{\frac{1}{4}}^{1} y\, dx = \int_{\frac{1}{4}}^{\frac{1}{2}} 1 \cdot dx + \int_{\frac{1}{2}}^{1} \frac{(6x - 1)\, dx}{\sqrt{4x - 1}}$$
$$= \frac{1}{4} + \int_{\frac{1}{2}}^{1} \frac{\tfrac{3}{2}(4x - 1) + \tfrac{1}{2}}{\sqrt{4x - 1}}\, dx,$$

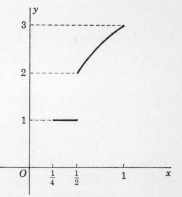

Figure 143

or

$$A = \tfrac{1}{4} + \tfrac{3}{2} \int_{\frac{1}{2}}^{1} (4x - 1)^{\frac{1}{2}}\, dx + \tfrac{1}{2} \int_{\frac{1}{2}}^{1} (4x - 1)^{-\frac{1}{2}}\, dx.$$

It is then a simple matter to show that $A = \sqrt{3} - \tfrac{1}{4}$.

As a check, note that

$$A = \int_{\frac{1}{4}}^{1} y\, dx$$

$$= \operatorname*{Lim}_{c \to \frac{1}{4}^{+}, k \to \frac{1}{2}^{-}} \int_{c}^{k} [xf(x)]'\, dx + \operatorname*{Lim}_{a \to \frac{1}{2}^{+}} \int_{a}^{1} [xf(x)]'\, dx$$

$$= \operatorname*{Lim}_{c \to \frac{1}{4}^{+}, k \to \frac{1}{2}^{-}} \left[\, xf(x)\, \right]_{c}^{k} + \operatorname*{Lim}_{a \to \frac{1}{2}^{+}} \left[\, xf(x)\, \right]_{a}^{1}$$

$$= \operatorname*{Lim}_{k \to \frac{1}{2}^{-}} kf(k) - \operatorname*{Lim}_{c \to \frac{1}{4}^{+}} cf(c) + f(1) - \operatorname*{Lim}_{a \to \frac{1}{2}^{+}} af(a).$$

Hence

$$A = \tfrac{1}{2} \cdot 1 - \tfrac{1}{4} \cdot 1 + \sqrt{3} - \tfrac{1}{2} \cdot 1 = \sqrt{3} - \tfrac{1}{4}.$$

151. *Improper Integrals*

In certain instances, a meaning may be assigned to the function

$$A = \int_a^b f(x)\, dx$$

under either or both of the following circumstances:

(a) Either a or b, or both, increase numerically without bound; or

(b) The integrand $f(x)$ has an infinite discontinuity at an endpoint or one or more interior points of the interval.

In either case, the integral is called an *improper integral*.

152. *Integrals with Infinite Limits*

If we keep a fixed, the integral

$$A = \int_a^b f(x)\, dx$$

becomes a function of b only. It may happen that as b increases without bound, the function A approaches a limit. If so, this limit is denoted by the symbol $\int_a^\infty f(x)\, dx$:

$$\int_a^\infty f(x)\, dx = \lim_{b \to \infty} \int_a^b f(x)\, dx.$$

Similarly,

$$\int_{-\infty}^b f(x)\, dx = \lim_{a \to -\infty} \int_a^b f(x)\, dx;$$

(1) $$\int_{-\infty}^\infty f(x)\, dx = \lim_{a \to -\infty} \int_a^c f(x)\, dx + \lim_{b \to \infty} \int_c^b f(x)\, dx,$$

where c may have any fixed value. If the limits occurring in the right members do not exist, the integrals on the left have no meaning.

An improper integral for which the defining limit or limits do not exist is said to be *divergent*. If the defining limits exist, the integral is called *convergent*. The terms *convergent* and *divergent* occur again in the study of infinite series (Chapters 30–32) with meanings similar to those used here. We make little use of the term convergent in connection with improper integrals; for such an integral we obtain its value and therefore have no need for a term which expresses merely the fact that it does have a value. The term convergent is employed widely in advanced calculus, which contains a study of tests to determine whether an improper integral exists, without necessarily evaluating the integral.

It should be noted that $\int_{-\infty}^\infty f(x)\, dx$ does not mean $\lim_{b \to \infty} \int_{-b}^b f(x)\, dx$.

If the former exists, then the latter also exists, and the two limits are equal; but the latter may exist when the former does not. For example,

$$\operatorname*{Lim}_{b \to \infty} \int_{-b}^{b} x \, dx = \operatorname*{Lim}_{b \to \infty} \left[\frac{x^2}{2} \right]_{-b}^{b} = \operatorname*{Lim}_{b \to \infty} \left(\frac{b^2}{2} - \frac{b^2}{2} \right) = 0;$$

but $\int_{-\infty}^{\infty} x \, dx$ is divergent, since neither limit in (1) exists.

Example (a). $\int_{1}^{\infty} \frac{dx}{x^2} = \operatorname*{Lim}_{b \to \infty} \int_{1}^{b} \frac{dx}{x^2} = \operatorname*{Lim}_{b \to \infty} \left[-\frac{1}{x} \right]_{1}^{b} = 1.$

The curve $y = \dfrac{1}{x^2}$ is shown in Fig. 144. Geometrically, the above integral means the limit of the shaded area as b becomes infinite. This limit we *define* as the "area bounded by" the curve, the x-axis, and the line $x = 1$, although it is not properly a bounded area in the literal sense. It is evident that a similar argument holds in general: An integral with an infinite

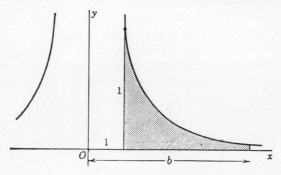

Figure 144

limit may be interpreted as the area under a curve which approaches the x-axis, usually without ever reaching it. In ordinary cases, the x-axis is an asymptote of the curve. However, even though the curve is asymptotic to Ox, the integral is not necessarily convergent (see, for example, Exs. 29–30 below).

Example (b). Find the area between the curve $y = \dfrac{x^2 - 1}{x^2 + 1}$ and its asymptote.

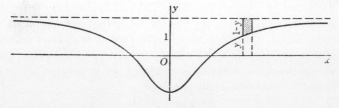

Figure 145

Since the curve is symmetric with respect to Oy, we may write

$$A = 2 \int_0^\infty \left(1 - \frac{x^2 - 1}{x^2 + 1}\right) dx.$$

Reduce the integrand to a common denominator:

$$A = 4 \int_0^\infty \frac{dx}{1 + x^2} = \lim_{b \to \infty} 4 \int_0^b \frac{dx}{1 + x^2} = \lim_{b \to \infty} \left[4 \operatorname{Arctan} x\right]_0^b = 2\pi.$$

EXERCISES

Evaluate the integrals in Exs. 1–20.

1. $\int_2^\infty \frac{dx}{x^3}.$ *Ans.* $\frac{1}{8}$.
2. $\int_0^\infty e^{-2y}\, dy.$ *Ans.* $\frac{1}{2}$.

3. $\int_{-\infty}^0 e^{4y}\, dy.$ *Ans.* $\frac{1}{4}$.
4. $\int_0^\infty x e^{-x^2}\, dx.$ *Ans.* $\frac{1}{2}$.

5. $\int_0^\infty \frac{dx}{9x^2 + 4}.$ *Ans.* $\frac{\pi}{12}$.
6. $\int_5^\infty \frac{dx}{4x^2 + 25}.$ *Ans.* $\frac{1}{10} \operatorname{Arctan} \frac{1}{2}$.

7. $\int_0^\infty \frac{dx}{2x + 1}.$ *Ans. Divergent.*
8. $\int_0^\infty \frac{dx}{(2x + 1)^4}.$ *Ans.* $\frac{1}{6}$.

9. $\int_0^\infty \frac{dx}{(7x + 2)^{\frac{3}{2}}}.$ *Ans.* $\frac{1}{7}\sqrt{2}$.
10. $\int_0^\infty \frac{dx}{(7x + 2)^{\frac{1}{2}}}.$ *Ans. Divergent.*

11. $\int_0^\infty \frac{x\, dx}{(x^2 + 4)^2}.$ *Ans.* $\frac{1}{8}$.
12. $\int_{-\infty}^\infty \frac{x\, dx}{(x^2 + 4)^2}.$ *Ans.* 0.

13. $\int_1^\infty \frac{dx}{x(x + 4)}.$ *Ans.* $\frac{1}{4}\ln 5$.
14. $\int_1^\infty \frac{dx}{x\sqrt{4x^2 - 1}}.$ *Ans.* $\frac{\pi}{6}$.

15. Do Ex. 14 a second way.
16. Do Ex. 14 a third way.

17. $\int_1^\infty \frac{dx}{x(x^2 + 1)}.$ *Ans.* 0.347.
18. $\int_1^\infty \frac{dx}{x\sqrt{x^2 + 1}}.$ *Ans.* 0.881.

19. $\int_0^\infty e^{-st}\, dt$; all real s. *Ans.* $\frac{1}{s}$, for $s > 0$; divergent for $s \leqq 0$.

20. $\int_0^\infty t e^{-st}\, dt$; $s > 0$. *Ans.* $\frac{1}{s^2}$.

21. Find the area between the curve $y = x e^{-\frac{1}{2}x^2}$ and its asymptote. *Ans.* 2.

22. Find the first quadrant area under the curve $y = x e^{-x}$. *Ans.* 1.

23. Find the area between the curve $y = \dfrac{a^3}{x^2 + a^2}$ and its asymptote. *Ans.* πa^2.

24. Find the area under the curve $y = \dfrac{1}{x^2 - 1}$ to the right of the line $x = 3$.

Ans. $\frac{1}{2}\ln 2$.

25. Find the area under the curve $y = \dfrac{1}{x(x + 1)^2}$ to the right of the line $x = 1$.

26. Find the area between the curve $y = \dfrac{x}{(1 + x^2)^2}$ and its asymptote.   *Ans.* 1.

27. Find the first quadrant area under the curve $y^2 = \dfrac{a^8}{(a^2 + x^2)^3}$ and to the right of the line $x = a$.   *Ans.* $a^2(1 - \tfrac{1}{2}\sqrt{2})$.

28. Find the area bounded by the curve $y = \dfrac{1}{(x^2 + 4)^2}$ and its asymptote.

29. Find the area under the hyperbola $xy = a^2$ to the right of the line $x = a$.
                                   Ans. Meaningless (integral is divergent).

30. Find the area under the curve $y = \dfrac{1}{x \ln x}$ to the right of the line $x = e$.

                                   Ans. Meaningless (divergent integral).

31. In § 99, find the area bounded by the path of the man, the path of the weight, and the original position of the rope. (Set up the integral with vertical element; see Ex. 21, page 186.)   *Ans.* $\tfrac{1}{4}\pi a^2$.

153. *Infinite Discontinuities of the Integrand*

Consider now the second class of improper integrals discussed in § 151, those in which the limits are finite, but the integrand has an infinite discontinuity at an endpoint or an interior point of the interval.

DEFINITIONS: *If $f(x)$ increases numerically without bound as $x \to b^-$,*

$$\int_a^b f(x)\,dx = \underset{c \to b^-}{\text{Lim}} \int_a^c f(x)\,dx;$$

if $f(x)$ increases numerically without bound as $x \to a^+$,

$$\int_a^b f(x)\,dx = \underset{c \to a^+}{\text{Lim}} \int_c^b f(x)\,dx.$$

Example (a). Find the area bounded by the curve $xy^2 = 1$, the axes, and the line $x = 1$.

We write

$$A = \int_0^1 y\,dx = \underset{c \to 0^+}{\text{Lim}} \int_c^1 \frac{dx}{\sqrt{x}}$$

$$= \underset{c \to 0^+}{\text{Lim}} \left[2\sqrt{x} \right]_c^1 = \underset{c \to 0^+}{\text{Lim}} (2 - 2\sqrt{c})$$

$$= 2.$$

When the integrand $f(x)$ has an infinite discontinuity at an interior point of the interval—say, at $x = c$, where $a < c < b$—we subdivide the interval.

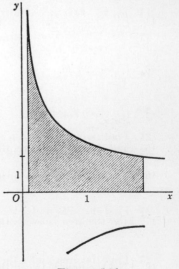

Figure 146

Example (*b*). Find the area under the curve $x^2y = 1$ from $x = -1$ to $x = 1$.

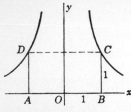

Figure 147

Since y becomes infinite at the interior point $x = 0$, we write

$$A = \int_{-1}^{1} y \, dx = \operatorname*{Lim}_{c_1 \to 0^-} \int_{-1}^{c_1} \frac{dx}{x^2} + \operatorname*{Lim}_{c_2 \to 0^+} \int_{c_2}^{1} \frac{dx}{x^2}$$

$$= \operatorname*{Lim}_{c_1 \to 0^-} \left[-\frac{1}{x} \right]_{-1}^{c_1} + \operatorname*{Lim}_{c_2 \to 0^+} \left[-\frac{1}{x} \right]_{c_2}^{1}.$$

Since these limits do not exist, the integral is divergent.

EXERCISES

Evaluate the integrals in Exs. 1–14.

1. $\int_0^1 \frac{dx}{x^{\frac{1}{4}}}.$ *Ans.* $\frac{4}{3}$.

2. $\int_0^1 \frac{dx}{x^{\frac{5}{4}}}.$ *Ans.* Divergent.

3. $\int_{-1}^1 \frac{dx}{x^{\frac{1}{3}}}.$ *Ans.* 0.

4. $\int_{-1}^1 \frac{dy}{y^{\frac{4}{3}}}.$ *Ans.* Divergent.

5. $\int_{-1}^7 \frac{du}{u+1}.$ *Ans.* Divergent.

6. $\int_{-1}^7 \frac{du}{(u+1)^{\frac{1}{3}}}.$ *Ans.* 6.

7. $\int_1^3 \frac{dy}{(y-2)^2}.$ *Ans.* Divergent.

8. $\int_1^3 \frac{dy}{(y-2)^{\frac{2}{3}}}.$ *Ans.* 6.

9. $\int_1^e \frac{dx}{x(\ln x)^{\frac{1}{3}}}.$ *Ans.* $\frac{3}{2}$.

10. $\int_{\frac{1}{e}}^e \frac{dx}{x(\ln x)^{\frac{1}{3}}}.$ *Ans.* 0.

11. $\int_{-a}^a \frac{dx}{\sqrt{a^2 - x^2}}.$ *Ans.* π.

12. $\int_{-a}^a \frac{x^4 \, dx}{\sqrt{a^2 - x^2}}.$ *Ans.* $\dfrac{3\pi a^4}{8}$.

13. $\int_0^{\frac{\pi}{2}} \sec^2 2\theta \, d\theta.$ *Ans.* Divergent.

14. $\int_{-\frac{\pi}{4}}^{\frac{\pi}{4}} \csc \theta \cot \theta \, d\theta.$ *Ans.* Divergent.

15. Find the area between the curve $xy^2 = (x-1)^2$ and the y-axis.   *Ans.* $\frac{8}{3}$.

16. Find the area between the curve $y^2 = \dfrac{1}{x(4-x)}$ and its asymptotes.

Ans. 2π.

17. Find the area between the curve $y^2 = \dfrac{x^4}{a^2 - x^2}$ and its asymptotes.

Ans. πa^2.

18. Find the area between the curve $y^2 = \dfrac{1}{x(1+x)^2}$ and the y-axis.   *Ans.* 2π.

19. Find the area in the fourth quadrant bounded by $y = \ln x$ and the axes. Solve in two ways.

20. Find the area between the curve $xy^2 = 1 - x$ and its asymptote. Solve in two ways.   *Ans.* π.

21. Find the area in the second quadrant under the curve $x^2 y = e^{\frac{1}{x}}$.   *Ans.* 1.

22. Find the area between the curves $y = \dfrac{1}{x}$, $y = \dfrac{1}{x + x^2}$, from $x = 0$ to $x = 2$.

$$\textit{Ans. } \ln 3 = 1.099.$$

23. Find the area between the curves $y = \dfrac{1}{x}$, $y = \dfrac{1}{2x + x^2}$, from $x = 0$ to $x = 2$.

Ans. Meaningless (divergent integral).

24. Find the area between the curves $y = \csc x$, $y = \cot x$, from $x = -\dfrac{\pi}{2}$ to $x = \dfrac{\pi}{2}$.   *Ans.* $2 \ln 2 = 1.386$.

25. Find the area between the cissoid $y^2 = \dfrac{x^3}{2a - x}$ and its asymptote.

$$\textit{Ans. } 3\pi a^2.$$

26. Find the area between the curve $y = \dfrac{1}{x(1 + x^2)}$ and the x-axis.

Ans. Meaningless (divergent integral).

27. Find the area in the first quadrant under the curve $y = \dfrac{1}{x^2 - 1}$.

Ans. Meaningless (divergent integral).

APPLICATIONS OF

INTEGRATION

154. *The General Method*

From the mode of development of Theorem 19, page 107, it might be thought that the theorem applies only in the computation of plane areas. But *any function of one variable may be represented graphically as a plane curve*. It follows that Theorem 19 may be used to evaluate

$$\lim_{\Delta x \to 0} \sum_{i=1}^{n} f(x_i)\, \Delta x$$

regardless of the physical meaning of the function $f(x)$. For, if the graph of the function were to be drawn (it is not necessary actually to do this), we can see that the quantity $f(x_i)\, \Delta x$ would represent a rectangular element of area, so that the theorem becomes applicable at once.

In this and succeeding chapters we shall develop a considerable variety of applications of integral calculus. In every case, the quantity to be computed will appear in the first instance as the limit of a sum; this limit will then be evaluated by application of Theorem 19. This general method is one of the most important and far-reaching in the whole field of science because it solves, directly or indirectly, a large share of the mathematical problems arising in engineering, physics, chemistry, astronomy, and biology.

155. *Solids of Revolution: Circular Disks*

Let a solid be generated by rotating the area OAB about the x-axis (the figure shows one quadrant of the solid). Imagine this solid cut into thin slices by *planes perpendicular to the axis of revolution* (a typical slice being formed by rotation of the area $PQRS$). Trim off the irregular outer edge (generated by revolving the area $S'RS$), to leave a thin *circular disk* (generated by revolving the rectangle $PQRS'$). The radius of this element is y_i, the thickness Δx, the volume $\pi y_i^2\, \Delta x$. Now, as the disks are taken thinner

298

and thinner, the aggregate volume of trimmings approaches zero, and the sum of all the elementary volumes $\pi y_i^2 \, \Delta x$ approaches as its limit *the volume of the solid*:

(1)
$$V = \operatorname*{Lim}_{n \to \infty} \sum_{i=1}^{n} \pi y_i^2 \, \Delta x = \pi \int_a^b y^2 \, dx.$$

In formula (1) we have resorted to equal divisions Δx in our use of Theorem 19. This simplification will be used regularly so as to avoid an unnecessary appearance of complexity in the setting up of the many definite integrals to be encountered in our later work. Formula (1) may be viewed as a definition of the volume under consideration.

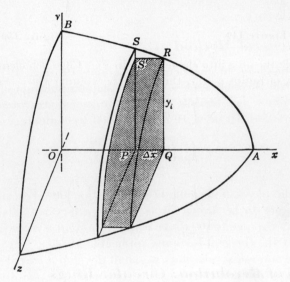

Figure 148

The student is strongly advised not to memorize this or any similar formulas, but to make sure that he fully understands the argument. Then, only the simplest elementary geometry is required to make up the correct integral in any given problem.

Example (a). The area bounded by a parabola, its axis, and its latus rectum revolves about the axis. Find the volume generated. See Fig. 149, page 300.

Let the equation of the parabola be $y^2 = 4ax$. Dividing the area into elements as in Fig. 149, we see that each rectangle generates a cylindrical volume-element of radius y, altitude dx, and volume $\pi y^2 \, dx$. Hence

$$V = \pi \int_0^a y^2 \, dx = 4\pi a \int_0^a x \, dx = 2\pi a^3.$$

Example (*b*). The above area rotates about the latus rectum. Find the volume generated.

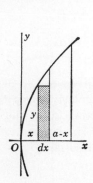

Figure 149

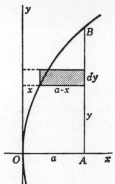

Figure 150

If we divide the area into elements as in Fig. 150, each element generates a circular disk of radius $a - x$, thickness dy, volume $\pi(a - x)^2 \, dy$. Hence

$$V = \pi \int_0^{2a} (a - x)^2 \, dy$$

$$= \pi \int_0^{2a} \left(a - \frac{y^2}{4a} \right)^2 \, dy$$

$$= \pi \int_0^{2a} \left(a^2 - \frac{y^2}{2} + \frac{y^4}{16a^2} \right) \, dy$$

$$= \frac{16}{15} \pi a^3.$$

156. *Solids of Revolution: Circular Rings*

In the general argument and examples of § 155, the axis of rotation formed part of the boundary of the rotating area; but the method works equally well when this is not the case. If, say, the area in Fig. 151, page 301, is to revolve about the *x*-axis, we may use as element the *circular ring*, or *washer*, formed by revolution of the rectangle* *PQRS*.

Example. Find the volume generated by revolving a circle about one of its tangents. (Figure 152, page 301.)

Let the circle

$$x^2 + y^2 = a^2$$

* Instead, we might find separately the volumes generated by rotating the areas *AMNBSA*, *AMNBPA* (using as elements the disks generated by the rectangles *P'Q'RS*, *P'Q'QP*), and subtract the latter from the former. But the method of circular rings gives us a chance to *simplify before integrating*, as is beautifully illustrated by the example in this section.

revolve about the line $x = a$. The volume-element is a circular ring of outer radius $SP' = a + x$, inner radius $PP' = a - x$, thickness dy:

$$V = \pi \int_{-a}^{a} [(a + x)^2 - (a - x)^2]\, dy,$$

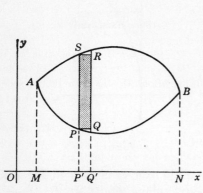

Figure 151	**Figure 152**

which reduces to

$$V = 8\pi a \int_{0}^{a} x\, dy.$$

Since this integral represents the area of the circular quadrant, we know its value:

$$V = 8\pi a \cdot \tfrac{1}{4}\pi a^2 = 2\pi^2 a^3.$$

EXERCISES

1. The area bounded by the curve $y = e^{-x}$, the axes, and the line $x = 2$ is revolved about the x-axis. Find the volume generated.   *Ans.* $\frac{1}{2}\pi(1 - e^{-4})$.

2. The area under one arch of the sine curve revolves about the x-axis. Find the volume generated.   *Ans.* $\frac{1}{2}\pi^2$.

3. Find the volume formed by revolving the area in Ex. 1 about the line $y = 1$.   *Ans.* $\frac{1}{2}\pi(1 - e^{-2})(3 - e^{-2})$.

4. The area bounded by the parabola $ay = x^2$, the x-axis, and the line $x = b$ is revolved about the x-axis. Find the volume generated.

$$Ans. \ \frac{\pi b^5}{5a^2}.$$

5. The area of Ex. 4 is revolved about the y-axis. Find the volume generated.

$$Ans. \ \frac{\pi b^4}{2a}.$$

6. The area in Ex. 4 is revolved about the line $x = b$. Find the volume generated.

$$Ans. \ \frac{\pi b^4}{6a}.$$

7. The area bounded by the y-axis, the line $y = 1$, and that arc of $y = \sin x$ between $x = 0$ and $x = \frac{1}{2}\pi$ is revolved about the line $y = 1$. Find the volume generated. *Ans.* $\frac{1}{4}\pi(3\pi - 8)$.

8. The area in Ex. 7 is revolved about the x-axis. Find the volume generated. *Ans.* $\frac{1}{4}\pi^2$.

9. The area bounded by the parabola $ay = x^2$ and the line $y = b$ is revolved about the x-axis. Find the volume generated. *Ans.* $\frac{8}{5}\pi b^2 \sqrt{ab}$.

10. The area bounded by the curve $a^2y = x^3$, the x-axis, and the line $x = a$ revolves about Ox. Find the volume generated. *Ans.* $\frac{1}{7}\pi a^3$.

11. The area bounded by the hyperbola $x^2 - y^2 = a^2$, the x-axis, and the line $x = 2a$ revolves about Ox. Find the volume. *Ans.* $\frac{4}{3}\pi a^3$.

12. Find the volume generated by revolving about Ox the area in the second quadrant under the curve $y = e^x$. *Ans.* $\frac{1}{2}\pi$.

13. Find the volume of a sphere. *Ans.* $\frac{4}{3}\pi a^3$.

14. Find the volume of a circular cone. *Ans.* $\frac{1}{3}\pi a^2 h$.

15. Find the volume of a prolate spheroid. *Ans.* $\frac{4}{3}\pi ab^2$.

16. Find the volume of an oblate spheroid, using the equations $x = a \cos \varphi$, $y = b \sin \varphi$. *Ans.* $\frac{4}{3}\pi a^2 b$.

17. The area bounded by $y = \ln x$, $x = e$, and the x-axis is revolved about the x-axis. Find the volume generated. *Ans.* $\pi(e - 2)$.

18. Find the volume generated by revolving the area in Ex. 17 about the line $x = e$. *Ans.* $\frac{1}{2}\pi(4e - 1 - e^2)$.

19. The area enclosed by the loop of the curve $y^2 = x(x - 3)^2$ is revolved about the x-axis. Find the volume generated.

Ans. $\dfrac{27\pi}{4}$.

20. Find the volume formed by revolving about the y-axis the area bounded by the parabola $x^2 = 4ay$, the line $x = a$, and the x-axis. *Ans.* $\frac{1}{8}\pi a^3$.

21. Find the volume formed by revolving the area of Ex. 20 about the line $x = a$.

Ans. $\dfrac{\pi a^3}{24}$.

22. Find the volume generated by revolving about Ox the area bounded by the hyperbola $xy = a^2$, the line $x = a$, and the x-axis. *Ans.* πa^3.

23. Solve Ex. 22, using for the hyperbola the equations $x = a \cot \varphi, y = a \tan \varphi$.

24. Solve Ex. 22, using the equations $x = a \sec \psi, y = a \cos \psi$.

25. Find the volume generated by revolving about the y-axis the area bounded by the curve $x^2 = 4(x - y)$, the y-axis, and the line $y = 1$. *Ans.* $\frac{2}{3}\pi$.

In Exs. 26–29, find the volume formed by revolving the area in Ex. 25 about the designated line.

26. $y = 1$.   *Ans.* $\frac{2}{5}\pi$.   **27.** $y = 0$.   *Ans.* $\frac{14}{15}\pi$.

28. $x = 2$.   *Ans.* 2π.   **29.** $x = 4$.   *Ans.* $\frac{14}{3}\pi$.

30. The area bounded by the curve $y = (x^2 - 4)^2$ and the x-axis revolves about the y-axis. Find the volume. *Ans.* $\frac{64}{3}\pi$.

31. Find the volume generated by revolving one arch of the cycloid $x = a(\theta - \sin \theta), y = a(1 - \cos \theta)$ (Fig. 138, page 286) about Ox. *Ans.* $5\pi^2 a^3$.

32. The area bounded by the curve $y = 3 - 2x + x^2$ and the line $y = 3$ is revolved about the line $y = 3$. Find the volume generated.   *Ans.* $\frac{16}{15}\pi$.

33. Find the volume formed by revolving about the line $y = 4$ the area of Ex. 23.

34. Find the volume generated by revolving about the line $x = 2a$ the area bounded by that line, the x-axis, and the curve $a^2y = x^3$.   *Ans.* $\frac{16}{5}\pi a^3$.

35. The area bounded by the parabola $y^2 = 4ax$, the y-axis, and the line $y = 2a$ revolves about the line $y = 2a$. Find the volume obtained.   *Ans.* $\frac{2}{3}\pi a^3$.

36. The area bounded by the parabola $x^2 - 2x + y = 3$, the y-axis, and the line $y = 4$ revolves about the line $y = 4$. Find the volume generated.   *Ans.* $\frac{1}{5}\pi$.

37. The area of Ex. 36 revolves about the line $x = 2$. Find the volume.

38. Find the volume formed by revolving the ellipse $\dfrac{x^2}{a^2} + \dfrac{y^2}{b^2} = 1$ about the line $y = b$.   *Ans.* $2\pi^2ab^2$.

39. Find the volume formed by revolving about the line $x = 1$ the area bounded by the curve $y = (x^2 - 1)^2$ and the x-axis.   *Ans.* $\frac{32}{15}\pi$.

40. Find the volume generated by revolving about Oy the area in the fourth quadrant bounded by the curve $y = \ln x$.   *Ans.* $\frac{1}{2}\pi$.

41. The area in the first quadrant between the curve $y(1 + x) = x$ and its horizontal asymptote revolves about the asymptote. Find the volume.   *Ans.* π.

42. Find the volume of a spherical segment of height h.   *Ans.* $\frac{1}{3}\pi h^2(3a - h)$.

43. Find the volume generated by revolving about the y-axis the area bounded by the curve $y = \dfrac{\sin x}{x}$ and the coordinate axes.   *Ans.* 4π.

44. Find the volume generated by revolving about Ox the area under the curve $xy = e^{\frac{1}{x}}$, to the right of $x = 1$.   *Ans.* $\frac{1}{2}\pi(e^2 - 1)$.

45. In Ex. 44, find the volume generated by revolving the area in the third quadrant about Ox.   *Ans.* $\frac{1}{2}\pi$.

46. Find the volume of the torus formed by revolving the circle $x^2 + y^2 = a^2$ about the line $x = b$ $(b > a)$.   *Ans.* $2\pi^2a^2b$.

47. Solve Ex. 46, using the equations $x = a \sin \theta$, $y = a \cos \theta$.

48. Find the volume formed by revolving the area enclosed by the curve $y^2 = (x + 1)^2(4 - x^2)$ about Ox.   *Ans.* $\frac{96}{5}\pi$.

49. Find the volume formed by revolving about the x-axis the area enclosed by the four-cusped hypocycloid $x^{\frac{2}{3}} + y^{\frac{2}{3}} = a^{\frac{2}{3}}$.

Ans. $\dfrac{32\pi a^3}{105}$.

50. Solve Ex. 49, using the parametric equations $x = a \sin^3 \theta$, $y = a \cos^3 \theta$.

51. Find the volume formed by revolving about the y-axis the area bounded by the curve $y^2 = 4(x - y - 1)$ and the line $x = 1$.   *Ans.* $\frac{16}{5}\pi$.

157. *Solids of Revolution: Cylindrical Shells*

The following method for computing volume of a solid of revolution frequently works out more simply than those of §§ 155–156; also, when two methods are feasible, solution both ways gives a valuable check.

Let a solid be formed by revolving the area OAB about Ox (Fig. 153 exhibits one quadrant). Divide the solid into thin shells, each with its axis in the axis of revolution; a typical shell is formed by rotation of the strip $PQRS$. Trim the outer end, leaving the *cylindrical shell* formed by rotation of the rectangle $PQRS'$. The inner radius is y_i, outer radius $y_i + \Delta y$, height x_i, volume

(1) $$\Delta V_i = \pi(y_i + \Delta y)^2 x_i - \pi y_i^2 x_i = 2\pi y_i x_i \, \Delta y + \pi x_i \, (\Delta y)^2.$$

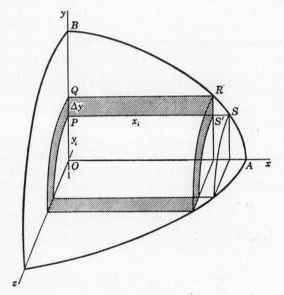

Figure 153

Hence the volume of the solid is

$$V = \operatorname*{Lim}_{\Delta y \to 0} \sum_{i=1}^{n} [2\pi y_i x_i \, \Delta y + \pi x_i \, (\Delta y)^2]$$

$$= \operatorname*{Lim}_{\Delta y \to 0} \sum_{i=1}^{n} 2\pi y_i x_i \, \Delta y + \operatorname*{Lim}_{\Delta y \to 0} \sum_{i=1}^{n} \pi x_i \, (\Delta y)^2.$$

Now, in regard to the second summation, we may write*

$$\operatorname*{Lim}_{\Delta y \to 0} \sum_{i=1}^{n} \pi x_i \, (\Delta y)^2 = \pi \operatorname*{Lim}_{\Delta y \to 0} \sum_{i=1}^{n} x_i \, \Delta y \cdot \operatorname*{Lim}_{\Delta y \to 0} \Delta y = 0,$$

since

$$\operatorname*{Lim}_{\Delta y \to 0} \sum_{i=1}^{n} x_i \, \Delta y = A,$$

* This particular method of proof requires that all the Δy's be taken equal. The result is true, however, without this restriction.

where A is the rotating area. It follows that in the expression for the volume-element, we may write

(2) $$V = \lim_{\Delta y \to 0} \sum_{i=1}^{n} 2\pi y_i x_i \, \Delta y = 2\pi \int_a^b yx \, dy.$$

In § 197 we shall lay down a definition for volume in general, and show that both the present formula and that of § 155 fall out as special cases when the solid is one of revolution.

In equation (2) the roles of x and y are in a sense accidental, being due to the particular position of the volume and axis of revolution in Fig. 153. The important conclusion to be drawn from (2) is that a volume of revolution may be obtained by taking the limit of the sum of (integrating) cylindrical shell elements, each of which is equal in volume to the *circumference times the height times the thickness*. This is the only formula to be remembered in connection with the present method.

Example (a). The area bounded by a parabola, its axis, and the latus rectum rotates about the latus rectum. Find the volume generated. (Fig. 154.)

With the shell as element,

$$V = 2\pi \int_0^a (a - x)y \, dx = 4\pi \sqrt{a} \int_0^a (ax^{\frac{1}{2}} - x^{\frac{3}{2}}) \, dx$$

$$= 4\pi \sqrt{a} \left[\tfrac{2}{3}ax^{\frac{3}{2}} - \tfrac{2}{5}x^{\frac{5}{2}} \right]_0^a = \tfrac{16}{15}\pi a^3.$$

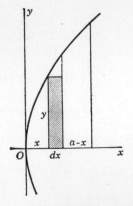

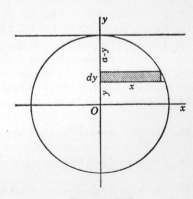

Figure 154   Figure 155

Example (b). Find the volume generated by revolving a circle about one of its tangents. (Fig. 155.)

Let the circle

$$x^2 + y^2 = a^2$$

rotate around the line $y = a$. The volume, with the shell as element, is

$$V = 2 \cdot 2\pi \int_{-a}^{a} (a - y)x \, dy$$

(1)
$$= 4\pi a \int_{-a}^{a} x \, dy - 4\pi \int_{-a}^{a} yx \, dy.$$

The first integral in (1) represents the area of the semicircle; the second, being the integral of an odd function between limits equally spaced from the origin, vanishes. Hence

$$V = 4\pi a \cdot \tfrac{1}{2}\pi a^2 = 2\pi^2 a^3.$$

EXERCISES

In Exs. 1–32, solve by the method of cylindrical shells.

1. Find the volume generated by revolving about Oy the area in the first quadrant bounded by the curve $y = 4 - x^2$ and the axes. *Ans.* 8π.

2. Find the volume formed by revolving the area of Ex. 1 about the line $x = 2$.

Ans. $\dfrac{40\pi}{3}$.

3. Find the volume of a sphere.

4. Find the volume of a prolate spheroid. *Ans.* $\tfrac{4}{3}\pi ab^2$.

5. Find the volume of an oblate spheroid, using the equations $x = a \cos \varphi$, $y = b \sin \varphi$. *Ans.* $\tfrac{4}{3}\pi a^2 b$.

6. Find the volume of a circular cone.

7. Find the volume generated by revolving about the line $x = 2a$ the area bounded by that line, the x-axis, and the curve $a^2 y = x^3$. *Ans.* $\tfrac{16}{5}\pi a^3$.

8. Find the volume formed by revolving about the line $y = 2a$ the area bounded by that line, the y-axis, and the parabola $y^2 = 4ax$. *Ans.* $\tfrac{2}{3}\pi a^3$.

9. Ex. 5, page 301.   **10.** Ex. 6, page 301.   **11.** Ex. 9, page 302.

12. Ex. 12, page 302.   **13.** Ex. 25, page 302.   **14.** Ex. 39, page 303.

15. The area bounded by the parabola $x^2 - 2x + y = 3$, the y-axis, and the line $y = 4$ revolves about the line $y = 4$. Find the volume. *Ans.* $\tfrac{1}{5}\pi$.

16. The area bounded by the parabola $y^2 + x - 2y = 1$, the x-axis, and the line $x = 2$ revolves about Ox. Find the volume.

17. The area of Ex. 16 revolves about the line $x = 2$. Find the volume.

Ans. $\tfrac{1}{5}\pi$.

18. The area enclosed by the loop of the curve $y^2 = x(1 - x)^2$ is revolved about the y-axis. Find the volume generated. *Ans.* $\tfrac{16}{35}\pi$.

19. The area of Ex. 18 is revolved about the line $x = 1$. Find the volume formed.

Ans. $\tfrac{64}{105}\pi$.

20. The area in the first quadrant between the curve $y(1 + x) = x$ and its horizontal asymptote revolves about the asymptote. Find the volume. *Ans.* π.

21. Find the volume of a spherical segment of height h. *Ans.* $\tfrac{1}{3}\pi h^2(3a - h)$.

22. The area enclosed by the hypocycloid of four cusps, $x^{\frac{2}{3}} + y^{\frac{2}{3}} = a^{\frac{2}{3}}$, is revolved about Oy. Use the parametric equations $x = a \sin^3 \varphi$, $y = a \cos^3 \varphi$, in finding the volume formed.

Ans. $\dfrac{32\pi a^3}{105}$.

23. Find the volume generated by revolving about Oy the area under that arch of the curve $y = \sin x$ for which x varies from 0 to π.   *Ans.* $2\pi^2$.

24. Find the volume generated by revolving about Oy the left-hand half of the area of Ex. 23.   *Ans.* 2π.

25. Find the volume formed by revolving about Oy the area in the first quadrant bounded by $y = \cos x$ and the two axes.   *Ans.* $\pi(\pi - 2)$.

26. Find the volume formed by revolving about the line $x = 1$ the area bounded by $x = 1$, $y = e^{-x}$, and the axes.

$$Ans. \; \frac{2\pi}{e}.$$

27. Find the volume generated by revolving about the y-axis the area enclosed by the curve $a^2y^2 = x^2(a^2 - x^2)$.   *Ans.* $\frac{1}{4}\pi^2a^3$.

28. The area bounded by the curve $y = (x^2 - 4)^2$ and the x-axis revolves about the y-axis. Find the volume.   *Ans.* $\frac{64}{3}\pi$.

29. A round hole of radius a is bored through the center of a sphere of radius $2a$. Find the volume cut out.   *Ans.* $\frac{4}{3}\pi(8 - 3\sqrt{3})a^3$.

30. Find the volume of the torus formed by revolving the circle $x^2 + y^2 = a^2$ about the line $x = b$.   *Ans.* $2\pi^2a^2b$.

31. Solve Ex. 30, using the equations $x = a \sin \theta$, $y = a \cos \theta$.

32. Find the volume formed by revolving about Oy the area bounded by the curve $y = \dfrac{\sin x}{x}$ and the coordinate axes.   *Ans.* 4π.

In Exs. 33–53, use any legitimate method.

33. Find the volume generated by revolving the area under the curve $y = e^x$, from $x = 0$ to $x = 1$, about the line $x = 1$.   *Ans.* $2\pi(e - 2)$.

34. Find the volume generated by revolving about Oy the area in the second quadrant under the curve $y = e^x$.   *Ans.* 2π.

35. The area bounded by the parabola $y^2 = 4ax$ and its latus rectum revolves about the directrix. Find the volume generated.   *Ans.* $\frac{128}{15}\pi a^3$.

36. The area enclosed by $y^2 = x^4(1 - x^2)$ is revolved about the x-axis. Find the volume generated.   *Ans.* $\frac{4}{35}\pi$.

37. The area of Ex. 36 is revolved about Oy. Find the volume formed.

$$Ans. \; \frac{8\pi}{15}.$$

38. The area under the curve $y = \ln x$ from $x = 1$ to $x = e$ is revolved about the y-axis. Find the volume generated.   *Ans.* $\frac{1}{2}\pi(1 + e^2)$.

39. Find the volume formed by revolving about Ox the area in the first quadrant bounded by the curves $y = 3x - x^3$, $x = 0$, $y = 2$.   *Ans.* $\frac{72}{35}\pi$.

40. Find the volume formed by revolving about Ox the area between the curves $x^2 = 2ay$, $x^2 = 4ay - a^2$.   *Ans.* $\frac{2}{15}\pi a^3$.

41. Find the volume formed by revolving the area of Ex. 40 about Oy.

$$Ans. \; \frac{1}{8}\pi a^3.$$

42. Find the volume generated by revolving the first arch of the cycloid $y = a(\theta - \sin \theta)$, $y = a(1 - \cos \theta)$ about Oy. (Fig. 138, page 286.)   *Ans.* $6\pi^3a^3$.

43. Find the volume formed by revolving one arch of the cycloid (Ex. 42) about the tangent at the vertex.   *Ans.* π^2a^3.

44. Find the volume formed by revolving about Oy the area bounded by the curve $x^2y^2 = a^2(a^2 - x^2)$. *Ans.* $\pi^2 a^3$.

45. Find the volume obtained by revolving about Ox the area under the curve $x^3y = a^4$ to the right of the line $x = a$. *Ans.* $\frac{1}{5}\pi a^3$.

46. Find the volume generated by revolving about Oy the area bounded by the curve $ay^3 = (x^2 - a^2)^2$ and the x-axis. *Ans.* $\frac{3}{5}\pi a^3$.

47. Find the volume bounded by the cylinder $x^2 + y^2 = 2a^2$ and the hyperboloid $x^2 + y^2 - z^2 = a^2$. *Ans.* $\frac{4}{3}\pi a^3$.

48. Find the volume bounded by the surfaces $x^2 + y^2 = 4az$, $x^2 + y^2 = z^2$. *Ans.* $\frac{32}{3}\pi a^3$.

49. Find the volume bounded by the hyperboloid $x^2 + y^2 - z^2 = a^2$ and the cone $x^2 + y^2 = 2z^2$. *Ans.* $\frac{4}{3}\pi a^3$.

50. Find the volume enclosed by the surfaces $x^2 + y^2 - z^2 + 2a^2 = 0$, $x^2 + y^2 = az$. *Ans.* $\frac{2}{3}\pi a^3(5 - 2\sqrt{2})$.

51. Find the volume common to the sphere $x^2 + y^2 + z^2 = a^2$ and the cone $x^2 + y^2 = z^2$. *Ans.* $\frac{4}{3}\pi a^3(1 - \frac{1}{2}\sqrt{2})$.

52. Find the volume inside the cone $x^2 + y^2 = z^2$ and the paraboloid $x^2 + y^2 + az = 2a^2$. *Ans.* $\frac{5}{6}\pi a^3$.

53. Find the volume formed by revolving about Ox the area under the tractrix. See § 99, and particularly Ex. 21, page 186.

$$Ans. \ \frac{\pi a^3}{3}.$$

158. *Miscellaneous Solids*

The volume of any solid can be expressed as a definite integral, provided we know the *area of every plane section parallel to some fixed plane*. We divide the solid into thin slices by means of n planes parallel to the fixed plane, trim off the outer edge exactly as in § 155 (which is a special case of the present problem), and take as element the slab remaining: The volume of this slab, of course, is the thickness times the area of the face, which by hypothesis is known.

The only plane figures whose area we are supposed to know offhand are the rectangle, the triangle, the trapezoid, the circle, the circular sector ($\frac{1}{2}r^2\alpha$), and the ellipse (πab). Thus the only solids whose volumes we can find at this time are those that can be divided into parallel slices of one of these shapes. More complicated volumes are found by iterated integration (Chapter 28).

Example (a). A woodsman chops halfway through a tree of diameter $2a$, one face of the cut being horizontal, the other inclined at 45°. Find the volume of wood cut out.

Figure 156 shows one-half of the required solid. If we pass cutting planes parallel to the yz-plane, the element is a *triangular plate* of width y, altitude z, and thickness dx. Hence

$$V = 2 \int_0^a \tfrac{1}{2}yz \, dx.$$

But $z = y$, and $y^2 = a^2 - x^2$, so that

$$V = \int_0^a (a^2 - x^2)\, dx = \tfrac{2}{3}a^3.$$

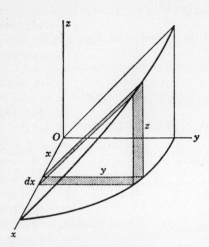

| Figure 156 | Figure 157 |

Example (*b*). Solve Example (*a*) by another method.

Planes parallel to the zx-plane cut the solid into *rectangular plates* of length x, height z, thickness dy (Fig. 157). Hence

$$V = 2 \int_0^a xz\, dy.$$

But $z = y$, $x^2 + y^2 = a^2$, $y\, dy = -x\, dx$, $x = a$ when $y = 0$, $x = 0$ when $y = a$, so that

$$V = 2 \int_0^a xy\, dy = -2 \int_a^0 x^2\, dx = \tfrac{2}{3}a^3.$$

EXERCISES

1. Find the volume in the first octant under the plane $z = y$ and inside the cylinder $y^2 = 4 - x$. Solve in two ways. *Ans.* 4.

2. Find the volume cut from the paraboloid $\dfrac{x^2}{a^2} + \dfrac{y^2}{b^2} = \dfrac{4z}{c}$ by the plane $z = c$.

Ans. $2\pi abc$.

3. Find the volume of an ellipsoid. *Ans.* $\tfrac{4}{3}\pi abc$.

4. Find the volume of an elliptic cone bounded by a right section.

Ans. $\tfrac{1}{3}\pi abh$.

5. Find the volume in the first octant inside the cylinder $\dfrac{x^2}{a^2} + \dfrac{y^2}{b^2} = 1$, under the plane $z = mx$. Solve in two ways. *Ans.* $\tfrac{1}{3}ma^2b$.

6. Find the volume of a tetrahedron with three mutually perpendicular faces.
Ans. $\frac{1}{6}abc$.

7. Find the volume in the first octant enclosed by the cylinder $y^2 = ax$ and the planes $x = a$, $z = x$. *Ans.* $\frac{2}{5}a^3$.

8. Find the volume in the first octant bounded by the cylinder $y^2 - x^2 = a^2$ and the planes $x = a$, $z = y$. *Ans.* $\frac{2}{3}a^3$.

9. Find the volume in the first octant bounded by the surfaces $x = 1$, $x^2 = y + 2z$. *Ans.* $\frac{1}{20}$.

10. Find the volume in the first octant inside the cylinder $y^2 + z^2 = a^2$ and outside the cylinder $y^2 = ax$. *Ans.* $\frac{1}{16}\pi a^3$.

11. Find the volume in the first octant bounded by the surfaces $x + y = a$, $z^2 = 4ay$. Solve in two ways. *Ans.* $\frac{8}{15}a^3$.

12. Find the volume in the first octant bounded by the surfaces $y + z = a$, $z^2 = ax$. *Ans.* $\frac{1}{12}a^3$.

13. Find the volume of a right pyramid with a square base of side $2a$. Solve in two ways. *Ans.* $\frac{4}{3}a^2h$.

14. Find the volume of a wedge cut from a circular cone by two planes through the axis. *Ans.* $\frac{1}{6}\alpha a^2h$.

15. Find the volume of a spherical wedge. *Ans.* $\frac{2}{3}\alpha a^3$.

16. By two methods, find the volume common to two equal cylinders of revolution whose axes intersect at right angles. *Ans.* $\frac{16}{3}a^3$.

17. Find the volume in the first octant bounded by the surfaces $az = xy$, $y^2 + ax = 4a^2$. Solve in two ways. *Ans.* $\frac{16}{3}a^3$.

18. Find the volume in the first octant under the surface $az = xy$, bounded by the cylinder $y^2 = ax$ and the plane $x = a$. *Ans.* $\frac{1}{6}a^3$.

19. A carpenter chisels a square hole of side 2 in. through a round post of radius 2 in., the axis of the hole intersecting that of the post at right angles. Find the volume of wood cut out. *Ans.* $4\sqrt{3} + \frac{8}{3}\pi = 15.3$ cu. in.

20. A hyperbolic paraboloid is generated by a line moving parallel to the zx-plane intersecting the lines $x = a$, $z = 0$ and $z = y$, $x = 0$. Find the volume enclosed by this surface, the coordinate planes, and the plane $y = b$. *Ans.* $\frac{1}{4}ab^2$.

21. A hyperbolic paraboloid is generated by a line moving parallel to the zx-plane and intersecting the lines $x = y = z$ and $x = a$, $z = 0$. Find the volume bounded by this surface, the xy-plane, and the plane $y = x$. *Ans.* $\frac{1}{12}a^3$.

22. A surface is generated by a line parallel to the xy-plane intersecting the parabolas $z^2 = ax$, $y = 0$, and $y^2 = a^2 - az$, $x = 0$. Find the volume in the first octant bounded by this surface and the planes $x = 0$, $y = 0$. *Ans.* $\frac{8}{105}a^3$.

23. A surface is generated by a line parallel to the zx-plane intersecting the parabola $y^2 = 4ax$, $z = 0$, and the line $z = b$, $x = 0$. Find the volume in the first octant bounded by this surface and the plane $y = a$. *Ans.* $\frac{1}{24}a^2b$.

24. Find the volume in the first octant bounded by the hyperbolic paraboloid generated by a straight line moving always parallel to the xy-plane and passing through the lines $y + z = a$ in the yz-plane and $x = b$ in the xz-plane. *Ans.* $\frac{1}{4}a^2b$.

25. In Ex. 24, derive the equation of the paraboloid; then find the volume by a second method. *Ans.* $xz - ax - by - bz + ab = 0$.

26. Find the volume in the first octant bounded by the surfaces $y + z = a$, $x^2 + ay = a^2$. Solve in two ways. *Ans.* $\frac{2}{5}a^3$.

27. Find the volume bounded by the cylinder $x^2 + y^2 = 2a^2$ and the planes $z = 0$, $x = 0$, $y = x$, $y = z$.   *Ans.* $\frac{2}{3}a^3$.

28. Find the volume bounded by the cylinder $x^2 = ay$ and the planes $z = 0$, $y = x$, $y = z$.   *Ans.* $\frac{1}{15}a^3$.

29. A circular conoid is generated by a straight line which moves always parallel to the xy-plane and passes through the line $y = h$ in the yz-plane and the circle $x^2 + z^2 = a^2$ in the xz-plane. Find the volume of the conoid.   *Ans.* $\frac{1}{2}\pi a^2 h$.

30. In Ex. 29, derive the equation of the conoid; then find the volume by a second method.   *Ans.* $h^2x^2 = (a^2 - z^2)(h - y)^2$.

31. Solve Ex. 29 if the line $y = h$ is replaced by the line $y + z = h(h > a)$.   *Ans.* $\frac{1}{2}\pi a^2 h$.

32. A cylinder is generated by a line moving always parallel to the line $y + z = a$, $x = 0$, and following the circle $x^2 + y^2 = a^2$, $z = 0$. Find the volume in the first octant inside the cylinder.   *Ans.* $\frac{1}{3}a^3$.

33. A cylinder is generated by a line moving always parallel to the line $x + z = a$, $y = 0$, and following the curve $y^2 + az = a^2$, $x = 0$. Find the volume in the first octant inside the cylinder.   *Ans.* $\frac{4}{15}a^3$.

34. Find the volume in the first octant bounded by the surfaces $yz = z - x$, $z = 1$. Solve in two ways.   *Ans.* $\frac{1}{4}$.

35. Find the volume in the first octant bounded by the surfaces $yz = z^2 - x$, $z = 1$.   *Ans.* $\frac{1}{8}$.

36. Find the volume in the first octant bounded by the surfaces $z = y - xy$, $x + y = 1$. Solve in two ways.   *Ans.* $\frac{1}{8}$.

37. The vertex of a cone is at $(a,0,0)$; the base is the curve $y^2 + z^2 = 2by$, $x = 0$. Find the volume of the cone.   *Ans.* $\frac{1}{3}\pi ab^2$.

159. *Length of a Curve*

In § 46, page 89, we defined the differential ds of arc length by

$$(1) \qquad ds = \sqrt{(dx)^2 + (dy)^2}.$$

Instead of (1) it is sometimes convenient to use the equivalent forms

$$(2) \qquad ds = \left[1 + \left(\frac{dy}{dx}\right)^2\right]^{\frac{1}{2}} dx = \left[1 + \left(\frac{dx}{dy}\right)^2\right]^{\frac{1}{2}} dy$$

or, if x and y are known in terms of a parameter t, the form

$$(3) \qquad ds = \left[\left(\frac{dx}{dt}\right)^2 + \left(\frac{dy}{dt}\right)^2\right]^{\frac{1}{2}} dt.$$

In agreement with (1) we now define the length s of a curve along an arc C by

$$(4) \qquad s = \int_C ds = \int_a^b \sqrt{1 + \left(\frac{dy}{dx}\right)^2} \, dx,$$

where a and b are the abscissas of the endpoints of C, and where $\dfrac{dy}{dx}$ must be replaced by its value in terms of x from the equation of the curve.

If it is more convenient to integrate with respect to y, we put

(5)
$$s = \int_c^d \sqrt{\left(\frac{dx}{dy}\right)^2 + 1}\; dy.$$

If x and y are given in terms of a parameter t,

(6)
$$s = \int_{t_1}^{t_2} \sqrt{\left(\frac{dx}{dt}\right)^2 + \left(\frac{dy}{dt}\right)^2}\; dt.$$

We assume, of course, that in any instance the integrand is a single-valued function of the variable of integration. If this condition is not satisfied, C must consist of several portions for each of which the condition holds, and each portion may be considered separately.

The equation of the curve may be known in polar, rather than in rectangular, coordinates. From $x = r \cos \theta$, $y = r \sin \theta$, it follows, by methods to be developed in § 189, that

$$dx = \cos \theta\, dr - r \sin \theta\, d\theta, \qquad dy = \sin \theta\, dr + r \cos \theta\, d\theta.$$

Then (1) yields

(7)
$$ds = \sqrt{(dr)^2 + r^2(d\theta)^2} = \left[\left(\frac{dr}{d\theta}\right)^2 + r^2\right]^{\frac{1}{2}} d\theta.$$

The student should verify (Ex. 1, below) that formula (4) yields the desired result for the distance between any two points (x_1, y_1), (x_2, y_2) along the straight line joining them. See also Ex. 2 below.

Example (a). Find the length of the curve $y = \ln \sin x$ from $x = \frac{1}{4}\pi$ to $x = \frac{1}{2}\pi$.

From $y = \ln \sin x$, we obtain $y' = \cot x$, so that the desired length is given by

$$\begin{aligned}
s &= \int_{\frac{1}{4}\pi}^{\frac{1}{2}\pi} \sqrt{1 + \cot^2 x}\; dx \\
&= \int_{\frac{1}{4}\pi}^{\frac{1}{2}\pi} \csc x\; dx = \Big[\ln\,(\csc x - \cot x)\Big]_{\frac{1}{4}\pi}^{\frac{1}{2}\pi} \\
&= \ln\,(1 - 0) - \ln\,(\sqrt{2} - 1) = -\ln\,(\sqrt{2} - 1) \\
&= -\ln \frac{2 - 1}{\sqrt{2} + 1} = \ln\,(1 + \sqrt{2}).
\end{aligned}$$

Example (b). Find the length of one arch of the cycloid $x = a(\theta - \sin \theta)$, $y = a(1 - \cos \theta)$, (Fig. 138, page 286).

Here θ is a parameter; we use formula (6) above.   From

$$dx = a(1 - \cos \theta)\, d\theta$$

and

$$dy = a \sin \theta\, d\theta,$$

we obtain

$$ds = \sqrt{a^2(1 - \cos\theta)^2 + a^2 \sin^2\theta}\; d\theta.$$

Because of symmetry, we can integrate from $x = 0$ to $x = \pi a$ (from $\theta = 0$ to $\theta = \pi$) and double the result. Hence,

$$s = 2\int_0^\pi a\sqrt{1 - 2\cos\theta + \cos^2\theta + \sin^2\theta}\; d\theta$$

$$= 2a\int_0^\pi \sqrt{2 - 2\cos\theta}\; d\theta.$$

Now $1 - \cos\theta = 2\sin^2\tfrac{1}{2}\theta$, so

$$s = 2a\int_0^\pi \sqrt{4\sin^2\tfrac{1}{2}\theta}\; d\theta = 4a\int_0^\pi \sin\tfrac{1}{2}\theta\; d\theta$$

$$= -8a\left[\cos\tfrac{1}{2}\theta\right]_0^\pi = 8a.$$

EXERCISES

1. Verify that equation (4) of this section yields the desired result for the distance between two points (x_1, y_1), (x_2, y_2) along the straight line joining those points.

2. Use the polar equation $r = a$ and equation (7) of this section to compute the length of arc of one quadrant of a circle.

In Exs. 3–23, find the length of the curve over the given interval.

3. One branch of the curve $9y^2 = 4x^3$ from $x = 0$ to $x = 3$.   *Ans.* $\frac{14}{3}$.

4. The curve $y = \ln x$ from $x = \sqrt{3}$ to $x = 2\sqrt{2}$.   *Ans.* $1 + \frac{1}{2}\ln\frac{3}{2}$.

5. The curve $y = \ln\cos x$ from $x = 0$ to $x = \frac{1}{4}\pi$. Use x as the variable of integration.   *Ans.* $\ln(1 + \sqrt{2})$.

6. Solve Ex. 5, using y as the variable of integration.

7. One branch of the curve $ay^2 = x^3$ from $x = 0$ to $x = 5a$.   *Ans.* $\frac{335}{27}a$.

8. Solve Ex. 7, using the parametric equations $x = at^2$, $y = at^3$.

9. The four-cusped hypocycloid $x^{\frac{2}{3}} + y^{\frac{2}{3}} = a^{\frac{2}{3}}$.   *Ans.* $6a$.

10. Solve Ex. 9, using the parametric equations $x = a\sin^3 t$, $y = a\cos^3 t$.

11. One branch of the parabola $y^2 = 4ax$ from the vertex to the end of the latus rectum, integrating with respect to x.   *Ans.* $2.295a$.

12. Solve Ex. 11, using y as the variable of integration.

13. Solve Ex. 11, using the equations $x = a\tan^2\psi$, $y = 2a\tan\psi$.

14. The curve $y = e^x$ from $x = 0$ to $x = 1$, using x as the variable of integration.

15. Solve Ex. 14 using y as the variable of integration.

16. The catenary $y = a\cosh\dfrac{x}{a}$ from $x = 0$ to $x = x_1$.   *Ans.* $a\sinh\dfrac{x_1}{a}$.

17. The curve $y = \frac{4}{5}x^{\frac{5}{4}}$, from $x = 0$ to $x = 9$. Evaluate the integral in two ways.   *Ans.* $\frac{232}{15}$.

18. One branch of the curve $9y^2 = 4(1 + x^2)^3$, from $x = 0$ to $x = 2$.   *Ans.* $\frac{22}{3}$.

19. The curve $y = \text{Arcsin } e^{-x}$, from $x = 0$ to $x = \ln \frac{5}{4}$.   *Ans.* $\ln 2$.

20. One branch of the curve $25y^2 = (x + 2)^2(2x - 1)^3$, from $x = \frac{1}{2}$ to $x = 3$.

Ans. $\frac{58}{5}$.

21. The curve $y = \frac{1}{2}x(x^2 - 1)^{\frac{1}{2}} - \frac{1}{2}\ln(x + \sqrt{x^2 - 1})$, from $x = 1$ to $x = \frac{5}{4}$.

Ans. $\frac{9}{32}$.

22. One branch of the curve $3y^2 = (2x + 3)^3$, from $x = -1$ to $x = 1$.   *Ans.* $\frac{56}{9}$.

23. The curve $6xy = x^4 + 3$ from the minimum point to $x = 2$.   *Ans.* $\frac{17}{12}$.

24. Find the perimeter of the loop of the curve $9ay^2 = x(x - 3a)^2$.

Ans. $4\sqrt{3}\,a$.

25. Find the perimeter of the loop of the curve $9y^2 = x^2(2x + 3)$.   *Ans.* $2\sqrt{3}$.

26. Find the length of the tractrix (§ 99) from the starting point to $y = h$. (See Ex. 21, page 186.)

Ans. $a \ln \dfrac{a}{h}$.

27. A point moves in a plane curve according to the law $x = 1 - \cos 2t$, $y = 2 \cos t$. Find the length of the path.   *Ans.* $2\sqrt{5} + \ln(2 + \sqrt{5}) = 5.92$ ft.

28. A point moves according to the law $x = e^{-3t}$, $y = e^{-2t}$. Find the entire distance traveled ($t > 0$).   *Ans.* $\frac{1}{27}(13^{\frac{3}{2}} - 8) = 1.44$ ft.

29. A point moves according to the law $x = e^{-t}$, $y = e^{-t} - e^{-2t}$. Find the length of its path ($t > 0$).   *Ans.* 1.15 ft.

30. Find the length of the cycloid $x = a(\theta - \sin \theta)$, $y = a(1 - \cos \theta)$ from $(0, 0)$ to any point (x_1, y_1) on the curve ($0 \leqq \theta \leqq \pi$). Check the answer against Example (b).   *Ans.* $4a - \sqrt{4a^2 - 2ay_1}$.

In Exs. 31–35, the equation of the curve is given in polar coordinates. Find the length of the arc described.

31. The total length of the cardioid $r = a(1 + \cos \theta)$.   *Ans.* $8a$.

32. The total length of the cardioid $r = a(1 - \sin \theta)$.

33. The total length of the curve $r = a \cos^2 \theta$.

Ans. $\dfrac{2a}{3}[6 + \sqrt{3}\ln(2 + \sqrt{3})]$.

34. The logarithmic spiral $r = ae^{k\theta}$ from $\theta = 0$ to $\theta = \pi$.

Ans. $k^{-1}a(1 + k^2)^{\frac{1}{2}}(e^{k\pi} - 1)$.

35. The spiral of Archimedes $r = a\theta$ from $\theta = 0$ to $\theta = \pi$.

Ans. $\frac{1}{2}a[\pi(1 + \pi^2)^{\frac{1}{2}} + \ln\{\pi + (1 + \pi^2)^{\frac{1}{2}}\}]$.

36. Show that for the curve $r = \sin^{2k}\theta$ for k any positive integer, the integral encountered in applying formula (7) of this section is an elementary integral. That is, show that the integration can be performed by the techniques studied earlier in this course.

37. Find the length of the curve $y = (e^{2x} - 1)^{\frac{1}{2}} + \text{Arcsin } e^{-x}$, from $x = 0$ to $x = 1$.   *Ans.* $e - 1$.

38. Find the length of the curve

$$y = (1 - x^2)^{\frac{1}{2}} + \ln \frac{x}{1 + (1 - x^2)^{\frac{1}{2}}},$$

from $x = \frac{3}{5}$ to $x = \frac{4}{5}$.   *Ans.* $\ln \frac{4}{3}$.

160. *Surfaces of Revolution*

The problem of this section is to find the area of the surface generated by rotating a plane curve C about a line in its plane—say, for definiteness, about the x-axis. For variety, let us revert to fundamentals to obtain the desired formula. In Fig. 158 we cut the pertinent section along the axis of revolution into equal segments Δx which project onto elements Δs_i along the curve C. Next inscribe in C a broken line of n segments $\Delta s_i'$. In the rotation, each segment $\Delta s_i'$ generates the frustrum of a circular cone, the radii of whose bases are y_i, $y_i + \Delta y_i$. By elementary geometry, the surface area of this conical frustrum is *the circumference of the middle section multiplied by the slant height*, or $2\pi(y_i + \frac{1}{2}\Delta y_i)\,\Delta s_i'$. It can be shown that

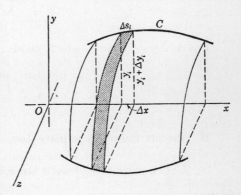

Figure 158

$$\lim_{n \to \infty} \sum_{i=1}^{n} 2\pi(\tfrac{1}{2}\Delta y_i)\,\Delta s_i' = 0.$$

Therefore

$$A = \lim_{n \to \infty} \sum_{i=1}^{n} 2\pi y_i\,\Delta s_i' = 2\pi \int_C y\,ds.$$

Example. Find the surface area generated by revolving about the y-axis the hyperbola

$$x^2 - y^2 = a^2$$

from $y = 0$ to $y = 2a$.

At once

$$A = 2\pi \int_{y=0}^{y=2a} x\,ds.$$

From the equation $x^2 - y^2 = a^2$, we obtain $x\,dx - y\,dy = 0$, so that

$$ds = \sqrt{1 + \left(\frac{dx}{dy}\right)^2}\,dy$$

$$= \sqrt{1 + \frac{y^2}{x^2}}\,dy.$$

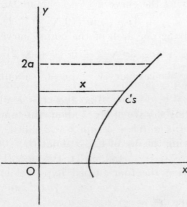

Figure 159

Thus we have

$$A = 2\pi \int_0^{2a} x \sqrt{1 + \frac{y^2}{x^2}}\, dy$$

$$= 2\pi \int_0^{2a} \sqrt{x^2 + y^2}\, dy$$

$$= 2\pi \int_0^{2a} \sqrt{a^2 + 2y^2}\, dy.$$

Put $\sqrt{2}\, y = a \tan \theta$, which yields

$$A = \frac{2\pi a^2}{\sqrt{2}} \int_0^\beta \sec^3 \theta\, d\theta,$$

where $\beta = \operatorname{Arctan} 2\sqrt{2}$.

We already know (page 250) that

$$\int \sec^3 \theta\, d\theta = \tfrac{1}{2}\left[\sec \theta \tan \theta + \ln (\sec \theta + \tan \theta)\right] + C.$$

Hence

$$A = \frac{\pi a^2}{\sqrt{2}}\left[\sec \theta \tan \theta + \ln (\sec \theta + \tan \theta)\right]_0^\beta.$$

But $\tan \beta = 2\sqrt{2}$, $\sec \beta = 3$, $\tan 0 = 0$, and $\sec 0 = 1$. Therefore

$$A = \frac{\pi a^2}{\sqrt{2}}[6\sqrt{2} + \ln (3 + 2\sqrt{2})].$$

EXERCISES

1. Find the surface area of a sphere of radius a.   *Ans.* $4\pi a^2$.

2. Solve Ex. 1, using the equations $x = a \cos \theta$, $y = a \sin \theta$.

3. Find the surface area generated by revolving the curve $a^2 y = x^3$ about Ox, from $x = 0$ to $x = a$.   *Ans.* $\frac{1}{27}\pi a^2(10\sqrt{10} - 1)$.

4. Find the surface area generated by revolving one arch of the cosine curve about Ox.   *Ans.* $2\pi[\sqrt{2} + \ln (1 + \sqrt{2})]$.

5. Find the surface area formed by revolving the catenary $y = a \cosh \dfrac{x}{a}$ about Oy, from $x = 0$ to $x = a$.   *Ans.* $2\pi a^2(1 - e^{-1})$.

6. Find the surface area generated by revolving the arc of Ex. 5 about the tangent at the vertex.   *Ans.* $\pi a^2(1 + \frac{1}{2}\sinh 2 - 2 \sinh 1)$.

7. Find the surface area generated by revolving the arc of Ex. 5 about Ox.   *Ans.* $\pi a^2(1 + \frac{1}{2}\sinh 2)$.

8. Find the surface area formed by revolving the four-cusped hypocycloid $x^{\frac{2}{3}} + y^{\frac{2}{3}} = a^{\frac{2}{3}}$ about Ox.   *Ans.* $\frac{12}{5}\pi a^2$.

9. Solve Ex. 8, using the parametric equations $x = a \sin^3 t$, $y = a \cos^3 t$.

10. Find the surface area of a torus.   *Ans.* $4\pi^2 ab$.

11. Find the surface area generated by revolving an arch of the cycloid $x = a(\theta - \sin \theta)$, $y = a(1 - \cos \theta)$ about its base.   *Ans.* $\frac{64}{3}\pi a^2$.

12. Find the surface area of a zone cut from a sphere by two parallel planes at a distance h apart.   *Ans.* $2\pi ah$.

13. Find the surface area cut from a sphere by a circular cone of half-angle α with its vertex at the center of the sphere. (Use $x = a \cos \theta$, $y = a \sin \theta$.)

Ans. $2\pi a^2(1 - \cos \alpha)$.

14. Find the surface area generated by revolving about Oy that part of the curve $y = \ln x$ lying in the fourth quadrant, using x as the variable of integration.

Ans. $\pi[\sqrt{2} + \ln (1 + \sqrt{2})]$.

15. Solve Ex. 14, using y as the variable of integration.

16. Find the surface area generated by revolving about Ox the arc of the curve $6xy = x^4 + 3$, from the minimum point to $x = 2$.   *Ans.* $\frac{47}{16}\pi$.

17. In Ex. 16, revolve the arc about Oy.   *Ans.* $(\frac{15}{4} + \ln 2)\pi$.

18. Find the surface area generated by revolving about Ox the curve $8a^2y^2 = x^2(a^2 - x^2)$.   *Ans.* $\frac{1}{2}\pi a^2$.

19. Find the area cut off from the paraboloid $x^2 + y^2 = 4az$ by the plane $z = a$, using z as the variable of integration.   *Ans.* $\frac{8}{3}\pi a^2(2\sqrt{2} - 1)$.

20. Solve Ex. 19, using x or y as the variable.

21. Solve Ex. 19, using the equations $x = 2a \cot \psi$, $z = a \cot^2 \psi$.

22. Find the surface area generated by revolving about the y-axis that arc of the curve $a^2y = x^3$ from $x = 0$ to $x = a$.

Ans. $\dfrac{\pi a^2}{12} [3 \sqrt{10} + \ln (3 + \sqrt{10})]$.

CENTROIDS

161. *Density*

A mass is said to be *homogeneous* if the masses contained in any two equal volumes are equal. In all other cases the mass is *heterogeneous*. In the present chapter we confine our attention to homogeneous masses.

The *density* of a homogeneous mass is the ratio of the mass M to the volume V that it occupies. That is, the density is the mass per unit volume.

A *mass point* may be imagined as the limiting form approached by a body whose dimensions approach zero, while the density increases in such a way that the mass remains finite. Similarly we may think of masses of one dimension and of two dimensions—i.e., of material curves and surfaces. Such masses are represented approximately, for example, by slender wires and thin sheets of metal. In these cases we define the density as "linear density," or mass per unit length, and "surface density," or mass per unit area.

162. *First Moment of Mass*

The product of a mass m, concentrated at a point P, by the distance l of P from a given point, line, or plane, is called the *first moment* of m with respect to the point, line, or plane (also called *simple moment*, or *mass moment*). Denoting this moment by G, we have

$$G = ml.$$

Second moments, those involving the square of the distance from P to a point, line, or plane, will be considered in Chapter 25.

If a system of points $P_1, P_2, \cdots, P_n$, having masses $m_1, m_2, \cdots, m_n$, respectively, be referred to rectangular coordinate axes, the first moments of the system with respect to the three coordinate planes are

$$(1) \qquad G_{yz} = \sum_{i=1}^{n} m_i x_i, \qquad G_{zx} = \sum_{i=1}^{n} m_i y_i, \qquad G_{xy} = \sum_{i=1}^{n} m_i z_i.$$

If the particles all lie in one of the coordinate planes, the moments with respect to coordinate planes reduce to moments with respect to coordinate axes.

318

The idea of mass moment may be extended to the case of a continuous mass by thinking of the body as composed of an indefinitely large number of particles. (A definition will be laid down in § 211.) The actual computation of such a moment is usually effected by means of definite integrals; we return to this question presently.

163. *Centroid*

Given any mass M, let G_{yz}, G_{zx}, G_{xy} denote the first moments of the mass with respect to the coordinate planes. The point C, whose coordinates $\bar{x}$, $\bar{y}$, $\bar{z}$ are given by the formulas

(1) $$M\bar{x} = G_{yz}, \qquad M\bar{y} = G_{zx}, \qquad M\bar{z} = G_{xy},$$

has the property that the moment of the mass with respect to each coordinate plane is the same as if the whole mass were concentrated at that point. For, the moments for a particle of mass M at the point C are $M\bar{x}$, $M\bar{y}$, $M\bar{z}$, and by (1), these are equal to the moments for the original distribution.

It can be shown that this property holds for first moments with respect to any other plane. For a system of mass particles the proof is as follows: Let

(2) $$x \cos \alpha + y \cos \beta + z \cos \gamma = p$$

be the equation of any plane in the normal form; let $\bar{p}$, p_1, $\cdots$, p_n be the distances of the points C, P_1, $\cdots$, P_n from this plane. Then

$$p_1 = x_1 \cos \alpha + y_1 \cos \beta + z_1 \cos \gamma - p,$$

$$\cdot \qquad \qquad \cdot$$
$$\cdot \qquad \qquad \cdot$$
$$\cdot \qquad \qquad \cdot$$

$$p_n = x_n \cos \alpha + y_n \cos \beta + z_n \cos \gamma - p,$$

so that by simple addition

$$\sum_{i=1}^{n} m_i p_i = \left(\sum_{i=1}^{n} m_i x_i \right) \cos \alpha + \left(\sum_{i=1}^{n} m_i y_i \right) \cos \beta + \left(\sum_{i=1}^{n} m_i z_i \right) \cos \gamma - \left(\sum_{i=1}^{n} m_i \right) p$$
$$= M\bar{x} \cos \alpha + M\bar{y} \cos \beta + M\bar{z} \cos \gamma - Mp$$
$$= M(\bar{x} \cos \alpha + \bar{y} \cos \beta + \bar{z} \cos \gamma - p) = M\bar{p}.$$

The point C is called the *centroid* (also called *center of mass*, or *center of gravity*). Hence:

The centroid of a mass is a point such that the first moment of the mass with respect to any plane is the same as if the whole mass were concentrated at that point.

The first moment of a mass with respect to any plane through the centroid is zero.

In the determination of centroids, the following considerations are often useful (the first two apply only to homogeneous masses):

(a) *If the body has a geometrical center, that point is the centroid.*

(b) *Any plane or line of symmetry must contain the centroid.*

(c) *If the body consists of several portions for each of which the centroid can be found, each portion may be imagined concentrated at its centroid for the sole purpose of computing first moments.*

In many applications, we are concerned with centroids of purely geometric figures (volumes, areas, lines), *no idea of mass being involved.* However, it is unnecessary to write out a separate theory for such cases; the above discussion applies to plane areas, for instance, if we merely replace the word "mass" throughout by "area." To see this, note that for a homogeneous body of given size and shape, both the mass and its moment with respect to any plane are proportional to the density δ. Hence, in the formulas for $\bar{x}$, $\bar{y}$, $\bar{z}$, the factor δ cancels out from both members, leaving the coordinates of the centroid independent of the density. We may therefore take $\delta = 1$, so that the "mass" is numerically equal to the area.

164. *Centroid of a System of Particles*

Combining (1), § 162, with (1), § 163, we see that the coordinates of the centroid of a *system of particles* are given by the formulas

$$M\bar{x} = \sum_{i=1}^{n} m_i x_i, \qquad M\bar{y} = \sum_{i=1}^{n} m_i y_i, \qquad M\bar{z} = \sum_{i=1}^{n} m_i z_i.$$

By use of (c), § 163, problems involving distributed masses may frequently be reduced to consideration of a set of particles, as in the following examples.

Example (a). Find the centroid of a metal plate having the shape shown in Fig. 160 (or, what amounts to the same thing, the centroid of the area itself).

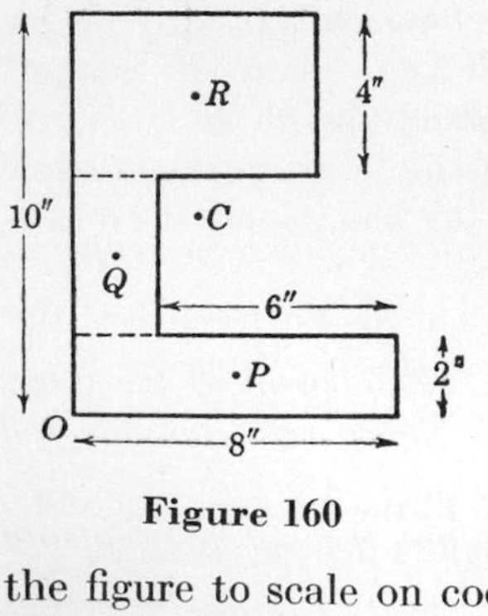

Dividing the area into rectangles by the dotted lines, we have 16 units at P: $(4, 1)$, 8 units at Q: $(1, 4)$, and 24 units at R: $(3, 8)$. Hence

$$M\bar{x} = 16 \cdot 4 + 8 \cdot 1 + 24 \cdot 3 = 144,$$
$$\bar{x} = \tfrac{144}{48} = 3,$$
$$M\bar{y} = 16 \cdot 1 + 8 \cdot 4 + 24 \cdot 8 = 240,$$
$$\bar{y} = \tfrac{240}{48} = 5.$$

Figure 160

In problems of this type, mistakes are easy to make. The danger is greatly reduced if we draw the figure to scale on coordinate paper. In most cases, the centroid can be fairly accurately located by estimate. A very valuable rough check is obtained if in each problem we *compare our answer with the estimate*; if a mistake of any great magnitude has been made, it will certainly be evident.

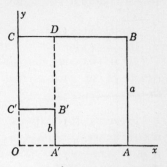

Figure 161

It is frequently convenient to adopt the fiction of *negative mass*. That this is allowable is clear; for, our theory nowhere requires that M be positive.

Example (b). Find the centroid of a square plate with a square cut out of one corner.

Place the axes as shown. We might consider the figure as composed of two rectangles $C'B'DC$, $A'ABD$; but the algebra is much simpler if we consider it as a square plate $OABC$, together with a plate $OA'B'C'$ of numerically equal but negative density:

$$M\bar{x} = M\bar{y} = a^2 \cdot \tfrac{1}{2}a - b^2 \cdot \tfrac{1}{2}b,$$

$$\bar{x} = \bar{y} = \frac{a^3 - b^3}{2(a^2 - b^2)} = \frac{a^2 + ab + b^2}{2(a + b)}.$$

EXERCISES

In Exs. 1–6, find the centroid of the given system.

1. Equal masses at $(2, 0)$, $(1, 1)$, $(5, 2)$, $(-3, -5)$.   *Ans.* $(\tfrac{5}{4}, -\tfrac{1}{2})$.

2. Equal masses at $(0, 0)$, $(3, -8)$, $(2, 2)$, $(-3, 6)$.   *Ans.* $(\tfrac{1}{2}, 0)$.

3. Masses of 1, 2, 3, 4 units at $(4, 2)$, $(0, 0)$, $(3, 4)$, $(-2, 5)$, respectively.
     Ans. $(\tfrac{1}{2}, \tfrac{17}{5})$.

4. Masses of 2, 2, 4, 6 units at $(3, 1)$, $(4, 1)$, $(2, -5)$, $(-1, -4)$, respectively.
     Ans. $(\tfrac{8}{7}, -\tfrac{20}{7})$.

5. Masses of 1, 3, 4 units at $(0, -3, -1)$, $(4, 5, 3)$, $(1, -3, -4)$, respectively.
     Ans. $(2, 0, -1)$.

6. Masses of 2, 3, 4 units at $(4, \tfrac{1}{2}, 1)$, $(3, 4, 0)$, $(-2, -1, 4)$, respectively.
     Ans. $(1, 1, 2)$.

7. Two posts of equal radius, 6 ft. and 4 ft. tall, stand upright 5 ft. apart. Find the centroid.   *Ans.* 2 ft. from taller post, 2.6 ft. above the ground.

8. Two posts of equal radius, 7 ft. and 3 ft. tall, stand upright 20 ft. apart. Find the centroid.   *Ans.* 6 ft. from taller post, 2.9 ft. above the ground.

9. Show that the centroid of two particles divides the line joining them into segments inversely proportional to the masses.

10. Show that the centroid of three equal particles lies at the intersection of the medians of the triangle having the three points as vertices. (Deduce from Ex. 9.)

11. A slender rod 40 in. long is bent so as to form a right angle. If the segments are 8 in. and 32 in. long, find the centroid.
     Ans. Coordinates in inches relative to the corner: $(12.8, 0.8)$.

12. Three rods, of lengths 10, 10, 16 ft., form a triangle. Find the centroid.
     Ans. On the altitude to the longest side, $\tfrac{5}{3}$ ft. from that side.

13. Weights of 2, 3, 7, and 8 lb. rest on the four corners of a table 5 ft. square. Find the centroid of the four weights.

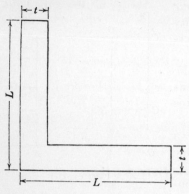

14. Find the centroid of a cross-section of an angle iron (Fig. 162), the outside flange width L being 3 in. and the thickness $\frac{1}{2}$ in.

15. Solve Ex. 14, if the flange width remains 3 in., and the thickness is increased to 1 in.

16. For the angle iron of Fig. 162, for what proportions does the centroid lie at the inner corner? *Ans.* $L = 2.62t$.

17. Find the centroid of a nonsymmetrical angle iron, like that of Fig. 162, except that one flange is 3 in. wide and $\frac{1}{2}$ in. thick, the other 4 in. wide and $\frac{3}{4}$ in. thick.

Figure 162

18. The legs of a table are 2 ft. 6 in. long; the legs weigh 5 lb. each, the top 10 lb. Find the centroid. *Ans.* 20 in. above the floor.

19. If in Ex. 18, the top of the table is taken as 1 in. thick, how much does the centroid rise? *Ans.* $\frac{1}{8}$ in.

20. From a square of side $2a$ a circle of radius $b(b < a)$ is stamped out. If the circle is tangent to two sides of the square, find the centroid (tangents as axes).

$$Ans. \ \bar{x} = \bar{y} = \frac{4a^3 - \pi b^3}{4a^2 - \pi b^2}.$$

21. Check the answer to Example (*a*) by solving in another way (different subdivision).

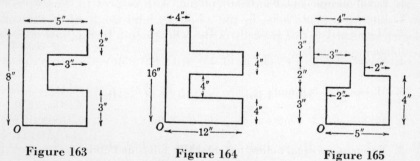

Figure 163   **Figure 164**   **Figure 165**

22. Find the centroid of the area in Fig. 163. Check by solving in two ways.

23. Find in two ways the centroid of the area in Fig. 164.

24. In Fig. 165, find the centroid. *Ans.* $(\frac{125}{62}, \frac{231}{62})$.

25. The base of a box is 4 ft. by 3 ft., the depth is 2 ft. If there is no top, find the centroid. *Ans.* 0.7 ft. from the base.

26. Solve Ex. 25 if the bottom is twice as heavy, per unit area, as the sides.
Ans. 0.54 ft. from the base.

27. A sphere of radius 3 in. rests on a cylinder of radius 4 in. and height 8 in. Find the height of the centroid. *Ans.* 5.54 in.

28. Find the centroid of a cylindrical basin of radius 4 in. and depth 3 in.
Ans. $\frac{9}{10}$ in. above the base.

29. Solve Ex. 28 if the bottom is twice as heavy, per unit area, as the sides.

Ans. $\frac{9}{14}$ in. above the base.

30. A circular disk of radius b, density k, is inset in a disk of radius a, density 1. If the two circles are tangent, find the centroid.

$$Ans. \text{ From point of tangency, } \bar{x} = \frac{a^3 + (k-1)b^3}{a^2 + (k-1)b^2}.$$

31. Solve Ex. 30 if the circumference of the smaller passes through the center of the larger $(2b < a)$.

$$Ans. \text{ From center, } \bar{x} = \frac{(k-1)b^3}{a^2 + (k-1)b^2}.$$

165. *Determination of Centroids by Integration*

To find the centroid of a continuous mass, we must as a rule resort to integration. In the most general case multiple integrals (Chapters 28–29) must be used, but in many cases of practical importance the result may be obtained by methods analogous to those of Chapter 23.

In the following discussion we restrict ourselves to one-, two-, or three-dimensional bodies of the forms considered in Chapter 23. Nevertheless the formulas obtained are applicable, with proper interpretation, to *all* masses. Let us choose, as in that chapter, a suitable geometrical element (of volume, area, or length), and denote the mass contained in this element by Δm_i. Let x_i, y_i, z_i be the *coordinates of the centroid of* Δm_i. Then the product $x_i \Delta m_i$ is the simple mass moment of Δm_i with respect to the yz-plane (or the y-axis, for a plane mass in the xy-plane), and the limit of the sum of all such moments is the moment of the whole mass. In this way we obtain the following formulas:

$$(1) \qquad M\bar{x} = \operatorname*{Lim}_{n \to \infty} \sum_{i=1}^{n} x_i \, \Delta m_i = \int x_c \, dm,$$

$$(2) \qquad M\bar{y} = \operatorname*{Lim}_{n \to \infty} \sum_{i=1}^{n} y_i \, \Delta m_i = \int y_c \, dm,$$

$$(3) \qquad M\bar{z} = \operatorname*{Lim}_{n \to \infty} \sum_{i=1}^{n} z_i \, \Delta m_i = \int z_c \, dm,$$

where x_c, y_c, z_c are the *coordinates of the centroid of the element.*

The subscript is inserted to make sure that we never forget the meaning of the multipliers x_c, y_c, z_c. Of course in any problem these variables, as well as the mass element, must be expressed in terms of some one variable.

As usual, we have omitted writing, in equations (1)–(3), those terms which will drop out in the limit as $n \to \infty$. For instance, it often happens that the x-coordinate is, exactly, $x_i + \frac{1}{2}\Delta x$, so that the first limit above is

$$M\bar{x} = \lim_{n \to \infty} \sum_{i=1}^{n} (x_i + \tfrac{1}{2}\Delta x) \, \Delta m_i.$$

But

$$\lim_{n \to \infty} \sum_{i=1}^{n} \Delta m_i = \int dm = M$$

and $\Delta x \to 0$ as $n \to \infty$, so that

$$\lim_{n \to \infty} \sum_{i=1}^{n} \tfrac{1}{2}\Delta x \, \Delta m_i = 0.$$

166. *Centroid of a Plane Area: Rectangular Coordinates*

In any system of coordinates, formulas (1) and (2) above become, for a plane area,

(1) $$A\bar{x} = \int x_c \, dA, \qquad A\bar{y} = \int y_c \, dA.$$

In rectangular coordinates, the area element dA is, of course, the usual rectangular element.

Example. Find the centroid of the area in the first quadrant bounded by the parabola $y^2 = 4ax$ and its latus rectum.

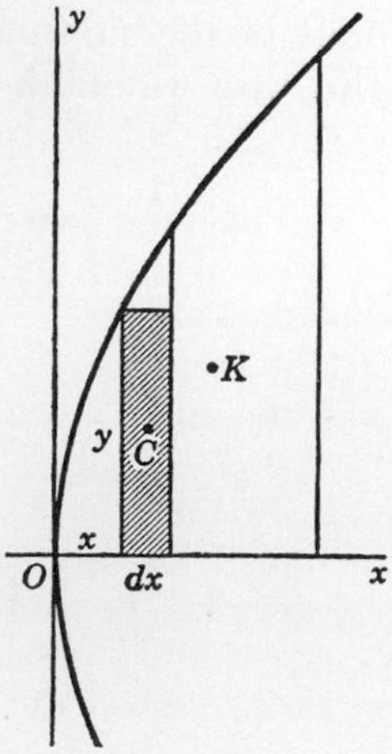

Figure 166

With the vertical element, the area is

$$A = \int_0^a y \, dx = 2\sqrt{a} \int_0^a \sqrt{x} \, dx = \tfrac{4}{3}a^2.$$

The centroid C of the element is $(x, \frac{1}{2}y)$: by (1),

$$A\bar{x} = \int_0^a xy \, dx = 2\sqrt{a} \int_0^a x^{\frac{3}{2}} \, dx = \tfrac{4}{5}a^3,$$

$$A\bar{y} = \int_0^a \tfrac{1}{2}y \cdot y \, dx = 2a \int_0^a x \, dx = a^3.$$

Thus the coordinates of the centroid K are

$$\bar{x} = \tfrac{3}{5}a, \qquad \bar{y} = \tfrac{3}{4}a,$$

which checks very well by estimate.*

Anyone who thoroughly understands this simple example should have little difficulty, either here or later, with the subject of centroids. One has not fully

* The student is strongly advised not to write out formulas for $\bar{x}$, $\bar{y}$, as quotients of integrals. Aside from clumsiness of form, the continual turning back and forth from one integral to the other wastes time and increases the likelihood of mistake. The best technique is to take up in turn the three tasks—of finding A, $A\bar{x}$, $A\bar{y}$—and complete each before the next is started.

mastered it, however, until he sees clearly that this example is exactly the same, in kind, as Example (*a*), § 164. There, we replaced three rectangles by equivalent particles at the respective centroids and found the total moment by simple arithmetic; here, we replace *n* rectangles by particles in exactly the same way and find the limit of the sum of elementary moments by integration.

We shall have occasion to use the following result.

THEOREM 26. *The centroid of a triangular area is at the intersection of the medians.*

The proof of this theorem is a very easy problem in integration (Ex. 8 below). Also, a special device may be noted. Divide the triangle into strips parallel to the base. The centroid of each strip is in the median, so that the same must be true for the centroid of the whole. And by symmetry of argument, if the centroid lies in one median it must lie in all three.

Figure 167

EXERCISES

In Exs. 1–34, find the centroid of the area. (Where *A* is given, it has been found in a previous exercise.) In each case, draw a figure and estimate the coordinates of the centroid.

1. The semicircular area inside $x^2 + y^2 = a^2$ with $y \geqq 0$.   *Ans.* $\left(0, \dfrac{4a}{3\pi}\right)$.

2. The elliptic quadrant inside $\dfrac{x^2}{a^2} + \dfrac{y^2}{b^2} = 1$ for $x \geqq 0$, $y \geqq 0$.   *Ans.* $\left(\dfrac{4a}{3\pi}, \dfrac{4b}{3\pi}\right)$.

3. Ex. 2, using the equations $x = a \cos \varphi$, $y = b \sin \varphi$.

4. The area in the first quadrant under the curve $y = 4 - x^2$. Find each coordinate in two ways.   *Ans.* $(\frac{3}{4}, \frac{8}{5})$.

5. The area bounded by the curve $y = 2(1 + x^3)$ and the coordinate axes.
     Ans. $(-\frac{2}{5}, \frac{6}{7})$.

6. The area bounded by the curve $y^2 = 4ax$, the x-axis, and the line $x = x_1$. ($A = \frac{2}{3}x_1y_1$.)   *Ans.* $(\frac{3}{5}x_1, \frac{3}{8}y_1)$.

7. The area bounded by the curve $x^2 = 4ay$, the x-axis, and the line $x = x_1$. Find each coordinate in two ways.   *Ans.* $(\frac{3}{4}x_1, \frac{3}{10}y_1)$.

8. A triangle. (Solve for a right triangle by integration; deduce the general answer.)

9. The area in the first quadrant under that arch of $y = \sin \frac{1}{4}x$ nearest the y-axis.   *Ans.* $(2\pi, \frac{1}{8}\pi)$.

10. The area in the first quadrant bounded by the curve $y = e^{-x}$, the axes, and the ordinate $x = \ln 5$.   *Ans.* $(1 - \frac{1}{4}\ln 5, \frac{3}{10})$.

11. The whole area in the first quadrant between the curve $y = e^{-x}$ and the axes.
     Ans. $(1, \frac{1}{4})$.

12. The area bounded by the curve $2y^2 + 2y - x - 2 = 0$ and the line $x = 2y$. ($A = \frac{8}{3}$.)   *Ans.* $(-\frac{4}{5}, 0)$.

13. The area bounded by the curve $y = \ln x$, the x-axis, and the line $x = e$. $(A = 1.)$

$$Ans. \left(\frac{e^2 + 1}{4}, \frac{e - 2}{2}\right).$$

14. The area bounded by $y^2(2 - x)^3 = 1$, the y-axis, and the line $x = -2$. $(A = 2\sqrt{2} - 2.)$ 　　　　　　　　　　$Ans.$ $(2 - 2\sqrt{2}, 0).$

15. One arch of the cycloid $x = a(\theta - \sin \theta)$, $y = a(1 - \cos \theta)$. $(A = 3\pi a^2.)$

$$Ans. (\pi a, \tfrac{5}{6}a).$$

16. The area between the curves $2y = x^2$, $y = x^3$. 　　　$Ans.$ $(\tfrac{3}{10}, \tfrac{3}{70}).$

17. The area in the first quadrant under the curve $y = \dfrac{a^3}{x^2 + a^2}.$ $(A = \tfrac{1}{2}\pi a^2.)$

$$Ans. \text{ Nonexistent.}$$

18. The area in the first quadrant under the curve $y = \dfrac{x}{(1 + x^2)^2}.$ $(A = \tfrac{1}{2}.)$

19. The area bounded by the parabola $y^2 = 4ax$, its axis prolonged, and the tangent at the upper end of the latus rectum.

$$Ans. \left(-\frac{a}{5}, \frac{a}{2}\right).$$

20. The area bounded by the parabola $x^2 - 4x + y = 5$ and the lines $x = 0$, $y = 9$. 　　　　　　　　　　　　　　$Ans.$ $(\tfrac{1}{2}, \tfrac{39}{5}).$

21. The fourth-quadrant area bounded by the parabola $y^2 + 2x - 2y = 3$. Obtain each coordinate in two ways. 　　　　　$Ans.$ $(0.53, -0.35).$

22. The area bounded by $y = (1 - x^2)^2$ and the x-axis. $(A = \tfrac{16}{15}.)$

$$Ans. (0, \tfrac{8}{21}).$$

23. The area bounded by the curve $xy^3 = 1$ and the lines $x = 0$, $y = 1$.

$$Ans. (\tfrac{1}{5}, 2).$$

24. The area between the curve $y = xe^x$ and its asymptote. 　$Ans.$ $(-2, -\tfrac{1}{8}).$

25. The area in the first quadrant bounded by the hypocycloid $x = a \cos^3 t$, $y = a \sin^3 t$. $(A = \tfrac{3}{32}\pi a^2.)$

$$Ans. \ \bar{x} = \bar{y} = \frac{256a}{315\pi}.$$

26. The area in the first quadrant between the two parabolas $x^2 - 4ay + a^2 = 0$, $x^2 = 2ay$. 　　　　　　　　　　　　　　$Ans.$ $(\tfrac{3}{8}a, \tfrac{1}{5}a).$

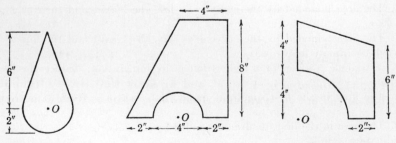

Figure 168　　　　　　　Figure 169　　　　　　　Figure 170

27. The area in Fig. 168.　　　　　**28.** The area in Fig. 169.
29. The area in Fig. 170.

30. The area of the loop of the curve $y^2 = x(1 - x^2)^2$. $(A = \frac{16}{21}.)$ *Ans.* $(\frac{7}{15}, 0)$.

31. The area in the first quadrant enclosed by the curve $a^2y^2 = x^2(a^2 - x^2)$ and the axes. $\left(A = \dfrac{a^2}{3}.\right)$ *Ans.* $\left(\dfrac{3\pi a}{16}, \dfrac{a}{5}\right)$.

32. The area of the loop of the curve $y^2 = x^2(1 - x)$. $(A = \frac{8}{15}.)$ *Ans.* $(\frac{4}{7}, 0)$.

33. The area bounded by $xy = \ln x$, the x-axis, and the maximum ordinate. $(A = \frac{1}{2}.)$ *Ans.* $(2, 2 - 5e^{-1})$.

34. The area under $x^2y = 1$ from $x = 1$ to $x = c$, $c > 1$.

35. What happens in Ex. 34 as $c \to \infty$?   *Ans.* $\bar{x} \to \infty$, $\bar{y} \to \frac{1}{6}$.

36. Devise a method for finding graphically the centroid of any quadrilateral.

167. *Centroid of a Plane Area: Polar Coordinates*

In a definite integration, if we always make sure that the *limit of the sum of elements* represents the quantity required, nothing else matters. In two different problems using the same coordinates and dealing with the same kind of physical entity (e.g., a plane area), or even at different stages of the same problem, we may at any time shift from one type of element to another, according to convenience.

Figure 171 represents an enlargement of a single element of polar area. We may adjust the technique of § 166 to the use of polar coordinates once we have the location of the centroid of the sector in Fig. 171. Actually, we shall first obtain the centroid of the sector in Fig. 172 and then find the centroid in Fig. 171 by rotation of axes.

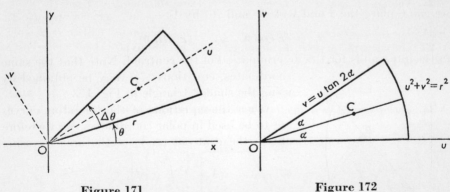

Figure 171   Figure 172

In Fig. 172 the area is $A = \alpha r^2$, and we know that the centroid of the sector lies on the line of symmetry. Hence $\bar{u} = \bar{v} \cot \alpha$. By the methods of § 166,

$$(1) \qquad A\bar{v} = \int_0^{r \sin 2\alpha} v[(r^2 - v^2)^{\frac{1}{2}} - v \cot 2\alpha] \, dv.$$

The integrations to be performed in (1) are simple. The student should show that

$$\bar{v} = \frac{r}{3\alpha}\left(1 - \cos^3 2\alpha - \sin^2 2\alpha \cos 2\alpha\right)$$
$$= \frac{r(1 - \cos 2\alpha)}{3\alpha} = \frac{2r \sin^2 \alpha}{3\alpha}.$$

Since $\bar{u} = \bar{v} \cot \alpha$, we may now write the coordinates of the centroid in Fig. 172:

(2) $$\bar{u} = \frac{2}{3} r \cos \alpha \, \frac{\sin \alpha}{\alpha}, \qquad \bar{v} = \frac{2}{3} r \sin \alpha \, \frac{\sin \alpha}{\alpha}.$$

To obtain Fig. 172 from Fig. 171, choose $\alpha = \frac{1}{2}\Delta\theta$ and rotate the axes through the angle $(\theta + \frac{1}{2}\Delta\theta)$. By the rotation formulas of analytic geometry it follows that the centroid of the sector in Fig. 171 has the coordinates

(3) $$\bar{x} = \bar{u} \cos (\theta + \tfrac{1}{2}\Delta\theta) - \bar{v} \sin (\theta + \tfrac{1}{2}\Delta\theta),$$
(4) $$\bar{y} = \bar{u} \sin (\theta + \tfrac{1}{2}\Delta\theta) + \bar{v} \cos (\theta + \tfrac{1}{2}\Delta\theta).$$

Because of (2) with $\alpha = \frac{1}{2}\Delta\theta$, equations (3) and (4) lead to

(5) $$\bar{x} = \frac{2}{3} r \cos (\theta + \Delta\theta) \, \frac{\sin \frac{1}{2}\Delta\theta}{\frac{1}{2}\Delta\theta},$$

(6) $$\bar{y} = \frac{2}{3} r \sin (\theta + \Delta\theta) \, \frac{\sin \frac{1}{2}\Delta\theta}{\frac{1}{2}\Delta\theta}.$$

Since

$$\operatorname*{Lim}_{\Delta\theta \to 0} \frac{\sin \frac{1}{2}\Delta\theta}{\frac{1}{2}\Delta\theta} = 1,$$

we can replace the $\bar{x}$ and $\bar{y}$ of (5) and (6) by

(7) $$x_c = \tfrac{2}{3} r \cos \theta, \quad y_c = \tfrac{2}{3} r \sin \theta$$

in the integrands for the determination of the centroid. Note that the same coordinates, equations (7), may be obtained by using the shaded triangle in Fig. 173.

When the equations of the bounding curves are to be used in polar coordinates, we therefore obtain the centroid $(\bar{x}, \bar{y})$ of the area by using

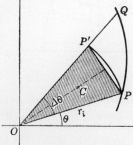

Figure 173

(8) $$A = \tfrac{1}{2} \int_\alpha^\beta r^2 \, d\theta,$$

$$A\bar{x} = \tfrac{1}{2} \int_\alpha^\beta \tfrac{2}{3} r \cos \theta \cdot r^2 \, d\theta,$$

$$A\bar{y} = \tfrac{1}{2} \int_\alpha^\beta \tfrac{2}{3} r \sin \theta \cdot r^2 \, d\theta.$$

Example. Using polar coordinates, find the centroid of the area between the curves $x^2 = ay$, $y = x$.

In polar coordinates, the equation of the parabola is

$$r^2 \cos^2 \theta = ar \sin \theta, \qquad r = a \tan \theta \sec \theta;$$

$$A = \tfrac{1}{2}\int_0^{\frac{\pi}{4}} r^2\, d\theta = \tfrac{1}{2}a^2 \int_0^{\frac{\pi}{4}} \tan^2\theta \sec^2\theta\, d\theta = \tfrac{1}{6}a^2 \left[\tan^3\theta\right]_0^{\frac{\pi}{4}} = \tfrac{1}{6}a^2;$$

$$A\bar{x} = \tfrac{1}{2}\int_0^{\frac{\pi}{4}} \tfrac{2}{3}r\cos\theta \cdot r^2\, d\theta,$$

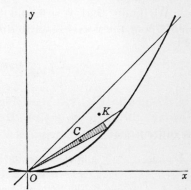

$$A\bar{x} = \tfrac{1}{3}a^3 \int_0^{\frac{\pi}{4}} \tan^3\theta \sec^2\theta\, d\theta$$

$$= \tfrac{1}{12}a^3,$$

$$\bar{x} = \tfrac{1}{2}a;$$

$$A\bar{y} = \tfrac{1}{2}\int_0^{\frac{\pi}{4}} \tfrac{2}{3}r\sin\theta \cdot r^2\, d\theta$$

$$= \tfrac{1}{3}a^3 \int_0^{\frac{\pi}{4}} \tan^4\theta \sec^2\theta\, d\theta$$

$$= \tfrac{1}{15}a^3,$$

$$\bar{y} = \tfrac{2}{5}a.$$

Figure 174

168. *A Theorem of Pappus*

The following theorem, known as the *Second Proposition of Pappus*, is useful in a variety of ways (see also Ex. 20, page 337).

THEOREM 27. *The volume of any solid of revolution is equal to the generating area times the circumference of the circle described by the centroid of the area.*[*]

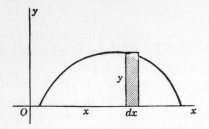

Figure 175

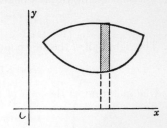

Figure 176

For definiteness, take the axis of revolution as x-axis, and suppose first that this forms part of the boundary of the rotating area (Fig. 175). The proof is very easy. By §§ 155, 166,

$$V = \pi \int_a^b y^2\, dx, \qquad A\bar{y} = \int_a^b \tfrac{1}{2}y \cdot y\, dx,$$

so that

$$V = 2\pi A\bar{y} = A \cdot 2\pi\bar{y}.$$

But this last formula, translated into words, is the theorem.

[*] The case in which the axis of revolution crosses the generating area is excluded.

The proof is readily extended to cover the situation shown in Fig. 176.

Example. Find the centroid of the semicircular area in the first and fourth quadrants, bounded by $x^2 + y^2 = a^2$.

We know that $\bar{y} = 0$ and that the area is $A = \frac{1}{2}\pi a^2$. Revolving that area about the y-axis generates a sphere of volume $\frac{4}{3}\pi a^3$. Hence, by Theorem 27,

$$\tfrac{4}{3}\pi a^3 = \tfrac{1}{2}\pi a^2 \cdot 2\pi\bar{x},$$

$$\bar{x} = \frac{4a}{3\pi}.$$

EXERCISES

In Exs. 1–12, find the centroid, using polar coordinates.

1. The area in the first and fourth quadrants between the circles $x^2 + y^2 = a^2$ and $x^2 + y^2 = b^2$.

$$Ans.\ \bar{x} = \frac{4}{3\pi} \cdot \frac{a^2 + ab + b^2}{a + b}.$$

2. The upper half of the area bounded by the curve $r^2 = a^2 \cos\theta$. ($A = a^2$.)

$$Ans.\ \bar{y} = \tfrac{4}{15}a.$$

3. The area bounded by the curve $r = a(1 + \sin\theta)$. ($A = \frac{3}{2}\pi a^2$.)

$$Ans.\ (0, \tfrac{5}{6}a).$$

4. The right half of the area of Ex. 3.

$$Ans.\ \left(\frac{16a}{9\pi}, \frac{5a}{6}\right).$$

5. The first quadrant area bounded by the curve $r = a\sin 2\theta$. ($A = \frac{1}{8}\pi a^2$.)

$$Ans.\ \bar{x} = \bar{y} = \frac{128a}{105\pi}.$$

6. The right half of the area bounded by the curve $r = a(2 - \sin\theta)$. ($A = \frac{9}{4}\pi a^2$.)

$$Ans.\ \left(\frac{80a}{27\pi}, -\frac{17a}{18}\right).$$

7. One quadrant of the area of the curve $r = 2a\cos^2\theta$. ($A = \frac{3}{8}\pi a^2$.)

$$Ans.\ \left(\frac{1024a}{315\pi}, \frac{64a}{21\pi}\right).$$

8. The area bounded by the curves $y = 2x$, $y^2 = 4ax$. $\qquad$ *Ans.* $(\frac{2}{5}a, a)$.

9. The area in the first quadrant bounded by the curves $y = x^3$, $y = 2x$. ($A = 1$.)

10. One loop of the curve $r = a\cos 2\theta$. ($A = \frac{1}{8}\pi a^2$.)

11. The area between the curves $x^2 = ay$, $y^2 = ax$. (Deduce from the example of § 167.)

12. The upper half of the area bounded by the curve $r = a(3 - 2\cos\theta)$. ($A = \frac{11}{2}\pi a^2$.)

$$Ans.\ \left(-\frac{20a}{11\pi}, \frac{52a}{11\pi}\right).$$

13. Prove Theorem 27 by another method.

14. Prove Theorem 27 for the case shown in Fig. 176.

In Exs. 15–25, use the Second Proposition of Pappus, Theorem 27.

15. Find the volume of a right circular cylinder.

16. Find the volume of the torus of Ex. 46, p. 303. *Ans.* $2\pi^2 a^2 b$.

17. Find the volume generated by revolving the area bounded by the ellipse $\dfrac{x^2}{a^2} + \dfrac{y^2}{b^2} = 1$ about the tangent at one end of the minor axis. *Ans.* $2\pi^2 ab^2$.

18. The ellipse $\dfrac{x^2}{a^2} + \dfrac{y^2}{b^2} = 1$ and the circle $x^2 + y^2 = ab$ with $a > b$ are rotated about the line $x = a$. Compare the volumes obtained.

19. Find the centroid of a right triangle.

20. Find the centroid of a semicircular area.

21. Find the centroid of half of a circular ring. (Cf. Ex. 1.)

22. Find the centroid of the area in Fig. 169, page 326.

23. Find the centroid of the area in Fig. 170, page 326.

24. Find the volume formed by rotating about Oy the quadrilateral whose vertices are $(1, 4)$, $(13, 9)$, $(18, -3)$, $(6, -8)$. *Ans.* 3211π.

25. Find the volume formed by rotating about Ox the area bounded by the lines $3x + 5y + 14 = 0$, $2y = x + 1$, $3x + 5y + 25 = 0$, $x - 2y = 10$. (Do not find the vertices.) *Ans.* 66π.

169. *Centroid of a Solid of Revolution*

Since the centroid of a solid of revolution lies on the axis, a single coordinate determines its position. If, say, the revolution takes place around the x-axis, the general formulas of § 165 reduce to

$$V\bar{x} = \int x_c\, dV,$$

where of course dV is a disk, ring, or shell, according to convenience, and x_c is the x-coordinate of the centroid of the volume element.

Example (*a*). The area bounded by the parabola $y^2 = 4ax$, the x-axis, and the latus rectum revolves about the x-axis. Find the centroid of the solid generated.

Cutting the generating area into rectangles as shown, we have as the element a circular disk of volume $\pi y^2\, dx$. The centroid C of the element is of course at its center, i.e., on the x-axis at a distance x from O. Hence

$$V\bar{x} = \pi \int_0^a xy^2\, dx = 4\pi a \int_0^a x^2\, dx = \tfrac{4}{3}\pi a^4.$$

By Example (*a*), § 155, $V = 2\pi a^3$, so that

$$\bar{x} = \frac{\tfrac{4}{3}\pi a^4}{2\pi a^3} = \frac{2}{3}\,a.$$

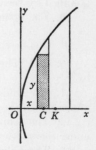

Figure 177

Example (*b*). Solve Example (*a*) by another method.

With the cylindrical shell as element,

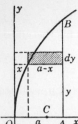

$$dV = 2\pi y(a - x) \, dy.$$

By the midpoint formula of analytic geometry,

$$x_c = \tfrac{1}{2}(a + x).$$

Thus

$$V\bar{x} = 2\pi \cdot \tfrac{1}{2} \int_0^{2a} y(a^2 - x^2) \, dy.$$

Figure 178   Putting $y \, dy = 2a \, dx$ and changing limits, we get

$$V\bar{x} = 2\pi a \int_0^a (a^2 - x^2) \, dx = 2\pi a \left[a^2x - \tfrac{1}{3}x^3 \right]_0^a = \tfrac{4}{3}\pi a^4,$$

as before.

EXERCISES

In Exs. 1–28, find the centroid.

1. A hemisphere of radius R. Solve in two ways.

Ans. At distance $\tfrac{3}{8}R$ from the center.

2. The volume formed by revolving about Oy the area in the first quadrant bounded by $y^2 = 4ax$, $y = 0$, $x = a$. Solve in two ways.   *Ans.* $(0, \tfrac{5}{6}a, 0)$.

3. The volume formed by rotating the area of Ex. 2 about the latus rectum. Solve in two ways.   *Ans.* $(a, \tfrac{5}{8}a, 0)$.

4. The upper half of the oblate spheroid formed by revolving the ellipse $\dfrac{x^2}{a^2} + \dfrac{y^2}{b^2} = 1$ about Oy. Solve in two ways.   *Ans.* $(0, \tfrac{3}{8}b, 0)$.

5. A circular cone. Solve in two ways.   *Ans. At distance $\tfrac{1}{4}h$ from the base.*

6. The volume formed by revolving about Ox the area enclosed by the loop of the curve $y^2 = x^2(1 - x)$.   *Ans.* $(\tfrac{3}{5}, 0, 0)$.

7. The volume formed by revolving about Oy the top half of the loop of Ex. 6.   *Ans.* $(0, \tfrac{21}{128}, 0)$.

8. The volume formed by revolving about Ox the area in the first quadrant bounded by the curve $y^2 = x^2(1 - x^2)$ and the x-axis.   *Ans.* $(\tfrac{5}{8}, 0, 0)$.

9. The volume formed by revolving about Oy the area of Ex. 8.

$$Ans. \left(0, \frac{2}{3\pi}, 0 \right).$$

10. The volume formed by revolving about the line $x = -1$ the area bounded by $y = x^3$, $y = 0$, $x = 1$.   *Ans.* $(-1, \tfrac{25}{84}, 0)$.

11. The volume generated by revolving about Ox the area in the second quadrant under the curve $y = e^x$. ($V = \tfrac{1}{2}\pi$.)   *Ans.* $\bar{x} = -\tfrac{1}{2}$.

12. The volume generated by revolving about Oy the area in the second quadrant under the curve $y = e^x$. ($V = 2\pi$.)   *Ans.* $\bar{y} = \tfrac{1}{8}$.

13. The volume formed by revolving about the line $x = 2a$ the area bounded by that line, the x-axis, and the curve $a^2y = x^3$. ($V = \tfrac{16}{5}\pi a^3$.)   *Ans.* $\bar{y} = \tfrac{10}{7}a$.

14. The volume generated by revolving about Ox the area in the third quadrant under the curve $y^2 = \dfrac{1}{(1-x)^3}$. *Ans.* $\bar{x} = -1$.

15. The volume formed by revolving about Ox the area under the curve $xy = 1$, from $x = 1$ to $x = b$. What happens as b increases?

$$Ans.\ \bar{x} = \frac{b \ln b}{b - 1}.$$

16. One-half of a torus (cut by a plane perpendicular to the axis). Solve in two ways. ($V = \pi^2 a^2 b$.)

$$Ans.\ \bar{y} = \frac{4a}{3\pi}.$$

17. The volume formed by rotating about Oy the area in the third quadrant bounded by the curve $y^2 = x + 1$. Solve in two ways. *Ans.* $\bar{y} = -\frac{5}{16}$.

18. The volume formed by rotating the area of Ex. 17 about Ox. Solve in two ways. *Ans.* $\bar{x} = -\frac{1}{3}$.

19. The volume generated by revolving about the directrix the area in the first quadrant bounded by the parabola $y^2 = 4ax$, its axis, and its latus rectum. ($V = \frac{64}{15}\pi a^3$.) *Ans.* $\bar{y} = \frac{25}{32}a$.

20. The volume generated by revolving about Ox the area bounded by $y = \ln x$, $y = 0$, $x = e$.

$$Ans.\ \bar{x} = \frac{e^2 - 1}{4(e - 2)}.$$

21. The volume generated by revolving the area of Ex. 20 about Oy.

$$Ans.\ \bar{y} = \frac{e^2 - 1}{2(e^2 + 1)}.$$

22. The volume cut off from the hyperboloid $x^2 + y^2 - z^2 + a^2 = 0$ by the plane $z = 2a$. *Ans.* $\bar{z} = \frac{27}{16}a$.

23. The upper half of the solid bounded by the surfaces $x^2 + y^2 = 2a^2$, $x^2 + y^2 - z^2 = a^2$. ($V = \frac{2}{3}\pi a^3$.) *Ans.* $\bar{z} = \frac{3}{8}a$.

24. The upper half of the solid bounded by the surfaces $x^2 + y^2 - z^2 = a^2$, $x^2 + y^2 = 2z^2$. ($V = \frac{2}{3}\pi a^3$.) *Ans.* $\bar{z} = \frac{3}{8}a$.

25. The volume inside the surfaces $x^2 + y^2 = z^2$, $x^2 + y^2 + az = 2a^2$. ($V = \frac{5}{6}\pi a^3$.) *Ans.* $\bar{z} = \frac{11}{10}a$.

26. The volume bounded by the surfaces $x^2 + y^2 = 3a^2 - 2az$, $x^2 + y^2 = az$. *Ans.* $\bar{z} = \frac{5}{6}a$.

27. The volume formed by revolving about Ox the area in the first quadrant between the parabolas $x^2 = 2ay$, $x^2 = 4ay - a^2$. ($V = \frac{1}{15}\pi a^3$.) *Ans.* $\bar{x} = \frac{15}{32}a$.

28. The volume formed by revolving the area of Ex. 27 about Oy. ($V = \frac{1}{8}\pi a^3$.)

$$Ans.\ \bar{y} = \frac{1}{4}a.$$

29. A top consists of a cone of radius 2 in. and height 2 in., surmounted by a cylinder of radius $\frac{1}{4}$ in. and height 2 in. Find the centroid.

Ans. 1.57 in. from vertex of cone.

30. A wooden buoy consists of a cone and hemisphere placed base to base; the common radius is 2 ft., the height of the cone 6 ft. Find the centroid.

Ans. 5.4 ft. from vertex.

31. Find the centroid of the volume formed by rotating about Oy the area under the curve $y = e^{-\frac{1}{2}x^2}$. *Ans.* $\bar{y} = \frac{1}{4}$.

32. Solve Ex. 31 by inspection. (In $V\bar{y}$, put $x^2 = \frac{1}{2}z^2$; compare $V\bar{y}$ and V.)

33. If a plane area, *symmetric with respect to Oy*, rotates about an external line parallel to Oy, show that $\bar{y}$ for the solid thus formed is equal to $\bar{y}$ for the area. State the result as a general theorem. Check Ex. 16 above with Ex. 1, page 325.

34. Find the centroid of the solid formed by rotating an isosceles triangle about an external line perpendicular to the base. (Ex. 33.)

35. Find graphically the centroid of the solid formed by rotating an isosceles trapezoid about an external line perpendicular to the base. (Ex. 36, page 327, and Ex. 33 above.)

36. If V_x, V_y denote the volumes formed by revolving a plane area (lying all in one quadrant) about Ox and Oy in turn, show that the mass moments $V_x\,\bar{x}$, $V_y\,\bar{y}$ are equal. Check Ex. 16.

170. *Centroids of Miscellaneous Solids*

Example (a). Find the centroid of one-half of the solid in the examples of § 158.

With the triangular element (Fig. 156), we know by § 166 that the centroid of the element is $(x_c,\,y_c,\,z_c) \equiv (x,\,\frac{2}{3}y,\,\frac{1}{3}z)$. Thus

$$V\bar{x} = \int_0^a x \cdot \frac{1}{2}yz\,dx.$$

But $z = y$, $x\,dx = -y\,dy$:

$$V\bar{x} = \frac{1}{2}\int_0^a xy^2\,dx$$

$$= -\frac{1}{2}\int_a^0 y^3\,dy = \frac{1}{8}a^4.$$

In § 158 we found $V = \frac{1}{3}a^3$, so that

$$\bar{x} = \frac{\frac{1}{8}a^4}{\frac{1}{3}a^3} = \frac{3}{8}a.$$

Next,

$$V\bar{y} = \int_0^a \frac{2}{3}y \cdot \frac{1}{2}yz\,dx$$

$$= \frac{1}{3}\int_0^a y^3\,dx = \frac{1}{3}\int_0^a (a^2 - x^2)^{\frac{3}{2}}\,dx.$$

Putting $x = a \sin \theta$, we find

$$V\bar{y} = \frac{1}{16}\pi a^4,$$

$$\bar{y} = \frac{\frac{1}{16}\pi a^4}{\frac{1}{3}a^3} = \frac{3}{16}\pi a.$$

Since for all the elements $z_c = \frac{1}{3}z = \frac{1}{3}y = \frac{1}{2}y_c$,

$$\bar{z} = \frac{1}{2}\bar{y} = \frac{3}{32}\pi a.$$

Example (b). Solve Example (a) by another method.

For the rectangular element (Fig. 157), the centroid is easily seen to be $(x_c, y_c, z_c) \equiv (\frac{1}{2}x, y, \frac{1}{2}z)$. Thus

$$V\bar{x} = \int_0^a \tfrac{1}{2}x \cdot xz \, dy = \tfrac{1}{2} \int_0^a x^2 y \, dy = -\tfrac{1}{2} \int_a^0 x^3 \, dx,$$

as before. Next,

$$V\bar{y} = \int_0^a y \cdot xz \, dy = \int_0^a y^2 x \, dy = \int_0^a y^2 \sqrt{a^2 - y^2} \, dy.$$

Putting $y = a \sin \theta$, we obtain the same result as above.

EXERCISES

Find the centroid of the given solid.

1. An elliptic cone cut off by a right section. $(V = \frac{1}{3}\pi abh.)$ *Ans.* $\bar{z} = \frac{1}{4}h$.

2. The volume cut from the paraboloid $\dfrac{x^2}{a^2} + \dfrac{y^2}{b^2} = \dfrac{z}{c}$ by the plane $z = c$.

Ans. $\bar{z} = \frac{2}{3}c$.

3. The volume in the first octant under the plane $z = y$ and inside the parabolic cylinder $y^2 = 4 - x$. Solve in two ways. $(V = 4.)$ *Ans.* $(\frac{4}{3}, \frac{16}{15}, \frac{8}{15})$.

4. A pyramid with a square base, whose apex lies vertically above one corner of the base.   *Ans.* $(\frac{3}{8}a, \frac{3}{8}a, \frac{1}{4}h)$.

5. The volume in the first octant enclosed by the cylinder $y^2 = ax$ and the planes $x = a, z = x.$ $(V = \frac{2}{5}a^3.)$ *Ans.* $(\frac{5}{7}a, \frac{5}{12}a, \frac{5}{14}a)$.

6. The volume in the first octant bounded by the surfaces $y + z = a, z^2 = ax.$ $(V = \frac{1}{12}a^3.)$

7. The volume in the first octant bounded by the surfaces $x^2 = y + 2z, x = 1.$ $(V = \frac{1}{20}.)$

8. The volume in the first octant inside the cylinder $y^2 + z^2 = a^2$ and outside the cylinder $y^2 = ax.$ $(V = \frac{1}{16}\pi a^3.)$

$$\textit{Ans.} \left(\frac{a}{4}, \frac{32a}{15\pi}, \frac{16a}{15\pi}\right).$$

9. One-eighth of the solid bounded by two equal circular cylinders whose axes intersect at right angles. $(V = \frac{2}{3}a^3.)$ *Ans.* $(\frac{9}{64}\pi a, \frac{9}{64}\pi a, \frac{3}{8}a)$.

10. The volume in the first octant bounded by the surfaces $y + z = a$, $x^2 + ay = a^2.$ $(V = \frac{2}{5}a^3.)$

11. The volume bounded by the cylinder $x^2 = ay$ and the planes $z = 0, y = x$, $y = z.$ $(V = \frac{1}{15}a^3.)$

12. The volume in the first octant bounded by the surfaces $yz = z - x, z = 1.$ Solve in two ways. $(V = \frac{1}{4}.)$

13. The volume in the first octant bounded by the surfaces $y^2 = 4a^2 - ax$, $az = xy.$ $(V = \frac{16}{3}a^3.)$

14. The volume in the first octant bounded by the surfaces $x + y = a, z^2 = 4ay.$ Solve in two ways. $(V = \frac{8}{15}a^3.)$

15. The volume enclosed by the plane $y = x$, the xy-plane, and the hyperbolic paraboloid with rulings parallel to the zx-plane intersecting the lines $x = a$, $z = 0$, and $x = y = z$. ($V = \frac{1}{12}a^3$.)

16. One-quarter of the circular conoid generated by a line parallel to the xy-plane following the line $y = h$, $x = 0$, and the circle $x^2 + z^2 = a^2$, $y = 0$. ($V = \frac{1}{8}\pi a^2 h$.)

$$Ans. \left(\frac{8a}{9\pi}, \frac{h}{3}, \frac{4a}{3\pi}\right).$$

17. The volume of Ex. 16 by a second method. (Ex. 30, page 311, and Ex. 2, page 325.)

18. The volume in the first octant inside the cylinder formed by a line parallel to the line $y + z = a$, $x = 0$, and following the circle $x^2 + y^2 = a^2$, $z = 0$. ($V = \frac{1}{3}a^3$.)

$$Ans. \left(\tfrac{3}{8}a, \tfrac{3}{32}\pi a, \tfrac{3}{32}\pi a\right).$$

171. *Centroid of an Arc; of a Surface of Revolution*

The centroid of a curved arc or of a surface of revolution can be found by choosing an element as in § 159 or § 160 respectively.

Example. Find the centroid of a semicircular wire.

Taking the bounding diameter as axis of y, we have $\bar{y} = 0$, and

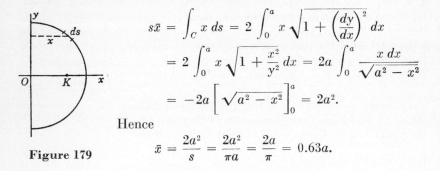

$$s\bar{x} = \int_C x \, ds = 2 \int_0^a x \sqrt{1 + \left(\frac{dy}{dx}\right)^2} \, dx$$

$$= 2 \int_0^a x \sqrt{1 + \frac{x^2}{y^2}} \, dx = 2a \int_0^a \frac{x \, dx}{\sqrt{a^2 - x^2}}$$

$$= -2a \left[\sqrt{a^2 - x^2} \right]_0^a = 2a^2.$$

Hence

$$\bar{x} = \frac{2a^2}{s} = \frac{2a^2}{\pi a} = \frac{2a}{\pi} = 0.63a.$$

Figure 179

EXERCISES

In Exs. 1–17, find the centroid.

1. The example above, using y as the variable of integration.

2. The example above, using the equations $x = a \cos \theta$, $y = a \sin \theta$.

3. A circular arc of half-angle α. $Ans. \; \bar{x} = \dfrac{a \sin \alpha}{\alpha}.$

4. Half the arc of the hypocycloid $x^{\frac{2}{3}} + y^{\frac{2}{3}} = a^{\frac{2}{3}}$. ($s = 3a$.) $Ans. \; \bar{x} = \tfrac{2}{5}a.$

5. Half the arc of the hypocycloid $x = a \cos^3 \varphi$, $y = a \sin^3 \varphi$.

6. The arc from cusp to vertex of the cycloid $x = a(\theta - \sin \theta)$, $y = a(1 - \cos \theta)$. ($s = 4a$.) $Ans. \; \left(\tfrac{4}{3}a, \tfrac{4}{3}a\right).$

7. The entire arc which is cut off on the curve $9y^2 = 4x^3$ by the line $x = 3$.

$$Ans. \; \left(\tfrac{58}{35}, 0\right).$$

8. The entire arc of the loop of the curve $9ay^2 = x(x - 3a)^2$. $(s = 4\sqrt{3}\,a.)$

$$Ans. \left(\frac{7a}{5}, 0\right).$$

9. The entire arc of the loop of the curve $9y^2 = x^2(2x + 3)$. $(s = 2\sqrt{3}.)$

Ans. $(-\frac{4}{5}, 0)$.

10. The entire arc of the cardioid $r = a(1 + \cos\theta)$.   *Ans.* $(\frac{4}{5}a, 0)$.

11. The two arcs of the curve $9y^2 = 4(1 + x^2)^3$ between $x = 0$ and $x = 2$. $(s = \frac{44}{3}.)$ *Ans.* $(\frac{15}{11}, 0)$.

12. A hemispherical surface area.   *Ans.* $\bar{x} = \frac{1}{2}a$.

13. A hemispherical surface area, using the equations $x = a\cos\theta$, $y = a\sin\theta$.

14. A spherical zone.   *Ans.* Midway between the bounding planes.

15. The lateral surface area of a circular cone.   *Ans.* $\bar{x} = \frac{1}{3}h$.

16. The surface area cut from a sphere by one sheet of a cone of half-angle 60°.

Ans. $\bar{x} = \frac{3}{4}a$.

17. One-half the surface area of a torus (cut by a plane at right angles to the axis). $(A = 2\pi^2 ab.)$

$$Ans. \ \bar{y} = \frac{2a}{\pi}.$$

18. If an arc, *symmetric with respect to Oy*, rotates about an external axis parallel to Oy, show that $\bar{y}$ for the surface area thus formed is the same as $\bar{y}$ for the arc. Formulate the result as a theorem. Check Ex. 17.

19. One arch of the cycloid $x = a(\theta - \sin\theta)$, $y = a(1 - \cos\theta)$ rotates about Oy. Find the centroid of the surface area generated. (Exs. 6, 18.)   *Ans.* $\bar{y} = \frac{4}{3}a$.

20. Prove the First Proposition of Pappus:

The surface area of a solid of revolution is equal to the length of the generating arc times the circumference of the circle described by the centroid of the arc.

Solve Exs. 21–25 by the First Proposition of Pappus.

21. Find the surface area of a circular cone.

22. Find the surface area of a torus.

23. Find the centroid of a semicircular wire.

24. Find the surface area of a circular cone frustum.

25. Find the centroid of a semicircular wire plus a wire of the same density joining the ends.

$$Ans. \ \bar{x} = \frac{2a}{\pi + 2}$$

MOMENTS OF INERTIA

172. *Moment of Inertia*

The product of a mass m, concentrated at a point P, by the square of the distance r of P from a fixed line, or *axis*, is called the second moment, or the *moment of inertia*, of m with respect to that axis:

$$I = mr^2.$$

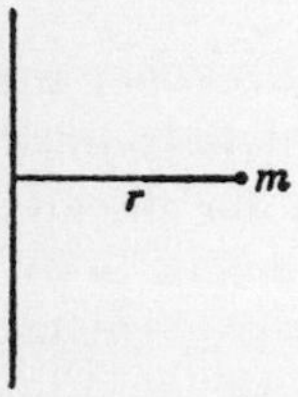

The moment of inertia of a system of such masses is, of course, the sum

$$(1) \qquad I = \sum_{i=1}^{n} m_i r_i^2.$$

Figure 180

Moment of inertia with respect to the x-axis will be denoted by I_x; similarly I_y and I_z. Since the distance from the x-axis to a point (x, y, z) is $\sqrt{y^2 + z^2}$, we have by (1)

$$(2) \qquad I_x = \sum_{i=1}^{n} m_i(y_i^2 + z_i^2); \text{ etc.}$$

It is fundamentally important to realize that the moment of inertia of a particle of given mass, with respect to a given axis, is *independent of the direction* from that axis, being dependent on the distance only. Thus for a given particle, I_z is the same whether the particle is at $(5, 0, 0)$, or $(0, 5, 2)$, or $(3, -4, 6)$, or any other point for which

$$x^2 + y^2 = 25.$$

Example. Find I_z for the following set of particles: 2 units at $(1, 3, -2)$, 3 units at $(-3, 2, 6)$, 4 units at $(0, 0, 2)$, 1 unit at $(-3, 0, 1)$.

By (2), properly adapted, we have

$$I_z = 2(1 + 9) + 3(9 + 4) + 4(0) + 1(9) = 68.$$

By thinking of a continuous mass as an aggregate of particles, we may obtain an intuitive conception of the meaning of moment of inertia for such a mass. A formal definition will be stated in § 211.

338

173. *Radius of Gyration*

Let M denote the mass of the physical object (solid, plane sheet, system of particles, etc.) under consideration. Since $M \neq 0$, we may always divide I by M; from the fact that moment of inertia is mass times square of distance, it follows that $\dfrac{I}{M}$ will be the square of a length:

$$\frac{I}{M} = R^2,$$

or

(1) $$I = MR^2.$$

The length R is called the *radius of gyration*, or *radius of inertia*, of M with respect to the given axis of moments. The radius of gyration is the distance from the axis at which a *particle* of mass M must be placed in order to have the same moment of inertia as the original mass.

We confine our attention now to *homogeneous* bodies. In this case, the mass M is proportional to the density δ. It follows from the definition of moment of inertia that I is also proportional to δ. Thus in (1) the density factor δ cancels out, so that the radius of gyration of a homogeneous body, with respect to any axis, is *independent of the density*.

Just as in the case of first moment, by taking $\delta = 1$, we may speak of "moment of inertia" of areas, volumes, etc., no idea of mass being involved. In many important applications, this is just the case in which we are interested.

174. *Moment of Inertia by Integration*

The actual computation of the moment of inertia of a continuous mass is effected by integration in much the same way that the moment of the first order (§ 165) is determined.

Choose an element (of volume, area, or length) in some suitable way, and denote the mass of this element by Δm_i. Let r_i denote the radius of gyration of the element. Then $r_i^2 \, \Delta m_i$ is the moment of inertia of the element. Add together all the elementary moments and take the limit of the sum:

(1) $$I = \operatorname*{Lim}_{n \to \infty} \sum_{i=1}^{n} r_i^2 \, \Delta m_i = \int r^2 \, dm,$$

where r is the *radius of gyration of the mass element* with respect to the axis of moments. Of course the integrand must be expressed in terms of a single variable, and the integration must be extended over the whole mass.

Just as in finding centroids we must take an element the position of whose centroid is known, so here the essential point is to *choose an element whose radius of gyration is known.* The way in which the integral (1) is built up will be explained piecemeal, for the cases of greatest importance.

175. *Moment of Inertia of a Plane Area*

To find the moment of inertia of a plane area with respect, say, to the y-axis, let us take as element a rectangle parallel to that axis. [A second method will appear in Example (*b*)

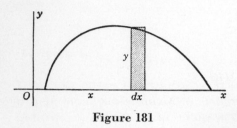

below.] Then, the radius of gyration *r* of the element is simply *x*, since (apart from terms which drop out in the limit) the entire element is at a distance *x* from the axis of moments:

$$I_y = \int_a^b x^2 y \, dx.$$

Figure 181

It is definitely inadvisable to memorize this formula; again, the reader should concentrate on understanding the argument.

Example (*a*). Find the moment of inertia of the area bounded by a parabola, its axis, and its latus rectum, with respect to the axis.

Taking the horizontal element, we have

$$I_x = \int_0^{2a} y^2(a - x) \, dy = \int_0^{2a} y^2 \left(a - \frac{y^2}{4a} \right) dy$$

$$= \left[\frac{ay^3}{3} - \frac{y^5}{20a} \right]_0^{2a} = \frac{16}{15} a^4.$$

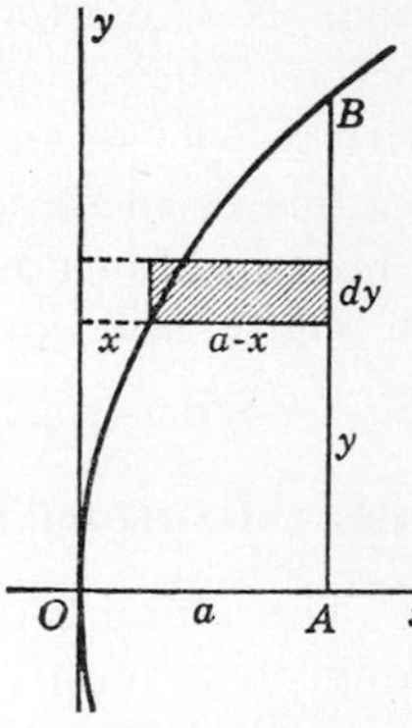

By Example (*a*), § 58, the mass, or area, is $M = \frac{4}{3}a^2$, so that

$$I_x = \frac{16}{15} a^4 \cdot \frac{M}{\frac{4}{3}a^2} = \frac{4}{5} Ma^2.$$

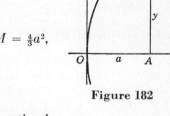

Figure 182

This shows that the square of the radius of gyration is

$$R^2 = \tfrac{4}{5}a^2.$$

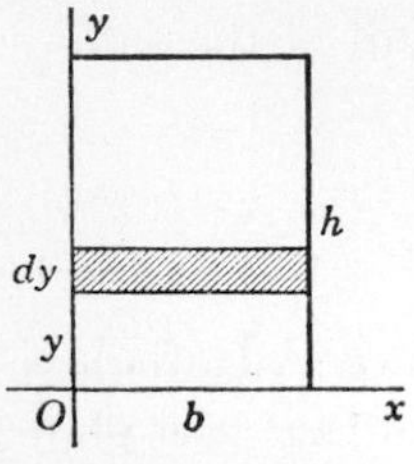

To find the moment of inertia of a rectangle with respect to the base, we have

$$I_x = \int_0^h y^2 x \, dy = b \int_0^h y^2 \, dy = \tfrac{1}{3}bh^3.$$

Since $M = bh$, the result may be written as

Figure 183   (1) $$I_x = \frac{bh^3}{3} = \frac{1}{3} Mh^2.$$

This formula, which should be memorized, says in words:

The moment of inertia of a rectangle with respect to the base is one-third the mass, or area, times the square of the altitude.

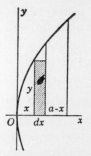

Figure 184

Example (*b*). Solve Example (*a*) by another method. Taking the vertical element, we have by (1)

$$I_x = \int_0^a \tfrac{1}{3}y^2 \cdot y \, dx = \tfrac{1}{3} \int_0^a y^3 \, dx$$

$$= \tfrac{8}{3}a^{\frac{3}{2}} \int_0^a x^{\frac{3}{2}} \, dx = \tfrac{16}{15}a^4.$$

Example (*c*). Find the moment of inertia, with respect to the line $x = 1$, of the area enclosed by the loop of the curve $y^2 = x^2(1 - x)$. See Fig. 185.

Choosing a vertical element (Fig. 185), one parallel to the line $x = 1$, we obtain at once

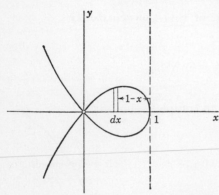

Figure 185

$$I_{x=1} = 2 \int_0^1 (1 - x)^2 y \, dx.$$

Here $y = x \sqrt{1 - x}$, so that we have

$$I_{x=1} = 2 \int_0^1 x(1 - x)^{\frac{3}{2}} \, dx.$$

One of the many ways of evaluating this integral is to use the substitution $1 - x = v$. Another is to employ Wallis' formula. Put $x = \sin^2 \varphi$, and thus obtain

$$I_{x=1} = 4 \int_0^{\frac{\pi}{2}} \sin^2 \varphi \cos^5 \varphi \sin \varphi \cos \varphi \, d\varphi$$

$$= 4 \int_0^{\frac{\pi}{2}} \sin^3 \varphi \cos^6 \varphi \, d\varphi$$

$$= 4 \frac{2 \cdot 5 \cdot 3 \cdot 1}{9 \cdot 7 \cdot 5 \cdot 3 \cdot 1} = \frac{8}{63}.$$

176. *Polar Moment of Inertia*

It is frequently necessary to find the moment of inertia of a plane mass, or area, with respect to a line perpendicular to the plane. Take the plane in which the area lies as xy-plane, and the perpendicular line as z-axis. The distance of each particle from the z-axis is merely its distance from the origin, so that this moment may equally well be considered as moment of inertia *with respect to the origin.* Since, for a particle at (x, y), the distance is the polar radius vector $\sqrt{x^2 + y^2}$, moment of inertia with respect to the origin is called *polar moment of inertia.* For a system of particles,

$$(1) \qquad I_z = I_0 = \sum_{i=1}^{n} m_i(x_i{}^2 + y_i{}^2).$$

THEOREM 28. *The moment of inertia of a plane mass with respect to a line perpendicular to its plane is equal to the sum of the moments with respect to two lines in the plane intersecting at right angles in the foot of the perpendicular.*

That is, for a mass (or area) in the xy-plane,

$$I_z = I_0 = I_x + I_y.$$

For a system of particles, the truth of this theorem follows at once from (1):

$$I_z = \sum_{i=1}^{n} m_i(x_i{}^2 + y_i{}^2) = \sum_{i=1}^{n} m_i y_i{}^2 + \sum_{i=1}^{n} m_i x_i{}^2 = I_x + I_y.$$

Later (§ 211), it will be a simple matter to complete the proof.

EXERCISES

In Exs. 1–4, find the moment of inertia with respect to each of the coordinate axes.

1. Masses of 3 units at $(1, 0)$, 4 units at $(0, -2)$, 2 units at $(3, -3)$, and 3 units at $(4, -2)$. *Ans.* $I_x = 46; I_y = 69.$
2. Masses of 2 units at $(0, -2)$, 2 units at $(1, -3)$, 3 units at $(2, 0)$, and 4 units at $(3, 1)$. *Ans.* $I_x = 30; I_y = 50.$
3. Masses of 2 units at $(0, 3, 0)$, 3 units at $(2, -4, 1)$, 1 unit at $(-1, -2, -3)$. *Ans.* $I_x = 82; I_y = 25; I_z = 83.$
4. Masses of 2 units at $(1, 1, 4)$, 3 units at $(2, 0, 0)$, and 4 units at $(-2, -3, 1)$. *Ans.* $I_x = 74; I_y = 66; I_z = 68.$

In Exs. 5–44, find the moment of inertia. The symbol M denotes the total mass of the system.

5. Equal particles at each corner of a square, with respect to one side of the square. *Ans.* $\frac{1}{2}Ma^2.$
6. Equal particles at three corners of a square, with respect to a side through the vacant corner. *Ans.* $\frac{2}{3}Ma^2.$
7. Equal particles at each corner of a cube, with respect to an edge of the cube.
8. Equal particles at seven corners of a cube, with respect to an edge through the vacant corner. *Ans.* $\frac{8}{7}Ma^2.$
9. A straight rod or wire with respect to a perpendicular through one end.
10. A straight rod with respect to a perpendicular through a trisection point. Solve by integration; check by Ex. 9.

11. A wire bent in the form of a square, with respect to one side.   *Ans.* $\frac{5}{12}Ma^2$.

12. A circular wire with respect to its axis (line through the center perpendicular to the plane).

13. The area bounded by the parabola $y^2 = 4ax$ and the latus rectum, with respect to Oy.   *Ans.* $\frac{3}{7}Ma^2$.

14. The area bounded by $y^2 = 4ax$ and its latus rectum, with respect to the latus rectum.   *Ans.* $\frac{64}{105}a^4$.

15. The area bounded by $y^2 = 4ax$ and its latus rectum, with respect to the line $y = 2a$.   *Ans.* $\frac{64}{5}a^4$.

16. The area of the loop of $y^2 = x^2(1 - x)$, Fig. 185, with respect to Oy.

Ans. $\frac{64}{315}$.

17. The area under the curve $y = \sin x$ from $x = 0$ to $x = \frac{1}{2}\pi$, with respect to the y-axis.   *Ans.* $\pi - 2$.

18. The area under the curve $y = \sin x$ from $x = 0$ to $x = \pi$, with respect to the y-axis.   *Ans.* $\pi^2 - 4$.

19. The area of Ex. 18 with respect to the x-axis.   *Ans.* $\frac{4}{9}$.

20. The area under the curve $xy = \ln x$ from $x = 1$ to $x = e$, with respect to the y-axis.   *Ans.* $\frac{1}{4}(e^2 + 1)$.

21. The first quadrant area under the curve $y = e^{-x}$, with respect to the x-axis.

Ans. $\frac{1}{9}$.

22. The area of Ex. 21, with respect to the y-axis.   *Ans.* 2.

23. The area of the loop of $y^2 = x^4(1 - x)$ with respect to Oy.

$$Ans. \ \frac{2^9}{11 \cdot 9 \cdot 7 \cdot 5} = \frac{512}{3465}.$$

24. The area of Ex. 23, with respect to the line $x = 1$.   *Ans.* $\frac{32}{693}$.

25. The area enclosed by the curve $y^2 = x^5(1 - x)^3$, with respect to Oy.

26. The area of Ex. 25, with respect to the line $x = 1$.   *Ans.* $\dfrac{5\pi}{1024}$.

27. The area bounded by the curve $2x^2 + 2x - y - 2 = 0$ and the line $y = 2x$, with respect to the line $x = 1$.   *Ans.* $\frac{16}{5}$.

28. A triangle with respect to the line through the vertex parallel to the base. (Solve for the right triangle and deduce the general answer.)   *Ans.* $\frac{1}{2}Mh^2$.

29. A triangle with respect to the base.   *Ans.* $\frac{1}{6}Mh^2$.

30. Ex. 29 another way.

31. A circular area with respect to a diameter.   *Ans.* $\frac{1}{4}Ma^2$.

32. Solve Ex. 31 by inspection. (Set up I_y and I_x, each with vertical element; add the former to three times the latter and note that $I_x = I_y$.)

33. An ellipse with respect to each of its axes.   *Ans.* $\frac{1}{4}Ma^2$, $\frac{1}{4}Mb^2$.

34. The area in the fourth quadrant bounded by the curve $y = \ln x$, with respect to Oy.   *Ans.* $\frac{1}{9}$.

35. A rectangle of sides b, h, with respect to the line bisecting the sides of length h.   *Ans.* $\frac{1}{12}bh^3$.

36. The area bounded by the curve $y = 1 + x^3$ and the axes, with respect to Oy.

37. The area in Fig. 165, page 322, with respect to the right side.   *Ans.* 348.3.

38. The area in Fig. 160, page 320, with respect to the base.   *Ans.* 1728.

39. The area in Fig. 160, with respect to the left side.   *Ans.* 640.

40. The area in Fig. 160, with respect to O. (Exs. 38–39.)

41. The area in Fig. 162, page 322, with respect to the base.

42. The area in Fig. 168, page 326, with respect to the line of symmetry.

43. The area in Fig. 170, page 326, with respect to the left side.   *Ans.* 417.7.

44. A circular area with respect to a perpendicular to the plane through the center. (Ex. 31 and § 176.)   *Ans.* $\frac{1}{2}Ma^2$.

45. Solve Ex. 44 by integration. (Take as element a circular ring.)

46. Find the moment of inertia of a circular sector of angle α, with respect to a line through the center perpendicular to the plane. (Deduce the answer from Ex. 44.)

Ans. $\frac{1}{2}Ma^2$.

47. Using the answer to Ex. 46, show that the polar moment of inertia of an area bounded by a polar curve and two radius vectors is

$$I_0 = \tfrac{1}{4} \int_\alpha^\beta r^4 \, d\theta.$$

In Exs. 48–52, find the moment of inertia with respect to the origin. (Ex. 47.)

48. The area of the curve $r^2 = a^2 \cos \theta$.   *Ans.* $\frac{1}{4}\pi a^4$.

49. The area of the curve $r^2 = a^2 \cos 2\theta$.   *Ans.* $\frac{1}{8}\pi a^4$.

50. The triangle bounded by the lines $y = 0$, $x = b$, $y = \dfrac{h}{b} x$. Check by § 176 (Exs. 28–29).   *Ans.* $\frac{1}{12}bh(h^2 + 3b^2)$.

51. The area bounded by the parabola $y^2 = ax$ and the line $y = x$.

52. The area bounded by the curve $a^2y = x^3$ and the line $y = x$.

53. Find the moment of inertia of a circular area with respect to a point on the circumference.   *Ans.* $\frac{3}{2}Ma^2$.

54. Find the moment of inertia of a rectangle with respect to one corner.

Ans. $\frac{1}{3}bh(b^2 + h^2)$.

177. *Moment of Inertia of a Solid of Revolution*

No additional theory is needed to find the moment of inertia of a solid of revolution with respect to its axis, but other solids are out of reach at present (§ 211).

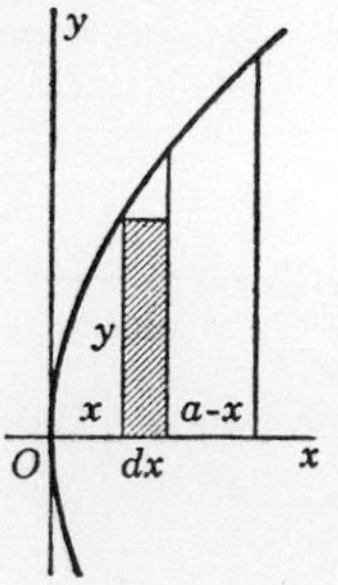

Example (*a*). A solid is generated by revolving about Oy the area bounded by the parabola $y^2 = 4ax$, the x-axis, and the latus rectum. Find the moment of inertia of the solid with respect to Oy.

Take as volume element the cylindrical shell $2\pi xy \, dx$. The radius of gyration of this shell is x:

Figure 186

$$I_y = 2\pi \int_0^a x^2 \cdot xy \, dx = 4\pi \sqrt{a} \int_0^a x^{\frac{5}{2}} \, dx = \tfrac{8}{9}\pi a^5.$$

The mass, or volume, is

$$M = 2\pi \int_0^a xy \, dx = \tfrac{8}{5}\pi a^3,$$

whence

$$I_y = \tfrac{5}{9}Ma^2.$$

To find the moment of inertia of a circular cylinder with respect to its axis, divide the cylinder into shells:

$$I_y = 2\pi \int_0^r x^2 \cdot xy \, dx = 2\pi h \int_0^r x^3 \, dx,$$

or

(1)
$$I_y = \frac{\pi r^4 h}{2} = \frac{1}{2} M r^2.$$

That is, *the moment of inertia of a cylinder with respect to its axis is one-half the mass times the square of the radius.*

Since the circular disk is a cylinder of small altitude, this gives us a valuable second method for moment of inertia of a solid of revolution with respect to its axis.

Example (b). Find I_x for the solid formed by revolving about Ox the area of Fig. 186.

Take as volume element the disk $\pi y^2 \, dx$. Then by (1),

$$I_x = \pi \int_0^a \frac{1}{2} y^2 \cdot y^2 \, dx = \frac{\pi}{2} \cdot 16a^2 \int_0^a x^2 \, dx$$
$$= \tfrac{8}{3}\pi a^5.$$

178. The Translation Theorem

Let the term *centroidal line* be used to denote a line through the centroid.

THEOREM 29. *The moment of inertia of a mass with respect to any line equals the moment with respect to the parallel centroidal line plus the mass times the square of the distance between the lines.*

That is, if l is any line, c the parallel centroidal line, h the distance between them, then

$$I_l = I_c + M h^2.$$

This theorem applies to *all* masses. For brevity, the proof will be deferred to § 212, at which time the general proof can be given.

Example. Find the moment of inertia of a right triangle with respect to its centroid (i.e., with respect to a line through the centroid perpendicular to the plane).

By Ex. 29, page 343,

$$I_y = \tfrac{1}{6}Ma^2, \qquad I_x = \tfrac{1}{6}Mb^2,$$

so that

$$I_0 = \tfrac{1}{6}M(a^2 + b^2),$$
$$I_c = I_0 - M \cdot \overline{OC}^2 = I_0 - M \cdot \tfrac{1}{9}(a^2 + b^2)$$
$$= \tfrac{1}{18}M(a^2 + b^2).$$

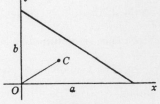

Figure 187

EXERCISES

In Exs. 1–20, find the moment of inertia with respect to the axis of revolution.

1. A sphere. *Ans.* $\frac{2}{5}Ma^2$.   **2.** A circular cone. *Ans.* $\frac{3}{10}Ma^2$.

3. An oblate spheroid. Solve by two methods. *Ans.* $\frac{2}{5}Ma^2$.

4. A prolate spheroid, using the equations $x = a\cos\varphi$, $y = b\sin\varphi$.

Ans. $\frac{2}{5}Mb^2$.

5. A torus. See Ex. 46, page 303. *Ans.* $(b^2 + \frac{3}{4}a^2)M$.

6. The volume formed by revolving about Ox the area bounded by $y^2 = 4ax$, $x = 0$, $y = 2a$.

7. The volume formed by revolving the area of Ex. 6 about the line $y = 2a$.

Ans. $\dfrac{8\pi a^5}{15}$.

8. The volume formed by revolving about Ox the area in the first quadrant under the curve $y = e^{-x}$.

Ans. $\dfrac{\pi}{8}$.

9. The volume formed by revolving about Ox the area under the curve $y = \ln x$ from $x = 1$ to $x = e$. *Ans.* $\frac{3}{2}\pi(3e - 8)$.

10. The volume generated by revolving the area of Ex. 9 about Oy.

Ans. $\dfrac{\pi(3e^4 + 1)}{8}$.

11. The volume generated by revolving about Ox the area under the curve $y = \sin x$ from $x = 0$ to $x = \pi$. *Ans.* $\frac{3}{16}\pi^2$.

12. The volume generated by revolving about Ox the area of the loop of the curve $y^2 = x^2(1 - x)$ of Fig. 185, page 341.

Ans. $\dfrac{\pi}{210}$.

13. The volume formed by revolving the area of Fig. 160, page 320, about the left side.

14. The volume formed by revolving the area of Fig. 160 about the base.

15. The volume formed by revolving the area of Fig. 163, page 322, about the base.

16. The volume generated by revolving the area of Fig. 162, page 322, about its base.

17. The volume bounded by the surfaces $x^2 + y^2 = 4az$, $x^2 + y^2 = 4z^2$.

Ans. $\frac{16}{15}\pi a^5$.

18. The volume bounded by the quadric surfaces $x^2 + y^2 - z^2 = a^2$, $x^2 + y^2 = 2a^2$. *Ans.* $\frac{32}{15}\pi a^5$.

19. The volume bounded by the quadric surfaces $x^2 + y^2 - z^2 = a^2$, $x^2 + y^2 = 2z^2$. *Ans.* $\frac{16}{15}\pi a^5$.

20. The volume inside the surfaces $x^2 + y^2 = 3z^2$, $x^2 + y^2 + az = 4a^2$.

In Exs. 21–23, find the moment of inertia.

21. A circular wire with respect to a **diameter.** *Ans.* $\frac{1}{2}Ma^2$.

22. A circular wire with respect to a tangent. (Use $x = a \cos \theta$, $y = a \sin \theta$.)
$$Ans. \ \tfrac{3}{2}Ma^2.$$

23. The arc of the catenary $y = a \cosh \dfrac{x}{a}$, from the vertex to the point (x_1, y_1),

with respect to Ox. $\left(s = a \sinh \dfrac{x_1}{a}. \right)$
$$Ans. \ a^2 s + \tfrac{1}{3}s^3.$$

In Exs. 24–28, find the moment of inertia with respect to the axis of revolution.

24. A spherical surface area, using rectangular coordinates. $Ans. \ \tfrac{2}{3}Ma^2.$
25. A spherical surface area, using the parametric equations $x = a \cos \theta$, $y = a \sin \theta$.
26. The lateral surface area of a cone of revolution. $Ans. \ \tfrac{1}{2}Ma^2.$
27. The surface area of a torus. See Ex. 46, page 303. $Ans. \ (b^2 + \tfrac{3}{2}a^2)M.$
28. A cylindrical drum. $Ans. \ \pi r^4 + 2\pi r^3 h.$

In Exs. 29–39, obtain the required moment of inertia by using the theorem of § 178, with reference to previous exercises.

29. A square plate with respect to (a) a line through the center parallel to a side; (b) a perpendicular through the center; (c) a line trisecting two opposite sides (two cases); (d) a diagonal. $Ans. \ (a) \ \tfrac{1}{12}Ma^2; \ (b) \ \tfrac{1}{6}Ma^2; \ (d) \ \tfrac{1}{12}Ma^2.$
30. An isosceles triangle with respect to a line (a) parallel to the base bisecting the altitude; (b) through the vertex perpendicular to the plane.
$$Ans. \ (a) \ \tfrac{1}{12}Mh^2; \ (b) \ \tfrac{1}{2}M(h^2 + \tfrac{1}{3}a^2).$$
31. A circular wire with respect to (a) a tangent; (b) any line perpendicular to the plane. $Ans. \ (a) \ \tfrac{3}{2}Ma^2; \ (b) \ M(a^2 + h^2).$
32. A circular area with respect to (a) a tangent; (b) a perpendicular through a point in the circumference.
33. The volume of a sphere with respect to a tangent.
34. A spherical surface area with respect to a tangent.
35. The volume of a torus with respect to a tangent parallel to the axis.
36. The area of Fig. 160, page 320, with respect to a line through the centroid parallel to the base. $Ans. \ 528.$
37. The area of Fig. 160 with respect to a line through the centroid parallel to the sides. $Ans. \ 208.$
38. The area of Fig. 160 with respect to the centroid. (Exs. 36–37.)
39. The area of Fig. 160 with respect to a line through P perpendicular to the plane. (Ex. 38.) $Ans. \ 1552.$

FLUID PRESSURE.

WORK

179. *Distributed Force*

In Chapter 12 we touched briefly upon the problem of a force or forces acting upon a single particle.

We have frequently to consider a force not acting at a single point, but distributed over an area or throughout a volume. Examples are the pressure of a carload of sand against the sides of the car, the attraction between two electrified plates, the gravitational attraction between two spheres or other solids. If the mass upon which the force acts be thought of as composed ultimately of particles, such a distributed force may be regarded as comprising the totality of forces acting on the separate particles.

180. *Fluid Pressure*

Given a plane area submerged vertically in a homogeneous fluid, let us for definiteness take the x-axis in the surface with the y-axis *positive downward*. (Of course, in any particular problem, the axes should be so chosen as to make the analytic geometry simple.) Divide the area into rectangles of length x_i, width Δy, and depth y_i below the surface. Now the force on any submerged *horizontal* area is equal to the weight of the column of fluid standing on this area. Hence the force on our elementary rectangle is, apart from terms which will drop out when the limit (the definite integral) is taken,*

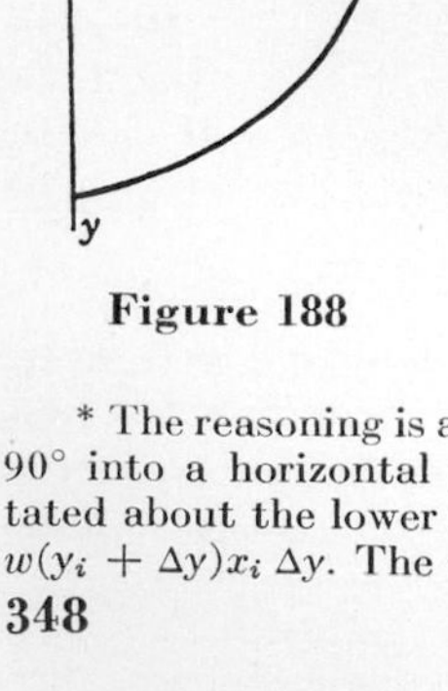

$$\Delta F_i = wy_ix_i \,\Delta y,$$

where w is the weight of the fluid per unit volume. Therefore

Figure 188

---

* The reasoning is as follows: If the rectangle were rotated about its upper side through 90° into a horizontal position at depth y_i, the force would be $wy_ix_i \,\Delta y$; if it were rotated about the lower side to a horizontal position at depth $y_i + \Delta y$, the force would be $w(y_i + \Delta y)x_i \,\Delta y$. The actual force is greater than the former and less than the latter.

$$F = \lim_{n \to \infty} \sum_{i=1}^{n} w y_i x_i \, \Delta y = w \int_c^d y x \, dy,$$

where c and d are the least and greatest depths below the surface.

Under the integral sign, we have multiplied the area $x \, dy$ of the element by its depth y below the surface, so that the integral represents the first moment of the submerged area with respect to the axis in the surface.

THEOREM 30. *The force on a submerged vertical plane area equals the product of the weight per unit volume, the submerged area, and the depth of the centroid of the area below the surface:*

(1) $$F = wA\bar{y}.$$

When numerical results are desired, we shall use $w = 62.5$ lb. per cu. ft., which is a close approximation to the weight of water.

Example. Find the force on one face of the submerged triangle of **Fig.** 189.

The equation of the line through $(0, 3)$, $(2, 1)$ is

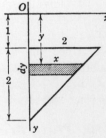

$$x + y = 3.$$

Thus the force is

$$F = w \int_1^3 y x \, dy = w \int_1^3 y(3 - y) \, dy$$

$$= w \left[\tfrac{3}{2} y^2 - \tfrac{1}{3} y^3 \right]_1^3 = \tfrac{10}{3} w.$$

Figure 189

Check. The area is $A = \tfrac{1}{2} \cdot 2 \cdot 2 = 2$, the depth of the centroid is $1 + \tfrac{2}{3} = \tfrac{5}{3}$; the force, by (1), is $F = w \cdot 2 \cdot \tfrac{5}{3} = \tfrac{10}{3} w.$

EXERCISES

In Exs. 1–17, solve by direct integration. When the position of the centroid is already known, check by Theorem 30.

1. Find the force on one face of a plank 16 ft. by 6 in., submerged vertically with its upper end in the surface.   *Ans.* $64w$.

2. Solve Ex. 1, if the upper end is 6 ft. below the surface.   *Ans.* $112w$.

3. Find the force on one face of a right triangle of sides $AB = 4$ ft., $AC = 3$ ft., submerged with AC vertical and AB in the surface.   *Ans.* $6w$.

4. Solve Ex. 3 if AB is 3 ft., C 6 ft., below the surface.

5. Solve Ex. 3 if AB is 6 ft., C 3 ft., below the surface.

6. What force must be withstood by a vertical dam 80 ft. long and 20 ft. deep?
                                                            Ans. 500 tons.

7. What force must be withstood by a trapezoidal dam 100 ft. long at the top, 80 ft. long at the bottom, and 20 ft. deep?   *Ans.* $17{,}333w$.

8. A horizontal cylindrical boiler 6 ft. in diameter is half full of water. Find the force on one end. *Ans.* 1125 lb.

9. Solve Ex. 8 if the boiler is full of water. *Ans.* $27\pi w$.

10. Find the force that must be withstood by a bulkhead closing a water main 6 ft. in diameter, if the surface of the water in the reservoir is 30 ft. above the center of the bulkhead. *Ans.* $270\pi w$.

11. Find the force on one end of a parabolic trough full of water, if the depth is 2 ft. and the width across the top 2 ft. *Ans.* $\frac{32}{15}w$.

12. The ends of a trough have the shape of an inverted arch of the curve $y = a \cos \dfrac{x}{a}$. If the trough is filled with a liquid weighing w lb. per cu. ft., find the force on one end. *Ans.* $\frac{1}{4}\pi w a^3$.

13. The vertical face of a dam is in the shape of an inverted arch of the cycloid $x = a(\theta - \sin \theta)$, $y = a(1 - \cos \theta)$. Find the maximum force that the dam must withstand. *Ans.* $\frac{5}{2}\pi w a^3$.

14. A trough 6 ft. deep and 8 ft. wide has semi-elliptical ends. If the trough is full of water, find the force on one end. *Ans.* $96w$.

15. Solve Ex. 14, using the equations $x = 4 \cos \varphi$, $y = 6 \sin \varphi$.

16. Find the force on one face of a square 2 ft. on a side, submerged with one diagonal vertical and one corner in the surface. *Ans.* $4\sqrt{2}\,w$.

17. A triangular trough of width $2a$ and depth $2a$ is filled to depth a with a liquid of unit weight $2w$, this overlaid with a stratum of depth a and unit weight w. (a) Find the force on one end; (b) find the force if the liquids were thoroughly mixed. *Ans.* (a) $\frac{3}{2}wa^3$; (b) $\frac{5}{3}wa^3$.

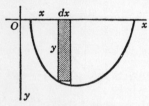

18. Show that for an area submerged as in Fig. 190, the force is

Figure 190

$$F = \tfrac{1}{2}w \int_a^b y^2\, dx.$$

Solve Exs. 19–24 by the method of Ex. 18.

19. Ex. 3.   **20.** Example, § 180.   **21.** Ex. 8.
22. Ex. 11.   **23.** Ex. 12.   **24.** Ex. 13.

25. A physical mixture consisting of equal parts of two liquids of unit weights w_1 and w_2 ($w_1 < w_2$) is poured into a rectangular tank. Show that when the liquids have had time to separate, the force on the sides of the tank has increased in the ratio $\dfrac{w_1 + 3w_2}{2(w_1 + w_2)}$.

181. *Resultant of Parallel Forces*

Given a set of parallel forces $f_1, f_2, \cdots, f_n$ whose resultant (algebraic sum) is not 0, the problem of finding the line of action of the resultant is analogous to that of finding the centroid of a set of mass particles.

The simplest case arises when all the forces lie in one plane; for concreteness, consider a straight beam bearing concentrated loads. Take the line of the beam as x-axis, and mark an origin—say, at the left end. Multiply each force by its distance (i.e., the distance of its line of action) from the origin. *The sum of these first moments must equal the moment of the resultant:* that is,

$$F\bar{x} = \sum_{i=1}^{n} f_i x_i.$$

Example (a). A straight beam bears concentrated loads as shown. Find the position of the resultant, and the reactions at the ends.

Taking moments about A, we have

$$F\bar{x} = 4 \cdot 60 + 8 \cdot 40 + 16 \cdot 100 = 2160,$$
$$\bar{x} = \tfrac{2160}{200} = 10.8 \text{ ft.}$$

The moment, about A, of the reaction R_2 must balance the moments of the forces, so that $20R_2 = 2160$, $R_2 = 108$ lb. We could find R_1 from the fact that

$$R_1 + R_2 = 200,$$

but as a check let us find it independently, by taking moments about B:

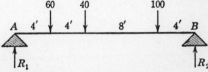

Figure 191

$$20R_1 = 16 \cdot 60 + 12 \cdot 40 + 4 \cdot 100 = 1840, \qquad R_1 = 92 \text{ lb.}$$

If the parallel forces do not all lie in the same plane, take the xy-plane perpendicular to the forces. Let (x_i, y_i) be the point where the line of action of f_i pierces the xy-plane. Taking moments first with respect to the y-axis, then with respect to the x-axis, we obtain the equations

$$F\bar{x} = \sum_{i=1}^{n} f_i x_i, \qquad F\bar{y} = \sum_{i=1}^{n} f_i y_i,$$

where $(\bar{x}, \bar{y})$ is the point where the line of action of the resultant F pierces the xy-plane.

Example (b). A table 20 ft. by 10 ft., weighing 4 oz. per sq. ft., bears loads at the corners as shown. Find the point of application of the resultant.

The weight of the table top may be replaced by a force of 50 lb. at the center. Taking moments about OC as y-axis and about OA as x-axis, we find

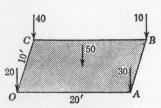

Figure 192

$$F\bar{x} = 10 \cdot 50 + 20 \cdot 30 + 20 \cdot 10 = 1300,$$
$$\bar{x} = \tfrac{1300}{150} = \tfrac{26}{3} \text{ ft.;}$$
$$F\bar{y} = 5 \cdot 50 + 10 \cdot 40 + 10 \cdot 10 = 750,$$
$$\bar{y} = \tfrac{750}{150} = 5 \text{ ft.}$$

182. *Center of Pressure*

Let us return to the problem of fluid pressure. In taking moments, we may replace the force

$$\Delta F_i = w y_i x_i \, \Delta y,$$

acting on the elementary rectangle, by a concentrated force of the same magnitude at the center of the rectangle (just as, in the example above, we replaced the weight of the table by a force at its center).

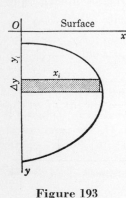

Figure 193

The moments of this force with respect to Oy and Ox are respectively $w y_i x_i \, \Delta y \cdot \frac{1}{2} x_i$, $w y_i x_i \, \Delta y \cdot y_i$. Adding all these elementary moments and taking the limits of the sums, we obtain the formulas

$$F \bar{x} = \lim_{n \to \infty} \sum_{i=1}^{n} \tfrac{1}{2} w y_i x_i^2 \, \Delta y = \tfrac{1}{2} w \int_c^d y x^2 \, dy,$$

$$F \bar{y} = \lim_{n \to \infty} \sum_{i=1}^{n} w y_i^2 x_i \, \Delta y = w \int_c^d y^2 x \, dy,$$

where $(\bar{x}, \bar{y})$ is the point of application of a single force F that would balance the distributed force. This point is called the *center of pressure*.

Once more, the student is advised not to memorize these formulas but to concentrate on understanding the mechanics of the problem.

Example. Find the center of pressure on the submerged triangle of Fig. 189. (Example, § 180.)

We have

$$F \bar{x} = \frac{1}{2} w \int_1^3 y x^2 \, dy = \frac{1}{2} w \int_1^3 y (3 - y)^2 \, dy$$

$$= \frac{1}{2} w \left[\frac{9 y^2}{2} - 2 y^3 + \frac{1}{4} y^4 \right]_1^3 = 2w,$$

$$\bar{x} = \frac{2w}{\frac{10}{3} w} = \frac{3}{5};$$

$$F \bar{y} = w \int_1^3 y^2 x \, dy = w \int_1^3 y^2 (3 - y) \, dy$$

$$= w \left[y^3 - \frac{1}{4} y^4 \right]_1^3 = 6w,$$

$$\bar{y} = \frac{6w}{\frac{10}{3} w} = \frac{9}{5}.$$

EXERCISES

1. A man weighing 200 lb. stands on the end of a plank supported as shown in Fig. 194. If the plank weighs 4 lb. per ft., what weight W must be applied at A to hold the plank in position?   *Ans.* 40 lb. (critical value).

2. In Ex. 1, what must be the weight of the plank per foot, if it is to remain in position due to its own weight?

3. In Ex. 1, with W removed, a child weighing 60 lb. walks from A toward B. How far can he go?   *Ans.* 5 ft.

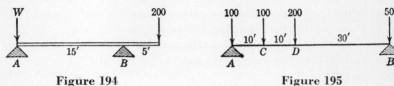

Figure 194   **Figure 195**

4. A straight beam is loaded as shown in Fig. 195. If the weight of the beam is negligible, find (a) the point of application of the resultant; (b) the reactions at the supports.   *Ans.* (a) $\bar{x} = 16$ ft. 8 in.; (b) 300 lb., 150 lb.

5. Solve Ex. 4 if the beam weighs 2 lb. per foot.

6. Solve Ex. 4 if the segment AD bears a uniformly distributed load of 5 lb. per ft.

7. Solve Ex. 4 if the segment AD bears a uniformly distributed load of 5 lb. per ft. and the segment DB a distributed load increasing uniformly from 5 lb. per ft. at D to 15 lb. per ft. at B.   *Ans.* (a) $\bar{x} = 23$ ft. 3 in.

8. A platform 20 ft. square, weighing $1\frac{1}{2}$ lb. per sq. ft., bears loads of 100 lb. at (5, 4), 200 lb. at (15, 5), 50 lb. at (8, 12), 50 lb. at (20, 0). At what point would a single support hold the platform in place?   *Ans.* (10.9, 8).

9. A weight W is to be raised by a lever with the force F at one end and the fulcrum A at the other. If the weight is a ft. from the fulcrum, and the lever weighs

Figure 196   **Figure 197**

w lb. per ft., what should be the length of the lever to lift the weight most easily? (Fig. 196.)

$$Ans. \ l = \sqrt{\frac{2Wa}{w}}.$$

10. Solve Ex. 9 if the lever projects a distance b beyond the fulcrum (Fig. 197).

$$Ans. \ \text{If} \ \sqrt{\frac{2Wa - b^2w}{w}} > a, \ l = b + \sqrt{\frac{2Wa - b^2w}{w}}; \ \text{otherwise}, \ l = a + b.$$

11. A platform 20 ft. square, of negligible weight, bears a single concentrated load. The reactions are, at (0, 0), 50 lbs.; at (20, 0), 80 lb.; at (20, 20), 100 lb.; at (0, 20), 70 lb. Where is the load?

12. Solve Ex. 11 if the platform weighs 4 oz. per sq. ft.   *Ans.* (13, 12).

In Exs. 13–18, find the depth of the center of pressure.

13. A rectangle submerged vertically with one edge in the surface.   *Ans.* $\frac{2}{3}a$.

14. A rectangle submerged vertically with its upper edge at depth c.

15. An isosceles triangle submerged with the line of symmetry vertical and the vertex in the surface.   *Ans.* $\frac{3}{4}h$.

16. An isosceles triangle submerged with the line of symmetry vertical and the base in the surface.   *Ans.* $\frac{1}{2}h$.

17. One end of a horizontal cylindrical tank, half filled.

18. One end of the parabolic trough of Ex. 11, page 350.

19. Find the center of pressure in Ex. 3, page 349.

20. Find the center of pressure in Ex. 4, page 349.

21. Find the center of pressure in Ex. 5, page 349.

22. Find the center of pressure on the right half of the square of Ex. 16, page 350.

23. Find integrals for the center of pressure on the submerged area of Ex. 18, page 350. See Ex. 13 above.

183. *Work*

Let a constant force be acting continuously upon a body so as to move it through a distance d. The product of the magnitude F of the force, and the distance d, is called the work done in moving the body through the distance d,

Work = (magnitude of force)(distance over which it acts),
W = F · d.

If, for instance, you use a constant 20-lb. force to push a block 10 ft., then the work you do is
$$W = (20 \text{ lb.})(10 \text{ ft.})$$
$$= 200 \text{ ft-lb.}$$

The above basic concept of work is readily extended to the determination of the work done by a variable force, as is illustrated in the example below.

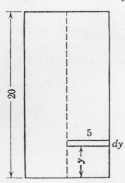

Figure 198

Example. A cylindrical tank, with a base radius of 5 ft. and a height of 20 ft., is filled with water. Find the work done in pumping all the water out the top of the tank.

A cross-section of the tank is exhibited in Fig. 198. Consider a representative element, as shown, at a distance y from the base of the tank. The circular disk, formed by revolving that element about the axis of the tank, has a volume $\pi(5^2) \, dy$ cu. ft. Water weighs about 62.5 lb. per cu. ft. Therefore, the circular disk of water weighs $62.5(25\pi) \, dy$ lb., and it is to be raised a distance of $(20 - y)$ ft.

The work to be done in raising the circular disk of water to the top of the tank is $62.5(25\pi)(20 - y) \, dy$.

To empty the whole tank, the work required is

(1) $$W = 62.5(25\pi) \int_0^{20} (20 - y)\, dy.$$

From (1) it follows that

$$W = \frac{3125\pi}{2} \left[-\frac{(20 - y)^2}{2} \right]_0^{20}$$
$$= 9.82(10)^5 \text{ ft-lb.}$$

EXERCISES

In order to simplify the numerical work, let w denote the weight in pounds per cubic foot of the liquid in Exs. 1–13.

1. Suppose the tank of the example above is only half full (the bottom half!): find the work done in pumping the water out the top of the tank.

Ans. $3750\pi w$ ft-lb.

2. A hemispherical tank of diameter 8 ft. is full of liquid. Find the work done in pumping the liquid out the top of the tank.   *Ans.* $64\pi w$ ft-lb.

3. For the tank of Ex. 2, suppose the surface of the liquid is 1 ft. from the top of the tank. Find the work done in pumping the liquid out the top.

Ans. $\frac{225}{4}\pi w$ ft-lb.

4. A cistern is built in the form of a hemisphere of radius r, surmounted by a right circular cylinder with base radius r and height h. If the cistern is full of water, find the work done in pumping the water out the top of the cistern.

Ans. $\frac{1}{12}\pi w r^2(3r^2 + 8rh + 6h^2)$.

5. Let a cistern of the shape of that in Ex. 4 have its cylinder height equal its hemisphere radius, $h = r$. If the cistern is half full, 50% of capacity volume, find the work done in pumping the water out the top of the cistern.   *Ans.* $\frac{77}{12}\pi w r^4$.

6. Let the cistern of Ex. 5 be three-fourths full. Find the work done in pumping the water out the top.

Ans. $\dfrac{383\pi w r^4}{288}$.

7. If the cistern of Ex. 4 is filled only to the top of the hemisphere, find the work done in pumping the water out the top.   *Ans.* $\frac{1}{12}\pi w r^3(3r + 8h)$.

8. A tank is made in the shape of a right circular cylinder surmounted by a frustrum of a cone, a vertical cross-section being shown in Fig. 199. The tank is full of water. Find the work needed to pump all the water out the top.

Ans. $\dfrac{314\pi w}{3}$ ft-lb.

9. A conical reservoir of top radius r and height h is filled with oil. Find the work needed to pump the oil out the top of the reservoir.   *Ans.* $\frac{1}{12}\pi w r^2 h^2$.

10. If the reservoir of Ex. 9 is filled only to one-eighth of its capacity, find the work needed.   *Ans.* $\frac{5}{192}\pi w r^2 h^2$.

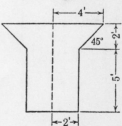

Figure 199

11. A tank is made in the form of a cone, of base radius r and height h, surmounted by a right circular cylinder of base radius r and height H. The tank is full of water. Find the work done in pumping all the water out the top of the tank.

Ans. $\frac{1}{12}\pi wr^2(h^2 + 4hH + 6H^2)$.

12. If the tank of Ex. 11 is filled only to a distance c units $(c < H)$ from the top of the tank, find the work done.   *Ans.* $\frac{1}{12}\pi wr^2(h^2 + 4hH + 6H^2 - 6c^2)$.

13. Solve Ex. 12, if $H < c < H + h$.

$$Ans. \ \frac{\pi wr^2}{12h^2}(h + H - c)^3(h + H + 3c).$$

It is known empirically that (within the so-called elastic limit) for an elastic spring, the force f needed to stretch it beyond its natural length is proportional to the elongation s; $f = k \cdot s$. The number k is called the spring constant.

14. A spring of natural length 10 in. is such that a force of 6 lb. will stretch it 2 in. Show that the spring constant is 3 lb. per in., and find the work done in stretching the spring from its natural length to a length of 14 in.   *Ans.* 24 in-lb.

15. Find the work necessary to stretch the spring of Ex. 14 an additional 4 in., from a length of 14 in. to one of 18 in.   *Ans.* 72 in-lb.

16. It takes twice as much work to stretch a certain spring from 9 to 10 in., as it does to stretch it from 8 to 9 in. Find the natural length of the spring.

Ans. 7.5 in.

PARTIAL DIFFERENTIATION

184. *Functions of Several Variables*

So far, we have been concerned with functions of a single argument. A function may, however, depend upon several independent variables.

Example. The hypotenuse of a right triangle is a function of the perpendicular sides:

$$(1) \qquad\qquad h = \sqrt{a^2 + b^2}.$$

Geometrically a function of two variables x and y may be represented as the z-coordinate of a surface in space. Thus an equation of first degree represents a plane; equation (1) represents one sheet of a circular cone.

185. *Limits; Continuity*

Consider a function

$$(1) \qquad\qquad z = f(x, y)$$

representing a surface in space. When x and y approach the respective values x_1, y_1, the function z is said to *approach a limit* z_1 if the point (x, y, z) of the surface (1) approaches a limiting point (x_1, y_1, z_1). In other words, if the difference between the variable z and the fixed value z_1 can be made as small as desired, by taking x sufficiently near the fixed x_1, and y sufficiently near the fixed y_1, then z is said to approach z_1; in symbols,

$$\operatorname*{Lim}_{\substack{x \to x_1 \\ y \to y_1}} f(x, y) = z_1.$$

A function $f(x, y)$ is *continuous* at the point (x_1, y_1) (compare with § 13) if $f(x_1, y_1)$ exists, and

$$\operatorname*{Lim}_{\substack{x \to x_1 \\ y \to y_1}} f(x, y) = f(x_1, y_1).$$

Similar definitions are laid down for functions of more than two variables.

In what follows, it is assumed that all functions occurring are continuous at all points under consideration.

186. *Partial Derivatives*

If y be kept *fixed*, the function

$$z = f(x, y)$$

becomes a function of x alone, and its derivative may be found by the ordinary rules. This derivative is called the *partial derivative of z with respect to x* and is denoted by

$$\frac{\partial z}{\partial x}, \quad \frac{\partial f}{\partial x}, \quad \text{or} \quad f_x(x, y).$$

The partial derivative with respect to y has a similar meaning.

When z is defined implicitly as a function of x and y by the equation

$$F(x, y, z) = 0,$$

the partial derivatives may still be found by the rule of § 33.

The idea of partial differentiation may be extended at once to functions of any number of variables. We have only to remember that in differentiating with respect to any one variable, *all the other variables are treated as constants*.

Example (a). If $V = \pi r^2 h$, then

$$\frac{\partial V}{\partial r} = 2\pi r h, \qquad \frac{\partial V}{\partial h} = \pi r^2.$$

Thus, if the altitude of a circular cylinder is kept fixed, the volume changes at a rate equal to the lateral area; etc.

Example (b). If $z^2 + 2zx = x^2 - y^2$, then

$$2z \frac{\partial z}{\partial x} + 2z + 2x \frac{\partial z}{\partial x} = 2x, \qquad \frac{\partial z}{\partial x} = \frac{x - z}{x + z},$$

$$2z \frac{\partial z}{\partial y} + 2x \frac{\partial z}{\partial y} = -2y, \qquad \frac{\partial z}{\partial y} = \frac{-y}{x + z}.$$

It is basic that before any partial differentiations can be performed, the independent and dependent variables must be stipulated. As an example, consider the system of equations

(1) $$v^2 + x^2 + uxy - t^2 = 0,$$
(2) $$u^2 + v^2 + y^2 - 3xt = 0.$$

Equations (1) and (2) determine two of the five variables present as functions of the other three. There are, therefore, two dependent variables and three independent variables in the system.

Suppose that we seek $\frac{\partial u}{\partial x}$. Then surely u is one of the dependent variables and x is one of the independent variables. Before we can proceed to perform any differentiation we must know what to hold constant during that differentiation. The solution is not unique until the character of each of the variables has been stipulated.

If in (1) and (2) we decide to use u and v as the two dependent variables, then x, y, and t are the independent ones. We must then hold y and t constant while differentiating (1) and (2) with respect to x. We thus obtain

$$(3) \qquad 2v \frac{\partial v}{\partial x} + 2x + xy \frac{\partial u}{\partial x} + uy = 0,$$

$$(4) \qquad 2u \frac{\partial u}{\partial x} + 2v \frac{\partial v}{\partial x} - 3t = 0.$$

From (3) and (4) it follows, by elimination of $\dfrac{\partial v}{\partial x}$, that

$$(5) \qquad \frac{\partial u}{\partial x} = \frac{2x + 3t + uy}{2u - xy}.$$

Instead of $\dfrac{\partial u}{\partial x}$ in (5) it is much safer to write

$$\left(\frac{\partial u}{\partial x} \right)_{y,t}$$

in which the subscripts indicate what variables were held constant during the manipulations performed.

Next let us return to equations (1) and (2) and consider u and y to be the dependent variables. Then x, v, and t are to be independent variables, and in any differentiation with respect to x, we must hold v and t constant. Then (1) and (2) yield

$$(6) \qquad 2x + xy \frac{\partial u}{\partial x} + uy + ux \frac{\partial y}{\partial x} = 0,$$

$$(7) \qquad 2u \frac{\partial u}{\partial x} + 2y \frac{\partial y}{\partial x} - 3t = 0,$$

from which it follows that

$$(8) \qquad \left(\frac{\partial u}{\partial x} \right)_{v,t} = \frac{4xy + 2uy^2 + 3xut}{2x(u^2 - y^2)}$$

in contrast to (5) above.

In physical problems the ambiguity discussed here should not arise. The purpose to which the partial derivative is to be put, together with other details of the problem, must dictate which are to be the independent and the dependent variables. The study of an artificial system such as (1) and (2) above should clarify the student's feeling for the meaning of partial differentiation. In thermodynamics and physical chemistry the ideas discussed in this section play a useful role.

187. *Geometric Interpretation*

To keep y constant, say $y = y_1$, in the equation $z = f(x, y)$ means geometrically that we cut the surface by the plane $y = y_1$. The partial derivative $\dfrac{\partial z}{\partial x}$ is therefore the *slope of the curve of intersection* of the surface and the plane $y = y_1$; i.e., the slope of the tangent PT. The partial derivative $\dfrac{\partial z}{\partial y}$ may be interpreted similarly.

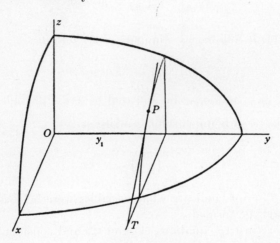

Figure 200

Example. Find the equations of the tangent to the parabola

$$(x + y)^2 + 32z = 256, \qquad x = 5$$

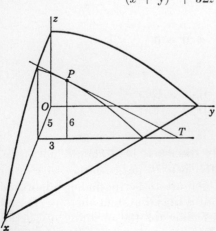

Figure 201

at P: (5, 3, 6). (Fig. 201.)

Since x is constant, we differentiate partially with respect to y:

$$2(x + y) + 32\frac{\partial z}{\partial y} = 0,$$

$$\frac{\partial z}{\partial y} = -\frac{1}{16}(x + y),$$

$$\left[\frac{\partial z}{\partial y}\right]_P = -\frac{1}{2}.$$

Thus the equations of the tangent PT are

$$z - 6 = -\tfrac{1}{2}(y - 3), \qquad x = 5,$$

or

$$y + 2z = 15, \qquad x = 5.$$

188. *Higher Derivatives*

The derivatives $\dfrac{\partial z}{\partial x}$, $\dfrac{\partial z}{\partial y}$ are themselves functions of x and y, and their partial derivatives can in turn be found. They are denoted by the following symbols:

$$\frac{\partial}{\partial x}\left(\frac{\partial z}{\partial x}\right) = \frac{\partial^2 z}{\partial x^2} = f_{xx}(x, y),$$

$$\frac{\partial}{\partial y}\left(\frac{\partial z}{\partial x}\right) = \frac{\partial^2 z}{\partial y\,\partial x} = f_{xy}(x, y),$$

$$\frac{\partial}{\partial x}\left(\frac{\partial z}{\partial y}\right) = \frac{\partial^2 z}{\partial x\,\partial y} = f_{yx}(x, y),$$

$$\frac{\partial}{\partial y}\left(\frac{\partial z}{\partial y}\right) = \frac{\partial^2 z}{\partial y^2} = f_{yy}(x, y).$$

The process can, of course, be repeated to find still higher derivatives. It can be shown that the two "cross-derivatives" $\dfrac{\partial^2 z}{\partial y\,\partial x}$, $\dfrac{\partial^2 z}{\partial x\,\partial y}$ are identical, provided they are continuous:

$$\frac{\partial^2 z}{\partial y\,\partial x} \equiv \frac{\partial^2 z}{\partial x\,\partial y}.$$

EXERCISES

In Exs. 1–16, find the first partial derivatives of the given function.

1. $z = x^3 - xy^2 + 3y^2$.   Ans. $\dfrac{\partial z}{\partial x} = 3x^2 - y^2;\ \dfrac{\partial z}{\partial y} = 2y(3 - x)$.

2. $z = 3x^2y - y^3 + 4x - 7$.   Ans. $\dfrac{\partial z}{\partial x} = 2(3xy + 2);\ \dfrac{\partial z}{\partial y} = 3(x^2 - y^2)$.

3. $u = \cos(xy)$.   4. $u = \csc(xy)$.

5. $y = (x^2 + v^2)^{-\frac{1}{2}}$.   6. $y = (x^2 - v^2)^{\frac{2}{3}}$.

7. $s = \left(\dfrac{t + 2y}{t}\right)^2$.   8. $s = \dfrac{t - 2v}{t^2 + 4v^2}$.

9. $r = \sin^2(\theta - 2\varphi)$.   10. $r = \tan^2(3\theta - 2\varphi)$.

11. $z = \ln(x^2 + 3y^2)$.   12. $v = \ln[u^2(x^2 - 4y^2)]$.

13. $u = e^{-2xy}$.   14. $v = ue^{-u^2 + x^2}$.

15. $z = \text{Arctan}(x - y)$.   16. $\alpha = \text{Arcsin}(x + 2y)$.

17. If (x, y) and (r, θ) are the rectangular and polar coordinates of a point, find the partial derivatives of x and y with respect to r and θ.

$$Ans.\ \frac{\partial x}{\partial \theta} = -r\sin\theta.$$

18. In Ex. 17, find the partial derivatives of r and θ with respect to x and y.

$$Ans.\ \frac{\partial \theta}{\partial x} = -\frac{y}{x^2 + y^2}.$$

In Exs. 19–24, find $\dfrac{\partial z}{\partial x}, \dfrac{\partial z}{\partial y}$.

19. $x^2 - y^2 + z^2 = a^2$.

20. $z^2 - 4xz + y^2 = 4$.

21. $x^2 + z^2 = 6yz$.

22. $xy - xz + yz = 4$.

23. $xyz = x - y + z$.

24. $x^2z - 2z^2y = 3x$.

In Exs. 25–30, find the equations of the tangent line in the given plane.

25. Tangent to the parabola $z = x^2 + 3y^2$, $x = 1$, at the point $(1, 2, 13)$.
    Ans. $x = 1$, $z = 12y - 11$.

26. Tangent to the parabola $z = x^2 - 2y^2 + 4$, $y = 2$, at the point $(1, 2, -3)$.
    Ans. $y = 2$, $z = 2x - 5$.

27. Tangent to the circle $x^2 + 4y^2 + z^2 = 17$, $y = 1$, at the point $(-2, 1, -3)$.
    Ans. $y = 1$, $2x + 3z = -13$.

28. Tangent to the ellipse $x^2 + 4y^2 + z^2 = 9$, $x = 2$, at the point $(2, -1, 1)$.
    Ans. $x = 2$, $z = 4y + 5$.

29. Tangent to the curve $z^2 = 2xy + x^2$, $z = 3$, at the point $(1, 4, 3)$. What kind of curve is this?
    Ans. $z = 3$, $5x + y = 9$.

30. Tangent to the curve $xy + xz + yz = 0$, $x = 6$, at $(6, -2, 3)$. What kind of curve is this?
    Ans. $x = 6$, $9y + 4z = -6$.

31. Given $z = (3x^2 - y)^2$, find $\dfrac{\partial^2 z}{\partial x^2}, \dfrac{\partial^2 z}{\partial x\, \partial y}, \dfrac{\partial^2 z}{\partial y\, \partial x}, \dfrac{\partial^2 z}{\partial y^2}$.

32. Given $v = (3t - x)e^{-2t}$, find $\dfrac{\partial^2 v}{\partial t^2}, \dfrac{\partial^2 v}{\partial x^2}, \dfrac{\partial^2 v}{\partial x\, \partial t}, \dfrac{\partial^2 v}{\partial t\, \partial x}$.

33. Given $u = \cos(x - 2y)$, verify that $\dfrac{\partial^3 u}{\partial y\, \partial x^2} = \dfrac{\partial^3 u}{\partial x\, \partial y\, \partial x} = \dfrac{\partial^3 u}{\partial x^2\, \partial y}$.

34. For the u of Ex. 33, obtain $\dfrac{\partial^3 u}{\partial x^3}, \dfrac{\partial^3 u}{\partial y^2\, \partial x}$, and $\dfrac{\partial^3 u}{\partial y\, \partial x\, \partial y}$.

35. If $w = 2x^3 - 5xy^2$, show that $x\dfrac{\partial w}{\partial x} + y\dfrac{\partial w}{\partial y} = 3w$.

36. If $u = x^2 - 4yz + 3y^2$, show that $x\dfrac{\partial u}{\partial x} + y\dfrac{\partial u}{\partial y} + z\dfrac{\partial u}{\partial z} = 2u$.

37. If $z = \dfrac{xy}{x^2 + y^2}$, show that $x\dfrac{\partial z}{\partial x} + y\dfrac{\partial z}{\partial y} = 0$.

38. If $u = \sqrt{x^3 - 2y^3}$, show that $x\dfrac{\partial u}{\partial x} + y\dfrac{\partial u}{\partial y} = \dfrac{3}{2}u$.

39. If $u = \ln(x^2 + y^2)$, show that $\dfrac{\partial^2 u}{\partial x^2} + \dfrac{\partial^2 u}{\partial y^2} = 0$, which is called Laplace's equation in two dimensions.

40. If $\theta = \operatorname{Arctan} \dfrac{y}{x}$, show that $\dfrac{\partial^2 \theta}{\partial x^2} + \dfrac{\partial^2 \theta}{\partial y^2} = 0$. See also Ex. 39.

41. Show that $u = e^{-\alpha^2 t} \sin \alpha x$ satisfies the heat equation $\dfrac{\partial u}{\partial t} = \dfrac{\partial^2 u}{\partial x^2}$ for all values of α.

42. Determine the relation that must hold between α and β if $u = e^{\alpha x} \sin \beta y$ is to satisfy Laplace's equation $\dfrac{\partial^2 u}{\partial x^2} + \dfrac{\partial^2 u}{\partial y^2} = 0$.   *Ans.* $\beta = \pm \alpha$.

43. If $u = e^{\sqrt{m^2 + n^2}\, x} \cos my \sin nz$, show that $\dfrac{\partial^2 u}{\partial x^2} + \dfrac{\partial^2 u}{\partial y^2} + \dfrac{\partial^2 u}{\partial z^2} = 0$, which is Laplace's equation in three dimensions.

44. Find the relation connecting α, β, γ if $u = e^{\alpha t} \cos \beta x \sin \gamma y$ is to satisfy the heat equation $\dfrac{\partial^2 u}{\partial x^2} + \dfrac{\partial^2 u}{\partial y^2} = \dfrac{\partial u}{\partial t}$.

45. For the function $z = x^2 y^2 + y^{\frac{1}{3}}$, show that $\dfrac{\partial^2 z}{\partial y \, \partial x} \neq \dfrac{\partial^2 z}{\partial x \, \partial y}$ at $(0, 0, 0)$.

46. Find all the possible values of $\dfrac{\partial v}{\partial t}$ from the system

$$uv + xyt = 0,$$
$$x^2 + v^2 - 2ut = 0.$$

47. Find the different possible values of $\dfrac{\partial y}{\partial u}$ from the system of equations in Ex. 46.

48. Let $f_1(z)$ and $f_2(z)$ be functions whose second derivatives are continuous and let a be a constant. Show that

$$y = f_1(x - at) + f_2(x + at)$$

satisfies the wave equation

$$\frac{\partial^2 y}{\partial t^2} = a^2 \frac{\partial^2 y}{\partial x^2}.$$

49. A function $f(x, y)$ of two arguments x and y is said to be *homogeneous* of degree n in x and y if a function φ of one argument exists such that $f(x, y) = y^n \varphi \left(\dfrac{x}{y} \right)$. Prove Euler's theorem: *If $f(x, y)$ is homogeneous of degree n in x and y,*

$$x \frac{\partial f}{\partial x} + y \frac{\partial f}{\partial y} = nf.$$

Re-examine Ex. 35–38 above.

189. *The Total Differential*

In studying functions of one variable,

$$y = f(x),$$

we found much use for the differential

$$dy = f'(x) \, dx = \frac{dy}{dx} \, dx.$$

We shall now set up the corresponding quantity for functions of more than one variable.

Let u be a function of the two independent variables x and y. Consider

$$(1) \qquad u = f(x, y).$$

If we change x by the amount Δx and y by the amount Δy, u will change by an amount Δu. Then, from (1),

$$(2) \qquad u + \Delta u = f(x + \Delta x, y + \Delta y)$$

so that

$$(3) \qquad \Delta u = f(x + \Delta x, y + \Delta y) - f(x, y).$$

For a function $g(x)$ of one variable the first law of the mean, Theorem 22, § 104, is

$$(4) \qquad g(b) - g(a) = (b - a)g'(x_1), \qquad a < x_1 < b.$$

If in (4) we put $a = x$ and $b = x + \Delta x$, we may write

$$x_1 = x + \alpha \, \Delta x, \qquad 0 < \alpha < 1.$$

Then (4) assumes the form

$$(5) \qquad g(x + \Delta x) - g(x) = g'(x + \alpha \, \Delta x) \, \Delta x, \qquad 0 < \alpha < 1.$$

In order to employ (5) in (3) we first rewrite (3) in the form

$$(6) \qquad \Delta u = f(x + \Delta x, y + \Delta y) - f(x + \Delta x, y) + [f(x + \Delta x, y) - f(x, y)].$$

Consider the last two terms in (6). If y is held fixed, we may use $g(x) = f(x, y)$ in (5) to obtain

$$(7) \qquad f(x + \Delta x, y) - f(x, y) = \Delta x \, f_x(x + \alpha \, \Delta x, y), \qquad 0 < \alpha < 1.$$

In (7) the subscript x indicates partial differentiation with respect to x (y being held fixed).

For the first two terms on the right in (6) we use (5) applied to the function $f(x + \Delta x, y)$ with x and Δx being held fixed. Thus we write from (5),

$$(8) \qquad f(x + \Delta x, y + \Delta y) - f(x + \Delta x, y)$$
$$= \Delta y \, f_y(x + \Delta x, y + \beta \, \Delta y), \qquad 0 < \beta < 1.$$

By employing (7) and (8), we may now write equation (6) in the form

$$(9) \qquad \Delta u = \Delta x \, f_x(x + \alpha \, \Delta x, y) + \Delta y \, f_y(x + \Delta x, y + \beta \, \Delta y),$$
$$0 < \alpha < 1, 0 < \beta < 1.$$

In using (5) to obtain (7) and (8) we assumed that the first partial derivatives of f, i.e., of u, exist. If we also assume that those partial derivatives are continuous functions of their arguments, we may rewrite (9) as

$$(10) \qquad \Delta u = \Delta x[f_x(x, y) + \epsilon] + \Delta y[f_y(x, y) + \eta],$$

in which $\epsilon \to 0$ and $\eta \to 0$ as $\Delta x \to 0$ and $\Delta y \to 0$. Since $u = f(x, y)$, we may put (10) in the form

$$(11) \qquad \Delta u = \frac{\partial u}{\partial x} \Delta x + \frac{\partial u}{\partial y} \Delta y + \epsilon \, \Delta x + \eta \, \Delta y.$$

As Δx and $\Delta y \to 0$ independently, the first two terms on the right in (11) yield an approximation to Δu, the change in u. Therefore we proceed to use those terms in defining a differential for a function of two variables in much the same way that we laid down the corresponding definition in the one variable case in § 45.

We define the total differential du of a function u of two independent variables x and y by

$$(12) \qquad du = \frac{\partial u}{\partial x} \Delta x + \frac{\partial u}{\partial y} \Delta y.$$

For the particular function $u = x$, we obtain $\dfrac{\partial u}{\partial x} = 1$, $\dfrac{\partial u}{\partial y} = 0$, so (12) yields

$$(13) \qquad dx = \Delta x.$$

In the same way the function $u = y$ leads us to write

$$(14) \qquad dy = \Delta y.$$

Therefore we define the differentials dx and dy of the independent variables by (13) and (14). This also permits us to rewrite the definition (12) as

$$(15) \qquad du = \frac{\partial u}{\partial x} dx + \frac{\partial u}{\partial y} dy.$$

If x and y are functions of a third variable t, then u becomes a function of t alone, and its differential has been defined in § 45. It can be shown that the value of du as given by (15) agrees with the earlier definition.

For functions of more than two arguments a similar formula holds. Thus if

$$u = f(x, y, z),$$

the total differential of u is

$$(16) \qquad du = \frac{\partial u}{\partial x} dx + \frac{\partial u}{\partial y} dy + \frac{\partial u}{\partial z} dz.$$

190. *Approximate Formulas*

It follows from the discussion in the preceding section that when Δx and Δy are small, du and Δu are *nearly equal*. Hence the differential can be used as an approximation to the increment, for functions of two (or more) variables, exactly as in § 47.

Example (*a*). Find the error in the value of a fraction produced by small errors in the numerator and denominator.

Let the fraction be

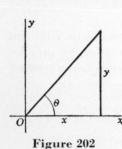

Figure 202

$$(1) \qquad f = \frac{y}{x}.$$

Then the change in f due to small changes in y and x is approximately, if Δx and Δy are small compared to x,

$$df = \frac{x\,\Delta y - y\,\Delta x}{x^2}.$$

Example (*b*). In Fig. 202, if $x = 9.986$, $y = 7.013$, find $\tan \theta$.

In Example (*a*), take $y = 7$, $\Delta y = 0.013$; $x = 10$, $\Delta x = -0.014$. Then

$$\tan \theta = \frac{7.013}{9.986} = 0.7 + \frac{10(0.013) - 7(-0.014)}{100}$$

$$= 0.7 + \frac{0.13 + 0.098}{100} = 0.7023.$$

EXERCISES

In Exs. 1–13, find the total differential.

1. $z = y^4 - 4xy^3$.   *Ans.* $dz = 4(y^3 - 3xy^2)\,dy - 4y^3\,dx.$

2. $z = x^2y - u^2 + x$.   *Ans.* $dz = (2xy + 1)\,dx + x^2\,dy - 2u\,du.$

3. $z = \sqrt{x^2 + y^2}$.   *Ans.* $dz = \dfrac{x\,dx + y\,dy}{\sqrt{x^2 + y^2}}.$

4. $\theta = \operatorname{Arctan} \dfrac{y}{x}.$ *Ans.* $d\theta = \dfrac{x\,dy - y\,dx}{x^2 + y^2}.$

5. $\theta = \operatorname{Arcsin} \dfrac{y}{r}.$ *Ans.* $d\theta = \dfrac{r\,dy - y\,dr}{r\sqrt{r^2 - y^2}}.$

6. $z = \dfrac{y}{\sqrt{x^2 + y^2}}.$ *Ans.* $dz = \dfrac{x(x\,dy - y\,dx)}{(x^2 + y^2)^{\frac{3}{2}}}.$

7. $u = \ln (xyz)$.   **8.** $u = \ln \sqrt{x^2 + y^2 + z^2}$.

9. $x = \dfrac{v}{u^2}.$ **10.** $x = e^{-2yt^2}$.

11. $r = \sin \theta \cos \varphi \cos \psi$.   **12.** $r = \cos \theta \sin \varphi \cos \psi$.

13. $u = e^{-\alpha^2 t} \cos \alpha x$; α constant.

14. Find the error in the product xy, due to small errors in x and y.

15. Compute the product 0.5102 by 0.6303 to four decimal places. (Ex. 14.)

16. A lot is approximately 60 ft. by 150 ft. If each of the measurements is uncertain by 3 in., find the maximum uncertainty in the area.

17. A certain giant saguaro in the Arizona desert has no protruding limbs and is roughly a circular cylinder in shape. At the present time, its rate of growth is found to be an increase in height of 0.8 in. per year, and an increase in diameter of

0.1 in. per year. Find the rate of increase of its volume, given that the saguaro is 40 ft. tall and 2 ft. in diameter.   *Ans.* 1.26 cu. ft. per year.

18. In Ex. 17, compute the rate of change of the lateral surface area (disregarding the spines, which is not always advisable).   *Ans.* 1.47 sq. ft. per year.

19. A sprinter runs 100 yd. in about 10 sec. If the time may be in error by as much as $\frac{1}{10}$ sec., and the distance by as much as 6 in., find the greatest possible error in the velocity.   *Ans.* 0.35 ft. per sec.

20. Find the error in the common logarithm of the product of two numbers x and y due to small errors in the numbers.

21. A box is approximately 3 ft. by 4 ft. by 5 ft. If each dimension is in excess by 0.1 in., find the excess volume.   *Ans.* 677 cu. in.

22. In Ex. 21, find the length of a diagonal.

23. A closed cylindrical tank of circular cross-section has a radius of 2 ft. and a height of 6 ft. Find the approximate volume of asbestos required to line the tank completely with a lining one inch thick.   *Ans.* 8.4 cu. ft.

24. A bin is 10 ft. by 9 ft. by 8 ft. Find approximately the change in the volume when the bin is completely lined with paper $\frac{1}{16}$ in. thick.   *Ans.* −2.52 cu. ft.

25. A right triangle is constructed and the tangent of one of the acute angles is found by measuring the opposite side y and the adjacent side x. If $y = 2.5 \pm 0.1$, $x = 1.5 \pm 0.1$, what is the greatest possible error in the tangent? [Example (*a*), § 190.]   *Ans.* About 0.18.

26. In Ex. 25, find the greatest possible error in the angle. (Ex. 4.)

                    Ans. About 2° 42′.

27. In Ex. 25, find the greatest possible error in the sine of the angle.

28. It is desired to draw a line through the points (0, 0), (3, 4). If the line is actually drawn through (−0.04, 0.11) and (3.01, 3.94), find the error in the slope of the line.   *Ans.* −0.08.

29. Find approximately the error in the function x^2y due to small errors in x and y.

30. The base of a box is a square of side 6.005; the depth is 8.997. Find the volume. (Ex. 29.)

31. Find the hypotenuse of a right triangle whose sides are 6.03, 7.96.

32. The cosine of an angle is measured: $\cos \theta = \dfrac{x}{r}$. Find the error in computing $\cos 2\theta$ due to errors in x and r.

33. The tangent of an angle is measured: $\tan \theta = \dfrac{y}{x}$. Find the error in computing $\sin 2\theta$ due to errors in x and y.

34. For the angle of Ex. 33, find the error in computing $\cos 2\theta$.

$$Ans. \quad \frac{4xy(y\,dx - x\,dy)}{(x^2 + y^2)^2}.$$

35. Find an approximate formula for the change in volume of a right circular cylinder if small changes are made in the base radius r and the height h.

                    Ans. $dV = \pi(2rh\,dr + r^2\,dh)$.

36. Find an approximate formula for the change in total surface area for the cylinder of Ex. 35.   *Ans.* $dA = 2\pi(2r\,dr + h\,dr + r\,dh)$.

37. Do Ex. 36 for lateral surface area only.

191. *Differentiation of Implicit Functions*

Let z be defined implicitly as a function of the two independent variables x and y by the equation

(1) $$F(x, y, z) = 0.$$

We already know how to obtain the derivatives of z with respect to x, and with respect to y, in an efficient manner; see Example (*b*), § 186. There are times, as in the next section, when it is expedient to have a formula for each of these derivatives.

For the function in equation (1), put

$$u = F(x, y, z);$$

then

$$du = \frac{\partial F}{\partial x} dx + \frac{\partial F}{\partial y} dy + \frac{\partial F}{\partial z} dz.$$

But since $u = 0$, $du = 0$ likewise, and

$$\frac{\partial F}{\partial x} dx + \frac{\partial F}{\partial y} dy + \frac{\partial F}{\partial z} dz = 0.$$

Further, since z is a function of x and y, we may write

$$dz = \frac{\partial z}{\partial x} dx + \frac{\partial z}{\partial y} dy.$$

Eliminating dz between these two equations, we find

$$\left(\frac{\partial F}{\partial x} + \frac{\partial F}{\partial z} \frac{\partial z}{\partial x} \right) dx + \left(\frac{\partial F}{\partial y} + \frac{\partial F}{\partial z} \frac{\partial z}{\partial y} \right) dy = 0.$$

To find $\frac{\partial z}{\partial x}$, keep y fixed, so that $dy = 0$. Then

$$\frac{\partial F}{\partial x} + \frac{\partial F}{\partial z} \frac{\partial z}{\partial x} = 0,$$

whence

(2) $$\frac{\partial z}{\partial x} = - \frac{\dfrac{\partial F}{\partial x}}{\dfrac{\partial F}{\partial z}}, \qquad \frac{\partial F}{\partial z} \neq 0.$$

Similarly

(3) $$\frac{\partial z}{\partial y} = - \frac{\dfrac{\partial F}{\partial y}}{\dfrac{\partial F}{\partial z}}, \qquad \frac{\partial F}{\partial z} \neq 0.$$

192. *Tangent Plane to a Surface*

It can be shown that all the lines tangent to a surface

(1) $$z = f(x, y)$$

at a point P: (x_1, y_1, z_1) lie in a plane, the *tangent plane* to the surface at that point. (It is assumed that z, $\dfrac{\partial z}{\partial x}$, and $\dfrac{\partial z}{\partial y}$ are continuous at P.) This plane is determined by any two tangent lines.

Let us assume the equation of the tangent plane in the form

$$z - z_1 = m_1(x - x_1) + m_2(y - y_1),$$

when m_1 and m_2 are to be determined. Now the line of intersection of this plane with the plane $y = y_1$ has the slope m_1. But this line is the tangent lying in the plane $y = y_1$, and, by § 187, its slope is the value of $\dfrac{\partial z}{\partial x}$ at P:

$$m_1 = \left[\frac{\partial z}{\partial x} \right]_P.$$

Similarly we find

$$m_2 = \left[\frac{\partial z}{\partial y} \right]_P.$$

Thus the equation of the plane tangent to the surface (1) at (x_1, y_1, z_1) is

(2) $$z - z_1 = \left[\frac{\partial z}{\partial x} \right]_P (x - x_1) + \left[\frac{\partial z}{\partial y} \right]_P (y - y_1).$$

More generally, let the equation of the surface be given in the implicit form

(3) $$F(x, y, z) = 0.$$

We may imagine equation (3) solved for z and may then write the equation of the tangent plane by (2). Substituting for $\dfrac{\partial z}{\partial x}$ and $\dfrac{\partial z}{\partial y}$ the values given by (2) and (3) of § 191, and clearing of fractions, we find

(4) $$\left[\frac{\partial F}{\partial x} \right]_P (x - x_1) + \left[\frac{\partial F}{\partial y} \right]_P (y - y_1) + \left[\frac{\partial F}{\partial z} \right]_P (z - z_1) = 0.$$

193. *Normal Line*

The *normal* to a surface at a point P is the line through P perpendicular to the tangent plane.

It will be recalled from solid analytic geometry that the direction cosines of any line perpendicular to the plane

$$Ax + By + Cz + D = 0$$

are *proportional to the coefficients A, B, C.* Hence, since the normal is perpendicular to the tangent plane (4), § 192, we have at once the following theorem.

THEOREM 31. *The direction cosines of the normal to the surface*

$$F(x, y, z) = 0$$

at a point are proportional to the values of $\dfrac{\partial F}{\partial x}, \dfrac{\partial F}{\partial y}, \dfrac{\partial F}{\partial z}$ *at that point.*

This theorem is fundamental in the geometry of surfaces.

By analytic geometry, the equations of a line through (x_1, y_1, z_1) with direction cosines proportional to a, b, c are

(1)
$$\frac{x - x_1}{a} = \frac{y - y_1}{b} = \frac{z - z_1}{c}.$$

From this the equations of the normal at any point may be written down at once.

Example. Find the tangent plane and normal line to the sphere

(2)
$$x^2 + y^2 + z^2 = a^2$$

at any point $P: (x_1, y_1, z_1)$ on the surface.

With

$$F(x, y, z) = x^2 + y^2 + z^2 - a^2 = 0,$$

we have

$$\frac{\partial F}{\partial x} = 2x, \qquad \frac{\partial F}{\partial y} = 2y, \qquad \frac{\partial F}{\partial z} = 2z,$$

or at P,

$$\left[\frac{\partial F}{\partial x}\right]_P = 2x_1, \qquad \left[\frac{\partial F}{\partial y}\right]_P = 2y_1, \qquad \left[\frac{\partial F}{\partial z}\right]_P = 2z_1.$$

Substituting in (4), § 192, and simplifying, we find

$$x_1 x + y_1 y + z_1 z = x_1^2 + y_1^2 + z_1^2,$$

or, since the coordinates of P satisfy (2),

$$x_1 x + y_1 y + z_1 z = a^2.$$

By Theorem 31 and equations (1) above, the equations of the normal are

$$\frac{x - x_1}{x_1} = \frac{y - y_1}{y_1} = \frac{z - z_1}{z_1}.$$

These equations may be simplified (Ex. 21 below).

EXERCISES

In Exs. 1–14, find the equation of the tangent plane and the equations of the normal line at the given point.

1. The cone $x^2 + 3y^2 = z^2$ at $(2, 2, 4)$. Draw the figure.

$$\text{Ans. } x + 3y - 2z = 0; \frac{x-2}{1} = \frac{y-2}{3} = \frac{z-4}{-2}.$$

2. The ellipsoid $4x^2 + y^2 + z^2 = 36$ at $(2, 2, 4)$. Draw the figure.

Ans. Tangent plane: $4x + y + 2z = 18$.

3. The paraboloid $4z = x^2 + 4y^2$ at $(2, 1, 2)$. Draw the figure.

Ans. Tangent plane: $x + 2y - 2z = 0$.

4. The cylinder $y^2 = 4ax$ at $(a, 2a, a)$. Draw the figure.

$$\text{Ans. } x - y + a = 0; \frac{x-a}{1} = \frac{y-2a}{-1} = \frac{z-a}{0}.$$

5. The cone $x^2 + 2z^2 = y^2$ at $(1, 3, -2)$. *Ans.* Tangent plane: $x = 3y + 4z$.

6. The paraboloid $z = xy$ at $(3, 4, 12)$.

$$\text{Ans. Normal: } \frac{x-3}{4} = \frac{y-4}{3} = \frac{z-12}{-1}.$$

7. The paraboloid $z = x^2 - y^2$ at $(3, 3, 0)$.

Ans. Tangent plane: $z = 6(x - y)$.

8. The hyperboloid $x^2 - 3y^2 - z^2 + 3 = 0$ at $(2, 1, -2)$.

$$\text{Ans. Normal: } \frac{x-2}{2} = \frac{y-1}{-3} = \frac{z+2}{2}.$$

9. The paraboloid $yz = x$ at the origin. *Ans.* $x = 0; y = z = 0$.

10. The cubic surface $xy^2 + 3x - z^2 = 4$ at $(2, 1, -2)$.

11. The surface $y = x(2z - 1)$ at $(4, 4, 1)$.

12. The paraboloid $Ax^2 + Cz^2 = 2Gy$ at $(x_1, y_1\, z_1)$.

Ans. Tangent plane: $Ax_1x + Cz_1z = G(y + y_1)$.

13. The cylinder $Ax^2 + Cz^2 = 1$ at (x_1, y_1, z_1).

Ans. Tangent plane: $Ax_1x + Cz_1z = 1$.

14. The quadric surface $Ax^2 + By^2 + Cz^2 = K$ at (x_1, y_1, z_1).

Ans. Tangent plane: $Ax_1x + By_1y + Cz_1z = K$.

15. Find the equations of the tangent at the point $(1, 2, 2)$ to the circle $x^2 + y^2 + z^2 = 9$, $x + y + z = 5$; draw the figure.

16. Find the equations of the tangent at the point $(1, 1, 1)$ to the ellipse $x^2 + y^2 = 2z^2$, $x + y + 2z = 4$.

17. Show that the surfaces $x^2 - y^2 + 4z^2 = 1$ and $x^2 - y^2 + 2(z + 1)^2 = 5$ are tangent at the point $(1, 2, 1)$.

18. Show that the sphere $x^2 + y^2 + z^2 = 2a^2$ and the hyperbolic cylinder $xy = a^2$ are tangent to each other at the point $(a, a, 0)$. Draw the figure.

19. Show that the surfaces $2x^2 + 2y^2 - z^2 = 25$, $x^2 + y^2 = 5z$ are tangent to each other at $(4, 3, 5)$. Draw the figure.

20. Prove that the tetrahedron formed by the coordinate planes and a tangent plane to the surface $xyz = a^3$ is of constant volume.

21. Prove that every normal to a sphere passes through the center.

22. State and prove a converse of the theorem of Ex. 21.

23. Two surfaces are said to intersect at right angles (or be perpendicular to each other) at a common point P if their normals at P intersect at right angles. Prove that two surfaces

$$F(x, y, z) = 0, \qquad G(x, y, z) = 0$$

intersect at right angles at P if

$$\left[\frac{\partial F}{\partial x}\right]_P \cdot \left[\frac{\partial G}{\partial x}\right]_P + \left[\frac{\partial F}{\partial y}\right]_P \cdot \left[\frac{\partial G}{\partial y}\right]_P + \left[\frac{\partial F}{\partial z}\right]_P \cdot \left[\frac{\partial G}{\partial z}\right]_P = 0.$$

24. Prove that the ellipsoid $2x^2 + y^2 + z^2 = 7$ and the cylinder $y^2 = 4x$ are perpendicular to each other at $(1, 2, 1)$. (Ex. 23.)

25. Prove that the paraboloid $2x^2 + y^2 = 6az + 6a^2$ and the cone $z^2 = xy$ intersect at right angles at $(a, 4a, 2a)$.

26. Determine a and b so as to make the paraboloid $y = ax^2 + bz^2$ perpendicular to the ellipsoid $x^2 + y^2 + 2z^2 = 7$ at the point $(1, 2, 1)$.   *Ans. $a = 3$, $b = -1$.*

27. Determine b and c so as to make the surfaces $x^2 = by + cz$ and $x^2 + y^2 = 2z(y - 4) + 25$ perpendicular at the point $(3, -2, 1)$.

28. Find the angle between the sphere $x^2 + y^2 + z^2 = 14$ and the ellipsoid $3x^2 + 2y^2 + z^2 = 20$ at the point $(1, 2, 3)$.   *Ans. $23° \, 33'$.*

194. *The Chain Rule; Change of Variables*

The useful chain rule

$$\frac{dy}{dx} = \frac{dy}{du}\frac{du}{dx}$$

of § 29 can be extended to involve any number of independent variables.

As an example, consider F a function of two independent variables x and y:

(1) $F = g_1(x, y).$

Let x and y be functions of two other independent variables u and v. Then

(2) $x = x(u, v), \qquad y = y(u, v),$

or, equivalently,

(2)′ $u = u(x, y), \qquad v = v(x, y).$

It follows that F is a function of u and v,

(3) $F = g_2(u, v).$

Of course g_2 is neither necessarily nor usually the same function as g_1. In simple instances g_2 may be found by direct substitution of the x and y of (2) into the g_1 of equation (1).

From (3) we obtain, as in § 189,

(4) $\Delta F = \dfrac{\partial F}{\partial u} \Delta u + \dfrac{\partial F}{\partial v} \Delta v + \epsilon \, \Delta u + \eta \, \Delta v$

in which ϵ and $\eta \rightarrow 0$ as Δu and $\Delta v \rightarrow 0$. As usual, we postulate the existence and (if need be) the continuity of any derivatives which enter our work.

From (4) it follows that

$$(5) \qquad \frac{\Delta F}{\Delta x} = \frac{\partial F}{\partial u}\frac{\Delta u}{\Delta x} + \frac{\partial F}{\partial v}\frac{\Delta v}{\Delta x} + \epsilon \frac{\Delta u}{\Delta x} + \eta \frac{\Delta v}{\Delta x}$$

so that if we let Δx and $\Delta y \rightarrow 0$, Δu and Δv will also $\rightarrow 0$, and (5) leads us to the chain rule

$$(6) \qquad \frac{\partial F}{\partial x} = \frac{\partial F}{\partial u}\frac{\partial u}{\partial x} + \frac{\partial F}{\partial v}\frac{\partial v}{\partial x}.$$

In the same way we obtain

$$(7) \qquad \frac{\partial F}{\partial y} = \frac{\partial F}{\partial u}\frac{\partial u}{\partial y} + \frac{\partial F}{\partial v}\frac{\partial v}{\partial y}.$$

The student should find it easy to remember (6) if he thinks of it in the following way. The derivative of a function F with respect to an old variable x is the sum of terms each of which is the product of the derivative of F with respect to a new variable by the derivative of that new variable with respect to x. The sum includes one such product term for each new variable.

It is true that the chain rule also applies in the other direction; that is,

$$(8) \qquad \frac{\partial F}{\partial u} = \frac{\partial F}{\partial x}\frac{\partial x}{\partial u} + \frac{\partial F}{\partial y}\frac{\partial y}{\partial u},$$

but most often we wish to move from the old variables to the new ones so that (6) is the basic formula needed.

Iteration of (6) leads easily (but with considerable labor) to formulas for change of variables in higher derivatives.

One frequent use of the chain rule in more advanced mathematics is in changing independent variables in partial differential equations. We choose as an example the change from rectangular to polar coordinates in what are called the Cauchy-Riemann equations, which are (9) and (10) below.

It is vital that in performing partial differentiations, the operator keep in mind what independent variables go together so that he knows what variables to hold constant during a specific operation.

Example. In the following equations,

$$(9) \qquad \frac{\partial u}{\partial x} = \frac{\partial v}{\partial y},$$

$$(10) \qquad \frac{\partial u}{\partial y} = -\frac{\partial v}{\partial x},$$

change independent variables from the rectangular coordinates x, y to a polar coordinate system r, θ given by

$$(11) \qquad x = r \cos \theta, \qquad y = r \sin \theta.$$

In order to use the chain rule (6) efficiently we prefer to have the new variables expressed in terms of the old ones. From (11), or our previous knowledge, we write

$$(12) \qquad r^2 = x^2 + y^2, \qquad \theta = \text{Arctan} \frac{y}{x}.$$

Because of (6) we have

$$(13) \qquad \frac{\partial u}{\partial x} = \frac{\partial u}{\partial r} \frac{\partial r}{\partial x} + \frac{\partial u}{\partial \theta} \frac{\partial \theta}{\partial x}$$

together with corresponding formulas involving u and y, v and x, v and y.

In seeking $\frac{\partial r}{\partial x}$ and $\frac{\partial \theta}{\partial x}$ from (12), or from (11), we must differentiate throughout with respect to x holding y constant. From (12) we obtain

$$r \frac{\partial r}{\partial x} = x, \qquad \frac{\partial \theta}{\partial x} = \frac{-\dfrac{y}{x^2}}{1 + \dfrac{y^2}{x^2}} = \frac{-y}{x^2 + y^2}.$$

We need these derivatives in terms of the new variables r and θ. Hence we proceed as follows:

$$\frac{\partial r}{\partial x} = \frac{x}{r} = \frac{r \cos \theta}{r} = \cos \theta,$$

$$\frac{\partial \theta}{\partial x} = \frac{-r \sin \theta}{r^2} = \frac{-\sin \theta}{r}.$$

We are now able to employ equation (13) to get

$$(14) \qquad \frac{\partial u}{\partial x} = \cos \theta \frac{\partial u}{\partial r} - \frac{\sin \theta}{r} \frac{\partial u}{\partial \theta}.$$

The student should use a similar procedure to obtain

$$(15) \qquad \frac{\partial u}{\partial y} = \sin \theta \frac{\partial u}{\partial r} + \frac{\cos \theta}{r} \frac{\partial u}{\partial \theta}.$$

Naturally equations (14) and (15) may be rewritten with v replacing u throughout.

Then the original system of equations (9) and (10) becomes the system

$$(16) \qquad \cos \theta \frac{\partial u}{\partial r} - \frac{\sin \theta}{r} \frac{\partial u}{\partial \theta} = \sin \theta \frac{\partial v}{\partial r} + \frac{\cos \theta}{r} \frac{\partial v}{\partial \theta},$$

$$(17) \qquad \sin \theta \frac{\partial u}{\partial r} + \frac{\cos \theta}{r} \frac{\partial u}{\partial \theta} = - \cos \theta \frac{\partial v}{\partial r} + \frac{\sin \theta}{r} \frac{\partial v}{\partial \theta}.$$

Multiply each member of (16) by $\cos \theta$, each member of (17) by $\sin \theta$

and add the results to arrive at

(18)
$$\frac{\partial u}{\partial r} = \frac{1}{r} \frac{\partial v}{\partial \theta}.$$

Multiply each member of (16) by $\sin \theta$, each member of (17) by $\cos \theta$ and subtract to get

(19)
$$\frac{1}{r} \frac{\partial u}{\partial \theta} = -\frac{\partial v}{\partial r}.$$

We have shown that a change from rectangular coordinates x, y to polar coordinates r, θ, transforms the system of equations (9) and (10) into the system (18) and (19).

EXERCISES

1. Obtain $\dfrac{\partial r}{\partial x}$ and $\dfrac{\partial \theta}{\partial x}$ directly from equations (11) above.

2. Obtain $\dfrac{\partial r}{\partial y}$ and $\dfrac{\partial \theta}{\partial y}$ directly from equations (11) above.

3. Let x and y be rectangular coordinates. Convert the expression

$$\left(\frac{\partial F}{\partial x}\right)^2 + \left(\frac{\partial F}{\partial y}\right)^2$$

into polar coordinates r and θ.

$$Ans. \left(\frac{\partial F}{\partial r}\right)^2 + \frac{1}{r^2}\left(\frac{\partial F}{\partial \theta}\right)^2.$$

4. Let F be a function of the independent variables x, y, z. Introduce new variables u, v, w by

$$u = \tfrac{1}{2}(y + z),$$
$$v = \tfrac{1}{2}(2x - y - z),$$
$$w = \tfrac{1}{2}(z - y).$$

Convert the first partial derivatives of F with respect to the old variables x, y, z into expressions involving only the new variables. Obtain a check on your answers by using a specific function; for instance,

$$F = x^2 - y^2 + z^2.$$

$$Ans. \ \frac{\partial F}{\partial x} = \frac{\partial F}{\partial v}, \ \frac{\partial F}{\partial y} = \frac{1}{2}\left(\frac{\partial F}{\partial u} - \frac{\partial F}{\partial v} - \frac{\partial F}{\partial w}\right), \ etc.$$

5. Let F be a function of x, y, and z. Introduce new variables u, v, w by

$$u = \tfrac{1}{2}(x + y - z), \qquad v = \tfrac{1}{2}(x - y - z), \qquad w = z.$$

Obtain the first partial derivatives of F with respect to x, y, z in terms of the new variables. Thus show, among other things, that $\dfrac{\partial F}{\partial z} \neq \dfrac{\partial F}{\partial w}$ even though $w = z$.

ITERATED INTEGRALS

195. *Iterated Integration*

The operation of integration may be iterated and thus yields another valuable tool as we shall see in § 197–212. Consider a definite integral

$$(1) \qquad \int_{x_1}^{x_2} f(x, y) \, dx$$

in which the integrand is a function of the two variables x and y, either or both of which may be absent from $f(x, y)$ in specific problems. The limits of integration x_1 and x_2 must never depend upon x, the variable of integration. We may permit x_1 and x_2 to depend upon y. Thus $x_1 = x_1(y)$ and $x_2 = x_2(y)$, although in special cases either of or both x_1 and x_2 may be independent of y. The integral (1) so described is a function of y:

$$(2) \qquad \varphi(y) = \int_{x_1(y)}^{x_2(y)} f(x, y) \, dx.$$

If x_1, x_2, and f are reasonably well-behaved functions of y, $\varphi(y)$ will itself be an integrable function, and we may well consider an integral

$$(3) \qquad I = \int_a^b \varphi(y) \, dy,$$

in which a and b must, of course, be independent of y.

It is customary to combine (2) and (3) and write

$$(4) \qquad I = \int_a^b \int_{x_1}^{x_2} f(x, y) \, dx \, dy$$

to mean that $f(x, y)$ is to be integrated with respect to x (as indicated by the inner differential dx) between the limits x_1 and x_2, and the result of that definite integration is to be integrated with respect to y between the limits a and b.

In evaluating (4) it is important to remember that

376

(a) During the x (inner) integration the y (other variable of integration) is held constant;

(b) The inner limits of integration x_1 and x_2 must be independent of x (the inner variable of integration);

(c) The outer limits of integration a and b must be independent of both variables of integration x and y.

In § 197 we shall encounter the first of many instances in which a mathematical or physical problem leads us naturally to iterated integration. For the moment we concentrate on obtaining practice in evaluating iterated integrals.

Example (a). Evaluate $\displaystyle\int_0^2 \int_0^y (x^2 + 3y^2)\, dx\, dy.$

We proceed as follows:

$$\int_0^2 \int_0^y (x^2 + 3y^2)\, dx\, dy = \int_0^2 \left[\tfrac{1}{3}x^3 + 3xy^2 \right]_{x=0}^{x=y} dy$$

$$= \int_0^2 (\tfrac{1}{3}y^3 + 3y^3)\, dy$$

$$= \frac{10}{3} \int_0^2 y^3\, dy = \frac{5}{6}\left[y^4 \right]_0^2 = \frac{5 \cdot 16}{6} = \frac{40}{3}.$$

Example (b). Evaluate $\displaystyle\int_0^2 \int_x^{x^2} \frac{x^3\, dy\, dx}{(xy + 4)^2}.$

Note that the integration in this example is in the order: y integration first, x integration second. We obtain

$$\int_0^2 \int_x^{x^2} \frac{x^3\, dy\, dx}{(xy + 4)^2} = \int_0^2 \left[\frac{-x^2}{xy + 4} \right]_x^{x^2} dx$$

$$= \int_0^2 \left[\frac{-x^2}{x^3 + 4} + \frac{x^2}{x^2 + 4} \right] dx$$

$$= \int_0^2 \left[1 - \frac{4}{x^2 + 4} - \frac{x^2}{x^3 + 4} \right] dx$$

$$= \left[x - 2 \operatorname{Arctan} \tfrac{1}{2}x - \tfrac{1}{3} \ln (x^3 + 4) \right]_0^2$$

$$= 2 - 2 \operatorname{Arctan} 1 - \tfrac{1}{3} \ln 12 - 0 + 0 + \tfrac{1}{3} \ln 4$$

$$= 2 - \tfrac{1}{2}\pi - \tfrac{1}{3} \ln 3 = 0.0630.$$

196. *Plane Area by Iterated Integration*

An iterated integral with unity as integrand may be interpreted as an area. For instance, the integral

$$\int_0^3 \int_{y^2}^9 dx\, dy$$

$$\int_0^3 (9 - y^2)\, dy$$

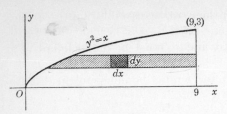

Figure 203

may be viewed as follows: We consider an elementary rectangle of dimensions dx and dy. First sum those rectangles in the x-direction (y being held constant) from $x = y^2$, the lower inner limit of integration, to $x = 9$, the upper inner limit of integration. This yields the area of the horizontal element shown lightly shaded in Fig. 203. The horizontal elements are then summed (integrated) in the y-direction from $y = 0$ to $y = 3$. We thus obtain the area in the first quadrant bounded by $y^2 = x$, $x = 9$, $y = 0$. Indeed,

$$A = \int_0^3 \int_{y^2}^9 dx\, dy = \int_0^3 \Big[x \Big]_{y^2}^9 dy$$
$$= \int_0^3 (9 - y^2)\, dy = \Big[9y - \tfrac{1}{3}y^3 \Big]_0^3 = 18.$$

Exercises in obtaining areas by iterated integration, in either rectangular or polar coordinates, are useful for practice in setting up iterated integrals. In presenting such problems, we are not advocating the use of two integrations when only one is needed.

Example (a). Find the area of a right triangle by iterated integration in rectangular coordinates. (Fig. 204.)

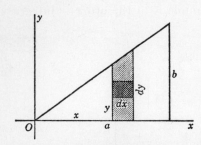

Figure 204

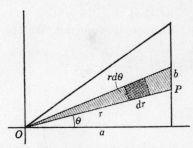

Figure 205

The equation of the bounding line is

$$y = \frac{b}{a} x;$$

therefore

$$A = \int_0^a \int_0^{\frac{b}{a}x} dy\, dx = \int_0^a \Big[y \Big]_0^{\frac{b}{a}x} dx$$
$$= \frac{b}{a} \int_0^a x\, dx = \frac{1}{2} ab.$$

Example (*b*): Solve Example (*a*) in polar coordinates.

From § 200 we borrow the expression $r\, dr\, d\theta$ for the element of area in polar coordinates. The upper limit for r is seen from Fig. 205 to be*

$$OP = a \sec \theta,$$

so that

$$A = \int_0^{\text{Arctan} \frac{b}{a}} \int_0^{a \sec \theta} r\, dr\, d\theta = \tfrac{1}{2} a^2 \int_0^{\text{Arctan} \frac{b}{a}} \sec^2 \theta\, d\theta$$

$$= \frac{1}{2}\, a^2 \left[\tan \theta \right]_0^{\text{Arctan} \frac{b}{a}} = \frac{1}{2}\, a^2 \cdot \frac{b}{a} = \frac{1}{2}\, ab.$$

EXERCISES

In Exs. 1–8, evaluate the given integral.

1. $\displaystyle\int_1^2 \int_0^{2y} (x^2 + y^2)\, dx\, dy.$ *Ans.* $\frac{35}{2}$.

2. $\displaystyle\int_0^1 \int_{2x^2}^{1+x} xy\, dy\, dx.$ *Ans.* $\frac{3}{8}$.

3. $\displaystyle\int_0^1 \int_1^{1+x^2} (y + 2x)^{-\frac{1}{2}}\, dy\, dx.$ *Ans.* $\frac{1}{3}(11 - 6\sqrt{3})$.

4. $\displaystyle\int_0^2 \int_{2x}^4 e^{-x-2y}\, dy\, dx.$ *Ans.* 0.0998.

5. $\displaystyle\int_0^{\frac{1}{2}\pi} \int_y^{\frac{1}{2}\pi} y \sin 2x\, dx\, dy.$ *Ans.* $\frac{1}{16}(\pi^2 - 4)$.

6. $\displaystyle\int_0^1 \int_y^{\sqrt{y}} \frac{x\, dx\, dy}{x^2 + y^2}.$ *Ans.* $\frac{1}{2} \ln 2$.

7. $\displaystyle\int_0^1 \int_{x^2}^x \frac{x\, dy\, dx}{x^2 + y^2}.$ *Ans.* $\frac{1}{2} \ln 2$.

8. $\displaystyle\int_0^1 \int_{x^2}^x \frac{x^2\, dy\, dx}{x^2 + y^2}.$ *Ans.* $\frac{1}{8}(4 - \pi)$.

Solve Exs. 9–20 by iterated integration in rectangular coordinates.

9. Find the area between the cubic $xy^2 = a^3$ and the lines $y = a$ and $x = 0$.

10. Check the answer to Ex. 9 by inverting the order of integration.

11. Find the area bounded by the parabola $y^2 = 4ax$ and its latus rectum.

12. Check the answer to Ex. 11 by inverting the order of integration.

13. Find the area between the curves $x^2 = 2ay$, $x^2 = 4ay - a^2$.   *Ans.* $\frac{1}{3}a^2$.

14. Find the area between the curve $y = 2x(x + 2)$ and the line $y = -2x$.
                                                                                           Ans. 9.

15. Find the area between the curve $y^2 = -4x$ and the line $y = -2(x + 2)$.
                                                                                           Ans. 9.

---

* Or, we may transform the equation $x = a$ to polar coordinates: $x = r \cos \theta = a$, $r = a \sec \theta$.

16. Find the area bounded by the curve $y = 4x - x^2$ and the lines $x = -2$ and $y = 4$.   *Ans.* $\frac{64}{3}$.

17. Find the area bounded by the curve $y = 12x - x^3$ and the line $y = 16$.

Ans. 108.

18. Find each of the two areas bounded by the curves $y = x^3 - 4x$ and $y = x^2 + 2x$.   *Ans.* $\frac{16}{3}$, $\frac{63}{4}$.

19. Ex. 18, page 117.   **20.** Ex. 32, page 117.

In Ex. 21–28, use iterated integration in polar coordinates to find the area bounded by the given curve.

21. $r = a(1 + \cos \theta)$.   *Ans.* $\frac{3}{2}\pi a^2$.   **22.** $r = a(1 - \sin \theta)$.   *Ans.* $\frac{3}{2}\pi a^2$.

23. $r = 2a \cos^2 \theta$.   **24.** $r = a \cos 2\theta$.

25. $r = a \sin 2\theta$.   *Ans.* $\frac{1}{2}\pi a^2$.   **26.** $r = a(2 - \cos \theta)$.   *Ans.* $\frac{9}{2}\pi a^2$.

27. $r^2 = a^2 \sin 2\theta$.   *Ans.* a^2.   **28.** $r^2 = a^2 \cos 2\theta$.   *Ans.* a^2.

29. Find the area of the inner loop of the curve $r = a(1 - 2 \sin \theta)$.   *Ans.* $0.54a^2$.

30. Find the area between the inner and the outer ovals of the curve $r^2 = a^2(1 - \sin \theta)$.   *Ans.* $4a^2$.

197. *Volume Under a Surface*

The method employed in § 158 for finding the volume of a solid succeeds only when the solid can be cut into slices such that the area of the face of each slice is known. We proceed to develop a method that is free of this restriction.

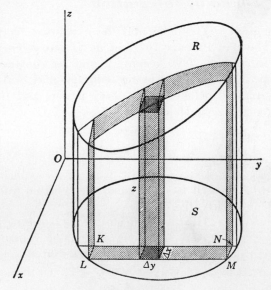

Figure 206

Consider the solid bounded by a portion R of the surface

$$z = f(x, y), \qquad z \geqq 0,$$

the area S into which R projects in the xy-plane, and the vertical cylinder through the boundaries of S and R.

Draw in S a set of n lines parallel to the y-axis and a set of m lines parallel to the x-axis, thus dividing S into rectangles of area $\Delta y \, \Delta x$, together with a number of irregular portions around the boundary. By passing through each line of the two sets a plane perpendicular to the xy-plane, we divide V into vertical rectangular columns together with smaller irregular columns. The upper boundary of each column is a portion of R.

Through that point of the upper boundary of each column which is nearest the xy-plane, pass a horizontal plane, thus forming a set of rectangular prisms lying wholly within V. As Δx and Δy both approach 0, the *limit of the sum* of all these prisms is the volume under the surface:

$$(1) \qquad V = \operatorname*{Lim}_{\substack{\Delta x \to 0 \\ \Delta y \to 0}} \sum_{i=1}^{n} \sum_{j=1}^{m} f(x_i, y_j) \, \Delta y \, \Delta x.$$

From the critical standpoint this formula, based directly on our intuitive conception of volume, may be regarded as a *definition*, analogous to the definition of area in § 55. The definition is valid whenever the limit exists. If z is a continuous function, existence of the limit can be proved.

198. *Volume Found by Integration*

The "double limit" (1) above may be evaluated by two successive applications of Theorem 19, page 107. Let us fix our attention on the rectangle $KLMN$ in S (Fig. 206), keeping x and Δx constant for the time being. The volume $\Delta V_i'$ whose base is this rectangle may be found by adding the volumes of all the included elementary prisms and then taking the limit as Δy approaches zero. Hence, by § 55,

$$\Delta V_i' = \operatorname*{Lim}_{m \to \infty} \sum_{j=1}^{m} f(x_i, y_j) \, \Delta y \, \Delta x = \left[\int_{y_i'}^{y_i''} f(x_i, y) \, dy \right] \Delta x.$$

Here primes are being used to distinguish one y_i from another, etc. The primes do not denote derivatives.

In the expression for $\Delta V_i'$ the coefficient of Δx is a function of x_i alone, since the limits y_i' and y_i'' are functions of x_i alone. Thus we may apply again the theorem of § 55, and find that the required volume under the surface $z = f(x, y)$ is

$$V = \operatorname*{Lim}_{n \to \infty} \sum_{i=1}^{n} \left[\int_{y_i'}^{y_i''} f(x_i, y) \, dy \right] \Delta x = \int_{a}^{b} \left[\int_{y'}^{y''} f(x, y) \, dy \right] dx,$$

where a and b are the extreme values of x on the boundary of S.

The quantity just found is an iterated integral:

(1)
$$V = \int_a^b \int_{y'}^{y''} f(x, y)\, dy\, dx.$$

Of course we might integrate first with respect to x, then with respect to y. The same reasoning as before would lead to the formula

(2)
$$V = \int_c^d \int_{x'}^{x''} f(x, y)\, dx\, dy,$$

y remaining constant during the first integration.

In the foregoing argument we have assumed our solid to be divided into rectangular columns perpendicular to the xy-plane. Sometimes, however, it is more convenient to erect columns perpendicular to one of the other coordinate planes. Such variations offer no difficulty, provided the geometric meaning of the successive integrations be kept clearly in mind. In every problem a sketch of the required volume should be made and the iterated integral built up by inspection of the figure.

Any function $f(x, y)$ of two independent variables may be interpreted as the z-coordinate of a variable point on a surface. If, then, in any problem we can express the required quantity as a double limit of the form (1), § 197, *no matter what may be the geometric or physical meaning of the given function $f(x, y)$,* the limit may be evaluated by an iterated integration (1) or (2). Thus the method described above is by no means confined to the determination of volumes, it applies to a great variety of problems.

Example (a). Find the volume in the first octant bounded by the plane $z = 2 - x - y$ and the cylinder $y = 1 - x^2$. (Fig. 207.)

By means of planes parallel to the yz-plane, cut the solid into thin slabs. Then, by planes parallel to the zx-plane, cross-cut the slabs into slender vertical columns of base $dy\, dx$, height z, volume $z\, dy\, dx$. (Since we are intending to integrate first with respect to y, we write $z\, dy\, dx$ rather than $z\, dx\, dy$.) In the first integration, adding up all the columns in the slab, x remains constant, and y varies from 0 (at P) to $1 - x^2$ (at Q). The second integration adds up all the slabs, from $x = 0$ (at O) to $x = 1$ (at A):

$$V = \int_0^1 \int_0^{1-x^2} z\, dy\, dx$$

$$= \int_0^1 \int_0^{1-x^2} (2 - x - y)\, dy\, dx$$

$$= -\tfrac{1}{2} \int_0^1 \left[(2 - x - y)^2 \right]_0^{1-x^2} dx$$

$$= -\tfrac{1}{2} \int_0^1 \left[(1 - x + x^2)^2 - (2 - x)^2 \right] dx = \tfrac{49}{60}.$$

Example (*b*). Solve Example (*a*) by a second method.

Cut the solid into slabs by planes parallel to the *zx*-plane, the slabs into columns by planes parallel to the *yz*-plane (Fig. 208). In the first

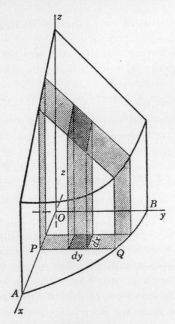

Figure 207   **Figure 208**

integration, x varies from 0 (at R) to $\sqrt{1-y}$ (at S); then y varies from 0 (at O) to 1 (at B):

$$V = \int_0^1 \int_0^{\sqrt{1-y}} z \, dx \, dy = \int_0^1 \int_0^{\sqrt{1-y}} (2 - x - y) \, dx \, dy$$

$$= -\tfrac{1}{2} \int_0^1 \left[(2 - x - y)^2 \right]_0^{\sqrt{1-y}} dy$$

$$= -\tfrac{1}{2} \int_0^1 \left[(2 - \sqrt{1-y} - y)^2 - (2 - y)^2 \right] dy = \tfrac{49}{60}.$$

EXERCISES

In each of the following exercises, the limits of integration should be obtained directly from a figure.

1. Find the volume in the first octant bounded by the planes $x = 1$, $z = x + y$, and the cylinder $y^2 = x$. Solve in two ways, integrating once in the order x, y, then in the order y, x.   *Ans.* $\tfrac{13}{20}$.

2. Find the volume in the first octant bounded by the surfaces $z = 1 + 2xy$, $y = 1 - x^2$. Solve in two ways.   *Ans.* $\tfrac{5}{6}$.

3. Find the volume in the first octant bounded by the surfaces $z = xy^2$, $x = 2y$, $y = 1$. Solve in two ways.   *Ans.* $\frac{2}{5}$.

4. Find in two ways the volume in the first octant bounded by the surfaces $az = x^2 + 2ay$, $y = x$, $x = a$.

$$Ans.\ \frac{7a^3}{12}.$$

5. Find the volume of a cylindrical column having as its base the area between the curves $y = x$, $y = x^2$, and cut off by the plane $x - y - z + 1 = 0$.   *Ans.* $\frac{11}{60}$.

6. Find the volume of a sphere by iterated integration.

7. Find by iterated integration the volume of a segment of an elliptic paraboloid. Use the equation

$$\frac{z - h}{h} + \frac{x^2}{a^2} + \frac{y^2}{b^2} = 0$$

with z ranging from $z = 0$ to $z = h$.   *Ans.* $\frac{1}{2}\pi abh$.

8. Find in two ways the volume in the first octant bounded by the surfaces $yz = ax$, $y^2 = az$, $z = a$.   *Ans.* $\frac{1}{6}a^3$.

9. Find the volume in the first octant bounded by the surfaces $y^2 + z^2 = ax$, $2y + z = 2a$.   *Ans.* $\frac{5}{6}a^3$.

10. Find in two ways the volume in the first octant bounded by the surfaces $z = x^2 y$, $y^2 = x$, $y = x^2$.   *Ans.* $\frac{3}{56}$.

11. Find the volume in the first octant bounded by the surfaces $az = xy$, $x^2 = 4ay$, $x - y = a$.   *Ans.* $\frac{1}{24}a^3$.

12. Find the volume under the surface $az = xy$, whose base is the area in the xy-plane bounded by the curves $y^2 = ax$, $x + y = 2a$, $y = 0$.

13. Find the volume in the first octant bounded by the cylinder $x^2 = 4y$ and the planes $x + y = 3$, $z = 1 + y$.   *Ans.* $\frac{112}{15}$.

14. Find in two ways the volume in the first octant under the plane $x + z = 1$, cut off by the surface $x^2 + y + z = 4$.   *Ans.* $\frac{7}{4}$.

15. Find the volume in the first octant bounded by the surfaces $y^2 + az = a^2$, $y^2 + z^2 = ax$. Solve in two ways.   *Ans.* $\frac{2}{7}a^3$.

16. Find the volume enclosed by the surfaces $z = x + y^2$, $y = x$, $x + y = 2$, $y = 0$, $z = 0$.   *Ans.* $\frac{7}{6}$.

17. Find the volume enclosed by the surfaces $z = x + y^2$, $y = x$, $x + y = 2$, $x = 0$, $z = 0$.   *Ans.* $\frac{3}{2}$.

18. Find the volume bounded by the coordinate planes and the surface $x^{\frac{1}{2}} + y^{\frac{1}{2}} + z^{\frac{1}{2}} = a^{\frac{1}{2}}$.   *Ans.* $\frac{1}{90}a^3$.

19. Find the entire volume inside the surface $x^{\frac{2}{3}} + y^{\frac{2}{3}} + z^{\frac{2}{3}} = a^{\frac{2}{3}}$.   *Ans.* $\frac{4}{35}\pi a^3$.

20. Find the centroid of the solid in the first octant bounded by the surfaces $az = x^2 + y^2$, $y = x$, $x = a$.   *Ans.* $(\frac{4}{5}a, \frac{9}{20}a, \frac{7}{15}a)$.

21. Find the centroid of the solid in Ex. 3.   *Ans.* $(\frac{10}{9}, \frac{5}{6}, \frac{5}{12})$.

22. Find the moment of inertia with respect to the z-axis of the solid in Ex. 3.

23. Find the centroid of the solid in Ex. 8.   *Ans.* $(\frac{2}{9}a, \frac{4}{7}a, \frac{3}{4}a)$.

24. Find the moment of inertia with respect to the x-axis of the solid in Ex. 8.

$$Ans.\ \frac{13}{80}a^5.$$

25. Find the centroid of the solid in Ex. 16.   *Ans.* $(\frac{8}{7}, \frac{13}{35}, \frac{47}{70})$.

26. Find the centroid of the solid bounded by the surfaces $z = 0$, $z = x$, $y = x$, $x^2 = ay$.   *Ans.* $(\frac{3}{5}a, \frac{1}{2}a, \frac{3}{10}a)$.

27. In Ex. 26, find the moment of inertia with respect to the z-axis.

Ans. $\frac{7}{120}a^5$.

28. Find the centroid of the solid in Ex. 18.   *Ans.* $\bar{x} = \bar{y} = \bar{z} = \frac{3}{28}a$.

29. Show that when an area in the xy-plane rotates about the x-axis, the volume generated is

$$V = 2\pi \int_a^b \int_{y'}^{y''} y \, dy \, dx.$$

30. In Ex. 29, show that the result of the first integration is either the circular disk or the cylindrical shell, depending on the order of integration.

199. *The Double Integral*

Being given a function f of two independent variables, defined at all points of a plane region S, let us divide S into k elements ΔS_i ($i = 1, 2, \cdots, k$) in such a way that as k increases and ΔS_i approaches zero, the maximum distance between any two points on the boundary of ΔS_i approaches zero. Multiply the area ΔS_i of each element by the value f_i of the function at some point of ΔS_i, add all these products together, and take the limit of the sum. This limit is called the *double integral of f over the region S,* and is denoted by the symbol $\iint_S f \, dS$:

$$(1) \qquad \operatorname*{Lim}_{k \to \infty} \sum_{i=1}^{k} f_i \, \Delta S_i = \iint_S f \, dS.$$

Let us take a moment to tie this up with the argument of § 197. There, the independent variables were the rectangular coordinates (x, y) of any point in S; the equation

$$z = f(x, y)$$

represented a surface in space; the elements of area ΔS were rectangles $\Delta y \, \Delta x$; and, since we took m cutting planes in one direction and n in the other, the number of elements was $k = mn$.

The double integral, like the iterated integral $\int_a^b \int_{y'}^{y''} f(x, y) \, dy \, dx,$

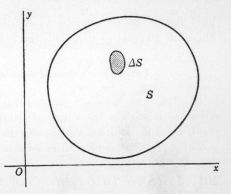

Figure 209

may always be interpreted as the volume under a surface. Since this volume, for a given surface, and given base S, is a definite fixed quantity, the value of a double integral is *independent of the mode of division* of S into elements, as long as the longest chord in every ΔS approaches zero.

Whenever the double integral exists, the iterated integral also exists, and gives us one means of evaluating the double integral. However, the latter does not tie us down to a particular coordinate system or to any particular mode of division of S. We shall take advantage of this in the next section.

200. *The Double Integral in Polar Coordinates*

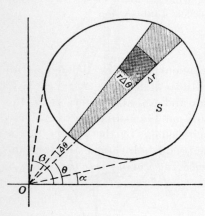

Figure 210

Let S be a plane area bounded by a curve whose equation is given in polar coordinates. We may divide S into elements ΔS by means of concentric circular arcs and radial lines, as in the figure. Then ΔS is the difference between two circular sectors of angle $\Delta\theta$ and radii r and $r + \Delta r$ respectively: i.e.,

$$\Delta S = \tfrac{1}{2}(r + \Delta r)^2\,\Delta\theta - \tfrac{1}{2}r^2\,\Delta\theta$$

$$= r\,\Delta r\,\Delta\theta + \tfrac{1}{2}(\Delta r)^2\,\Delta\theta.$$

Let $f(r,\ \theta)$ be a function of the polar coordinates defined at all points of S. Then, since $\tfrac{1}{2}(\Delta r)^2\,\Delta\theta$ may be neglected, the double integral of § 199 appears as

$$\iint_S f\,dS = \operatorname*{Lim}_{\substack{\Delta r\to 0 \\ \Delta\theta\to 0}} \sum \sum f(r,\ \theta)r\,\Delta r\,\Delta\theta.$$

This double limit can be evaluated by two successive applications of Theorem 19, just as in § 198; the result is

$$\operatorname*{Lim}_{\substack{\Delta r\to 0 \\ \Delta\theta\to 0}} \sum \sum f(r,\ \theta)r\,\Delta r\,\Delta\theta = \int_\alpha^\beta \int_{r'}^{r''} f(r,\ \theta)r\,dr\,d\theta,$$

where α, β are the least and greatest values of θ (Fig. 210), and r', r'' are the least and greatest values of r in the typical sector—α and β constant, r' and r'' functions of θ, in general.

201. *Volume in Cylindrical Coordinates*

Let (Fig. 211)

$$z = f(r,\ \theta)$$

be the equation of a surface in cylindrical coordinates (polar coordinates in the xy-plane with the rectangular z). To find the volume under any portion of this surface, divide the base into polar elements $r\,dr\,d\theta$ and erect on each element a column of height z, volume $zr\,dr\,d\theta$. Then

$$V = \operatorname*{Lim}_{\substack{\Delta r \to 0 \\ \Delta \theta \to 0}} \sum \sum zr\,\Delta r\,\Delta\theta = \int_\alpha^\beta \int_{r'}^{r''} zr\,dr\,d\theta.$$

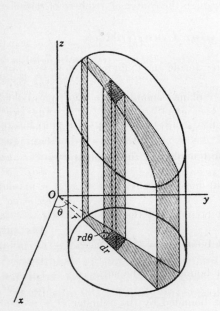

Figure 211

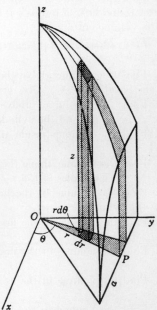

Figure 212

Example. Find the volume lying above the triangle bounded by the lines $x = 0$, $y = x$, $y = a$, and cut off by the surface (Fig. 212)

$$(1) \qquad\qquad x^2 + y^2 + az = 2a^2.$$

In cylindrical coordinates (1) becomes

$$r^2 + az = 2a^2;$$

the upper limit OP for r is found from

$$y = r\sin\theta = a;$$

$$V = \frac{1}{a} \int_{\frac{\pi}{4}}^{\frac{\pi}{2}} \int_0^{a\csc\theta} (2a^2 - r^2)r\,dr\,d\theta$$

$$= \frac{1}{a} \int_{\frac{\pi}{4}}^{\frac{\pi}{2}} \left[a^2 r^2 - \frac{1}{4}r^4 \right]_0^{a\csc\theta} d\theta$$

$$= a^3 \int_{\frac{\pi}{4}}^{\frac{\pi}{2}} (\csc^2\theta - \tfrac{1}{4}\csc^4\theta)\,d\theta = \tfrac{2}{3}a^3.$$

EXERCISES

In Exs. 1–24, use cylindrical coordinates.

1. Find the volume of a sphere.

2. A round hole of radius b is bored through the center of a sphere of radius a. Find the volume cut out.

$$Ans. \ \frac{4\pi}{3}\left[a^3 - (a^2 - b^2)^{\frac{3}{2}} \right].$$

3. Find the volume above the xy-plane, inside the cylinder $x^2 + y^2 = a^2$ and below the paraboloid $x^2 + y^2 = az$.   *Ans.* $\frac{1}{2}\pi a^3$.

4. Find the volume above the xy-plane common to the paraboloid $x^2 + y^2 + az = 4a^2$ and the cylinder $x^2 + y^2 = a^2$.   *Ans.* $\frac{7}{2}\pi a^3$.

5. Find the volume inside the cylinder $x^2 + y^2 = a^2$ and outside the cone $x^2 + y^2 = z^2$.   *Ans.* $\frac{4}{3}\pi a^3$.

6. Find the volume above the xy-plane bounded by the surfaces $x^2 + y^2 = a^2$, $z = y$, $z = 0$. (Examples, § 158.)   *Ans.* $\frac{2}{3}a^3$.

7. Find the volume in the first octant inside the cylinder $y^2 + z^2 = a^2$ and outside the cylinder $y^2 = ax$.   *Ans.* $\frac{1}{16}\pi a^3$.

8. Find the volume in the first octant bounded by the surfaces $y = x$, $x = a$, $xy = az$.   *Ans.* $\frac{1}{8}a^3$.

9. Find the volume in the first octant bounded by the surfaces $y = x$, $x = a$, $2az = x^2 + y^2$.   *Ans.* $\frac{1}{6}a^3$.

10. Find the volume in the first octant bounded by the surfaces $y = x$, $z = x$, $ay = x^2$.   *Ans.* $\frac{1}{12}a^3$.

11. Find the volume in the first octant bounded by the cylinder $x^2 + z^2 = a^2$ and the plane $x - y + z = 0$.   *Ans.* $\frac{2}{3}a^3$.

12. Find the volume inside the cylinder $x^2 + z^2 = 4a^2$ and outside the hyperboloid $x^2 + z^2 - y^2 = a^2$.   *Ans.* $4\sqrt{3}\,\pi a^3$.

13. Find the volume inside the cylinder $y^2 + z^2 = a^2$ and outside the hyperboloid $x^2 - y^2 - z^2 = a^2$.   *Ans.* $\frac{4}{3}\pi(2\sqrt{2} - 1)a^3$.

14. A square hole of side $2a$ whose axis is the z-axis is cut through the paraboloid of Ex. 4. Find the volume cut out.   *Ans.* $\frac{40}{3}a^3$.

15. A vertical cylinder is passed through the circle $r = a \cos \theta$. Find the volume of the cylinder inside a sphere of radius a with center at the origin.

$$Ans. \ \tfrac{2}{3}(\pi - \tfrac{4}{3})a^3.$$

16. Find the volume bounded by the surfaces $z = 0$, $x = 0$, $y = x$, $y = a$, $y^2 = a(z - x)$.   *Ans.* $\frac{5}{12}a^3$.

17. In Ex. 3, find the centroid of that part of the solid that lies in the first octant.

18. In Ex. 3, find the moment of inertia with respect to the z-axis.

19. Find the centroid of half of a circular cone.   *Ans.* $\left(\dfrac{a}{\pi}, 0, \dfrac{h}{4}\right).$

20. Find the moment of inertia of a sphere with respect to a diameter.

21. Find the centroid of one octant of a sphere.   *Ans.* $(\frac{3}{8}a, \frac{3}{8}a, \frac{3}{8}a)$.

22. In Ex. 5, find the centroid of the volume lying in the first octant.

23. Find the centroid of the volume in the first octant bounded by the surfaces $y = x$, $x = a$, $zx = ay$.   *Ans.* $(\frac{2}{3}a, \frac{4}{9}a, \frac{1}{3}a)$.

24. In Ex. 23, find the moment of inertia with respect to the z-axis.   *Ans.* $\frac{3}{16}a^5$.

25. Show that when an area bounded by the curve $r = f(\theta)$ rotates about the polar axis, the volume generated is

$$V = 2\pi \int_\alpha^\beta \int_{r'}^{r''} r^2 \sin\theta \, dr \, d\theta.$$

In Exs. 26–32, use the method of Ex. 25.

26. Find the volume of a sphere.

27. Find the volume of a circular cone.

28. Find the volume generated by revolving the cardioid $r = a(1 - \sin\theta)$ about its line of symmetry.   *Ans.* $\frac{8}{3}\pi a^3$.

29. The curve $r^2 = a^2 \sin\theta$ revolves about the y-axis. Find the volume generated.   *Ans.* $\frac{8}{15}\pi a^3$.

30. Find the volume of a torus. (Ex. 46, page 303.)   *Ans.* $2\pi^2 a^2 b$.

31. Find the volume cut from a sphere by one sheet of a cone of half-angle α with its vertex at the center of the sphere.   *Ans.* $\frac{2}{3}\pi a^3(1 - \cos\alpha)$.

32. Find the centroid of a circular cone.

Ans. On the axis, distance from base $= \frac{1}{4}$ altitude.

202. *Evaluation by Inversion of Order*

We have seen that inversion of the order of integration frequently affords a useful check on the value of an iterated integral. There are important integrals which cannot be evaluated in terms of elementary functions, as they stand, but which yield to elementary methods, when the order of integration is inverted.

Example. Evaluate $\displaystyle\int_0^1 \int_x^1 e^{y^2} \, dy \, dx$.

Here the first integration is impossible by elementary methods. We shall invert the order of integration. The inner integration runs from $y = x$ to $y = 1$; the outer one from $x = 0$ to $x = 1$. Therefore the integration covers the triangle bounded by $x = 0$, $y = x$, $y = 1$ (Fig. 213). The integrand is unaffected by a change of order of integration. Hence

$$\int_0^1 \int_x^1 e^{y^2} \, dy \, dx = \int_0^1 \int_0^y e^{y^2} \, dx \, dy$$

$$= \int_0^1 \left[x e^{y^2} \right]_0^y dy$$

$$= \int_0^1 y e^{y^2} \, dy$$

$$= \left[\tfrac{1}{2} e^{y^2} \right]_0^1$$

$$= \tfrac{1}{2}(e - 1).$$

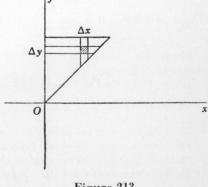

Figure 213

203. *Evaluation by Change of Coordinate System*

An integration impossible, by elementary methods, in rectangular co-ordinates, may become possible (even simple) in polar coordinates, or vice versa. We shall use two examples, of which the second is of vital importance in many advanced applications of mathematics to engineering and physics.

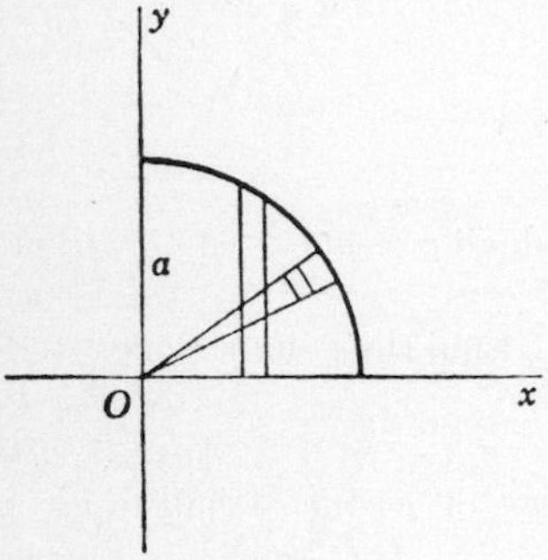

Example (a). Evaluate

$$\int_0^a \int_0^{\sqrt{a^2-x^2}} \sqrt{x^2 + y^2}\, dy\, dx.$$

In this example inversion of order of integration is useless; it would merely interchange the letters x and y throughout. We can perform the first integration, but not the second one, by elementary means. The integration runs from $y = 0$ to $y = \sqrt{a^2 - x^2}$, then from $x = 0$ to $x = a$; i.e., over the first quadrant of a circle of radius a, center at the origin. This suggests polar coordinates. The new element of area is $r\, dr\, d\theta$, and $\sqrt{x^2 + y^2}$ becomes r. Therefore,

Figure 214

$$\int_0^a \int_0^{\sqrt{a^2-x^2}} \sqrt{x^2 + y^2}\, dy\, dx = \int_0^{\frac{\pi}{2}} \int_0^a r \cdot r\, dr\, d\theta$$

$$= \int_0^{\frac{\pi}{2}} \frac{1}{3} a^3\, d\theta = \frac{\pi a^3}{6}.$$

Example (b). Evaluate $\int_0^\infty e^{-x^2}\, dx$.

This involves only a single integration but a nonelementary one. Put

$$B = \int_0^\infty e^{-x^2}\, dx.$$

Then, of course, it is also true that

$$B = \int_0^\infty e^{-y^2}\, dy.$$

Now consider the iterated integral

$$\int_0^\infty \int_0^\infty e^{-x^2-y^2}\, dx\, dy.$$

Since $e^{-x^2-y^2} = e^{-x^2} \cdot e^{-y^2}$, we may write

$$\int_0^\infty \int_0^\infty e^{-x^2-y^2}\, dx\, dy = \int_0^\infty \left[\int_0^\infty e^{-x^2}\, dx \right] e^{-y^2}\, dy = B \int_0^\infty e^{-y^2}\, dy = B^2.$$

Hence

$$B^2 = \int_0^\infty \int_0^\infty e^{-x^2-y^2} \, dx \, dy.$$

The region of integration in this last integral is the entire first quadrant. Turning to polar coordinates, we find that the element of area is $r \, dr \, d\theta$ and the integrand is e^{-r^2}. Therefore,

$$B^2 = \int_0^{\frac{\pi}{2}} \int_0^\infty e^{-r^2} r \, dr \, d\theta$$

$$= \int_0^{\frac{\pi}{2}} \left[-\tfrac{1}{2} e^{-r^2} \right]_0^\infty d\theta$$

$$= \int_0^{\frac{\pi}{2}} \tfrac{1}{2} \, d\theta = \tfrac{1}{4}\pi.$$

Since $B^2 = \tfrac{1}{4}\pi$, and $B > 0$, $B = \tfrac{1}{2}\sqrt{\pi}$. That is,

$$\int_0^\infty e^{-x^2} \, dx = \frac{\sqrt{\pi}}{2}.$$

EXERCISES

In Exs. 1–11, evaluate the integrals by inverting the order of integration.

1. $\displaystyle\int_0^1 \int_y^1 \frac{y \, dx \, dy}{\sqrt{x^2 + y^2}}.$ *Ans.* $\tfrac{1}{2}(\sqrt{2} - 1).$

2. $\displaystyle\int_0^1 \int_{2y}^2 y \sqrt{x^2 + y^2} \, dx \, dy.$ *Ans.* $\tfrac{1}{6}(5\sqrt{5} - 8).$

3. $\displaystyle\int_0^1 \int_x^1 x(x^2 + y^2)^{\frac{3}{2}} \, dy \, dx.$ *Ans.* $\tfrac{1}{30}(4\sqrt{2} - 1).$

4. $\displaystyle\int_0^2 \int_{\frac{1}{2}y}^1 \sin x^2 \, dx \, dy.$ *Ans.* $1 - \cos 1.$

5. $\displaystyle\int_0^\infty \int_x^\infty \frac{e^{-t} \, dt \, dx}{t}.$ *Ans.* $1.$

6. $\displaystyle\int_0^1 \int_x^1 x \sin y^3 \, dy \, dx.$ *Ans.* $0.077.$

7. $\displaystyle\int_0^1 \int_y^{\sqrt{y}} \frac{\sin x}{x} \, dx \, dy.$ *Ans.* $0.159.$

8. $\displaystyle\int_{-1}^0 \int_{-x}^1 \frac{x^2 \, dy \, dx}{1 + y^4}.$ *Ans.* $0.058.$

9. $\displaystyle\int_0^2 \int_{\frac{1}{2}y}^1 \frac{dx \, dy}{(1 + x^2)^3}.$ *Ans.* $\tfrac{3}{8}.$

10. $\displaystyle\int_0^1 \int_{\sqrt{x}}^1 \sqrt{1 + y^3}\, dy\, dx.$　　　　　　　　　　　*Ans.* 0.406.

11. $\displaystyle\int_0^4 \int_{\sqrt{y}}^2 \frac{y\, dx\, dy}{\sqrt{1 + x^5}}.$　　　　　　　　　　　*Ans.* 0.949.

In Exs. 12–22, evaluate the integrals by transforming to polar coordinates.

12. $\displaystyle\int_0^1 \int_0^{\sqrt{1-x^2}} e^{-x^2-y^2}\, dy\, dx.$　　　　　　　*Ans.* $\dfrac{\pi(e-1)}{4e}.$

13. $\displaystyle\int_0^1 \int_0^{\sqrt{1-x^2}} e^{x^2+y^2}\, dy\, dx.$　　　　　　　*Ans.* $\frac{1}{4}\pi(e-1).$

14. $\displaystyle\int_0^1 \int_y^1 \frac{x^6\, dx\, dy}{(x^2 + y^2)^{\frac{5}{2}}}.$　　　　　　　*Ans.* $\frac{5}{36}\sqrt{2}.$

15. $\displaystyle\int_0^a \int_0^{\sqrt{a^2-x^2}} x^2 \sqrt{x^2 + y^2}\, dy\, dx.$　　　　　　　*Ans.* $\dfrac{\pi a^5}{20}.$

16. $\displaystyle\int_0^a \int_0^x \frac{x^2\, dy\, dx}{\sqrt{x^2 + y^2}}.$　　　　　　　*Ans.* $\dfrac{a^3}{3}\ln(1 + \sqrt{2}).$

17. Ex. 1.　　　　　　　**18.** Ex. 2.　　　　　　　**19.** Ex. 3.
20. Ex. 4.　　　　　　　**21.** Ex. 6.　　　　　　　**22.** Ex. 8.

In Exs. 23–27, evaluate the integral by employing an appropriate method.

23. $\displaystyle\int_0^a \int_0^{\sqrt{a^2-y^2}} \frac{x^2\, dx\, dy}{(x^2 + y^2)^{\frac{1}{2}}}.$　　　　　　　*Ans.* $\frac{1}{4}\pi a.$

24. $\displaystyle\int_0^1 \int_y^1 \frac{\cos x}{x}\, dx\, dy.$　　　　　　　*Ans.* $\sin 1.$

25. $\displaystyle\int_0^1 \int_x^1 x \cos y^3\, dy\, dx.$　　　　　　　*Ans.* $\frac{1}{6}\sin 1.$

26. $\displaystyle\int_0^a \int_0^{\sqrt{a^2-y^2}} \frac{x^4\, dx\, dy}{(x^2 + y^2)^{\frac{1}{2}}}.$　　　　　　　*Ans.* $\frac{1}{16}\pi a^3.$

27. $\displaystyle\int_0^1 \int_0^y \frac{y^2\, dx\, dy}{(x^2 + y^2)^{\frac{3}{2}}}.$　　　　　　　*Ans.* $\frac{1}{2}\sqrt{2}.$

28. Evaluate $\displaystyle\int_0^{\frac{\pi}{2}} \int_0^{\sec\theta} \frac{r\, dr\, d\theta}{1 + r^2 \sin^2\theta}$ by transforming to rectangular coordi-

nates.　　　　　　　　　　　　　　　　　　　　　　　*Ans.* $\frac{1}{2}\pi.$

29. Use the result in Example (b), § 203, to evaluate

$$\int_0^\infty e^{-a^2x^2}\, dx, \quad \text{for } a > 0.$$　　　　　　*Ans.* $\dfrac{\sqrt{\pi}}{2a}.$

30. Evaluate the integral in Ex. 29 for $a < 0$.　　　　　　*Ans.* $\dfrac{-\sqrt{\pi}}{2a}.$

31. Find the volume generated by revolving about the x-axis the area between $y = e^{-x^2}$ and its asymptote.

$$Ans.\ 2\left(\frac{\pi}{2}\right)^{\frac{3}{2}}.$$

32. For the area of Ex. 31, find the moment of inertia with respect to Oy.

33. For the area of Ex. 31, find the moment of inertia with respect to Ox.

34. Evaluate $\displaystyle\int_0^\infty x^{-\frac{1}{2}}e^{-ax}\,dx$, for $a > 0$. Put $x = v^2$. $\qquad Ans.\ \sqrt{\dfrac{\pi}{a}}.$

35. Evaluate $\displaystyle\int_0^\infty x^{\frac{1}{2}}e^{-ax}\,dx$, for $a > 0$. $\qquad Ans.\ \frac{1}{2}\sqrt{\dfrac{\pi}{a^3}}.$

36. Evaluate $\displaystyle\int_0^1 \left(\ln\frac{1}{x}\right)^{\frac{1}{2}}\,dx$. $\qquad Ans.\ \frac{1}{2}\sqrt{\pi}.$

204. *Area of a Surface*

We have seen (§ 160) that the area of a surface of revolution may be found by simple integration. To find areas of curved surfaces in general, double integration is required.

Consider a region R on the surface

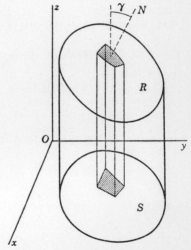

$$(1) \qquad z = f(x, y).$$

Let us pass through the boundary of R a vertical cylinder, cutting from the xy-plane a region S—i.e., S is the horizontal projection of R. Divide S into elements ΔS_i in any convenient way (§ 198), and denote by ΔR_i the portion of R lying above the ith element. Draw the tangent plane at some point (any point) of ΔR_i, and denote by $\Delta R_i'$ the element of area (above ΔS_i) on the tangent plane. Now the two elements ΔR_i and $\Delta R_i'$, on the surface and on the tangent plane, respec-

Figure 215

tively, are essentially equal in the sense that in taking the limit of the sum, we may *substitute the latter for the former*.

It is known from geometry (or if not known, is easily established—Ex. 30 below) that if two planes intersect at an acute angle, an area in one plane may be projected into the other by multiplying by the cosine of the included angle. The angle between the xy-plane and the tangent plane equals the angle between their normals—i.e., it is the angle between the z-axis and the normal to the surface at the point of contact of the tangent plane. Thus, if γ_i is the z-direction angle of the normal N_i,

$$\Delta R_i' \cos \gamma_i = \Delta S_i,$$

or

$$\Delta R_i' = \sec \gamma_i \, \Delta S_i.$$

Adding all the elements and taking the limit of the sum, we define the area R as

(2) $$R = \iint_S \sec \gamma \, dS.$$

Of course if it is more convenient to project the area into the yz- or zx-plane, the same formula holds with α or β in place of γ.

By § 193, the direction cosines of the normal to the surface (1) are proportional to $-\dfrac{\partial z}{\partial x}$, $-\dfrac{\partial z}{\partial y}$, 1, so that

$$\cos \gamma = \frac{1}{\sqrt{\left(\dfrac{\partial z}{\partial x}\right)^2 + \left(\dfrac{\partial z}{\partial y}\right)^2 + 1}}.$$

Thus (2) becomes in rectangular coordinates

(3) $$R = \int_a^b \int_{y'}^{y''} \sqrt{\left(\frac{\partial z}{\partial x}\right)^2 + \left(\frac{\partial z}{\partial y}\right)^2 + 1} \, dy \, dx.$$

Example (a). Find the area of the cylinder* (Fig. 216)

$$2az = 2a^2 - ax - y^2$$

intercepted in the first octant by the planes $y = x$, $y = a$.

We find

$$\frac{\partial z}{\partial x} = -\frac{1}{2}, \qquad \frac{\partial z}{\partial y} = -\frac{y}{a}.$$

In the order x, y (which is in this case much the simpler),

$$R = \int_0^a \int_0^y \sqrt{\frac{1}{4} + \frac{y^2}{a^2} + 1} \, dx \, dy$$

$$= \frac{1}{2a} \int_0^a \int_0^y \sqrt{5a^2 + 4y^2} \, dx \, dy$$

$$= \frac{1}{2a} \int_0^a \sqrt{5a^2 + 4y^2} \, y \, dy,$$

so that

$$R = \frac{1}{16a} \cdot \frac{2}{3} \left[(5a^2 + 4y^2)^{\frac{3}{2}} \right]_0^a = \frac{1}{24} (27 - 5^{\frac{3}{2}})a^2.$$

---

* Sections by planes $y = k$ are easily seen to be parallel straight lines, the yz-trace is a parabola, so that the surface is a parabolic cylinder with generators parallel to the zx-plane.

To use (2) in polar coordinates, we would usually work out $\sec \gamma$ in rectangular coordinates and transform the result to the polar system.

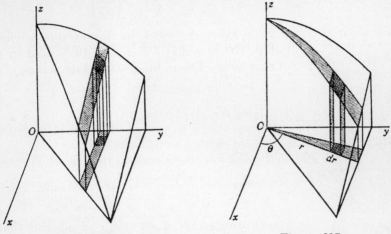

Figure 216   Figure 217

Example (b). Solve the problem above in polar coordinates.

Using the value of $\sec \gamma$ from Example (a), we have (Fig. 217)

$$R = \frac{1}{2a} \iint_S \sqrt{5a^2 + 4y^2} \, dS$$

$$= \frac{1}{2a} \int_{\frac{\pi}{4}}^{\frac{\pi}{2}} \int_0^{a \csc \theta} \sqrt{5a^2 + 4r^2 \sin^2 \theta} \; r \, dr \, d\theta$$

$$= \frac{1}{16a} \cdot \frac{2}{3} \int_{\frac{\pi}{4}}^{\frac{\pi}{2}} \frac{\left[(5a^2 + 4r^2 \sin^2 \theta)^{\frac{3}{2}} \right]_0^{a \csc \theta}}{\sin^2 \theta} \, d\theta$$

$$= \frac{(27 - 5^{\frac{3}{2}})a^2}{24} \int_{\frac{\pi}{4}}^{\frac{\pi}{2}} \csc^2 \theta \, d\theta = \frac{(27 - 5^{\frac{3}{2}})a^2}{24}.$$

205. *Surfaces of Revolution*

In § 160 we defined the area of a surface of revolution; in § 204 we defined curved area in general, including the former as a special case. Thus, for the surface of revolution, area has been defined in two ways; this is allowable only if the two definitions are equivalent. It is interesting and not difficult to see how the general formula works out in the special case.

Let a surface of revolution be formed by revolving about Ox, from $x = a$ to $x = b$, the curve

$$y = u, \qquad z = 0,$$

where u is a function of x. By § 160, the area generated is

$$S = 2\pi \int_C y\, ds = 2\pi \int_a^b u\, \sqrt{1 + \left(\frac{du}{dx}\right)^2}\, dx.$$

Any point Q of the given curve describes, in the rotation, a circle of radius $MQ = u$. Let $P:(x, y, z)$ be a random point of that circle. Then, directly from the figure,

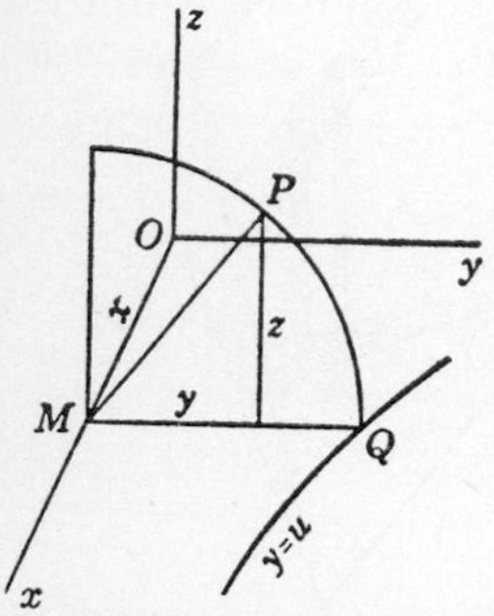

$$y^2 + z^2 = \overline{MP}^2 = \overline{MQ}^2 = u^2,$$

or, above the xy-plane,

$$z = \sqrt{u^2 - y^2}.$$

This gives

$$\frac{\partial z}{\partial x} = \frac{u\, \dfrac{du}{dx}}{\sqrt{u^2 - y^2}}, \qquad \frac{\partial z}{\partial y} = \frac{-y}{\sqrt{u^2 - y^2}}.$$

Figure 218

Substituting in (3), § 204, and remembering that the first octant contains only one-fourth of the surface, we find after a trifle of simplifying

$$R = 4 \int_a^b \int_0^u \frac{u\, \sqrt{1 + \left(\dfrac{du}{dx}\right)^2}\, dy\, dx}{\sqrt{u^2 - y^2}}$$

$$= 4 \int_a^b u\, \sqrt{1 + \left(\frac{du}{dx}\right)^2} \left[\operatorname{Arcsin} \frac{y}{u}\right]_0^u dx$$

$$= 2\pi \int_a^b u\, \sqrt{1 + \left(\frac{du}{dx}\right)^2}\, dx = S.$$

EXERCISES

In Exs. 1–12, use rectangular coordinates.

1. Find the surface area of a sphere.

2. Find the area on the cylinder $y^2 + z^2 = a^2$ included between the planes $y = x$, $y = 3x$.   *Ans.* $\frac{8}{3}a^2$.

3. Find the area of that part of the surface $az = ay + x^2$ lying above the xy-triangle bounded by the lines $y = 0$, $y = x$, $x = a$.   *Ans.* $\frac{1}{12}(6^{\frac{3}{2}} - 2^{\frac{3}{2}})a^2$.

4. Find the area on the cylinder $x^2 + z^2 = a^2$ included between the planes $y = 0$, $y = mx$.   *Ans.* $4ma^2$.

5. Solve Ex. 4, integrating in the other order.

6. Find the area of that part of the surface $9(z - y)^2 = 4x^3$ whose projection in the xy-plane is the triangle bounded by the lines $y = 0$, $y = x$, $x = 2$.

       Ans. $\frac{16}{15}(2 + \sqrt{2})$.

7. Solve Ex. 6, integrating in the other order.

8. Find the area cut off on the cylinder $y^2 + z^2 = a^2$ by the circular paraboloid $y^2 + z^2 = bx$.

9. Find the area on the cylinder $z^2 = 4ax$ and inside the cylinder $y^2 = 4ax$, from $x = 0$ to $x = 3a$.

$$Ans. \ \frac{112a^2}{3}.$$

10. How much of the conical surface $z^2 = x^2 + y^2$ lies above a square of side $2a$ in the xy-plane whose center is the origin?

11. Find the area of that part of the surface $a^2z = a^2x + y^3$ intercepted in the first quadrant by the cylinder $y^3 = a^2x$ and the plane $y = a$.   *Ans.* $\frac{1}{54}(11^{\frac{3}{2}} - 2^{\frac{3}{2}})a^2$.

12. A square hole of side $\sqrt{2}\,a$ is cut centrally through a sphere of radius a. Find the area cut from the surface of the sphere.   *Ans.* $4\pi(\sqrt{2} - 1)a^2$.

In Exs. 13–20, use polar coordinates.

13. Ex. 1.   **14.** Ex. 2.   **15.** Ex. 3.
16. Ex. 4.   **17.** Ex. 8.   **18.** Ex. 9.

19. How much of the surface area of the hyperbolic paraboloid $az = xy$ lies within the cylinder $x^2 + y^2 = a^2$, in the first octant?

20. The center of a sphere of radius a is on the surface of a cylinder of diameter a. Find the surface area on the sphere cut out by the cylinder.   *Ans.* $2(\pi - 2)a^2$.

21. A vertical cylinder is cut by a surface $z = f(x, y)$. Show that the area of the cylinder intercepted between the xy-plane and the cutting surface is

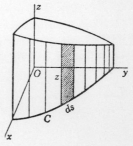

$$R = \int_C z \ ds,$$

where C is the horizontal projection of the curve of intersection.

Figure 219

In Exs. 22–29, use (or adapt) the formula of Ex. 21.

22. A woodsman chops halfway through a tree, the lower face of the cut being horizontal, the upper inclined at $45°$. Find the area of bark cut out. (Examples, § 158.)   *Ans.* $2a^2$.

23. Solve Ex. 22, integrating in the other order.

24. Solve Ex. 22 in polar coordinates.

25. Ex. 2.   **26.** Ex. 8.   **27.** Ex. 9.

28. In Ex. 20, find the surface area cut from the cylinder by the sphere.

29. A solid is bounded by two equal circular cylinders of radius a whose axes intersect at right angles. Find the total surface area of the solid.   *Ans.* $16a^2$.

30. Two planes intersect at an angle α. (a) Given, in one plane, a rectangle of area A with its base parallel to the line of intersection, show that the projection of this area in the other plane is $A \cos \alpha$. (b) Show that this formula holds for an area of any shape. (Divide into rectangular strips with their ends parallel to the line of intersection, and integrate.)

TRIPLE INTEGRALS

206. *The Triple Integral in Rectangular Coordinates*

Suppose we have given a continuous function $f(x, y, z)$ defined at all points of a three-dimensional region V. Let us pass through V three sets of planes parallel to the coordinate planes, thus dividing V into elementary

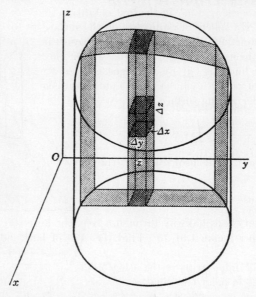

Figure 220

boxes of volume $\Delta x\, \Delta y\, \Delta z$, together with smaller irregular portions around the boundary. Now multiply the volume of each element by the value of the function at some point of the element, and form the sum of these products. The triple limit

$$\operatorname{Lim}_{\substack{\Delta z \to 0 \\ \Delta y \to 0 \\ \Delta x \to 0}} \Sigma\Sigma\Sigma f(x, y, z)\, \Delta z\, \Delta y\, \Delta x$$

is defined as the value of the *triple integral*, or *volume integral*, of $f(x, y, z)$ throughout the region V.

This limit may be evaluated by three successive integrations:

398

$$T = \operatorname*{Lim}_{\substack{\Delta z \to 0 \\ \Delta y \to 0 \\ \Delta x \to 0}} \Sigma\Sigma\Sigma f(x, y, z) \, \Delta z \, \Delta y \, \Delta x$$

(1)
$$= \int_a^b \int_{y'}^{y''} \int_{z'}^{z''} f(x, y, z) \, dz \, dy \, dx.$$

The first integration extends over a vertical column of base $\Delta y \, \Delta x$; the limits z', z'' are the extreme values of z in this column, and in general are functions of both x and y. The integration with respect to y is extended over a slice parallel to the yz-plane; the limits y' and y'' are the extreme values of y in this slice and are functions of x alone. In the final integration the limits are, of course, the extreme values of x in the whole region.

Since there are six permutations of the three letters x, y, z, five other orders of integration are possible, in addition to (1).

207. *Volume as a Triple Integral*

If in § 206 the given function be taken as unity, the integrand becomes merely the volume element, so that the result of integration is the volume itself:

$$V = \int_a^b \int_{y'}^{y''} \int_{z'}^{z''} dz \, dy \, dx.$$

Example. Find the volume sliced off from the paraboloid $x^2 + z^2 = ay$ by the plane $y = a$. (Fig. 221.)

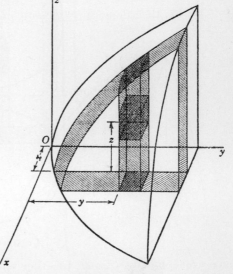

We read directly from the figure

$$V = 4 \int_0^a \int_{\frac{x^2}{a}}^a \int_0^{\sqrt{ay-x^2}} dz \, dy \, dx$$

$$= 4 \int_0^a \int_{\frac{x^2}{a}}^a \Big[z \Big]_0^{\sqrt{ay-x^2}} dy \, dx$$

$$= 4 \int_0^a \int_{\frac{x^2}{a}}^a \sqrt{ay - x^2} \, dy \, dx$$

$$= \frac{8}{3a} \int_0^a \Big[(ay - x^2)^{\frac{3}{2}} \Big]_{\frac{x^2}{a}}^a dx = \frac{\pi}{2} a^3.$$

Figure 221

For practice in reading limits, the student should verify the following integrals for the same volume:

$$V = 4 \int_0^a \int_0^{\sqrt{ay}} \int_0^{\sqrt{ay-x^2}} dz \, dx \, dy;$$

$$V = 4 \int_0^a \int_0^{\sqrt{a^2-x^2}} \int_{\frac{x^2+z^2}{a}}^a dy \, dz \, dx.$$

A figure should be drawn for each case.

208. *The Triple Integral: General Formulation*

We may generalize the setup of § 206 in two ways. First, let the given function f be a function, not necessarily of the rectangular x, y, z, but of any three independent variables. Second, let the region of integration be divided into k volume elements ΔV_i of any shape whatever, subject to the single condition that as k increases, *the maximum distance between any two points of ΔV_i approaches zero.*

Now multiply each ΔV_i by the value of f at some point of the element, and add all these products. The *limit of this sum* as k approaches infinity (always provided the limit exists) is the triple integral of f throughout V:

$$(1) \qquad \operatorname*{Lim}_{k \to \infty} \sum_{i=1}^{k} f_i \, \Delta V_i = \iiint_V f \, dV.$$

209. *The Triple Integral in Cylindrical Coordinates*

Divide the volume into elements by planes through the z-axis, cylinders around the z-axis, and planes perpendicular to the z-axis (Fig. 222). Then the base of the element is $r \, \Delta r \, \Delta \theta$, the altitude Δz, volume $r \, \Delta z \, \Delta r \, \Delta \theta$, so that

Figure 222

$$\operatorname*{Lim}_{\substack{\Delta z \to 0 \\ \Delta r \to 0 \\ \Delta \theta \to 0}} \Sigma\Sigma\Sigma f(r, \theta, z) r \, \Delta z \, \Delta r \, \Delta \theta$$

$$= \int_\alpha^\beta \int_{r'}^{r''} \int_{z'}^{z''} f(r, \theta, z) r \, dz \, dr \, d\theta.$$

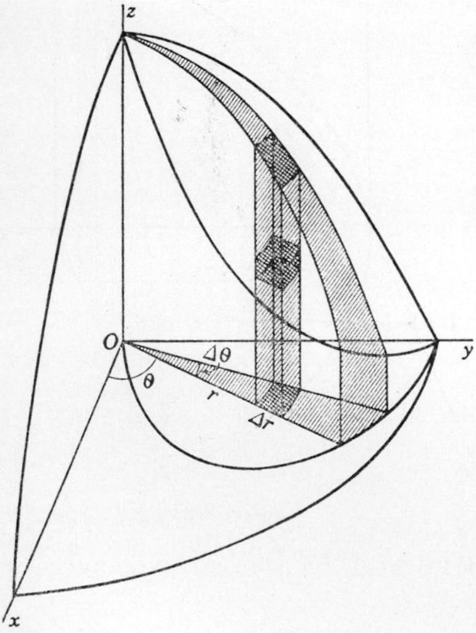

In particular, if

$$f(r, \theta, z) = 1,$$

the integral represents the volume of the region in question:

$$V = \int_\alpha^\beta \int_{r'}^{r''} \int_{z'}^{z''} r \, dz \, dr \, d\theta.$$

Example. Find the volume in the first octant inside the cylinder $x^2 + y^2 = ay$ and the paraboloid $x^2 + y^2 + az = a^2$. (Fig. 222.)

In cylindrical coordinates, the given equations are

$$r = a \sin \theta, \qquad r^2 + az = a^2;$$

$$V = \int_0^{\frac{\pi}{2}} \int_0^{a \sin \theta} \int_0^{\frac{a^2 - r^2}{a}} r \, dz \, dr \, d\theta$$

$$= \int_0^{\frac{\pi}{2}} \int_0^{a \sin \theta} \left[z \right]_0^{\frac{a^2 - r^2}{a}} r \, dr \, d\theta = \frac{1}{a} \int_0^{\frac{\pi}{2}} \int_0^{a \sin \theta} (a^2 - r^2) r \, dr \, d\theta$$

$$= -\frac{1}{4a} \int_0^{\frac{\pi}{2}} \left[(a^2 - r^2)^2 \right]_0^{a \sin \theta} d\theta = \frac{a^3}{4} \int_0^{\frac{\pi}{2}} (1 - \cos^4 \theta) \, d\theta = \frac{5}{64} \pi a^3.$$

EXERCISES

In Exs. 1–16, use triple integration in rectangular coordinates.

1. Find the volume in the first octant under the plane $x + 2y + z = 4$, integrating in the order z, x, y. *Ans.* $\frac{16}{3}$.

2. Ex. 1, integrating in the order z, y, x.

3. Ex. 1, integrating in the order y, x, z.

4. In Ex. 1, find the centroid. *Ans.* $(1, \frac{1}{2}, 1)$.

5. Find the volume in the first octant under the plane $x + 2y + 3z = 6$, integrating in the order x, y, z.

6. Check the answer to Ex. 5 by integrating in a different order.

7. Find the centroid of the volume in Ex. 5.

8. Find the volume in the first octant bounded by the surfaces $z = x^2 y$, $y = x$, $x = 1$, integrating in the order z, y, x. *Ans.* $\frac{1}{10}$.

9. Ex. 8, integrating in the order z, x, y.

10. Find the volume of a sphere.

11. Find the volume in the first octant bounded by the surfaces $yz = x^2 + z^2$, $z = x$, $z = a$, integrating in order y, z, x. *Ans.* $\frac{4}{9}a^3$.

12. Ex. 11, integrating in order y, x, z.

13. Find the volume in the first octant bounded by the surfaces $z^2 = xy$, $y = x$, $x = a$, integrating in order z, y, x. *Ans.* $\frac{2}{9}a^3$.

14. Ex. 13, integrating in order z, x, y.

15. Find the volume in the first octant bounded by the surfaces $a^2 z = a^3 - xy^2$, $y^2 = ax$, $y = a$, integrating in order z, y, x. *Ans.* $\frac{11}{42}a^3$.

16. Ex. 15, integrating in order z, x, y.

17. Find the volume in the first octant bounded by the surfaces $z = x + y$, $y = 1 - x^2$. *Ans.* $\frac{31}{60}$.

18. In Ex. 8, find the centroid. *Ans.* $(\frac{5}{6}, \frac{5}{9}, \frac{5}{24})$.

19. In Ex. 11, find the centroid. *Ans.* $(\frac{27}{64}a, \frac{21}{40}a, \frac{3}{4}a)$.

20. In Ex. 13, find the centroid. *Ans.* $(\frac{3}{4}a, \frac{9}{20}a, \frac{9}{32}a)$.

21. In Ex. 1, find I_x, I_y, I_z.

22. In Ex. 5, find I_x, I_y, I_z.

23. In Ex. 11, find I_x, I_y, I_z. *Ans.* $I_x = \frac{177}{175} Ma^2$.

24. In Ex. 13, find I_x, I_y, I_z. *Ans.* $I_y = \frac{18}{25} Ma^2$.

In Exs. 25–32, use triple integration with cylindrical coordinates.

25. Ex. 8.   **26.** Ex. 11.   **27.** Ex. 13.

28. Find the volume of a sphere.

29. Find the volume bounded by the xy-plane, the cylinder $x^2 + y^2 = ay$, and the paraboloid $x^2 + y^2 = az$.   *Ans.* $\frac{3}{32}\pi a^3$.

30. Find the volume in the first octant bounded by the cylinder $x^2 + y^2 = ay$ and the cone $a^2 z^2 = h^2(x^2 + y^2)$.   *Ans.* $\frac{2}{9}a^2 h$.

31. In Ex. 29, find the centroid.   *Ans.* $(0, \frac{2}{3}a, \frac{5}{18}a)$.

32. In Ex. 29, find I_x, I_y, I_z.   *Ans.* $I_x = \frac{175}{288}Ma^2$.

210. *Heterogeneous Masses*

The density of a homogeneous mass has been defined in § 161 as the ratio of the mass to the volume it occupies:

$$\delta = \frac{M}{V}.$$

For a *heterogeneous* mass, i.e., one whose density varies from point to point, we must introduce the idea of *density at a point*.

Consider an element of volume ΔV including a point P, and let ΔM denote the mass contained in ΔV. Then the ratio $\dfrac{\Delta M}{\Delta V}$ is the *average density* of ΔV. If ΔV approaches zero in such a way that P is always included, the ratio $\dfrac{\Delta M}{\Delta V}$ in general approaches a limit δ, called the *density at the point P*:

$$\delta = \operatorname*{Lim}_{\Delta V \to 0} \frac{\Delta M}{\Delta V} = \frac{dM}{dV}.$$

If the density at any point is given as a function of the coordinates, the mass can be found by integration. In the most general case we divide the space occupied by the body into volume elements ΔV_i as in § 208, multiply each element by the density δ_i at one of its points, and add all these products. The limit of this sum is the mass:

$$M = \iiint\limits_{V} \delta\, dV.$$

We shall use the term *homogeneous element* to mean that the density δ is essentially constant throughout the element in the sense that $\delta = \delta_i + \Delta\delta_i$ and

$$\operatorname*{Lim}_{\Delta V_i \to 0} \sum\sum\sum \Delta\delta_i\, \Delta V_i = 0.$$

That is, the variation in δ throughout the element makes a zero contribution to the mass integral. It is important to see two points clearly:

(*a*) The element must always be homogeneous, since otherwise, in building up the integral, we would not know what value to use for δ.

(*b*) Homogeneity of the element is the only requisite: The volume element may be of any character whatever, provided the mass contained in it is homogeneous, since then we know the values of both δ and dV.

If δ varies in some simple manner, it is possible in many cases to find a homogeneous element of one of the shapes used in Chapters 23 and 28; if so, we may find the volume by simple or at worst by double integration.

Example (*a*). Find the mass of a circular cone whose density varies as the distance from the axis. (Fig. 223.)

Let the cone be generated by revolving the line

$$\frac{x}{h} + \frac{y}{a} = 1$$

about Ox. If we divide the mass into cylindrical shells about the axis, each element will be homogeneous of density $\delta = ky$:

$$M = \int \delta \, dV = 2\pi k \int_0^a y \cdot yx \, dy$$
$$= 2\pi k \int_0^a y^2 \left(h - \frac{hy}{a} \right) dy = \tfrac{1}{6}\pi k a^3 h.$$

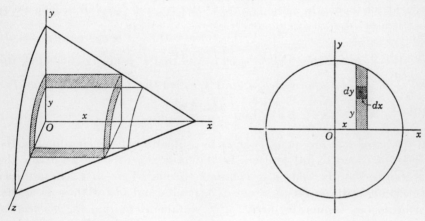

Figure 223   Figure 224

Example (*b*). Find the mass of a circular plate if the density is proportional to the sum of the distances from two perpendicular diameters. (Fig. 224.)

With the two diameters as axes, $\delta = k(x + y)$, whence

$$M = 4k \int_0^a \int_0^{\sqrt{a^2 - x^2}} (x + y) \, dy \, dx, \text{ etc.}$$

Example (*c*). Find the mass of a sphere whose density is proportional to the sum of the distances from three mutually perpendicular diametral planes.

Since the density varies with all three coordinates, a triple integral is required: in rectangular coordinates,

$$M = 8k \int_0^a \int_0^{\sqrt{a^2 - x^2}} \int_0^{\sqrt{a^2 - x^2 - y^2}} (x + y + z) \, dz \, dy \, dx.$$

211. *Centroids; Moments of Inertia*

In Chapters 24–25, in order to make the ideas of centroid and moment of inertia intelligible on an intuitive basis, we adopted the rough-and-ready expedient of considering the mass as an "aggregate of particles." We are now, for the first time, in position to state analytic definitions of first and second moments of mass.

Given a three-dimensional mass M occupying a volume V, with the density δ expressed as a function of the coordinates (including as a special case the homogeneous body—δ constant), take

$$\Delta M_i = \delta_i \, \Delta V_i$$

as in § 210. Multiply each element by the distance x_i of one of its points from the yz-plane, and add all the products. The limit of this sum is defined as the *first moment* of the mass with respect to the yz-plane. Similar definitions hold for moments with respect to the zx- and xy-planes. The point $(\bar{x}, \bar{y}, \bar{z})$ whose coordinates are given by the equations

$$M\bar{x} = \iiint\limits_V x\delta \, dV,$$

$$M\bar{y} = \iiint\limits_V y\delta \, dV,$$

$$M\bar{z} = \iiint\limits_V z\delta \, dV$$

is the *centroid* of the mass.

In analogous fashion we arrive at a suitable definition for *moment of inertia* with respect to the x-axis:

$$I_x = \iiint\limits_V (y^2 + z^2)\delta \, dV,$$

with similar definitions for I_y and I_z.

For area masses or line masses, the defining formulas are the two- and one-dimensional analogues of those above.

Example (a). In Example (a), § 210,

$$M\bar{x} = 2\pi k \int_0^a \frac{x}{2} \cdot y \cdot yx \, dy = \frac{\pi k h^2}{a^2} \int_0^a y^2 (a - y)^2 \, dy$$

$$= \frac{1}{30} \pi k a^3 h^2,$$

$$\bar{x} = \frac{\frac{1}{30}\pi k a^3 h^2}{\frac{1}{6}\pi k a^3 h} = \frac{1}{5} h.$$

Example (b). In Example (b), § 210,

$$I_x = 4k \int_0^a \int_0^{\sqrt{a^2-x^2}} y^2(x+y)\, dy\, dx.$$

212. *Translation Theorem on Moments of Inertia*

We are now able to prove the theorem of § 178, that if the lines l and c are parallel at a distance h apart, and if c passes through the centroid of the mass M, then

$$I_l = I_c + Mh^2.$$

Take the line c as x-axis, the line l as $y = h$, $z = 0$. With a volume element chosen in any suitable manner (the figure shows only one element), we have

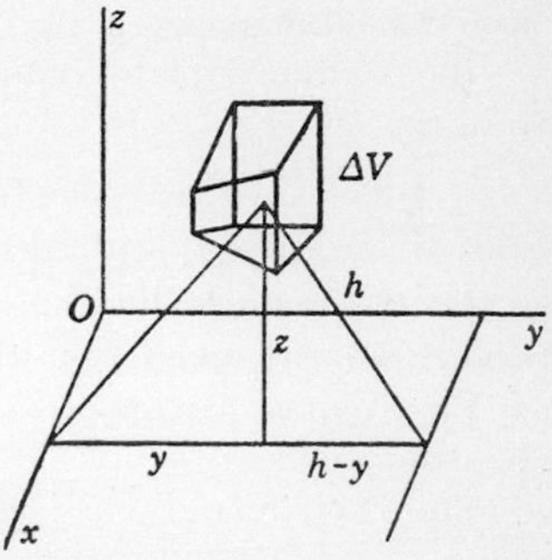

$$I_c = \iiint_V (y^2 + z^2)\, \delta\, dV,$$

$$I_l = \iiint_V [(h-y)^2 + z^2]\, \delta\, dV$$

$$= h^2 \iiint_V \delta\, dV - 2h \iiint_V y\delta\, dV + \iiint_V (y^2+z^2)\, \delta\, dV.$$

Figure 225

By § 210, the first of these three integrals is Mh^2; by § 211, the second is $-2hM\bar{y}$, and therefore vanishes, since the centroid is in the zx-plane; the third is I_c.

COROLLARY. *If two parallel lines l_1, l_2 are at distances h_1, h_2 from the centroid,*

$$I_{l_2} = I_{l_1} + M(h_2{}^2 - h_1{}^2).$$

EXERCISES

In Exs. 1–22, find the mass.

1. A straight rod, of length c, whose density is proportional to the distance from one end.   *Ans.* $\frac{1}{2}kc^2$.

2. A straight rod, of length c, whose density is proportional to the square of the distance from one end.   *Ans.* $\frac{1}{3}kc^3$.

3. A straight rod, of length c, whose density is proportional to the square of the distance from the center.   *Ans.* $\frac{1}{12}kc^3$.

4. Four rods forming a square of side c, with the density varying as the square of the distance from one corner.   *Ans.* $\frac{10}{3}kc^3$.

5. A rectangular plate, sides a and b, with density proportional to the square of the distance from a side of length b.   *Ans.* $\frac{1}{3}ka^3b$.

6. A rectangular plate, sides a and b, with density proportional to the product of the distances to two adjacent sides.   *Ans.* $\frac{1}{4}ka^2b^2$.

7. A semicircular wire, radius a, whose density varies as the distance from the bounding diameter. Use polar coordinates.   *Ans.* $2ka^2$.

8. A semicircular wire, radius a, whose density varies as the fourth power of the distance from the bounding diameter.

$$\text{Ans. } \frac{3k\pi a^5}{8}.$$

9. A circular plate, radius a, whose density varies as the square of the distance from a fixed diameter.   *Ans.* $\frac{1}{4}k\pi a^4$.

10. A circular plate, radius a, with density varying as the cube of the distance from the center.

$$\text{Ans. } \frac{2k\pi a^5}{5}.$$

11. A circular cylinder, base radius a and height h, whose density varies as the square of the distance from the base.   *Ans.* $\frac{1}{3}k\pi a^2 h^3$.

12. A circular cylinder, base radius a and height h, with density proportional to the distance from the axis of the cylinder.   *Ans.* $\frac{2}{3}k\pi a^3 h$.

13. A sphere, radius a, whose density varies as the distance from a fixed diametral plane.   *Ans.* $\frac{1}{2}k\pi a^4$.

14. A spherical surface, radius a, with density proportional to the distance from a fixed diameter.   *Ans.* $k\pi^2 a^3$.

15. A spherical surface, radius a, with density proportional to the distance from a fixed diametral plane.   *Ans.* $2k\pi a^3$.

16. A square, side a, whose density varies as the square of the distance from one corner.

$$\text{Ans. } \frac{2ka^4}{3}.$$

17. A square, side a, whose density varies as the distance from one corner. Use polar coordinates.   *Ans.* $\frac{1}{3}ka^3 \left[\sqrt{2} + \ln\left(1 + \sqrt{2}\right) \right]$.

18. A rectangular plate, sides a and b, whose density is proportional to the sum of the distances from two adjacent sides.   *Ans.* $\frac{1}{2}kab(a + b)$.

19. A circular plate, radius a, whose density is proportional to the distance from a fixed point on the circumference. Use polar coordinates, with the equation $r = 2a \cos \theta$.   *Ans.* $\frac{32}{9}ka^3$.

20. Use polar coordinates to solve Example (*b*), § 210.   *Ans.* $\frac{8}{3}ka^3$.

21. A cube, edge length a, with density varying as the square of the distance from one corner.   *Ans.* ka^5.

22. A cube, edge length a, whose density varies as the sum of the distances from three adjacent faces.   *Ans.* $\frac{3}{2}ka^4$.

23. Complete the solution in Example (*c*), § 210.   *Ans.* $\frac{3}{2}k\pi a^4$.

24. Solve Example (*c*), § 210, in cylindrical coordinates.

25. Show that the problem of determining fluid pressure on a submerged vertical area (§ 180) is equivalent to that of finding the mass of a thin plate whose density is proportional to the distance from a line in the plane.

In Exs. 26–38, find the centroid.

26. Ex. 1. *Ans.* $\frac{2}{3}$ way from the end of zero density.

27. Ex. 2. **28.** Ex. 4. **29.** Ex. 5. **30.** Ex. 6.

31. A semicircular plate, radius a, whose density varies as the square of the distance from the bounding diameter. Use polar coordinates.

Ans. On the line of symmetry, $\dfrac{32a}{15\pi}$ from the center.

32. A semicircular plate, radius a, whose density varies as the distance from the center.

33. One quadrant of a circular plate, radius a, with density proportional to the distance from one of the bounding radii.

34. One quadrant of a circular wire, radius a, with density varying as the distance from one of the bounding radii.

35. Ex. 19. *Ans.* On the line of symmetry, $\dfrac{6a}{5}$ from the point of zero density.

36. A circular plate, radius a, whose density is proportional to the square of the distance from a fixed point on the circumference.

Ans. On the line of symmetry, $\dfrac{4a}{3}$ from the point of zero density.

37. Ex. 21. *Ans.* $(\frac{7}{12}a, \frac{7}{12}a, \frac{7}{12}a)$. **38.** Ex. 22. *Ans.* $(\frac{5}{9}a, \frac{5}{9}a, \frac{5}{9}a)$.

In Exs. 39–48, find the indicated moment of inertia.

39. The rod of Ex. 1, with respect to the point of zero density. *Ans.* $\frac{1}{4}kc^4$.

40. The rod of Ex. 1, with respect to the point of maximum density. *Ans.* $\frac{1}{12}kc^4$.

41. The rod of Ex. 3, with respect to the center. *Ans.* $\dfrac{kc^5}{80}$.

42. The rod of Ex. 3, with respect to one endpoint. *Ans.* $\dfrac{kc^5}{30}$.

43. The circular plate of Ex. 9, with respect to the center.

44. The cylinder of Ex. 11, with respect to the plane of its base. *Ans.* $\frac{3}{5}Mh^2$.

45. The cylinder of Ex. 11, with respect to the plane at the end of maximum density. *Ans.* $\frac{1}{10}Mh^2$.

46. The sphere of Ex. 13, with respect to a diameter in the fixed plane (yz-plane).

Ans. $I_z = \frac{1}{2}Ma^2$.

47. The sphere of Ex. 13, with respect to the diameter perpendicular to the fixed plane. *Ans.* $I_x = \frac{1}{3}Ma^2$.

48. The cube of Ex. 21, with respect to an edge through the corner of zero density. *Ans.* $I_z = \frac{38}{45}Ma^2$.

49. Prove the theorem of § 176 for any continuous plane mass.

50. Prove the corollary, § 212.

51. Solve Example (b), § 211. (Find I_0, using polar coordinates; $I_x = \frac{1}{2}I_0$.)

SERIES OF

CONSTANT TERMS

213. *Infinite Series*

A *finite series*, or *series of n terms*, is an expression of the form

$$u_1 + u_2 + u_3 + \cdots + u_n,$$

where each term is formed by some definite rule. Familiar examples are the *arithmetic series* (also called arithmetic progression), in which each term is formed by adding a fixed amount to the preceding term; the *geometric series* (progression), in which each term bears a constant ratio to the preceding; and the expansion of $(1 + x)^m$ by the binomial theorem, where m is a positive integer.

One of the most powerful tools in modern mathematics results from the concept of an *infinite series*, denoted by the symbol

$$u_1 + u_2 + u_3 + \cdots + u_n + \cdots.$$

This symbol may be more compactly expressed by a simple extension of the Σ-notation introduced in § 54:

$$u_1 + u_2 + u_3 + \cdots + u_n + \cdots = \sum_{n=1}^{\infty} u_n.$$

In the next section we shall define the sum of an infinite series.

Example. The infinite geometric series with first term 1 and ratio $\frac{1}{2}$ is

$$(1) \qquad 1 + \frac{1}{2} + \frac{1}{4} + \frac{1}{8} + \cdots + \frac{1}{2^{n-1}} + \cdots = \sum_{n=1}^{\infty} \frac{1}{2^{n-1}}.$$

Instead, we may write either

$$1 + \sum_{n=1}^{\infty} \frac{1}{2^n} \quad \text{or} \quad \sum_{n=0}^{\infty} \frac{1}{2^n}.$$

The reader should verify that the above three forms are equivalent.

214. *Sum of an Infinite Series*

The *sum* of a finite series is merely the algebraic sum of all the terms, and can always be found (theoretically at least) by direct addition.

On the other hand, an infinite series has no sum in the ordinary sense of the term, since no matter how many terms we might add together, there would always be more to come.

Let us return to the example of the preceding section. Let the sum of the first n terms of the series

$$(1) \qquad 1 + \frac{1}{2} + \frac{1}{2^2} + \cdots + \frac{1}{2^{n-1}} + \cdots$$

be S_n; that is,

$$(2) \qquad S_n = 1 + \frac{1}{2} + \frac{1}{2^2} + \cdots + \frac{1}{2^{n-1}}.$$

Since this is a finite geometric series, we know its sum from algebra,

$$S_n = \frac{1 - (\frac{1}{2})^n}{1 - \frac{1}{2}} = 2 - \frac{1}{2^{n-1}}.$$

Note that, as n increases, $S_n \to 2$; i.e.,

$$(3) \qquad \lim_{n \to \infty} S_n = \lim_{n \to \infty} \left(2 - \frac{1}{2^{n-1}} \right) = 2.$$

It is only natural, then, to define as the sum of the series (1) the value of the limit in (3), a number which can be approached as closely as desired by adding a sufficient number of terms of the original series.

DEFINITION. *The* **sum** *of an infinite series is the limit, if it exists, of the sum of a finite number of terms, as the number of terms approaches infinity,*

$$S = \lim_{n \to \infty} S_n.$$

By replacing n by $(n - 1)$, we may also write

$$S = \lim_{n \to \infty} S_{n-1}.$$

Example. The sum of the first n terms of the infinite geometric series

$$a + ar + ar^2 + \cdots + ar^{n-1} + \cdots$$

is

$$S_n = \frac{a - ar^n}{1 - r}, \qquad r \neq 1.$$

Hence the sum of the series, if the sum exists, is

$$S = \lim_{n \to \infty} \frac{a - ar^n}{1 - r}.$$

When $|r| < 1$, the quantity ar^n approaches zero as $n \to \infty$, and

$$S = \frac{a}{1 - r}.$$

When $|r| > 1$, the quantity $|ar^n| \to \infty$, and the above limit does not exist; the series has no sum. The student should show that S_n does not approach a limit if $r = \pm 1$.

215. *Convergence and Divergence*

If the series has a sum S, i.e., if S_n approaches a limit when $n \to \infty$, the series is said to be *convergent*, or to *converge to the value* S; if the limit does not exist, the series is *divergent*.

For instance, the above example shows that a geometric series converges to the value $\frac{a}{1 - r}$ if $|r| < 1$; it diverges if $|r| \geq 1$.

In the elementary applications, divergent series are of no importance. Before being able to use a given series, we must determine whether it converges or diverges. If S_n can be expressed explicitly as a simple function of n, as in the case of the arithmetic and geometric series, we can usually determine the convergence or divergence of the series directly, and find the sum if it exists; but S_n cannot be so expressed in most cases.

If the series $\displaystyle\sum_{n=1}^{\infty} u_n$ converges,

$$\operatorname*{Lim}_{n \to \infty} S_n = S.$$

By a shift from n to $(n - 1)$, we see that also

$$\operatorname*{Lim}_{n \to \infty} S_{n-1} = S.$$

Now $S_n - S_{n-1} = u_n$ and if the series converges, $\operatorname*{Lim}_{n \to \infty} S_{n-1} = \operatorname*{Lim}_{n \to \infty} S_n$, so that

$$\operatorname*{Lim}_{n \to \infty} (S_n - S_{n-1}) = \operatorname*{Lim}_{n \to \infty} u_n = 0.$$

THEOREM 32. *If* $\displaystyle\sum_{n=1}^{\infty} u_n$ *converges,* $\operatorname*{Lim}_{n \to \infty} u_n = 0.$

This condition, though necessary, is not sufficient; i.e., if the nth term does not approach zero, the series diverges, but if the nth term does approach zero, the series still may diverge. This is illustrated by the "harmonic series"

$$1 + \frac{1}{2} + \frac{1}{3} + \frac{1}{4} + \cdots + \frac{1}{n} + \cdots,$$

which will be shown in § 216 to be divergent, although its nth term approaches zero as $n \to \infty$.

Theorem 32 is frequently employed in advanced mathematics. With it we can evaluate limits far too subtle for direct attacks. In the present course of study, the theorem is most useful when worded as a divergence test.

THEOREM 32a. *If u_n does not approach zero as $n \to \infty$,* $\sum\limits_{n=1}^{\infty} u_n$ *diverges.*

We shall make use of the following fundamental result without proof.

THEOREM 33. *If a variable steadily* $\begin{Bmatrix} increases \\ decreases \end{Bmatrix}$ *but never becomes* $\begin{Bmatrix} greater \\ less \end{Bmatrix}$ *than some fixed number A, the variable approaches a limit which is not* $\begin{Bmatrix} greater \\ less \end{Bmatrix}$ *than A.*

216. *The Harmonic Series*

The series

$$(1) \qquad 1 + \frac{1}{2} + \frac{1}{3} + \frac{1}{4} + \cdots + \frac{1}{n} + \cdots = \sum_{n=1}^{\infty} \frac{1}{n}$$

is called the *harmonic series*.

A common notation for the sum of the first n terms of this important series is H_n:

$$H_n = 1 + \frac{1}{2} + \frac{1}{3} + \cdots + \frac{1}{n} = \sum_{k=1}^{n} \frac{1}{k}.$$

We shall prove that the harmonic series diverges; $H_n \to \infty$, as $n \to \infty$. Of course, $1 + \frac{1}{2} > 1 + \frac{1}{3}$, $\frac{1}{3} + \frac{1}{4} > \frac{1}{4} + \frac{1}{4}$, $\frac{1}{5} + \frac{1}{6} > \frac{1}{6} + \frac{1}{6}$, etc. That is, the following n inequalities are true:

$$1 + \tfrac{1}{2} > 1 + \tfrac{1}{3},$$
$$\tfrac{1}{3} + \tfrac{1}{4} > \tfrac{1}{2},$$
$$\tfrac{1}{5} + \tfrac{1}{6} > \tfrac{1}{3},$$
$$\cdot$$
$$\cdot$$
$$\cdot$$
$$\frac{1}{2n-1} + \frac{1}{2n} > \frac{1}{n}.$$

Adding the corresponding members of these inequalities, we obtain

$$H_{2n} > H_n + \tfrac{1}{3}.$$

Thus $H_{2n} - H_n > \frac{1}{3}$. But, if the harmonic series converges, then a limit H exists such that as $n \to \infty$, $H_n \to H$, and also $H_{2n} \to H$. Then $H_{2n} - H_n \to 0$, which contradicts the inequality $H_{2n} - H_n > \frac{1}{3}$. Hence, the harmonic series cannot converge; it must diverge.

217. *The Factorial Notation*

The symbol $n!$ (read *factorial n*) is used to denote the *product of all the integers from 1 to n inclusive*:

$$n! = 1 \cdot 2 \cdot 3 \cdots (n-2)(n-1)n.$$

By special definition (introduced to facilitate the writing of certain formulas),

$$0! = 1.$$

It will be found as we proceed that factorials occur prominently in many important series.

In manipulating the factorial symbol, we must have constant recourse to the definition. For example,

$$\frac{6!}{3!} = \frac{1 \cdot 2 \cdot 3 \cdot 4 \cdot 5 \cdot 6}{1 \cdot 2 \cdot 3} = 4 \cdot 5 \cdot 6;$$
$$(n+2)! = (n-1)! \cdot n(n+1)(n+2).$$

EXERCISES

In Exs. 1–9, write out the first five terms of each series.

1. $\displaystyle\sum_{n=1}^{\infty} \frac{(-1)^{n+1}}{n^2}.$

2. $\displaystyle\sum_{n=0}^{\infty} \frac{n^2+1}{2^n}.$

3. $\displaystyle\sum_{n=0}^{\infty} \frac{2n+1}{n!}.$

4. $\displaystyle\sum_{n=0}^{\infty} \frac{(-1)^n n!}{(2n+1)!}.$

5. $\displaystyle\sum_{n=0}^{\infty} \frac{2n^2 - 5n + 6}{6 \cdot n!}.$ *Ans.* $1 + \frac{1}{2} + \frac{1}{3} + \frac{1}{4} + \frac{1}{8} + \cdots.$

6. $\displaystyle\sum_{n=0}^{\infty} \frac{1}{3n^4 - 18n^3 + 33n^2 - 17n + 1}.$ *Ans.* $1 + \frac{1}{2} + \frac{1}{3} + \frac{1}{4} + \frac{1}{77} + \cdots.$

7. $\displaystyle\sum_{n=1}^{\infty} \frac{1}{n^2}.$ *Ans.* $1 + \frac{1}{4} + \frac{1}{9} + \frac{1}{16} + \frac{1}{25} + \cdots.$

8. $\displaystyle\sum_{n=1}^{\infty} \frac{2n^2 - 9n + 19}{6(n^2 + n!)}.$ *Ans.* $1 + \frac{1}{4} + \frac{1}{9} + \frac{1}{16} + \frac{4}{145} + \cdots.$

9. $\displaystyle\sum_{n=1}^{\infty} \frac{1-(-1)^n}{n^2+1}.$ *Ans.* $1 + 0 + \frac{1}{5} + 0 + \frac{1}{13} + \cdots.$

Prove that the series in Ex. 10–18 are divergent.

10. $\dfrac{2}{5} + \dfrac{3}{10} + \dfrac{4}{15} + \dfrac{5}{20} + \cdots + \dfrac{n+1}{5n} + \cdots.$

11. $1 - 2 + 3 - \cdots + (-1)^{n+1}n + \cdots.$

12. $\dfrac{1}{3} + \dfrac{3}{5} + \dfrac{5}{7} + \cdots + \dfrac{2n-1}{2n+1} + \cdots.$

13. $1 + \dfrac{e}{2^2} + \dfrac{e^2}{3^2} + \dfrac{e^3}{4^2} + \cdots + \dfrac{e^{n-1}}{n^2} + \cdots.$

14. $\dfrac{1}{2} + \dfrac{1}{4} + \dfrac{1}{6} + \dfrac{1}{8} + \cdots + \dfrac{1}{2n} + \cdots.$

15. $\displaystyle\sum_{n=1}^{\infty} \sin \frac{n\pi}{2}.$ 16. $\displaystyle\sum_{n=0}^{\infty} \frac{\pi^n}{e^n}.$

17. $\displaystyle\sum_{n=1}^{\infty} \frac{(n+2)!}{n^2}.$ 18. $\displaystyle\sum_{n=0}^{\infty} \frac{(-1)^n 2^n}{1+n^5}.$

19. Show that every infinite arithmetic series, with terms not all zero, is divergent.

In each of Exs. 20–23, show that the given series are identical.

20. $\displaystyle\sum_{n=0}^{\infty} \frac{x^n}{n!}$ and $1 + x + \displaystyle\sum_{n=2}^{\infty} \frac{x^n}{n!}.$

21. $\displaystyle\sum_{n=0}^{\infty} \frac{x^{n+1}}{n+1}$ and $\displaystyle\sum_{n=1}^{\infty} \frac{x^n}{n}.$ In the first series replace n everywhere by $(n-1)$.

This is called a *shift in index*.

22. $\displaystyle\sum_{n=0}^{\infty} \frac{(-1)^n y^{2n+1}}{(2n+1)!}$ and $\displaystyle\sum_{n=1}^{\infty} \frac{(-1)^{n-1} y^{2n-1}}{(2n-1)!}.$

23. $\displaystyle\sum_{n=1}^{\infty} (n^2+1)z^{n+2}$ and $\displaystyle\sum_{n=3}^{\infty} (n^2-4n+5)z^n.$

218. *Tests for Convergence or Divergence*

Given an infinite series $\displaystyle\sum_{n=1}^{\infty} u_n$, it is of prime importance to us to discover whether the series converges or diverges. Convergent series are, in general, well behaved and of value to us. We shall make much use of convergent series in succeeding chapters. Divergent series have a delicate nature, and their use is ordinarily restricted to advanced mathematics.

It is usually not feasible to demonstrate convergence or divergence by showing directly that the limit in the definition of the sum (§ 214) exists or does not exist. Therefore we devise tests for convergence or divergence.

A test is a theorem which states that the series $\sum_{n=1}^{\infty} u_n$ is convergent (or divergent) if the general term u_n possesses certain specified properties. For example, Theorem 32a states that if u_n does not approach zero as $n \to \infty$, $\sum_{n=1}^{\infty} u_n$ is divergent. The bulk of this chapter is concerned with convergence tests.

No test for convergence is capable of effective testing of all series. At best, a test will show that certain series converge, that others diverge, but there will remain series for which it gives no answer.

It is important that the student realize that the convergence or divergence of a series is a property resulting from the behavior of the general term and from nothing else. It does not matter what the first ten billion terms (or any other fixed number of them) may be. Those terms affect the sum of the series, if it has one, but have no effect upon the matter of convergence.

LEMMA 4. *If n_0 is a fixed integer ≥ 1,* $\sum_{n=1}^{\infty} u_n$ *and* $\sum_{n=n_0}^{\infty} u_n$ *converge or diverge together.*

That is, if either series converges, the other converges, and if either series diverges, the other diverges.

Proof of Lemma 4 follows at once from the definition of the sum of a series.

219. *A Comparison Test*

Let
$$u_1 + u_2 + u_3 + \cdots + u_n + \cdots$$
be a series of *positive terms* to be tested.

THEOREM 34. (a) *If a series*
$$a_1 + a_2 + a_3 + \cdots + a_n + \cdots$$
of positive terms, known to be convergent, can be found such that
$$u_n \leq a_n,$$
then the series to be tested is convergent.

(b) *If a series*

$$b_1 + b_2 + b_3 + \cdots + b_n + \cdots$$

of positive terms, known to be divergent, can be found such that

$$u_n \geqq b_n,$$

then the series to be tested is divergent.

To prove (a), let S_n be the sum of the first n terms of the u-series, T_n the sum of the first n terms of the a-series, and T the sum of the a-series. Since all the terms u_n and a_n are positive, both S_n and T_n increase, as n increases. On the other hand, we have

$$S_n < T_n < T.$$

Therefore S_n always increases with n but never exceeds the fixed number T. Hence S_n approaches a limit, not greater than T, by Theorem 33 quoted at the end of § 215.

The proof of (b) is left to the student.

The success of the test depends on our ability to find a *convergent* series whose terms are *greater* than the corresponding terms of the series to be tested, or a *divergent* series whose terms are *less* than those of the series to be tested. To show that the terms of the u-series are greater than those of some convergent series, or less than those of some divergent series, proves nothing.

If we change the signs of all the terms, the sign of the sum S (if the sum exists) is changed, but its existence is not affected. Thus, if all the terms are negative, we may change all the signs before testing.

Example. Test for convergence the series

$$\frac{2}{1^2} + \frac{3}{2^2} + \frac{4}{3^2} + \cdots + \frac{n+1}{n^2} + \cdots .$$

We know (§ 216) that the harmonic series

$$1 + \frac{1}{2} + \frac{1}{3} + \cdots + \frac{1}{n} + \cdots$$

is divergent. Since

$$\frac{n+1}{n^2} = \frac{1}{n} + \frac{1}{n^2} > \frac{1}{n},$$

the given series is divergent.

220. *Other Comparison Tests*

The test in the preceding section has the advantage of simplicity of concept. That test is, however, more tedious to use than the slightly more sophisticated comparison tests contained in Theorems 35–37 below.

THEOREM 35. *If $u_n > 0$ and $a_n > 0$, and if*

$$(1) \qquad \operatorname*{Lim}_{n \to \infty} \frac{u_n}{a_n} = c \neq 0,$$

the series $\sum_{n=1}^{\infty} u_n$ *and* $\sum_{n=1}^{\infty} a_n$ *converge or diverge together.*

A shift of index in u_n from n to $(n + k)$ for any fixed k has no effect upon the limit in (1). Hence the theorem may be applied to series whose terms are all positive from some n-value onward.

Proof of Theorem 35. Because of (1) there exists a constant M_1 such that for all n

$$(2) \qquad \left| \frac{u_n}{a_n} - c \right| < M_1.$$

For n sufficiently large, M_1 can be made arbitrarily small, but that does not concern us here. From (2), and the fact that all the quantities involved are positive, it follows that

$$(3) \qquad u_n < (M_1 + c)a_n.$$

Because of (1), $\operatorname*{Lim}_{n \to \infty} \dfrac{a_n}{u_n} = c^{-1} \neq 0$, so we may also conclude that there exists a constant M_2 such that for all n

$$(4) \qquad a_n < (M_2 + c^{-1})u_n.$$

As in § 219, let the sum of the first n terms of the u-series be S_n; of the a-series, be T_n. Then by (3) and (4) there exist constants M_3 and M_4 such that

$$(5) \qquad S_n < M_3 T_n, \qquad T_n < M_4 S_n,$$

from which the conclusion in Theorem 35 follows at once.

Example. Test for convergence:

$$(6) \qquad \sum_{n=1}^{\infty} \frac{2n - 1}{5n^2 - 31n + 8}.$$

Note that for large n the general term in the series (6) behaves like $2n/(5n^2) = 2/(5n)$. Let us compare (6) with the harmonic series

$$(7) \qquad \sum_{n=1}^{\infty} \frac{1}{n}$$

which we know to be divergent. For $n > 5$, the terms of (6) are positive.

Since

$$\operatorname*{Lim}_{n \to \infty} \frac{2n - 1}{5n^2 - 31n + 8} \cdot \frac{n}{1} = \frac{2}{5} \neq 0,$$

we may conclude that (6) diverges because (7) diverges.

THEOREM 36. *If $u_n > 0$ and $a_n > 0$, and if*

$$(8) \qquad\qquad \operatorname*{Lim}_{n \to \infty} \frac{u_n}{a_n} = 0,$$

the series $\displaystyle\sum_{n=1}^{\infty} u_n$ *converges if* $\displaystyle\sum_{n=1}^{\infty} a_n$ *converges.*

Theorem 36 says nothing about what happens if the *a*-series diverges.

THEOREM 37. *If $u_n > 0$ and $d_n > 0$, and if*

$$(9) \qquad\qquad \operatorname*{Lim}_{n \to \infty} \frac{u_n}{d_n} = \infty,$$

the series $\displaystyle\sum_{n=1}^{\infty} u_n$ *diverges if* $\displaystyle\sum_{n=1}^{\infty} d_n$ *diverges.*

Theorem 37 says nothing about what happens if the *d*-series converges.

The value of the comparison tests increases as we add to the list of series which we know converge or diverge.

221. *An Integral Test*

Consider an infinite series,

$$\sum_{n=1}^{\infty} u_n,$$

of positive terms, such that the terms never increase with increasing n; i.e., $0 < u_{n+1} \leqq u_n$. For such a series the following test may determine whether the series converges or diverges.

INTEGRAL TEST

THEOREM 38. *If, for $x \geqq 1$, the function $f(x)$ is positive, continuous, and never increases with increasing x, then*

(a) If $\displaystyle\int_1^{\infty} f(x)\,dx$ *exists, the series* $\displaystyle\sum_{n=1}^{\infty} f(n)$ *converges;*

(b) If $\displaystyle\int_1^{\infty} f(x)\,dx$ *does not exist, the series* $\displaystyle\sum_{n=1}^{\infty} f(n)$ *diverges.*

Since, for continuous $f(x)$, $\int_a^\infty f(x)\,dx$ and $\int_1^\infty f(x)\,dx$ exist, or do not exist, together, the lower limit in the integral need not be taken as one; its value is unessential. See also Lemma 4, p. 414.

Let us prove part (a) of the integral test. Put

$$S_n = f(1) + f(2) + f(3) + \cdots + f(n).$$

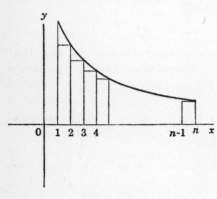

Now, as shown in Fig. 226, the area under the curve $y = f(x)$, from $x = 1$ to $x = n$, is

$$\int_1^n f(x)\,dx,$$

and the sum of the areas of the rectangles, from $x = 1$ to $x = n$, is

$$f(2) + f(3) + \cdots + f(n) = S_n - f(1).$$

Since $f(x)$ is continuous and never increases with increasing x,

$$S_n - f(1) \leqq \int_1^n f(x)\,dx.$$

Figure 226

But $\int_1^\infty f(x)\,dx$ exists; call its value A. Then

$$S_n - f(1) \leqq A,$$

or $S_n \leqq A + f(1)$, by which we have shown that S_n, always increasing, is bounded above. Then S_n approaches a limit as $n \to \infty$; the series $\sum_{n=1}^\infty f(n)$ converges.

The proof of part (b) is similar to the above, with rectangles formed by using horizontal lines drawn to the right where each ordinate, $x = 1, 2, 3, \cdots, n$, intersects the curve. Completion of the proof is left as an exercise.

It is important to notice that, in order to apply the integral test, it is necessary to find a continuous function $f(x)$ for which the values $f(n)$, for integral n, coincide with the terms of the series to be tested.

Example (a). Test the series $\sum_{n=0}^\infty \dfrac{1}{n^2 + 1}$.

The terms of this series are all positive, and they decrease steadily, since

$$\frac{1}{(n+1)^2 + 1} < \frac{1}{n^2 + 1}.$$

Consider the function $f(x) = \dfrac{1}{x^2 + 1}$. For $x = n$, this function yields the terms of the series. Also, $f(x)$ decreases steadily with increasing x. Further, $f(x)$ is continuous, and

$$\int_k^\infty \frac{dx}{x^2+1} = \Big[\text{Arctan } x \Big]_k^\infty = \frac{\pi}{2} - \text{Arctan } k,$$

so that $\int_k^\infty f(x)\, dx$ exists. Hence the series $\sum_{n=0}^\infty \frac{1}{n^2+1}$ converges.

Note that the lower limit k played no essential role, and also note that the fact that the series starts with the $n = 0$ term has no bearing whatever on the question of convergence.

Example (b). Test the series $\sum_{n=2}^\infty \frac{1}{n \ln n}$.

Here the series starts with $n = 2$, which does not interfere at all with the application of the integral test.

The function $f(x) = \dfrac{1}{x \ln x}$ yields the general term of our series for integral values, $x = n$. Now

$$f'(x) = -\frac{1 + \ln x}{x^2 \ln^2 x},$$

which is negative for $x \geqq 2$ (even for $x > 1$), so $f(x)$ decreases steadily. Consider the appropriate integral,

$$\int_2^\infty \frac{dx}{x \ln x} = \Big[\ln \ln x \Big]_2^\infty,$$

which does not exist. It follows that $\sum_{n=2}^\infty \frac{1}{n \ln n}$ is divergent.

222. *The p-Series*

The series

$$(1) \qquad 1 + \frac{1}{2^p} + \frac{1}{3^p} + \cdots + \frac{1}{n^p} + \cdots = \sum_{n=1}^\infty \frac{1}{n^p}$$

is called the *p-series*.

If $p = 1$, this is the harmonic series, which we know is divergent. If $p < 1$,

$$\frac{1}{n^p} > \frac{1}{n},$$

so that the series (1) diverges for $p < 1$ by comparison with the harmonic series.

If $p > 1$, we use the integral test. From $f(x) = \dfrac{1}{x^p}$, for fixed p, we obtain

$f'(x) = -\dfrac{p}{x^{p+1}}$, which is negative, for $x \geqq 1$; the function decreases with increasing x. The integral

$$\int_1^\infty \frac{dx}{x^p} = \left[\frac{1}{(1-p)x^{p-1}} \right]_1^\infty = 0 - \frac{1}{1-p}$$

exists, for $p > 1$. Hence the series (1) converges for $p > 1$.

In recapitulation, the p-series $\displaystyle\sum_{n=1}^\infty \frac{1}{n^p}$ diverges for $p \leqq 1$, converges for $p > 1$. It is quite useful in applying comparison tests.

Example. Test the series

$$(2) \qquad \frac{1}{1 \cdot 2} + \frac{1}{2 \cdot 3} + \frac{1}{3 \cdot 4} + \cdots + \frac{1}{n(n+1)} + \cdots.$$

The series

$$\frac{1}{1^2} + \frac{1}{2^2} + \frac{1}{3^2} + \frac{1}{4^2} + \cdots + \frac{1}{n^2} + \cdots$$

is the p-series with $p = 2$, therefore convergent. Since

$$\frac{1}{n^2 + n} < \frac{1}{n^2}$$

for all (positive integral) values of n, the series (2) converges.

EXERCISES

In Exs. 1–8, test for convergence by employing Theorem 34, page 414. You may use the p-series in comparisons.

1. $\displaystyle\sum_{n=1}^\infty \frac{1}{n^n}.$ *Ans.* Convergent.

2. $\dfrac{1}{2} + \dfrac{1}{2 \cdot 4} + \dfrac{1}{3 \cdot 8} + \dfrac{1}{4 \cdot 16} + \cdots + \dfrac{1}{n \cdot 2^n} + \cdots.$

3. $\dfrac{1}{5} + \dfrac{1}{11} + \dfrac{1}{17} + \cdots + \dfrac{1}{6n-1} + \cdots.$

4. $\displaystyle\sum_{n=0}^\infty \frac{1}{(2n-1)(n^2+1)}.$ *Ans.* Convergent.

5. $\displaystyle\sum_{k=2}^{\infty} \frac{\sqrt{k-1}}{k}.$ *Ans.* Divergent.

6. $\displaystyle\sum_{k=1}^{\infty} \frac{k^2+1}{k^3-7}.$

7. $\displaystyle\sum_{n=1}^{\infty} \frac{2n+1}{(1+n^2)^2}.$

8. $\displaystyle\sum_{n=1}^{\infty} \frac{n^3}{(n^2-2)^2}.$

In Exs. 9–16, test for convergence by employing Theorem 35, page 416.

9. $\displaystyle\sum_{n=0}^{\infty} \frac{2n^2+1}{3n^3+2}.$

10. $\displaystyle\sum_{n=1}^{\infty} \frac{n}{3n^4-n+4}.$

11. Ex. 3.　　　　**12.** Ex. 4.　　　　**13.** Ex. 5.
14. Ex. 6.　　　　**15.** Ex. 7.　　　　**16.** Ex. 8.

In Exs. 17–22, test for convergence by using Theorem 36 or 37, page 417.

17. $\displaystyle\sum_{n=1}^{\infty} \frac{e^n}{n}.$ *Ans.* Divergent.

18. $\displaystyle\sum_{n=1}^{\infty} \frac{\sin^2 n}{n^3}.$ *Ans.* Convergent.

19. $\displaystyle\sum_{n=0}^{\infty} e^{-n}(n+1).$

20. $\displaystyle\sum_{n=0}^{\infty} \frac{\ln(1+n)}{3n+2}.$

21. Ex. 1.　　　　**22.** Ex. 2.

23. Use Theorem 35, p. 416, with $u_n = \dfrac{P(n)}{Q(n)}$, $a_n = \dfrac{1}{n^{q-p}}$, to prove the validity of the following test.

POLYNOMIAL TEST. *If $P(n)$ is a polynomial of degree p, $Q(n)$ a polynomial of degree q, the series $\displaystyle\sum_{n=1}^{\infty} \frac{P(n)}{Q(n)}$ converges if $q > p + 1$, otherwise diverges.*

In Exs. 24–33, test by using the polynomial test.

24. $\displaystyle\sum_{n=2}^{\infty} \frac{n^3+1}{n^4(3n+1)}.$

25. $\displaystyle\sum_{k=0}^{\infty} \frac{1}{(2k+1)^2}.$

26. $\dfrac{3 \cdot 4}{2+1} + \dfrac{4 \cdot 5}{16+1} + \dfrac{5 \cdot 6}{54+1} + \cdots + \dfrac{(n+2)(n+3)}{2n^3+1} + \cdots.$

27. $\displaystyle\sum_{n=0}^{\infty} \frac{2n-1}{4(n+4)(n+1)}.$

28. Ex. 3.　　　　**29.** Ex. 4.　　　　**30.** Ex. 6.
31. Ex. 7.　　　　**32.** Ex. 8.　　　　**33.** Ex. 9.

In Exs. 34–43, test for convergence, using the integral test.

34. $\displaystyle\sum_{n=1}^{\infty} ne^{-n^2}$.   *Ans.* Convergent.   35. $\displaystyle\sum_{n=1}^{\infty} \frac{1}{1+\sqrt{n}}$.

36. $\dfrac{1}{2\sqrt{2}} + \dfrac{1}{5\sqrt{5}} + \dfrac{1}{10\sqrt{10}} + \cdots + \dfrac{1}{(1+k^2)^{\frac{3}{2}}} + \cdots$.

37. $\displaystyle\sum_{k=2}^{\infty} \frac{1}{k(\ln k)^2}$.   *Ans.* Convergent.   38. $\displaystyle\sum_{j=2}^{\infty} \frac{\ln j}{j}$.   *Ans.* Divergent.

39. $\displaystyle\sum_{n=1}^{\infty} \frac{n}{(1+n^2)^2}$.   40. $\displaystyle\sum_{n=1}^{\infty} \frac{n}{1+n^2}$.

41. Ex. 8.   42. Ex. 19.   43. Ex. 25.

44. Show that the series $\displaystyle\sum_{n=1}^{\infty} \frac{1}{an+b}$ is divergent for all values* of a and b.

45. Show that the series $\displaystyle\sum_{n=1}^{\infty} \frac{1}{an^2+bn+c}$ is convergent for all values* of a, b,

c $(a \neq 0)$.

46. Show that the series $\displaystyle\sum_{n=1}^{\infty} \frac{a_0 n + a_1}{b_0 n^2 + b_1 n + b_2}$ is divergent* for $a_0 \neq 0$.

47. Do Ex. 44 by the integral test.
48. Complete the proof of part (b) of the integral test.
49. Prove Theorem 36, p. 417.   50. Prove Theorem 37, p. 417.

51. Show, by using examples such as $\displaystyle\sum_{n=0}^{\infty} (-1)^n$, that you cannot, in general,

test for convergence by grouping terms together before testing.
52. Show that for series of positive terms, it is legitimate to group terms before testing for convergence.
53. Use the integral test on the harmonic series.

In Exs. 54–65, test by any available means.

54. $1 + \dfrac{1}{2^1} + \dfrac{1}{2^4} + \dfrac{1}{2^9} + \cdots + \dfrac{1}{2^{n^2}} + \cdots$.

55. $\displaystyle\sum_{m=0}^{\infty} \frac{\sin^2(2m+1)}{(m+1)^2}$.   *Ans.* Convergent.

---

* The case in which the denominator vanishes for a positive integral value of n is tacitly excluded, since then the series would not be defined.

56. $\displaystyle\sum_{n=0}^{\infty} \frac{(-1)^n n^2}{n+1}.$ *Ans.* Divergent.

57. $\displaystyle\sum_{n=0}^{\infty} \frac{2n+1}{(2n-1)^3 + n^2}.$ **58.** $\displaystyle\sum_{n=1}^{\infty} \frac{n^2}{3^n}.$

59. $\displaystyle\sum_{n=1}^{\infty} n^2 e^{-sn}, s > 0.$ **60.** $\displaystyle\sum_{n=1}^{\infty} n^2 e^{-sn}, s < 0.$

61. $\displaystyle\sum_{k=2}^{\infty} \frac{\sqrt{k}}{k^2+1}.$ *Ans.* Convergent.   **62.** $\displaystyle\sum_{n=1}^{\infty} \frac{n}{e^n}.$

63. $\dfrac{e+1}{\pi} + \dfrac{(e+1)^2}{\pi^2} + \dfrac{(e+1)^3}{\pi^3} + \cdots + \dfrac{(e+1)^n}{\pi^n} + \cdots.$

64. $\displaystyle\sum_{n=0}^{\infty} \frac{1}{2^{3n}}.$ **65.** $\displaystyle\sum_{n=1}^{\infty} \frac{100 n^2}{\pi^n}.$

223. *Absolute Convergence*

First we prove the following important result.

THEOREM 39. *If the series* $\displaystyle\sum_{n=1}^{\infty} |u_n|$ *converges, then* $\displaystyle\sum_{n=1}^{\infty} u_n$ *converges.*

In the finite sum

$$S_n = u_1 + u_2 + u_3 + \cdots + u_n,$$

let the positive terms be denoted by a's, the numerical values of the negative ones by b's. Then

$$S_n = A_k - B_m,$$

where $A_k = \Sigma a$'s, $B_m = \Sigma b$'s, and $k + m = n$.

For the series $\displaystyle\sum_{n=1}^{\infty} |u_n|$, the corresponding finite sum is

$$|u_1| + |u_2| + |u_3| + \cdots + |u_n| = A_k + B_m.$$

Th theorem states that if $(A_k + B_m)$ approaches a limit, then $(A_k - B_m)$ does also. But, since A_k and B_m are positive and increasing, if $(A_k + B_m)$ approaches a limit, then A_k and B_m must do so separately. Hence $(A_k - B_m)$ approaches a limit, and the proof is ended.

DEFINITION. *A series is said to be* **absolutely convergent** *if the series formed from it by replacing all its terms by their absolute values is convergent.*

Theorem 39 may now be reworded.

THEOREM 39a. *If a series is absolutely convergent, it is convergent.*

A series which is convergent but not absolutely convergent is called *simply convergent.*

Example. Test the series $\sum_{n=1}^{\infty} \dfrac{\sin \frac{1}{4}n\pi}{n^2}.$

The numerator takes on values which are positive, negative, or zero, depending on the value of n. However, $|\sin \frac{1}{4}n\pi| \leqq 1$, so

$$\left| \frac{\sin \frac{1}{4}n\pi}{n^2} \right| < \frac{1}{n^2}$$

and we know $\sum_{n=1}^{\infty} \dfrac{1}{n^2}$ is convergent. Hence, the given series is absolutely convergent by a comparison test, so it is also convergent.

224. *Ratio Test*

Given the series

(1) $$\sum_{n=1}^{\infty} u_n = u_1 + u_2 + u_3 + \cdots + u_n + \cdots,$$

form the ratio $\dfrac{u_{n+1}}{u_n}$ of a general term to the one *preceding* it.

RATIO TEST

THEOREM 40.

(a) *If* $\mathbf{Lim}\limits_{n \to \infty} \left| \dfrac{u_{n+1}}{u_n} \right| < 1$, *the series converges; indeed, converges absolutely.*

(b) *If* $\mathbf{Lim}\limits_{n \to \infty} \left| \dfrac{u_{n+1}}{u_n} \right| > 1$, *or if* $\left| \dfrac{u_{n+1}}{u_n} \right|$ *increases without bound, the series diverges.*

(c) *If* $\mathbf{Lim}\limits_{n \to \infty} \left| \dfrac{u_{n+1}}{u_n} \right| = 1$, *the test fails.*

(d) *If* $\left| \dfrac{u_{n+1}}{u_n} \right|$ *does not approch a limit and does not increase without bound, the test fails.*

Since the ratio test deals with absolute values, it applies to series in general, not merely to series of positive terms.

The ratio test stated here can be refined in many ways. For example, if $|u_{n+1}/u_n|$ remains always less than some constant which is itself less than unity, the series converges, whether the ratio approaches a limit or not. Such refinements are important in more advanced work, but the ratio test as stated above is sufficiently powerful for elementary work.

Proof of the Validity of the Ratio Test. Consider the first case:

$$\operatorname*{Lim}_{n \to \infty} \left| \frac{u_{n+1}}{u_n} \right| = L < 1.$$

Let us choose some number r between L and 1. By the definition of limit, the difference between the ratio $\left| \dfrac{u_{n+1}}{u_n} \right|$ and its limit L can be made as small as desired, by choosing n large enough; therefore a number k can be found such that for all values of $n \geq k$, we have

$$\left| \frac{u_{n+1}}{u_n} \right| < r.$$

Hence

$$|u_{k+1}| < |u_k|r,$$
$$|u_{k+2}| < |u_{k+1}|r < |u_k|r^2,$$
$$|u_{k+3}| < |u_{k+2}|r < |u_k|r^3,$$

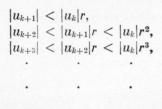

Figure 227

Discarding the first k terms of $\sum_{n=1}^{\infty} |u_n|$, we see that the remaining terms are less than the corresponding terms of the series

$$|u_k|r + |u_k|r^2 + |u_k|r^3 + \cdots + |u_k|r^m + \cdots.$$

But this last, being a geometric series with ratio $r < 1$, is convergent; hence the given series converges by a comparison test.

In case (b), it is easy to show that u_n does not approach zero.

Example (a). In the series

$$1 - \frac{1}{2} + \frac{2}{2^2} - \frac{3}{2^3} + \cdots + \frac{(-1)^n \cdot n}{2^n} + \frac{(-1)^{n+1}(n+1)}{2^{n+1}} + \cdots,$$

$$\operatorname*{Lim}_{n \to \infty} \left| \frac{u_{n+1}}{u_n} \right| = \operatorname*{Lim}_{n \to \infty} \frac{\dfrac{n+1}{2^{n+1}}}{\dfrac{n}{2^n}} = \operatorname*{Lim}_{n \to \infty} \frac{n+1}{2n} = \frac{1}{2}.$$

Thus the series converges.

Example (b). In the series

$$1 + 1 + \frac{1}{2!} + \frac{1}{3!} + \frac{1}{4!} + \cdots + \frac{1}{n!} + \frac{1}{(n+1)!} + \cdots,$$

$$\operatorname*{Lim}_{n \to \infty} \left| \frac{u_{n+1}}{u_n} \right| = \operatorname*{Lim}_{n \to \infty} \frac{n!}{(n+1)!},$$

so that

$$\text{Lim}_{n\to\infty} \left|\frac{u_{n+1}}{u_n}\right| = \text{Lim}_{n\to\infty} \frac{1\cdot 2\cdot 3\cdots n}{1\cdot 2\cdot 3\cdots n(n+1)} = \text{Lim}_{n\to\infty} \frac{1}{n+1} = 0.$$

Hence the series converges.

Example (c). For the *p*-series $\sum_{n=1}^{\infty} \frac{1}{n^p}$, we have

$$\text{Lim}_{n\to\infty} \frac{\dfrac{1}{(n+1)^p}}{\dfrac{1}{n^p}} = \text{Lim}_{n\to\infty} \frac{n^p}{(n+1)^p} = \text{Lim}_{n\to\infty} \frac{1}{\left(1+\dfrac{1}{n}\right)^p} = 1.$$

This is sufficient to show that the test fails in case (c); for the *p*-series converges if $p > 1$, diverges if $p \leqq 1$, so that there are both convergent and divergent series for which $L = 1$.

Failure of the test in case (d) follows at once, since the limit L, which is our criterion, is nonexistent. See Ex. 26 below.

EXERCISES

In Exs. 1–16, test for convergence by the ratio test.

1. $\displaystyle\sum_{n=1}^{\infty} \frac{(-1)^{n+1}n}{3^n}.$ *Ans.* Convergent.

2. $\dfrac{2^5}{\pi^2} + \dfrac{3^5}{\pi^3} + \dfrac{4^5}{\pi^4} + \cdots + \dfrac{n^5}{\pi^n} + \cdots.$

3. $\dfrac{1^2}{2^0} + \dfrac{2^2}{2^1} + \dfrac{3^2}{2^2} + \cdots + \dfrac{k^2}{2^{k-1}} + \cdots.$

4. $\displaystyle\sum_{n=0}^{\infty} \frac{(-1)^n}{(2n)!}.$ *Ans.* Convergent.

5. $\displaystyle\sum_{n=1}^{\infty} \frac{(n-2)(n+3)}{2\cdot 4\cdot 6\cdots(2n)}.$ *Ans.* Convergent.

6. $\displaystyle\sum_{n=1}^{\infty} \frac{1\cdot 4\cdot 7\cdots(3n+1)}{n^5}.$ *Ans.* Divergent.

7. $\displaystyle\sum_{n=0}^{\infty} \frac{(-1)^n(n+1)}{(2n+1)!}.$ 8. $\displaystyle\sum_{n=2}^{\infty} \frac{4n+1}{2^n n!(2n+1)}.$

9. $\displaystyle\sum_{n=1}^{\infty} \frac{1\cdot 3\cdot 5\cdot 7\cdots(2n-1)}{3\cdot 6\cdot 9\cdots(3n)}.$ *Ans.* Convergent.

10. $\dfrac{\pi}{3} - 2\left(\dfrac{\pi}{3}\right)^2 + 3\left(\dfrac{\pi}{3}\right)^3 - \cdots + (-1)^{n+1}n\left(\dfrac{\pi}{3}\right)^n + \cdots.$

11. $\displaystyle\sum_{n=1}^{\infty} \dfrac{n^{100}}{e^n}.$

12. $\displaystyle\sum_{k=0}^{\infty} \dfrac{1}{(2k+1)\cdot 5^{2k+1}}.$

13. $\displaystyle\sum_{n=0}^{\infty} \dfrac{(-1)^n(2n+1)}{(4n+1)\cdot 3^n}.$

14. $\displaystyle\sum_{n=1}^{\infty} \dfrac{(2n-1)\pi^{n+1}}{n^{200}}.$

15. $\displaystyle\sum_{n=1}^{\infty} \dfrac{3\cdot 6\cdot 9\cdots (3n)}{1\cdot 5\cdot 9\cdots (4n+1)}.$ *Ans.* Convergent.

16. $\displaystyle\sum_{n=1}^{\infty} \dfrac{(-1)^{n-1}(2n+1)!}{n!}.$ *Ans.* Divergent.

17. If $P(n)$ is a polynomial of any degree in n, show that *the series* $\displaystyle\sum_{n=1}^{\infty} \dfrac{P(n)}{k^n}$

converges provided $|k| > 1.$

In Exs. 18–29, show that the ratio test fails; test for convergence by some other method.

18. $\displaystyle\sum_{n=1}^{\infty} \dfrac{n+2}{n(n+3)(2n-1)}.$

19. $\displaystyle\sum_{n=2}^{\infty} \dfrac{\sqrt{n-1}}{n^2(n+1)}.$

20. $\dfrac{1}{1\cdot 3} + \dfrac{1}{3\cdot 5} + \dfrac{1}{5\cdot 7} + \cdots + \dfrac{1}{(2n-1)(2n+1)} + \cdots.$

21. $\dfrac{1}{2^3} + \dfrac{2^2}{3^3} + \dfrac{3^2}{4^3} + \cdots + \dfrac{(n-1)^2}{n^3} + \cdots.$

22. $\displaystyle\sum_{n=1}^{\infty} \dfrac{(-1)^n 3n}{n+1}.$ *Ans.* Divergent.

23. $\displaystyle\sum_{n=1}^{\infty} \dfrac{\sec^2 n}{n}.$ *Ans.* Divergent.

24. $\displaystyle\sum_{n=1}^{\infty} \dfrac{1}{n^2}\cos\dfrac{2n\pi}{n+1}.$ *Ans.* Convergent.

25. $\displaystyle\sum_{n=1}^{\infty} (-1)^n n^3.$ *Ans.* Divergent.

26. $\displaystyle\sum_{n=1}^{\infty} u_n$, where $u_n = \dfrac{1}{n}$ if n is odd, $u_n = \dfrac{1}{2^n}$ if n is even.   *Ans.* Divergent.

27. $\displaystyle\sum_{n=1}^{\infty} \dfrac{(3 + \cos n\pi)n}{2^n}$.   *Ans.* Convergent.

28. $\displaystyle\sum_{n=0}^{\infty} \dfrac{e^{\cos \frac{1}{4}n\pi}}{(n+1)(n+3)}$.   29. $\displaystyle\sum_{n=0}^{\infty} \dfrac{\cos \frac{1}{6}n\pi}{e^{2n}}$.

225. *Alternating Series*

A series whose terms are alternately positive and negative is called an *alternating series*. We shall obtain two extremely useful results concerning such series.

ALTERNATING SERIES TEST

THEOREM 41. *If after a certain point the terms of an alternating series never increase numerically, and if the limit of the nth term is zero, the series is convergent.*

THEOREM 42. *If a series has been shown to be convergent by the alternating series test, then the difference between the sum of the series and the sum of the first n terms is numerically less than the $(n + 1)$-st term:*

$$|S - S_n| < |u_{n+1}|.$$

Although formal proofs of these theorems are easily written out, the situation may be shown more vividly by plotting the successive terms as distances laid off end-to-end on an axis. Let $OP_1 = u_1$, $P_1P_2 = u_2$, $P_2P_3 = u_3$, and for any n, $P_nP_{n+1} = u_{n+1}$. It follows from the hypotheses that the suc-

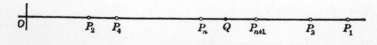

Figure 228

cessive segments are measured alternately right and left and become shorter and shorter, approaching the limit zero. For any n, the segment OP_n represents the sum S_n of the first n terms. Then P_n must approach some fixed limit-point Q, and OP_n, or S_n, approaches the limiting value $OQ = S$. This proves the validity of the alternating series test.

To prove Theorem 42, note that any two successive points P_n, P_{n+1} must fall on opposite sides of Q. Hence $|P_nQ| < |P_nP_{n+1}|$. But

$$P_nQ = OQ - OP_n = S - S_n, \quad P_nP_{n+1} = u_{n+1}.$$

It is important to realize that the theorem does not state a bound on the error for any convergent alternating series but only for those whose convergence can be demonstrated by the alternating series test.

Example (*a*). Test the series $\sum_{n=1}^{\infty} \frac{(-1)^{n-1}}{n}$.

This series is not absolutely convergent, since the series of absolute values is the harmonic series.

Let

$$u_n = \frac{(-1)^{n-1}}{n}.$$

Then

(1) The u_n alternate in sign;

(2) $\mathrm{Lim}_{n \to \infty} u_n = 0$;

(3) $\frac{1}{n+1} < \frac{1}{n}$, so $|u_{n+1}| < |u_n|$; the terms steadily decrease in numerical value.

Hence the series in question converges by the alternating series test. Since it is convergent but not absolutely convergent, it is simply convergent.

Let

$$S_n = 1 - \frac{1}{2} + \frac{1}{3} - \frac{1}{4} + \cdots + \frac{(-1)^{n-1}}{n},$$

the sum to n terms of the series, and let E_n be the error made by stopping with the nth term. Thus E_n is the difference between the sum of the series and the approximation S_n. By Theorem 42,

$$|E_n| < \frac{1}{n+1},$$

which in this instance is not particularly helpful, as is pointed out in Ex. 28 below. The next example has a more cheerful ending.

Example (*b*). Test the series $\sum_{n=0}^{\infty} \frac{(-1)^n}{(2n)!}$.

We already know (Ex. 4, page 426) that this series is absolutely convergent. Let us, in order to bound the error in computation with the series, test it by the alternating series test. It is easily seen that

(1) The terms alternate in sign;

(2) $\mathrm{Lim}_{n \to \infty} \frac{(-1)^n}{(2n)!} = 0$;

(3) $\frac{1}{(2n+2)!} < \frac{1}{(2n)!}$.

Therefore the alternating series test applies. Now consider the error made in using only the terms out to $n = 4$. Because the alternating series test worked, we know that

$$|E_4| < \frac{1}{(2 \cdot 5)!} = \frac{1}{10!} = \frac{1}{3{,}628{,}800} = 0.000\ 000\ 3.$$

That is, the approximation

$$S_4 = 1 - \frac{1}{2!} + \frac{1}{4!} - \frac{1}{6!} + \frac{1}{8!}$$

yields the sum of the series correct to six decimal places!

226. *Evaluation of the Sum of a Series*

So far we have striven merely to determine whether a given series is convergent or divergent—i.e., whether it does or does not have a sum. The existence of a sum having been established, the next problem is to determine its value. It follows from the definition of convergence that this can be done to any desired degree of approximation by merely adding together a sufficient number of terms at the beginning of the series. However, unless the series is "rapidly convergent"—i.e., unless the successive terms diminish rapidly in numerical value—the amount of computation involved in this process is apt to be prohibitive. (See Ex. 28 below.) More elaborate methods, beyond the range of this book, make it possible to sum many slowly convergent series with comparative ease.

In computing the sum of a series by addition of terms, it is necessary to know an upper limit for the error committed by stopping with any given term. In this connection Theorem 42 of the preceding section is useful.

If a series converges rapidly, it is usually easy to show that, even though the succeeding terms all have the same sign, the error committed by stopping at any point is only slightly greater than the first term neglected.

As a rule the terms retained in the computation are replaced by decimal approximations, and care must be taken to see that the errors thus introduced do not accumulate sufficiently to affect the result. If the sum is to be correct to k decimal places, each term must be computed to at least $k + 1$ places, and frequently more. The reader is warned against the very common mistake of stopping at too early a point in the series, so that the terms neglected are sufficient to vitiate the result.

Example. Find the sum of the series

$$\frac{1}{5} + \frac{1}{3 \cdot 5^3} + \frac{1}{5 \cdot 5^5} + \frac{1}{7 \cdot 5^7} + \cdots + \frac{1}{(2n + 1) \cdot 5^{2n+1}} + \cdots,$$

correct to four decimal places. (Ex. 12, page 427.)

To find the sum, we have

$$\frac{1}{5} = 0.2, \qquad \frac{1}{3 \cdot 5^3} = 0.002\,67, \qquad \frac{1}{5 \cdot 5^5} = 0.000\,06.$$

The fourth term is far too small in itself to affect the fifth place, and the error committed by stopping with the third term is but slightly greater than the fourth term. The argument is as follows:

$$\frac{1}{7 \cdot 5^7} + \frac{1}{9 \cdot 5^9} + \frac{1}{11 \cdot 5^{11}} + \cdots + \frac{1}{(2n+1)5^{2n+1}} + \cdots$$

$$< \frac{1}{7 \cdot 5^7} + \frac{1}{7 \cdot 5^9} + \frac{1}{7 \cdot 5^{11}} + \cdots + \frac{1}{7 \cdot 5^{2n+1}} + \cdots$$

$$< \frac{1}{7 \cdot 5^7}\left(1 + \frac{1}{5^2} + \frac{1}{5^4} + \cdots + \frac{1}{5^{2k}} + \cdots\right).$$

The series in parentheses is a geometric series whose sum is $\dfrac{1}{1 - \frac{1}{25}} = \dfrac{25}{24}.$
Thus the error in stopping with the third term is less than $\frac{25}{24}$ times the fourth term. Adding the three terms computed above, and discarding the fifth place as untrustworthy, we find the sum to be 0.2027.

EXERCISES

In Exs. 1–16, test the series (a) for absolute convergence; (b) for convergence.

1. $\displaystyle\sum_{n=0}^{\infty} \frac{(-1)^n}{3n+1}.$ *Ans.* Convergent.

2. $\displaystyle\sum_{n=0}^{\infty} \frac{(-1)^n}{(3n-1)^2}.$ *Ans.* Absolutely convergent.

3. $\displaystyle\sum_{n=0}^{\infty} \frac{(-1)^n(n+1)}{3n+1}.$ *Ans.* Divergent.

4. $\displaystyle\sum_{n=1}^{\infty} \frac{(-1)^{n-1}1000n^2}{3^n}.$ *Ans.* Absolutely convergent.

5. $\displaystyle\sum_{k=0}^{\infty} \frac{(-1)^k k!}{100^k}.$ *Ans.* Divergent.

6. $\displaystyle\sum_{k=0}^{\infty} \frac{(-1)^k(2k)!}{10^k}.$

7. $\displaystyle\sum_{n=0}^{\infty} \frac{(-1)^n 10^{4n}}{n!}.$

8. $\displaystyle\sum_{n=0}^{\infty} \frac{(-1)^n}{n^4+1}.$

9. $\displaystyle\sum_{n=0}^{\infty} \frac{(-1)^n(n+2)}{n^2+6n+10}.$

10. $\displaystyle\sum_{n=1}^{\infty} \frac{(-1)^{n+1} n e^n}{\pi^{2n} + 1}.$ 11. $\displaystyle\sum_{n=1}^{\infty} \frac{\cos n\pi}{4n + 1}.$

12. $1 - \dfrac{1}{2\sqrt{1}} + \dfrac{1}{3\sqrt{2}} - \dfrac{1}{4\sqrt{3}} + \cdots + \dfrac{(-1)^{n-1}}{n\sqrt{n-1}} + \cdots.$

13. $1 - \dfrac{1}{\sqrt{2}} + \dfrac{1}{\sqrt{3}} - \dfrac{1}{\sqrt{4}} + \cdots + \dfrac{(-1)^{n-1}}{\sqrt{n}} + \cdots.$

14. $\displaystyle\sum_{n=1}^{\infty} \frac{1}{n^2} \sin n.$ 15. $\displaystyle\sum_{n=1}^{\infty} \frac{\sin \frac{1}{4}n\pi}{n^4}.$ 16. $\displaystyle\sum_{n=1}^{\infty} \frac{n \cos \frac{1}{4}n\pi}{n+1}.$

17. $\displaystyle\sum_{n=1}^{\infty} u_n$, where $u_n = \dfrac{1}{n}$ if n is odd, $u_n = -\dfrac{1}{n^{\frac{3}{2}}}$ if n is even.   *Ans.* Divergent.

In Exs. 18–27, find the sum of the series, correct to the number of decimal places indicated in the respective answers.

18. $1 - \dfrac{1}{10} + \dfrac{2}{10^2} - \dfrac{3}{10^3} + \cdots + \dfrac{(-1)^n \cdot n}{10^n} + \cdots.$ *Ans.* 0.917 36.

19. $\displaystyle\sum_{n=0}^{\infty} \frac{(-1)^n}{(2n+1)!}.$ *Ans.* 0.841 47.   20. $\displaystyle\sum_{n=1}^{\infty} \frac{(-1)^{n-1} n^2}{10^{2n}}.$ *Ans.* 0.009 609.

21. $\displaystyle\sum_{n=1}^{\infty} \frac{(-1)^{n-1}}{n^2 \cdot 10^n}.$ *Ans.* 0.097 605.   22. $\displaystyle\sum_{n=0}^{\infty} \frac{(-1)^n}{(2n)!(n+1)}.$ *Ans.* 0.763 5.

23. $\displaystyle\sum_{n=0}^{\infty} \frac{(-1)^n (n+1)}{(n+4)!}.$ *Ans.* 0.028 5.

24. $\displaystyle\sum_{n=0}^{\infty} \frac{1}{(2n)!}.$ *Ans.* 1.543 1.   25. $\displaystyle\sum_{n=0}^{\infty} \frac{1}{(2n+1)!}.$ *Ans.* 1.175 2.

26. $\dfrac{1}{5} + \dfrac{2}{5^2} + \dfrac{3}{5^3} + \cdots + \dfrac{n}{5^n} + \cdots.$ *Ans.* 0.3125.

27. $\dfrac{1}{1 \cdot 2} + \dfrac{1}{2 \cdot 3} \cdot \dfrac{1}{10} + \dfrac{1}{3 \cdot 4} \cdot \dfrac{1}{10^2} + \cdots + \dfrac{1}{n(n+1)10^{n-1}} + \cdots.$

           Ans. 0.5176.

28. How many terms of the series $\displaystyle\sum_{n=0}^{\infty} \frac{(-1)^n}{n+1}$ must be taken, according to

Theorem 42, to insure correctness of the sum to four decimal places with an error of not more than 5 in the fifth decimal place?   *Ans.* 20,000.

POWER SERIES

227. *Convergence of Power Series*

A series of the form

$$a_0 + a_1 v + a_2 v^2 + \cdots + a_n v^n + \cdots = \sum_{n=0}^{\infty} a_n v^n,$$

where v is a variable and a_0, a_1, a_2, $\cdots$ are constants, is called a *power series*. Such series will be studied in this chapter.

A power series may converge for all values of the variable v, or for no values except zero, but usually it will converge for all values in some interval of definite length greater than zero, and diverge for all values outside that interval. The interval of convergence always extends equal distances on each side of the point $v = 0$.

In simple cases the interval of convergence can be determined by the ratio test.

Example (*a*). Find the interval of convergence of the series

$$1 + x + \frac{x^2}{2} + \frac{x^3}{3} + \cdots + \frac{x^n}{n} + \cdots.$$

Here

$$\operatorname*{Lim}_{n \to \infty} \left| \frac{u_{n+1}}{u_n} \right| = \operatorname*{Lim}_{n \to \infty} \left| \frac{\frac{x^{n+1}}{n+1}}{\frac{x^n}{n}} \right| = \operatorname*{Lim}_{n \to \infty} \frac{n}{n+1} \cdot |x| = |x|.$$

Therefore:

(*a*) The series converges when $|x| < 1$, i.e., $-1 < x < 1$.

(*b*) The series diverges when $|x| > 1$.

(*c*) The test fails when $x = \pm 1$. But when $x = 1$, the series is

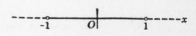

Figure 229

$$1 + 1 + \frac{1}{2} + \frac{1}{3} + \cdots + \frac{1}{n} + \cdots,$$

433

and therefore diverges; when $x = -1$, the series is

$$1 - 1 + \frac{1}{2} - \frac{1}{3} + \frac{1}{4} - \cdots + \frac{(-1)^n}{n} + \cdots,$$

which converges by § 225.

Hence the interval of convergence is $-1 \leqq x < 1$.

Example (b). Find the interval of convergence of the series

$$(x - 3) + 2(x - 3)^2 + 3(x - 3)^3 + \cdots + n(x - 3)^n + \cdots.$$

In this case

$$\operatorname*{Lim}_{n \to \infty} \left| \frac{(n + 1)(x - 3)^{n+1}}{n(x - 3)^n} \right| = \operatorname*{Lim}_{n \to \infty} \frac{n + 1}{n} \cdot |x - 3| = |x - 3|.$$

(*a*) The series converges if $|x - 3| < 1$, or $2 < x < 4$.

(*b*) The series diverges if $|x - 3| > 1$, or $x > 4$, $x < 2$.

(*c*) By Theorem 32a, page 411, the series diverges if $x = 2$ or $x = 4$.

Thus the interval is $2 < x < 4$.

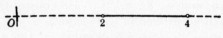

Figure 230

Example (c). Find the region of convergence of the series

$$\frac{1}{x} + \frac{2}{x^3} + \frac{2^2}{x^5} + \frac{2^3}{x^7} + \cdots + \frac{2^n}{x^{2n+1}} + \cdots.$$

The test limit is

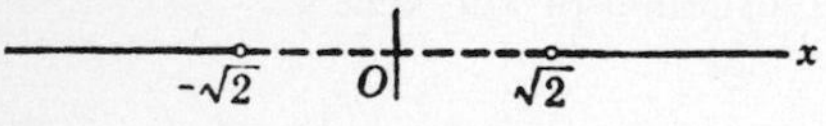

$$\operatorname*{Lim}_{n \to \infty} \frac{\dfrac{2^{n+1}}{x^{2n+3}}}{\dfrac{2^n}{x^{2n+1}}} = \operatorname*{Lim}_{n \to \infty} \frac{2}{x^2} = \frac{2}{x^2}.$$

Figure 231

Thus the series converges if $\dfrac{2}{x^2} < 1$, $|x| > \sqrt{2}$; it diverges at both endpoints.

EXERCISES

In Exs. 1–32, find the interval of convergence and test the series at the endpoints of the interval.

1. $\displaystyle\sum_{n=0}^{\infty} (-1)^n x^n.$ *Ans.* $-1 < x < 1.$

2. $\displaystyle\sum_{n=0}^{\infty} \frac{x^n}{3n + 1}.$ *Ans.* $-1 \leqq x < 1.$

3. $\displaystyle\sum_{n=1}^{\infty} \frac{(-1)^{n-1}y^{n-1}}{n^2 3^{n+1}}.$ $\qquad$ Ans. $-3 \leqq y \leqq 3.$

4. $\displaystyle\sum_{n=1}^{\infty} \frac{n^2 y^{2n}}{5^n}.$ $\qquad$ Ans. $-\sqrt{5} < y < \sqrt{5}.$

5. $\displaystyle\sum_{n=0}^{\infty} \frac{z^n}{n^3 + 1}.$ $\qquad$ 6. $\displaystyle\sum_{n=0}^{\infty} \frac{(-1)^n z^{2n}}{3n - 1}.$

7. $\displaystyle\sum_{n=1}^{\infty} \frac{(-1)^{n+1}x^{2n}}{(2n - 1)(2n)(2n + 1)}.$ $\qquad$ 8. $\displaystyle\sum_{n=1}^{\infty} \frac{(-1)^{n+1}x^n}{(n + 2)(n + 3)}.$

9. $\displaystyle\sum_{n=0}^{\infty} (-1)^n n! x^n.$ $\quad$ Ans. $x = 0.$ $\qquad$ 10. $\displaystyle\sum_{n=1}^{\infty} \frac{n! x^n}{2n - 1}.$ $\quad$ Ans. $x = 0.$

11. $\displaystyle\sum_{n=0}^{\infty} \frac{x^n}{n!}.$ $\qquad$ Ans. All values of x.

12. $\displaystyle\sum_{n=0}^{\infty} \frac{(-1)^n x^{2n}}{(2n)!}.$ $\qquad$ Ans. All values of x.

13. $\displaystyle\sum_{n=0}^{\infty} (n + 1)^2 (x + 2)^n.$ $\qquad$ Ans. $-3 < x < -1.$

14. $\displaystyle\sum_{n=0}^{\infty} \frac{(-1)^n (x - 2)^n}{(n + 1)^2}.$ $\qquad$ Ans. $1 \leqq x \leqq 3.$

15. $\displaystyle\sum_{n=0}^{\infty} \frac{(-1)^n}{(n + 1)x^n}.$ $\qquad$ Ans. $x \geqq 1,$ and $x < -1.$

16. $\displaystyle\sum_{n=0}^{\infty} \frac{n + 2}{2^n x^n}.$ $\qquad$ Ans. $x > \frac{1}{2},$ and $x < -\frac{1}{2}.$

17. $\displaystyle\sum_{n=0}^{\infty} \frac{(-1)^n x^{2n+1}}{(2n + 1)!}.$ $\qquad$ Ans. All values of x.

18. $\displaystyle\sum_{n=0}^{\infty} \frac{n! x^n}{(2n + 1)!}.$ $\qquad$ Ans. All values of x.

19. $\displaystyle\sum_{n=1}^{\infty} \frac{(-1)^n x^n}{n^2 2^{2n+1}}$ *Ans.* $-4 \leqq x \leqq 4$.

20. $\displaystyle\sum_{n=1}^{\infty} \frac{(n+1)x^{2n-1}}{n^2 + 3n + 1}$.   *Ans.* $-1 < x < 1$.

21. $\displaystyle\sum_{n=0}^{\infty} (-1)^n(2n+1)y^{2n}$.

22. $\displaystyle\sum_{n=1}^{\infty} (-1)^n n^2 y^{2n+1}$.

23. $\displaystyle\sum_{k=0}^{\infty} \frac{(-1)^k(2k+1)(x+1)^{2k}}{3^k}$.

24. $\displaystyle\sum_{k=0}^{\infty} \frac{(-1)^k(x+1)^{2k}}{3^k(2k+1)}$.

25. $\displaystyle\sum_{k=0}^{\infty} k!(x-2)^{k+1}$.

26. $\displaystyle\sum_{k=0}^{\infty} k(x-4)^k$.

27. $\displaystyle\sum_{n=1}^{\infty} \frac{n(x+2)^{n-1}}{(2n+1)^2}$.

28. $\displaystyle\sum_{n=1}^{\infty} \frac{(-1)^n(x+4)^{n-1}}{(3n-1)^3}$.

29. $\displaystyle\sum_{n=0}^{\infty} \frac{(-1)^n x^n}{(n!)^2}$.

30. $\displaystyle\sum_{n=1}^{\infty} \frac{n^3 x^n}{(2n+1)!}$.

31. $\displaystyle\sum_{n=0}^{\infty} \frac{(-1)^n 5^n}{(3n+1)x^n}$.

32. $\displaystyle\sum_{n=2}^{\infty} \frac{(-1)^n 2^{n+1}}{n^2 x^{n+2}}$.

In Exs. 33–37, find the interval of convergence but do not test the series at the endpoints of the interval.

33. $\displaystyle\sum_{n=1}^{\infty} \frac{1 \cdot 3 \cdot 5 \cdot 7 \cdots (2n-1)x^{2n}}{2^n n!}$.

34. $\displaystyle\sum_{n=1}^{\infty} \frac{n^n x^n}{n!}$.   *Ans.* $|x| < \dfrac{1}{e}$.

35. $\displaystyle\sum_{n=1}^{\infty} \frac{n! x^n}{n^n}$.

36. $\displaystyle\sum_{n=1}^{\infty} \frac{1 \cdot 3 \cdot 5 \cdot 7 \cdots (2n-1)x^{2n}}{2 \cdot 4 \cdot 6 \cdot 8 \cdots (2n+2)}$.

37. $\displaystyle 1 + \sum_{n=1}^{\infty} \frac{m(m-1) \cdots (m-n+1)x^n}{n!}$.   *Ans.* $|x| < 1$.

228. *Maclaurin Series*

Consider a power series in x with an interval of convergence. For any x within that interval, the sum of the series is determined; the sum is a function of x. This suggests a very important problem: Being given a function of x, to determine whether it has a power series expansion and, if it has one, to find that expansion.

In § 232 we shall justify many of the power series expansions to be employed in this book. At present we proceed on a purely formal basis. That is, we first develop techniques for obtaining the desired series and afterward prove the validity of the results.

Suppose that $f(x)$ does have a power series expansion:

(1) $$f(x) = c_0 + c_1x + c_2x^2 + \cdots + c_nx^n + \cdots,$$

where the coefficients c_0, c_1, c_2, $\cdots$ are constants to be determined. Setting $x = 0$, we get

$$f(0) = c_0;$$

i.e., c_0 is the value of the given function at $x = 0$. Differentiating each member of (1) (see Theorem 48, p. 456), we obtain

$$f'(x) = c_1 + 2c_2x + 3c_3x^2 + \cdots,$$

and setting $x = 0$, we find

$$f'(0) = c_1.$$

Proceeding in this way, we get successively

$$f''(0) = 2 \cdot 1c_2,$$

$$f'''(0) = 3 \cdot 2 \cdot 1c_3,$$

$$\cdot \quad \cdot$$
$$\cdot \quad \cdot$$
$$\cdot \quad \cdot$$

$$f^{(n)}(0) = n!c_n,$$

$$\cdot \quad \cdot$$
$$\cdot \quad \cdot$$
$$\cdot \quad \cdot$$

Hence (1) takes the following form, called the *Maclaurin series* for $f(x)$.

(2) $$f(x) = f(0) + f'(0)x + \frac{f''(0)}{2!}x^2 + \cdots + \frac{f^{(n)}(0)}{n!}x^n + \cdots.$$

It should be noted that we have not proved the validity of this result; we have merely proved that if there is a series of the form (1) whose sum is $f(x)$, that series is given by equation (2). The series (2) can always be formally written down whenever the function and its successive derivatives are defined at $x = 0$, but examples can be found in which the sum of the series is not the given function (see Ex. 65 below).

For all functions that we shall consider, *the interval within which the Maclaurin series is valid coincides with the interval of convergence of the series.* Within that interval the series is said to *represent the function*, and the function is said to be *expanded* in powers of x.

Example (a). Find the Maclaurin series for e^x.

At once,

$$f(x) = e^x, \qquad f(0) = 1,$$
$$f'(x) = e^x, \qquad f'(0) = 1,$$

$$\cdot \qquad \cdot \qquad \cdot \qquad \cdot$$
$$\cdot \qquad \cdot \qquad \cdot \qquad \cdot$$
$$\cdot \qquad \cdot \qquad \cdot \qquad \cdot$$

$$f^{(n)}(x) = e^x, \qquad f^{(n)}(0) = 1.$$

Therefore

$$e^x = 1 + x + \frac{x^2}{2!} + \frac{x^3}{3!} + \cdots + \frac{x^n}{n!} + \cdots.$$

This series converges for all values of x. (Ex. 11, page 435.)

Example (b). Expand $\sin x$ in powers of x.

Here

$$f(x) = \sin x, \qquad f(0) = 0,$$
$$f'(x) = \cos x, \qquad f'(0) = 1,$$
$$f''(x) = -\sin x, \qquad f''(0) = 0,$$
$$f'''(x) = -\cos x, \qquad f'''(0) = -1,$$
$$f^{(4)}(x) = \sin x, \qquad f^{(4)}(0) = 0.$$

Since we have now returned to the original function, it is clear that the sequence $0, 1, 0, -1$, occurring in the right-hand column, must repeat over and over. Hence, substituting in (2), we find

$$\sin x = x - \frac{x^3}{3!} + \frac{x^5}{5!} - \cdots + \frac{(-1)^n x^{2n+1}}{(2n+1)!} + \cdots.$$

The series converges for all values of x. (Ex. 17, page 435.)

The rather cumbersome* method, using Maclaurin's formula directly to obtain power series for elementary functions, is to be used only on certain basic functions, those given in the next section. For other elementary functions, we obtain their power series expansions by suitable manipulations performed on the basic series. For details, see §§ 237–239.

---

* Try this method for getting the general term of the series for $\dfrac{x^3}{(1+x^2)^2}$, and then compare with the neat device used in Exs. 4–5, page 457.

229. *The Basic Expansions*

We list for reference:

$$(1) \qquad e^x = \sum_{n=0}^{\infty} \frac{x^n}{n!}; \quad \text{for all values of } x.$$

$$(2) \qquad \cos x = \sum_{n=0}^{\infty} \frac{(-1)^n x^{2n}}{(2n)!}; \quad \text{for all values of } x.$$

$$(3) \qquad \sin x = \sum_{n=0}^{\infty} \frac{(-1)^n x^{2n+1}}{(2n+1)!}; \quad \text{for all values of } x.$$

$$(4) \qquad \frac{1}{1-x} = \sum_{n=0}^{\infty} x^n; \qquad -1 < x < 1.$$

$$(5) \qquad \ln(1+x) = \sum_{n=1}^{\infty} \frac{(-1)^{n+1} x^n}{n}; \qquad -1 < x \leqq 1.$$

$$(6) \quad (1+x)^m = 1 + \sum_{n=1}^{\infty} \frac{m(m-1)(m-2) \cdots (m-n+1)x^n}{n!};$$
$$|x| < 1.$$

It is advisable that the student write out several terms of each series, as an aid in remembering these important expansions.

Power series for $\cosh x$ and $\sinh x$ will be found in Exs. 1, 2, p. 456, and power series for Arctan x and Arcsin x in Exs. 1, 2, p. 462.

230. *Taylor Series*

The Maclaurin series for $f(x)$ is most useful near $x = 0$ where its convergence is rapid. In studying the function $f(x)$ near some other point $x = a$, it is natural to seek a series proceeding not in powers of x but in powers of $(x - a)$. Let

$$(1) \quad f(x) = c_0 + c_1(x - a) + c_2(x - a)^2 + \cdots + c_n(x - a)^n + \cdots,$$

and set $x = a$, which gives

$$c_0 = f(a).$$

Next differentiate with respect to x throughout equation (1) and then set $x = a$, proceeding just as we did in obtaining the coefficients in the Maclaurin series. The result is the *Taylor series* for $f(x)$:

(2) $f(x) = f(a) + f'(a)(x - a) + \dfrac{f''(a)}{2!} (x - a)^2 + \cdots$

$$+ \dfrac{f^{(n)}(a)}{n!} (x - a)^n + \cdots.$$

The Maclaurin series is the special case $a = 0$ of the Taylor series. The remarks made in § 228 concerning the validity of the Maclaurin series apply here as well.

Example. Expand the function $\ln x$ in powers of $x - 1$. Here $a = 1$:

$$f(x) = \ln x, \qquad\qquad\qquad f(1) = 0,$$

$$f'(x) = \frac{1}{x}, \qquad\qquad\qquad f'(1) = 1,$$

$$f''(x) = -\frac{1}{x^2}, \qquad\qquad\qquad f''(1) = -1,$$

$$f'''(x) = \frac{2}{x^3}, \qquad\qquad\qquad f'''(1) = 2,$$

$$f^{(4)}(x) = -\frac{2 \cdot 3}{x^4}, \qquad\qquad\qquad f^{(4)}(1) = -2 \cdot 3,$$

$$\qquad\cdot\qquad\qquad\cdot\qquad\qquad\qquad\cdot\qquad\qquad\cdot$$
$$\qquad\cdot\qquad\qquad\cdot\qquad\qquad\qquad\cdot\qquad\qquad\cdot$$
$$\qquad\cdot\qquad\qquad\cdot\qquad\qquad\qquad\cdot\qquad\qquad\cdot$$

$$f^{(n)}(x) = (-1)^{n-1}\frac{(n-1)!}{x^n}, \qquad f^{(n)}(1) = (-1)^{n-1}(n-1)!.$$

Hence, by (2),

$$\ln x = (x - 1) - \frac{(x - 1)^2}{2} + \frac{(x - 1)^3}{3}$$

$$- \cdots + (-1)^{n-1}\frac{(x - 1)^n}{n} + \cdots.$$

The series converges for $0 < x \leqq 2$.

In the higher development of mathematics, it would be hard to overstress the importance of the general Taylor series; but in the specific elementary applications to which we are necessarily limited in this beginning course, the special case, the Maclaurin series, is more useful than the general formula.

EXERCISES

In Exs. 1–11, use the Maclaurin series directly to expand the given function in powers of x; then determine the interval of convergence.

1. $\cos x$. See (2), § 229.
2. $\ln (1 + x)$. See (5), § 229.

3. $\dfrac{1}{1 - x}$. See (4), § 229.   4. $\dfrac{1}{1 + x}$.

5. $\sin 4x$.   **6.** $\ln (1 - 2x)$.

7. $e^{-\frac{1}{4}x}$.   **8.** $\dfrac{1}{1 - 3x}$.

9. $\sqrt{1 + x}$.   *Ans.* $1 + \dfrac{1}{2}\, x + \displaystyle\sum_{n=2}^{\infty} \dfrac{(-1)^{n+1}\, 1 \cdot 3 \cdot 5 \cdots (2n - 3)x^n}{2^n n!}$.

10. $\dfrac{1}{\sqrt{1 + x}}$.   *Ans.* $1 + \displaystyle\sum_{n=1}^{\infty} \dfrac{(-1)^n\, 1 \cdot 3 \cdot 5 \cdots (2n - 1)x^n}{2^n n!}$.

11. $(1 + x)^m$. See (6), § 229.

In Exs. 12–25, obtain the power series expansion for the given function by making an appropriate substitution in one of the basic expansions of § 229.

12. e^{-x^2}. Put $(-x^2)$ for x in (1), § 229.
13. $\ln (1 + 4x)$. Put $4x$ for x in (5), § 229.

14. Ex. 4.   **15.** Ex. 5.   **16.** Ex. 6.
17. Ex. 7.   **18.** Ex. 8.   **19.** $\cos 3x$.
20. $\sin 6x$.   **21.** $\ln (1 + 3x^2)$.   **22.** $\ln (1 - 2x^3)$.

23. $\dfrac{1}{1 + 2x^3}$.   **24.** e^{2x^2}.   **25.** $e^{-\frac{1}{2}x^2}$.

In Exs. 26–37, obtain the power series for the given function in the manner described.

26. $\ln (3 - x)$ from (5), § 229, with the aid of the relation

$$\ln (3 - x) = \ln \left[3 \left(1 - \frac{x}{3} \right) \right] = \ln 3 + \ln \left(1 - \frac{x}{3} \right).$$

27. $\ln (4 + 5x)$, from (5), § 229.   **28.** $\ln (4 - 5x)$, from (5), § 229.
29. $x^2 e^{-x}$, from (1), § 229.   **30.** $x^3 e^{-x^2}$, from (1), § 229.

31. $\dfrac{x^3}{1 - x^2}$, from (4), § 229.   **32.** $\dfrac{x^2}{1 + 2x}$, from (4), § 229.

33. $\sin x \cos x$, from (3), § 229.   **34.** $1 - \cos 2x$, from (2) § 229.

35. $\sqrt{1 - x^2}$, from Ex. 9.   **36.** $\dfrac{1}{\sqrt{1 + 3x}}$, from Ex. 10.

37. $\dfrac{1}{\sqrt{1 - x^2}}$, from Ex. 10.   *Ans.* $1 + \displaystyle\sum_{n=1}^{\infty} \dfrac{1 \cdot 3 \cdot 5 \cdots (2n - 1)x^{2n}}{2^n n!}$.

In Exs. 38–43, show that the given function cannot be expanded in a Maclaurin series.

38. $\csc x$.   **39.** $\cot x$.   **40.** $e^{\frac{1}{x}}$.

41. $\ln x$.   **42.** $x^2 \ln x$.   **43.** $x \csc^2 x$.

In Exs. 44–52, use the Taylor series directly to obtain the required expansion.

44. e^x in powers of $(x - 3)$.

$$Ans. \quad \sum_{n=0}^{\infty} \frac{e^3(x - 3)^n}{n!}.$$

45. e^x in powers of $(x + 2)$.   **46.** $\ln x$ in powers of $(x - 4)$.
47. $\ln x$ in powers of $(x + \frac{1}{2})$.   **48.** $\sqrt{x}$ in powers of $(x - 4)$.
49. $\cos x$ in powers of $(x - \frac{1}{4}\pi)$.   **50.** $\sin x$ in powers of $(x + \frac{1}{4}\pi)$.

51. $\dfrac{1}{1 - x}$ in powers of $(x + 4)$.   **52.** $\dfrac{1}{1 + x}$ in powers of $(x + 3)$.

In Exs. 53–61, use appropriate devices to obtain the desired expansion from the basic formulas of § 229 without resorting to Taylor's expansion directly.

53. Ex. 44. Write $e^x = e^3 \cdot e^{x-3}$.
54. Ex. 46. Write $\ln x = \ln [4 + (x - 4)] = \ln [4\{1 + \frac{1}{4}(x - 4)\}]$, etc.
55. Ex. 52. Write $\dfrac{1}{1 + x} = \dfrac{1}{-2 + (x + 3)} = \dfrac{-\frac{1}{2}}{1 - \frac{1}{2}(x + 3)}$, etc.

56. Ex. 45.   **57.** Ex. 47.   **58.** Ex. 48. Use Ex. 9.
59. Ex. 49.   **60.** Ex. 50.   **61.** Ex. 51.
62. Show that, if $P(x)$ is a polynomial of the nth degree in x,

$$P(x) = P(a) + P'(a)(x - a) + \frac{P''(a)}{2!}(x - a)^2 + \cdots + \frac{P^{(n)}(a)}{n!}(x - a)^n,$$

whatever may be the values of a and x.
63. Arrange the function $y = x^3 - 3x^2 + 2x - 5$ in powers of $x - 3$. (Ex. 62.)
$$Ans. \; y = 1 + 11(x - 3) + 6(x - 3)^2 + (x - 3)^3.$$
64. Arrange the function $y = x^4 - 3x^2 - 6x + 8$ in powers of $x - 2$. (Ex. 62.)
$$Ans. \; y = 14(x - 2) + 21(x - 2)^2 + 8(x - 2)^3 + (x - 2)^4.$$

65. The Maclaurin series for the function $f(x) = e^{-\frac{1}{x^2}}$ may be formally obtained, provided we define $f(0) = 0$. Prove that the series converges for all values of x but does not represent the function.

It is proved in more advanced courses that the derivatives of $f(x)$ exist and are continuous at $x = 0$.

The reader should show that the nth derivative of $f(x)$ is the product of $e^{-\frac{1}{x^2}}$ and a polynomial in $\dfrac{1}{x}$.

231. Remainder Theorems

Suppose that $f(y)$ and its derivative $f'(y)$ are continuous in a range $a \leq y \leq x$. We know that an integral of $f'(y)$ is $f(y)$, so that

$$(1) \qquad \int_a^x f'(y) \, dy = f(x) - f(a).$$

Let us rewrite (1) as

$$(2) \qquad f(x) = f(a) + \int_a^x f'(y) \, dy.$$

We shall use integration by parts on the integral in (2), differentiating $f'(y)$ to get $f''(y) \, dy$ and integrating dy to get $(y - x)$. The choice $(y - x)$ rather than y as an integral of dy is made to simplify the integrated portion at the upper limit of integration.

$$\begin{array}{c|c} f'(y) & dy \\ \hline f''(y) \, dy & -(x - y) \end{array}$$

If we assume the existence of $f''(y)$, the above integration by parts performed on equation (2) leads us to

$$f(x) = f(a) - \left[(x - y)f'(y) \right]_a^x + \int_a^x (x - y)f''(y) \, dy,$$

$$(3) \qquad f(x) = f(a) + (x - a)f'(a) + \int_a^x (x - y)f''(y) \, dy.$$

Let us now apply integration by parts again.

$$\begin{array}{c|c} f''(y) & (x - y) \, dy \\ \hline f'''(y) \, dy & -\tfrac{1}{2}(x - y)^2 \end{array}$$

The choice indicated in the table leads us from equation (3) to the form

$$f(x) = f(a) + (x - a)f'(a) - \tfrac{1}{2}\left[(x - y)^2 f''(y) \right]_a^x + \tfrac{1}{2}\int_a^x (x - y)^2 f'''(y) \, dy,$$

and thus to the equation

$$(4)$$
$$f(x) = f(a) + (x - a)f'(a) + \tfrac{1}{2}(x - a)^2 f''(a) + \tfrac{1}{2}\int_a^x (x - y)^2 f'''(y) \, dy.$$

The above process may be iterated, provided the derivatives of $f(y)$ involved all exist. In n steps, we are thus led to the following result.

THEOREM 43. *If in* $a \leqq y \leqq x$, $f(y)$ *and its first* $(n + 1)$ *derivatives exist,*

$$(5) \qquad f(x) = f(a) + \sum_{k=1}^n \frac{f^{(k)}(a)(x - a)^k}{k!} + R_n(x, a)$$

in which

$$(6) \qquad R_n(x, a) = \frac{1}{n!} \int_a^x (x - y)^n f^{(n+1)}(y) \, dy.$$

The term $R_n(x, a)$ in (5) and (6) is called the *remainder*. Equation (5) is a finite form of a Taylor series. The problem of showing that $f(x)$ is represented by its Taylor series in some interval around $x = a$ is precisely the problem of showing that in the interval

$$(7) \qquad\qquad \operatorname*{Lim}_{n \to \infty} R_n(x, a) = 0.$$

We shall now obtain another form for the remainder term R_n of equation (5). For this purpose let us extend the first law of the mean obtained in § 104.

Suppose that in the interval $a \leqq y \leqq x$, $f(y)$ and its first $(n + 1)$ derivatives exist. Define the remainder $R_n(x, a)$ by

$$(8) \qquad f(x) = f(a) + \sum_{k=1}^{n} \frac{f^{(k)}(a)(x - a)^k}{k!} + R_n(x, a).$$

Now consider the function

$$(9) \qquad \varphi(y) = f(x) - f(y) - \sum_{k=1}^{n} \frac{f^{(k)}(y)(x - y)^k}{k!} - \frac{(x - y)^{n+1} r_n(x, a)}{(n + 1)!}.$$

We wish to make $\varphi(y)$ satisfy the conditions of Rolle's theorem, § 103. From the fact that our proof is based upon Rolle's theorem, it can be seen that Theorem 44, page 445, is weaker than is necessary. The highest derivative involved need not exist at the endpoints of the interval.

By (9), $\varphi(x) = 0$ and

$$(10) \qquad \varphi(a) = f(x) - f(a) - \sum_{k=1}^{n} \frac{f^{(k)}(a)(x - a)^k}{k!} - \frac{(x - a)^{n+1} r_n(x, a)}{(n + 1)!}.$$

Because of (8) the $\varphi(a)$ of (10) will be zero if we choose $r_n(x, a)$ so that

$$R_n(x, a) = \frac{(x - a)^{n+1} r_n(x, a)}{(n + 1)!}.$$

From equation (9) it follows that

$$\varphi'(y) = -f'(y) - \sum_{k=1}^{n} \frac{f^{(k+1)}(y)(x - y)^k}{k!}$$

$$+ \sum_{k=1}^{n} \frac{f^{(k)}(y)(x - y)^{k-1}}{(k - 1)!} + \frac{(x - y)^n r_n(x, a)}{n!}.$$

A shift of index from k to $(k + 1)$ in the last summation above permits us to write

$$\varphi'(y) = -f'(y) - \sum_{k=1}^{n} \frac{f^{(k+1)}(y)(x - y)^k}{k!}$$

$$+ \sum_{k=0}^{n-1} \frac{f^{(k+1)}(y)(x - y)^k}{k!} + \frac{(x - y)^n r_n(x, a)}{n!},$$

or

(11) $$\varphi'(y) = -\frac{f^{(n+1)}(y)(x - y)^n}{n!} + \frac{(x - y)^n r_n(x, a)}{n!},$$

since all the other terms drop out. We now see that $\varphi'(y)$ exists in the interval $a \leq y \leq x$. Therefore Rolle's theorem may be applied to $\varphi(y)$. Hence there exists an x_1 in the open interval $a < x_1 < x$ such that $\varphi'(x_1) = 0$. Since $(x - x_1) \neq 0$, we may conclude from $\varphi'(x_1) = 0$ and equation (11) that

(12) $$r_n(x, a) = f^{(n+1)}(x_1), \qquad a < x_1 < x.$$

We have thus proved the following result.

THEOREM 44. *If in* $a \leq y \leq x$, $f(y)$ *and its first* $(n + 1)$ *derivatives exist,*

(13) $$f(x) = f(a) + \sum_{k=1}^{n} \frac{f^{(k)}(a)(x - a)^k}{k!} + R_n(x, a)$$

in which

(14) $$R_n(x, a) = \frac{(x - a)^{n+1} f^{(n+1)}(x_1)}{(n + 1)!}$$

for some x_1 *in the open interval* $a < x_1 < x$.

232. *Justification of Some Basic Expansions*

We now demonstrate the validity of some of the expansions given in § 229. We may conclude from Theorem 44 of the preceding section that, if all the derivatives of $f(x)$ exist, $f(x)$ is represented by its Taylor series

(1) $$f(x) = f(a) + \sum_{n=1}^{\infty} \frac{f^{(n)}(a)(x - a)^n}{n!}$$

in any x-interval such that

(2) $$\lim_{n \to \infty} \frac{(x - a)^{n+1} f^{(n+1)}(x_1)}{(n + 1)!} = 0, \qquad a < x_1 < x.$$

For Maclaurin series put $a = 0$ in the above statement.

First consider $f(x) = e^x$. We know that for all n

(3) $$f^{(n)}(x) = e^x.$$

Then, using $a = 0$, we have

(4) $$e^x = 1 + \sum_{n=1}^{\infty} \frac{x^n}{n!}$$

if only

(5) $$\lim_{n \to \infty} \frac{x^{n+1}e^{x_1}}{(n+1)!} = 0, \qquad 0 < x_1 < x.$$

But (5) is true for any fixed x, so (4) is valid for all positive x. The interval of validity of a Taylor (or Maclaurin) series is symmetric about the point $x = a$ (or zero). We need not discuss negative x separately in our justification of the basic Maclaurin expansions of § 229.

Next consider at once both the functions $\sin x$ and $\cos x$. We know the derivatives are each either plus or minus $\sin x$ or $\cos x$. Hence, for finite x_1,

$$|f^{(n+1)}(x_1)| \leqq 1.$$

It follows that $R_n \to 0$ as $n \to \infty$ for $f(x) = \cos x$ or $f(x) = \sin x$. Thus the expansions (2) and (3) of § 229 are valid for all finite x.

The validity of the expansion

(6) $$\frac{1}{1-x} = \sum_{n=0}^{\infty} x^n, \qquad -1 < x < 1$$

is easily justified by direct appeal to the definition of the sum of an infinite series. Let the sum of the terms out to x^n in the series on the right in (6) be $S_n(x)$:

(7) $$S_n(x) = \sum_{k=0}^{n} x^k.$$

By elementary algebra

$$S_n(x) = \frac{1 - x^{n+1}}{1 - x}.$$

Therefore, if $|x| < 1$,

$$\lim_{n \to \infty} S_n(x) = \frac{1}{1-x}.$$

If $|x| \geqq 1$, the series in (6) diverges because the general term does not $\to 0$ as $n \to \infty$. (Recall Theorem 32a, page 411.)

The student may show the validity of other expansions which appear in the book, if he wishes. We have accomplished the basic aim of exhibiting the ideas upon which such proofs of validity are based.

233. *Applications of Maclaurin Series*

The most elementary application of series, and one of great importance, is in computing tables of values of various functions, e.g., logarithms, trigonometric functions, etc.

Example (a). Compute $\sin 3°$ to five decimal places.

Setting $x = 3° = \dfrac{\pi}{60}$ in the series for $\sin x$ (§ 229), we get

$$\sin 3° = \sin \frac{\pi}{60} = \frac{\pi}{60} - \frac{1}{6}\left(\frac{\pi}{60}\right)^3 + \frac{1}{120}\left(\frac{\pi}{60}\right)^5 - \cdots$$
$$= 0.052\ 360 - 0.000\ 024 + \cdots .$$

Without computing the third term, we see that it is much too small to affect the sixth decimal place, and the error committed by stopping with any term is less than the next term by Theorem 42, page 428. Hence we need keep only two terms:

$$\sin 3° = 0.052\ 34.$$

Example (b). Since

$$\operatorname*{Lim}_{\theta \to 0} \frac{\sin \theta}{\theta} = 1,$$

it follows that for small values of the angle, $\sin \theta$ and θ are nearly equal. Within what interval can the sine be replaced by the angle if the allowable error is 0.0005?

From the equation

$$\sin \theta = \theta - \frac{\theta^3}{3!} + \frac{\theta^5}{5!} - \cdots + \frac{(-1)^n \theta^{2n+1}}{(2n+1)!} + \cdots$$

it follows that the error committed by stopping with the first term, i.e., by setting

$$\sin \theta = \theta,$$

is less than $\frac{1}{6}\theta^3$ for sufficiently small θ (say, $\theta < 1$), by Theorem 42, page 428. We therefore have

$$\frac{1}{6}\theta^3 < 0.0005,$$
$$\theta^3 < 0.003,$$
$$\theta < 0.1442 \text{ (radian)}$$
$$< 8° \ 15', \text{ approximately.}$$

That is, the sine of any angle less than $8° \ 15'$ can be replaced by the angle with an error less than 0.0005.

Example (c). Find the amount by which an arc of a great circle of the earth 1 mi. long recedes from its chord.

We have to find

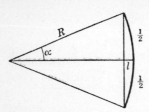

Figure 232

$$l = R - R \cos \alpha = R(1 - \cos \alpha).$$

Since α is very small, we may safely take, in (2) of § 229.

$$\cos \alpha = 1 - \tfrac{1}{2}\alpha^2,$$

$$l = \frac{1}{2} R\alpha^2 = \frac{(R\alpha)^2}{2R}.$$

By hypothesis, $R\alpha = \tfrac{1}{2}$, so that, with $R = 4000$ mi.,

$$l = \frac{\tfrac{1}{4}}{8000} \text{ mi.} = \frac{5280 \cdot 12}{4 \cdot 8000} \text{ in.} = 2 \text{ in., nearly.}$$

One of the most useful elementary applications of Maclaurin series is the evaluation of certain definite integrals. See § 240, page 460.

234. *The Value of e*

As a further application of Maclaurin series, let us compute the value of e to five decimal places. Taking $x = 1$ in (1), § 229, we have

$$e = 1 + 1 + \frac{1}{2!} + \frac{1}{3!} + \frac{1}{4!} + \cdots + \frac{1}{n!} + \cdots$$

This gives*

$$
\begin{array}{r}
1.000\ 000 \\
1.000\ 000 \\
0.500\ 000 \\
0.166\ 667 \\
0.041\ 667 \\
0.008\ 333 \\
0.001\ 389 \\
0.000\ 198 \\
0.000\ 025 \\
0.000\ 003 \\
\hline
2.718\ 28.
\end{array}
$$

The sum of all the remaining terms is but little greater than the first term neglected. Compare the terms neglected with the geometric series

$$\frac{1}{10!}\left(1 + \frac{1}{11} + \frac{1}{11^2} + \cdots + \frac{1}{11^n} + \cdots\right).$$

* Note that the fourth term can be obtained by dividing the third by 3, the fifth by dividing the fourth by 4, etc.

EXERCISES

In Exs. 1–8, use series to make the required computations.

1. cos 2° to five places.   2. sin 2° to five places.
3. sin 6° to five places.   4. cos 3° to five places.
5. sin 86° to four places.   6. cos 86° to four places.
7. ln (1.1) to four places.   8. ln (0.95) to four places.

9. Compute $\dfrac{1}{e}$ by series. *Ans.* 0.3679.

10. Find the tenth root of e. *Ans.* 1.10517.

11. Compute $(1.01)^{10}$ to four decimal places by the binomial theorem.
Ans. 1.1046.

12. Raise 0.99 to the tenth power. *Ans.* 0.9044.

13. Extract the square root of 102 to four decimal places by using power series, first writing
$$\sqrt{102} = \sqrt{100 + 2} = 10(1 + 0.02)^{\frac{1}{2}}.$$
Ans. 10.0995.

14. Extract the square root of 101 to four decimal places by using series.

15. Within what interval can $\sin \theta$ be replaced by θ, if the allowable error is 0.005? Check by the table.

16. Within what interval can $\cos \theta$ be taken equal to 1, with accuracy to three places (allowable error 0.0005)? Check by the table, pp. 566–570.

17. Solve the equation $\cos x = 8x$ to three figures by using series. *Ans.* 0.124.

18. Solve the equation $\cos x = 4x$. *Ans.* 0.243.

19. Solve Example (c), § 233, if the arc is 10 mi. long. *Ans.* 16 ft.

20. In Example (c), § 233, how much longer is the arc than the chord?
Ans. $\frac{1}{6000}$ in.

21. If a straight tunnel were to be bored through the earth from Detroit to Chicago (say, 300 mi.), how much distance would be saved? *Ans.* 371 ft.

22. In Ex. 21, find the greatest depth of the tunnel. *Ans.* 2.8 mi.

23. The gravitational attraction of the earth at a height h above sea-level is
$$A = \frac{gR^2}{(R + h)^2},$$
where R is the radius of the earth and $g = 32.16$ ft. per sec. per sec. At what altitude is $A = 32.00$?

24. Taking the earth's circumference as 40,000,000 meters, find the difference between the circumference and the perimeter of a regular inscribed polygon of 1,000,000 sides. *Ans.* Less than $\frac{1}{15}$ mm.

25. In the computation of e, § 234, find an upper limit for the error caused by stopping with ten terms. *Ans.* 0.000 000 3.

26. Use the forms of the remainder term in Theorems 43 and 44 of § 231 to show that: If $g(y)$ is continuous in the interval $a \leqq y \leqq x$, there exists an x_1 such that
$$\int_a^x (x - y)^n g(y)\, dy = \frac{(x - a)^{n+1} g(x_1)}{n + 1}, \qquad a < x_1 < x.$$

235. *Applications of Taylor Series*

If a power series is to be used for computation, the coefficients must be known numbers. Hence, even though it may be theoretically possible to expand a function $f(x)$ in powers of $(x - a)$ for any value of a (this is true, for instance, for e^x, $\sin x$ and $\cos x$), actually, for purposes of computation, the only readily available values of a are those for which $f(a)$, $f'(a)$, $f''(a)$, $\cdots$ are known, since these quantities appear in the coefficients. For example, if we wish to use the Taylor series for $\sin x$ for computation, the only values of a ready to hand $(0 < a < \frac{1}{2}\pi)$ are $\frac{1}{6}\pi$, $\frac{1}{4}\pi$, or $\frac{1}{3}\pi$.

Maclaurin series converges rapidly, in general, for *small* values of x. Taylor series converges rapidly for values of x near a—i.e., such that $x - a$ is small. Hence, of the available values of a [those for which $f(a), f'(a), \cdots$ are known], we should as a rule choose the one that is *nearest the value of x for which $f(x)$ is to be computed*. For example, to compute $\sin 46°$, we would take $a = \frac{1}{4}\pi$; to compute $\sin 58°$, we would take $a = \frac{1}{3}\pi$.

Example. Find the value of $e^{1.04}$ to four decimal places.

The Maclaurin series for e^x would converge fairly rapidly for $x = 1.04$, but the successive terms would not be easy to compute. Knowing the value of e from § 234, we may use $e^{1.04} = e \cdot e^{0.04}$,

$$e^{1.04} = e\left[1 + 0.04 + \frac{0.0016}{2!} + \frac{0.000\ 064}{3!} + \frac{0.000\ 002\ 56}{4!} + \cdots\right]$$
$$= 2.718\ 28(1 + 0.04 + 0.000\ 8 + 0.000\ 01) = 2.829\ 2.$$

236. *Approximate Formulas for Δy*

In (2), § 230, let us replace a by x and x by $x + \Delta x$. The formula then becomes

(1)　$f(x + \Delta x) = f(x) + f'(x)\,\Delta x + \dfrac{f''(x)}{2!}\,(\Delta x)^2 + \dfrac{f'''(x)}{3!}\,(\Delta x)^3 + \cdots$
$$+ \frac{f^{(n)}(x)}{n!}\,(\Delta x)^n + \cdots,$$

or, with

$$y = f(x), \qquad \Delta y = f(x + \Delta x) - f(x),$$

(2)　$\Delta y = y'\,\Delta x + \dfrac{y''}{2!}\,(\Delta x)^2 + \dfrac{y'''}{3!}\,(\Delta x)^3 + \cdots + \dfrac{y^{(n)}}{n!}(\Delta x)^n + \cdots.$

For values of x and Δx that cause the terms of the series to diminish rapidly, we have, as a first approximation to the value of Δy, the formula used in § 47,

$$\Delta y = y'\,\Delta x = dy,$$

the error in using this formula being approximately $\frac{1}{2}y''\,(\Delta x)^2$; as a second approximation we have

$$\Delta y = y' \, \Delta x + \tfrac{1}{2} y''(\Delta x)^2,$$

with an error nearly equal to $\tfrac{1}{6} y'''(\Delta x)^3$; etc.

Example. Taking $f(x) = \cos x$ in (1), we get

$$\cos (x + \Delta x) = \cos x - \sin x \, \Delta x - \tfrac{1}{2} \cos x (\Delta x)^2 + \cdots ,$$

which gives the first approximation

(3) $$\cos (x + \Delta x) = \cos x - \sin x \, \Delta x.$$

If the allowable error in the cosine is 0.0005, within what range may this formula be used to compute the cosines of angles near 45°?

The error in using (3) is approximately $-\tfrac{1}{2} \cos x (\Delta x)^2$. Since $x = 45°$, we have, numerically,

$$\tfrac{1}{2} \cdot 0.7071 \, (\Delta x)^2 < 0.000 \, 5,$$
$$(\Delta x)^2 < 0.001 \, 414,$$
$$\Delta x < 0.037 \, 6 = 2°, \text{ roughly.}$$

Hence the approximate formula (3) may safely be used to compute the cosines of angles between 43° and 47°.

EXERCISES

1. Using $e^x = e \cdot e^{x-1}$, compute $e^{0.95}$ to four figures. *Ans.* 2.586.

2. Compute $e^{0.98}$ to four figures. (Ex. 1.)

3. Using Ex. 49, p. 442, compute $\cos 44°$. *Ans.* 0.719.

4. Compute $\sin 44°$. *Ans.* 0.695.

5. Apply (1), § 236, to $y = \dfrac{1}{x}$.

Ans. $\dfrac{1}{x + \Delta x} = \displaystyle\sum_{n=0}^{\infty} \frac{(-1)^n(\Delta x)^n}{x^{n+1}} = \frac{1}{x} - \frac{\Delta x}{x^2} + \frac{(\Delta x)^2}{x^3} - \cdots + \frac{(-1)^n(\Delta x)^n}{x^{n+1}} + \cdots .$

6. Compute $\tfrac{1}{101}$ to eight decimal places. (Ex. 5.)

7. Compute $\tfrac{1}{998}$ to 15 decimal places by mental arithmetic with the aid of Ex. 5.

8. Given $\cos 6° = 0.99452$, find $\sec 6°$. *Ans.* 1.005 51.

9. Show that the error in using the approximate formula of Example (*a*), § 47, is $\pi(\Delta r)^2$. When $r = 10$ ft., what is the greatest allowable value of Δr if accuracy to 5% is required? *Ans.* About 1 ft.

10. Find the error in the approximate formula for the volume of a thin spherical shell (Ex. 1, page 92). What is the greatest allowable thickness for a radius of 5 ft., if accuracy to 1% is required? *Ans.* About 0.6 in.

11. Solve the example of § 236 for angles near 60°.

Ans. $57° \, 30' < x < 62° \, 30'.$

12. From (1), § 236, obtain an approximate formula for $\dfrac{1}{(x + \Delta x)^2}$.

$$Ans. \quad \frac{1}{(x + \Delta x)^2} = \frac{1}{x^2} - \frac{2 \, \Delta x}{x^3} + \frac{3(\Delta x)^2}{x^4} - \frac{4(\Delta x)^3}{x^5} + \cdots .$$

13. Compute $(\frac{1}{99})^2$ to ten places by mental arithmetic. (Ex. 12.)

14. Compute $(\frac{1}{98})^2$ to ten places. (Ex. 12.)

15. Use (1), § 236, to obtain an approximate formula for $\dfrac{1}{(x + \Delta x)^3}$.

$$Ans. \quad \frac{1}{(x + \Delta x)^3} = \frac{1 \cdot 2}{2x^3} - \frac{2 \cdot 3\,\Delta x}{2x^4} + \frac{3 \cdot 4(\Delta x)^2}{2x^5} - \frac{4 \cdot 5(\Delta x)^3}{2x^6} + \cdots$$

16. Compute $\frac{1}{729}$ to seven places. (Ex. 15.)

17. Compute $\frac{1}{1331}$ to six places. (Ex. 15.)

18. Show that $\ln (x + \Delta x) = \ln x + \dfrac{\Delta x}{x} - \dfrac{(\Delta x)^2}{2x^2} + \dfrac{(\Delta x)^3}{3x^3} - \cdots$.

19. If the allowable error in a logarithm is 0.00005, within what range can the formula $\ln (x + \Delta x) = \ln x + \dfrac{\Delta x}{x}$ be used?

20. Show that $(x + \Delta x)^{\frac{1}{2}} = x^{\frac{1}{2}} + \dfrac{\Delta x}{2x^{\frac{1}{2}}} - \dfrac{1}{2} \cdot \dfrac{(\Delta x)^2}{4x^{\frac{3}{2}}} + \dfrac{1 \cdot 3}{2 \cdot 4} \dfrac{(\Delta x)^3}{6x^{\frac{5}{2}}} - \cdots$

21. Extract $\sqrt{101}$ to seven decimal places. (Ex. 20.)

22. Evaluate $\sqrt{102}$ to seven decimal places. (Ex. 20.)

23. Make an accurate detail of the curve $y = x^4 - 4x^3 + 6x^2$ near the point $x = 1$. (Ex. 62, page 442.)

24. Solve Ex. 23 for the curve $y = \dfrac{\ln x}{x - 1}$. (Example, § 230.)

25. For the curve $y = 6x^4 - 24x^3 + 35x^2 - 22x + 6$, find all maximum, minimum, and inflection points. Make a detailed sketch in the interval $0.6 \leqq x \leqq 1.4$.

OPERATIONS WITH

POWER SERIES

237. *Algebraic Operations with Power Series*

Operations that can always be performed upon series of a finite number of terms, such as rearrangement of terms, insertion or removal of parentheses, etc., cannot be assumed offhand to be allowable with infinite series, and in fact it is easily shown that they are not allowable in all cases.

In dealing with power series, it is desirable to know whether certain elementary operations are permissible. We therefore state the following theorems regarding power series; the proofs belong to a more advanced treatment of the subject.

THEOREM 45. ADDITION. *Within any common interval of convergence, the term-by-term sum of the power series for $f(x)$ and $g(x)$ is the power series for $[f(x) + g(x)]$.*

In rough language, two convergent power series may be added term by term. That is, within an interval where the series

$$f(x) = \sum_{n=0}^{\infty} a_n x^n, \qquad g(x) = \sum_{n=0}^{\infty} b_n x^n,$$

are both convergent, the series obtained by adding them term by term will converge to $[f(x) + g(x)]$:

$$f(x) + g(x) = \sum_{n=0}^{\infty} (a_n + b_n) x^n.$$

Subtraction is included by a change of signs.

THEOREM 46. MULTIPLICATION. *Within any common interval* (*endpoints not necessarily included*) *of convergence of the power series*

$$f(x) = \sum_{n=0}^{\infty} a_n x^n, \qquad g(x) = \sum_{n=0}^{\infty} b_n x^n,$$

the power series formed by multiplying each term of one series by every term of the other series* converges to the product $f(x)g(x)$,

$$f(x)g(x) = a_0 b_0 + (a_0 b_1 + a_1 b_0)x + (a_0 b_2 + a_1 b_1 + a_2 b_0)x^2$$
$$+ \cdots + (a_0 b_n + a_1 b_{n-1} + \cdots + a_n b_0)x^n + \cdots.$$

THEOREM 47. DIVISION. *If the power series for $f(x)$ and $g(x)$ are convergent in some common interval, and if $g(0) \neq 0$, the power series formed by performing ordinary long division* (*as with polynomials*) *to form $\dfrac{f(x)}{g(x)}$ will converge in some interval including $x = 0$.*

The division is valid when the first m coefficients in the denominator series are zero, provided the first m coefficients in the numerator series are also zero.

In the division of one power series by another, neither the general term nor the interval of convergence of the quotient series can be determined by elementary means. Division of power series is one instance in which we are forced to be content with the first few terms of a series.

In using these theorems, the point to be noted is that within the limits indicated they enable us to treat infinite series *exactly like polynomials*, merely discarding all terms beyond those that we need to retain.

Example (*a*). Find the power series for $\dfrac{1}{x^2 - 3x + 2}$.

Since

$$\frac{1}{x^2 - 3x + 2} = \frac{1}{(1-x)(2-x)} = \frac{1}{1-x} - \frac{1}{2-x},$$

and

$$\frac{1}{1-x} = 1 + x + x^2 + \cdots + x^n + \cdots, \qquad -1 < x < 1,$$

and

$$\frac{-1}{2-x} = \frac{-\dfrac{1}{2}}{1 - \dfrac{x}{2}}$$

$$= -\frac{1}{2}\left(1 + \frac{x}{2} + \frac{x^2}{2^2} + \cdots + \frac{x^n}{2^n} + \cdots\right), \qquad -2 < x < 2,$$

---

* This is the "Cauchy product" of the two series. A similar result holds for the product of any two *absolutely* convergent series, the product series being absolutely convergent to the product of the sums of the series being multiplied.

we add the series term by term to obtain

$$\frac{1}{x^2 - 3x + 2} = \frac{1}{2} + \left(1 - \frac{1}{2^2}\right)x + \left(1 - \frac{1}{2^3}\right)x^2 + \cdots$$
$$+ \left(1 - \frac{1}{2^{n+1}}\right)x^n + \cdots, \qquad -1 < x < 1.$$

Example (*b*). Expand $\sin^2 x$ in powers of x to x^6 inclusive.
We have

$$\sin x = x - \frac{x^3}{3!} + \frac{x^5}{5!} - \cdots$$
$$= x - \tfrac{1}{6}x^3 + \tfrac{1}{120}x^5 - \cdots.$$

Squaring the trinomial and discarding all terms after x^6, we find

$$\sin^2 x = x^2 - \tfrac{1}{3}x^4 + \tfrac{2}{45}x^6 + \cdots.$$

By Theorem 46, this series converges for all values of x. See also the much
more efficient method in Exs. 15–16 below.

Example (*c*). Expand $x^2 \csc^2 x$ to x^4 inclusive.
By Example (*b*),

$$x^2 \csc^2 x = \frac{x^2}{\sin^2 x} = \frac{x^2}{x^2 - \tfrac{1}{3}x^4 + \tfrac{2}{45}x^6 + \cdots}$$
$$= \frac{1}{1 - \tfrac{1}{3}x^2 + \tfrac{2}{45}x^4 + \cdots}.$$

The work may be arranged as follows:

$$\begin{array}{r}
1 + \tfrac{1}{3}x^2 + \tfrac{1}{15}x^4 \\
\hline
1 - \tfrac{1}{3}x^2 + \tfrac{2}{45}x^4 \,\big|\, 1 \\
1 - \tfrac{1}{3}x^2 + \tfrac{2}{45}x^4 \\
\hline
\tfrac{1}{3}x^2 - \tfrac{2}{45}x^4 \\
\tfrac{1}{3}x^2 - \tfrac{1}{9}x^4 \\
\hline
\tfrac{1}{15}x^4;
\end{array}$$

$$x^2 \csc^2 x = 1 + \tfrac{1}{3}x^2 + \tfrac{1}{15}x^4 + \cdots.$$

The interval of convergence, obtained by more advanced methods, is $|x| < \pi$.

Example (*d*). In leveling, error is introduced, owing to the curvature of
the earth. Find the correction for 1 mi.
Employing the expansion in Ex. 9 below, we write

$$\sec \alpha = 1 + \frac{\alpha^2}{2} + \cdots,$$

and Fig. 233 shows that

$$\sec \alpha = \frac{R + x}{R} = 1 + \frac{x}{R}.$$

Since α is very small, we obtain

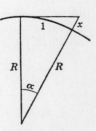

Figure 233

$$1 + \frac{\alpha^2}{2} = 1 + \frac{x}{R},$$

or

$$x = \frac{R\alpha^2}{2} = \frac{(R\alpha)^2}{2R} = \frac{1}{8000} \text{ mi.}$$
$$= \frac{5280 \cdot 12}{8000} \text{ in.} = 7.9 \text{ in.}$$

238. *Differentiation of Power Series*

Within its interval of convergence (endpoints excluded), term-by-term differentiation of a power series yields the power series for the derivative of the original sum-function, and the interval of convergence remains the same.

THEOREM 48. DIFFERENTIATION. *If*

$$f(x) = a_0 + a_1 x + a_2 x^2 + \cdots + a_n x^n + \cdots, \qquad |x| < h,$$

then

$$f'(x) = a_1 + 2a_2 x + \cdots + na_n x^{n-1} + \cdots, \qquad |x| < h.$$

Example. Derive the series for cos x from that for sin x.
We know that

$$\sin x = x - \frac{x^3}{3!} + \frac{x^5}{5!} - \cdots + \frac{(-1)^n x^{2n+1}}{(2n+1)!} + \cdots,$$

for all x. Therefore

$$\cos x = 1 - \frac{3x^2}{3!} + \frac{5x^4}{5!} - \cdots + \frac{(-1)^n (2n+1) x^{2n}}{(2n+1)!} + \cdots$$
$$= 1 - \frac{x^2}{2!} + \frac{x^4}{4!} - \cdots + \frac{(-1)^n x^{2n}}{(2n)!} + \cdots,$$

for all x, as given in § 229.

EXERCISES

In Exs. 1–31, expand the function in Maclaurin's series by appropriate application of Theorems 45–48 above and the basic expansions of § 229. Determine the interval of convergence (not testing endpoints), wherever Theorem 47 is not involved. If Theorem 47 is used, the interval is enclosed in parentheses in the answer.

1. cosh x. Compare your answer with (2), page 439.

$$\text{Ans. } 1 + \frac{x^2}{2!} + \frac{x^4}{4!} + \cdots + \frac{x^{2n}}{(2n)!} + \cdots, \text{ all values.}$$

2. sinh x. Compare your answer with (3), page 439.

$$\text{Ans. } x + \frac{x^3}{3!} + \frac{x^5}{5!} + \cdots + \frac{x^{2n+1}}{(2n+1)!} + \cdots, \text{ all values.}$$

3. $\ln \dfrac{1 + x}{1 - x}.$ *Ans.* $2\left(x + \dfrac{x^3}{3} + \dfrac{x^5}{5} + \cdots + \dfrac{x^{2n-1}}{2n - 1} + \cdots\right),\ |x| < 1.$

4. From the basic series (§ 229) for $\dfrac{1}{1 - x}$, find the series for $\dfrac{1}{(1 - x)^2}$ by differentiation.   *Ans.* $1 + 2x + 3x^2 + \cdots + nx^{n-1} + \cdots,\ |x| < 1.$

5. Obtain the series for $\dfrac{x^3}{(1 + x^2)^2}$ by replacing x by $(-x^2)$ in the answer to Ex. 4 and then multiplying throughout by x^3.

$$Ans.\ \frac{x^3}{(1 + x^2)^2} = \sum_{n=1}^{\infty} (-1)^{n-1} n x^{2n+1},\ |x| < 1.$$

6. $e^{-x} \cos x$, to the term in x^4.
    Ans. $1 - x + \frac{1}{3}x^3 - \frac{1}{6}x^4 + \cdots$, all values of x.

7. $e^{-x} \sin x$, to the term in x^5.
    Ans. $x - x^2 + \frac{1}{3}x^3 - \frac{1}{30}x^5 + \cdots$, all values of x.

8. $\tan x$, to the term in x^5.   *Ans.* $x + \frac{1}{3}x^3 + \frac{2}{15}x^5 + \cdots,\ (|x| < \frac{1}{2}\pi).$

9. $\sec x$, to the term in x^6.
    Ans. $1 + \frac{1}{2}x^2 + \frac{5}{24}x^4 + \frac{61}{720}x^6 + \cdots,\ (|x| < \frac{1}{2}\pi).$

10. $\ln^2 (1 + x)$, to the term in x^5.
    Ans. $x^2 - x^3 + \frac{11}{12}x^4 - \frac{5}{6}x^5 + \cdots,\ |x| < 1.$

11. $\dfrac{\ln (1 + x)}{1 + x}.$ Check by Ex. 10.

12. $x \csc x$, to the term in x^4.   *Ans.* $1 + \frac{1}{6}x^2 + \frac{7}{360}x^4 + \cdots,\ (|x| < \pi).$

13. $\tan^2 x$, to the term in x^6.   *Ans.* $x^2 + \frac{2}{3}x^4 + \frac{17}{45}x^6 + \cdots,\ (|x| < \frac{1}{2}\pi).$

14. $\sec^2 x$, to the term in x^6, by squaring the answer to Ex. 9. Check with Ex. 13.

15. $\cos^2 x$. Use $\cos^2 x = \frac{1}{2}(1 + \cos 2x)$.

$$Ans.\ 1 - \frac{2x^2}{2!} + \frac{2^3 x^4}{4!} - \frac{2^5 x^6}{6!} + \cdots + \frac{(-1)^n 2^{2n-1} x^{2n}}{(2n)!} + \cdots,\ \text{all values of } x.$$

16. $\sin^2 x$. Use $\sin^2 x = \frac{1}{2}(1 - \cos 2x)$; then check with Ex. 15.

17. $\csc x - \cot x$, to the term in x^5.
    Ans. $\frac{1}{2}x + \frac{1}{24}x^3 + \frac{1}{240}x^5 + \cdots,\ (|x| < \pi).$

18. $x \cot x$, to the term in x^4.   *Ans.* $1 - \frac{1}{3}x^2 - \frac{1}{45}x^4 + \cdots,\ (|x| < \pi).$

19. $\tanh x$, to the term in x^5. See Exs. 1–2.

20. $\dfrac{x^2}{(1 - 2x^3)^2}.$ See Exs. 4–5. $Ans.\ \displaystyle\sum_{n=1}^{\infty} n \cdot 2^{n-1} x^{3n-1}.$

21. $\dfrac{x^3}{(1 + 3x^4)^2}.$ See Exs. 4–5.   **22.** $\dfrac{1 + 3x}{1 - 2x^4}.$

23. $\dfrac{1 - 5x}{1 + x^3}.$

24. $e^{-x} \cos 2x$, to the term in x^5.
    Ans. $1 - x - \frac{3}{2}x^2 + \frac{11}{6}x^3 - \frac{7}{24}x^4 - \frac{41}{120}x^5 + \cdots.$

25. $e^{-x} \sin 2x$, to the term in x^5.   *Ans.* $2x - 2x^2 - \frac{1}{3}x^3 + x^4 - \frac{19}{60}x^5 + \cdots.$

26. $\dfrac{4x}{(1 + x)(1 - 3x)}$. Write as $\dfrac{1}{1 - 3x} - \dfrac{1}{1 + x}$.

$$Ans. \quad \sum_{n=1}^{\infty} [3^n - (-1)^n]x^n, \quad -\tfrac{1}{3} < x < \tfrac{1}{3}.$$

27. $\dfrac{x}{1 + x - 2x^2}$. Use $\dfrac{1}{1 - x} - \dfrac{1}{1 + 2x}$.

28. $\ln (1 - 3x + 2x^2)$.

$$Ans. \quad -3x - \frac{5}{2}x^2 - 3x^3 - \cdots - \frac{(1 + 2^n)x^n}{n} + \cdots, \quad |x| < \frac{1}{2}.$$

29. From Ex. 28, find the power series for $\dfrac{4x - 3}{1 - 3x + 2x^2}$.

30. Differentiate the series for e^x.

31. Obtain the series for $\cosh x$ from that for $\sinh x$.

32. From Ex. 9, find the first three terms of the power series for $\sec x \tan x$. Then check with Exs. 8–9.

33. Check Ex. 6 with Ex. 7, with the aid of differentiation.

34. Check Ex. 24 with Ex. 25, with the aid of differentiation.

35. Show that for values of x so small that the fourth and higher powers of $\dfrac{x}{a}$ may be neglected, the catenary $y = a \cosh \dfrac{x}{a}$ may be replaced by the parabola $x^2 = 2a(y - a)$.

36. Show that $\sin^3 x = \dfrac{3}{4} \displaystyle\sum_{n=1}^{\infty} \dfrac{(-1)^{n-1}(3^{2n} - 1)x^{2n+1}}{(2n + 1)!}$, for all x.

37. Use the result in Ex. 36 to show that $\sin^2 x \cos x = \dfrac{1}{4} \displaystyle\sum_{n=1}^{\infty} \dfrac{(-1)^{n-1}(3^{2n} - 1)x^{2n}}{(2n)!}$, for all x.

38. By first expressing $\sin^4 x$ in terms of $\cos 2x$ and $\cos 4x$, show that

$$\sin^4 x = \sum_{n=0}^{\infty} \frac{(-1)^n 2^{2n+3}(2^{2n+2} - 1)x^{2n+4}}{(2n + 4)!}, \text{ for all } x.$$

39. Use the result in Ex. 38 to conclude that

$$\sin^3 x \cos x = \sum_{n=0}^{\infty} \frac{(-1)^n 2^{2n+1}(2^{2n+2} - 1)x^{2n+3}}{(2n + 3)!}, \text{ for all } x.$$

40. In Example (d), § 237, find the correction for 4 mi. *Ans.* 10.56 ft.

41. Two ships have masts reaching 80 ft. above the water level. How far is each masthead visible from the other? *Ans.* About 22 mi.

42. What is the radius of vision (theoretically) from the top of a building 200 ft. high? *Ans.* 17.4 mi.

In Exs. 43–66, evaluate the limits with the aid of series.

43. $\lim\limits_{\theta \to 0} \dfrac{\theta - \sin \theta}{\theta^3}$ *Ans.* $\frac{1}{6}$.   **44.** $\lim\limits_{\theta \to 0} \dfrac{1 - \cos \theta}{\theta^2}$.   *Ans.* $\frac{1}{2}$.

45. $\lim\limits_{x \to 0} \dfrac{(1 + x)^m - (1 - x)^m}{x}$.   *Ans.* $2m$.

46. $\lim\limits_{x \to 0} \dfrac{\sinh x - \sin x}{x^3}$.   *Ans.* $\frac{1}{3}$.   **47.** $\lim\limits_{x \to 0} \dfrac{\cosh x - \cos x}{x^2}$.   *Ans.* 1.

48. $\lim\limits_{x \to 0} \dfrac{\sin x - \ln (1 + x)}{x^2}$.   *Ans.* $\frac{1}{2}$.

49. $\lim\limits_{y \to 0} \dfrac{y \cos y - \sin y}{y \sin^2 y}$.   **50.** $\lim\limits_{y \to 0} \dfrac{\tan y - y}{\sin^3 y}$.

51. $\lim\limits_{\theta \to 0} \dfrac{\tan^2 \theta - \theta^2}{\theta^2(1 - \cos \theta)}$.   **52.** $\lim\limits_{\theta \to 0} \dfrac{\tan^2 \theta - \sin^2 \theta}{\sinh^3 \theta \ln (1 + \theta)}$.

53. $\lim\limits_{\alpha \to 0} \dfrac{2 \sin \alpha - \tan 2\alpha}{\alpha^2 \sin \alpha}$.   **54.** $\lim\limits_{\alpha \to 0} \dfrac{1 - \cosh \alpha - \ln^2 (1 + \alpha)}{\tan^2 \alpha}$.

55. Ex. 1, page 200.   **56.** Ex. 15, page 201.   **57.** Ex. 17, page 201.
58. Ex. 19, page 201.   **59.** Ex. 20, page 201.   **60.** Ex. 27, page 201.
61. Ex. 30, page 201.   **62.** Ex. 33, page 201.   **63.** Ex. 34, page 201.
64. Ex. 35, page 201.   **65.** Ex. 36, page 201.   **66.** Ex. 44, page 202.

In Exs. 67–76, find the sum of the given series by using the appropriate value of x in some power series of known sum.

67. $1 + \dfrac{1}{2^2 \cdot 3} + \dfrac{1}{2^4 \cdot 5} + \cdots + \dfrac{1}{2^{2n} \cdot (2n + 1)} + \cdots$. Put $x = \frac{1}{2}$ in Ex. 3.

Ans. $\ln 3$.

68. $1 + \dfrac{2}{3} + \dfrac{3}{3^2} + \dfrac{4}{3^3} + \cdots + \dfrac{n}{3^{n-1}} + \cdots$. Use Ex. 4.   *Ans.* $\frac{9}{4}$.

69. $\sum\limits_{n=0}^{\infty} \dfrac{(-1)^n}{2^{2n} \cdot n!}$.   *Ans.* $e^{-\frac{1}{4}}$.   **70.** $\sum\limits_{n=0}^{\infty} \dfrac{5^{2n}}{(2n)!}$.   *Ans.* $\cosh 5$.

71. $\sum\limits_{n=0}^{\infty} \dfrac{(-1)^n}{(2n + 1)!}$.   **72.** $\sum\limits_{n=0}^{\infty} \dfrac{(-1)^n}{(2n)!}$.

73. $\sum\limits_{n=0}^{\infty} \dfrac{(-1)^n}{5^{2n} \cdot (2n)!}$.   **74.** $\sum\limits_{n=0}^{\infty} \dfrac{(-1)^n}{3^n \cdot (2n + 1)!}$.

75. $\sum\limits_{n=1}^{\infty} \dfrac{(-1)^{n-1}n}{3^{2n+1}}$. (Ex. 5.)   *Ans.* $\frac{3}{100}$.

76. $\sum\limits_{n=1}^{\infty} \dfrac{(-1)^n n}{2^{2n}}$. (Ex. 5.)   *Ans.* $\dfrac{-4}{25}$.

239. *Integration of Power Series*

Within its interval of convergence (sometimes even including endpoints), term-by-term integration of a power series yields the power series for the integral of the original sum-function, and the interval remains the same.

THEOREM 49. INTEGRATION. *If*

$$f(x) = a_0 + a_1x + a_2x^2 + \cdots + a_nx^n + \cdots, \qquad |x| < h,$$

then

$$\int f(x) \, dx = C + a_0x + \frac{a_1x^2}{2} + \frac{a_2x^3}{3} + \cdots + \frac{a_nx^{n+1}}{n+1} + \cdots, \qquad |x| < h.$$

The theorem may also be worded as follows. If

$$f(x) = \sum_{n=0}^{\infty} a_nx^n, \qquad |x| < h,$$

then

$$\int_{\alpha}^{\beta} f(x) \, dx = \sum_{n=0}^{\infty} \frac{a_n}{n+1} \Big[\beta^{n+1} - \alpha^{n+1} \Big],$$

if $|\alpha| < h$ and $|\beta| < h$.

Example. Derive the series for $\ln (1 + x)$ from that for $\dfrac{1}{1+x}$.

We know, from the basic series (4), page 439 (with x replaced by $-x$), that

$$\frac{1}{1+x} = 1 - x + x^2 - x^3 + \cdots + (-1)^nx^n + \cdots, \qquad |x| < 1.$$

Multiplying throughout by dx and integrating, we obtain

$$\ln (1 + x) = C + x - \frac{x^2}{2} + \frac{x^3}{3} - \frac{x^4}{4} + \cdots + \frac{(-1)^nx^{n+1}}{n+1} + \cdots,$$
$$|x| < 1.$$

Putting $x = 0$, we find that $C = 0$, so that finally

$$\ln (1 + x) = x - \frac{x^2}{2} + \frac{x^3}{3} - \frac{x^4}{4} + \cdots + \frac{(-1)^nx^{n+1}}{n+1} + \cdots, \qquad |x| < 1.$$

240. *Application to Definite Integrals*

An important application of Theorem 49 is in the approximate evaluation of definite integrals—particularly when the integral cannot be expressed in terms of elementary functions, but sometimes also when, although evaluation in the elementary sense is possible, the result would be of inconvenient form. Although the method is available, theoretically, whenever the interval of integration lies entirely within the interval of convergence of the series, it actually works well only if the integrated series converges rapidly at both limits of integration.

Example (a). Find the area under the curve

$$y = \frac{\sin x}{x}$$

from $x = 0$ to $x = 1$.

The area is

$$A = \int_0^1 y \, dx = \int_0^1 \frac{\sin x}{x} \, dx.$$

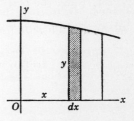

Figure 234

The integral occurring here cannot be evaluated in terms of elementary functions. But we have

$$\sin x = x - \frac{x^3}{6} + \frac{x^5}{120} - \frac{x^7}{5040} + \cdots + \frac{(-1)^n x^{2n+1}}{(2n+1)!} + \cdots,$$

$$\frac{\sin x}{x} = 1 - \frac{x^2}{6} + \frac{x^4}{120} - \frac{x^6}{5040} + \cdots + \frac{(-1)^n x^{2n}}{(2n+1)!} + \cdots,$$

whence (Theorem 49)

$$A = \int_0^1 \left(1 - \frac{x^2}{6} + \frac{x^4}{120} - \frac{x^6}{5040} + \cdots \right) dx$$

$$= \left[x - \frac{x^3}{18} + \frac{x^5}{600} - \frac{x^7}{35280} + \cdots \right]_0^1$$

$$= 1 - 0.05556 + 0.00167 - 0.00003 = 0.9461.$$

Example (b). Evaluate $\displaystyle\int_0^1 \frac{dx}{\sqrt{100 - x^3}}$.

This is an "elliptic integral," impossible to evaluate in elementary terms. But

$$\frac{1}{\sqrt{100 - x^3}} = \frac{1}{10 \sqrt{1 - \frac{1}{100} x^3}}.$$

Expanding the integrand in powers of x (Ex. 10, page 441), we find

$$\int_0^1 \frac{dx}{\sqrt{100 - x^3}} = \frac{1}{10} \int_0^1 \frac{dx}{\sqrt{1 - \frac{1}{100} x^3}} = \frac{1}{10} \int_0^1 \left(1 - \frac{1}{100} x^3 \right)^{-\frac{1}{2}} dx$$

$$= \frac{1}{10} \int_0^1 \left(1 + \frac{1}{2} \frac{x^3}{10^2} + \frac{1 \cdot 3}{2 \cdot 4} \frac{x^6}{10^4} + \cdots \right) dx$$

$$= \frac{1}{10} \left[x + \frac{1}{2 \cdot 4} \frac{x^4}{10^2} + \frac{1 \cdot 3}{2 \cdot 4 \cdot 7} \frac{x^7}{10^4} + \cdots \right]_0^1$$

$$= 0.10013.$$

EXERCISES

1. From the basic series for $\dfrac{1}{1-x}$, write down the series for $\dfrac{1}{1+y^2}$, multiply by dy, and integrate from 0 to x.

Ans. Arctan $x = \displaystyle\sum_{n=0}^{\infty} \frac{(-1)^n x^{2n+1}}{2n+1}$

$$= x - \frac{x^3}{3} + \frac{x^5}{5} - \cdots + \frac{(-1)^n x^{2n+1}}{2n+1} + \cdots, \ |x| \leqq 1.$$

2. From the series for $(1+x)^{-\frac{1}{2}}$, Ex. 10, page 441, obtain the series for $(1-y^2)^{-\frac{1}{2}}$, and then that for Arcsin x.

Ans. Arcsin $x = x + \displaystyle\sum_{n=1}^{\infty} \frac{1 \cdot 3 \cdot 5 \cdots (2n-1) x^{2n+1}}{2^n n! (2n+1)}, \ |x| < 1.$

3. Investigate the result of integrating, term by term, the series for e^x.

4. Check the series for sin x and cos x against each other by using integration.

5. Using the result in Ex. 9, page 457, obtain the power series for ln (sec x + tan x), out to the term in x^7.

Ans. ln (sec x + tan x) $= x + \dfrac{x^3}{6} + \dfrac{x^5}{24} + \dfrac{61x^7}{5040} + \cdots, \ (|x| < \tfrac{1}{2}\pi).$

6. In Ex. 13, page 457, we found that

$$\tan^2 x = x^2 + \tfrac{2}{3}x^4 + \tfrac{17}{45}x^6 + \cdots.$$

By integration of this series show that

$$\tan x = x + \frac{x^3}{3} + \frac{2x^5}{15} + \frac{17x^7}{315} + \cdots, \qquad (|x| < \tfrac{1}{2}\pi).$$

7. With the aid of Ex. 8, page 457, obtain the terms, out to the x^6 term, in the power series for ln cos x.

Ans. ln cos $x = -\dfrac{x^2}{2} - \dfrac{x^4}{12} - \dfrac{x^6}{45} + \cdots, \ (|x| < \tfrac{1}{2}\pi).$

8. Use the result in Ex. 6 above to show that

$$\text{ln cos } x = -\frac{x^2}{2} - \frac{x^4}{12} - \frac{x^6}{45} - \frac{17x^8}{2520} + \cdots, \qquad (|x| < \tfrac{1}{2}\pi).$$

9. From the series for cosh x, Ex. 1, page 456, obtain the series for sinh x by integration.

10. Put $x = 1$ in Ex. 45, page 134, to see that Arctan $\tfrac{1}{3}$ + Arctan $\tfrac{1}{2}$ = $\tfrac{1}{4}\pi$.

Use this result, and Ex. 1 above, to obtain a series for π.

Ans. $\pi = 4 \displaystyle\sum_{n=0}^{\infty} \frac{(-1)^n [(\tfrac{1}{3})^{2n+1} + (\tfrac{1}{2})^{2n+1}]}{2n+1}.$

11. Use Ex. 10 to compute π to three decimal places. It is best to compute 4 Arctan $\frac{1}{3}$ and 4 Arctan $\frac{1}{2}$, each from its own series, then add them to get π.

12. Put $x = \frac{1}{2}$ in the answer to Ex. 2, and compute π to two decimal places.

13. Integrate the series for $\dfrac{1}{1 - x^2}$, and compare with Ex. 3, page 457.

14. Find, to three decimal places, the area under the curve $y = e^{-x^2}$, from $x = 0$ to $x = \frac{1}{2}$. *Ans.* 0.461.

15. Find, to two decimal places, the centroid of the area in Ex. 14.
Ans. (0.24, 0.46).

16. Find, to four decimal places, the area under the curve $y = \cos(x^2)$ from $x = 0$ to $x = 1$. *Ans.* 0.9045.

17. Find, to four decimal places, the area under the curve $y = \sin(x^2)$ from $x = 0$ to $x = 1$.

18. Find the area under the curve $y = e^{-x^3}$, from $x = 0$ to $x = 1$. *Ans.* 0.807.

19. Find the area under the curve $y = \dfrac{e^{-x}}{x}$ from $x = 0.001$ to $x = 0.002$.

Ans. $\ln 2 - 0.001\ 00 = 0.692\ 15$.

20. Find, to five decimal places, the area under the curve $y = \dfrac{1 - \cos x}{x}$ from $x = 0$ to $x = \frac{1}{2}$. *Ans.* 0.061 85.

21. Find, to four decimal places, the centroid of the area in Ex. 20.
Ans. (0.3326, 0.0821).

22. Find, to three decimal places, the area under the curve $y = \dfrac{1 - \cos x}{x}$ from $x = 0$ to $x = 1$. *Ans.* 0.240.

23. Find, to three decimal places, the centroid of the area in Ex. 22.
Ans. (0.661, 0.157).

24. Find, to two decimal places, the area under the curve $y = \dfrac{\ln x}{x - 1}$ from $x = \frac{1}{2}$ to $x = 1$. *Ans.* 0.58.

25. Evaluate $\displaystyle\int_0^{0.1} \dfrac{dx}{\sqrt{1 + x^5}}$ to eight decimal places. *Ans.* 0.099 999 92.

26. Evaluate $\displaystyle\int_0^1 \dfrac{x^4\,dx}{\sqrt{25 + x^4}}$ to three places.

27. Find the area under the curve $y = x^3 - 3x^2 + 2x - 5$ from $x = 2.999$ to $x = 3$. (Ex. 63, page 442.)

28. Find the area under the curve $y = x^4 - 3x^2 - 6x + 8$ from $x = 1.99$ to $x = 2.01$. (Ex. 64, page 442.)

29. Find to three places the area under the curve $y = \dfrac{\cos x}{x}$ from $x = \dfrac{1}{2}$ to $x = 1$.

Ans. 0.515.

30. Use Ex. 9, page 441, and integration of series, to find to five decimal places the length of arc of the hyperbola $xy = 1$ from $x = 10$ to $x = 100$. *Ans.* 90.000 17.

31. Use Ex. 9, page 441, Wallis' formula, page 276, and integration of series, to show that the length of one arch of the curve $y = \cos x$ is 1.24π.

32. Evaluate $\displaystyle\lim_{x \to 0} \int_x^{2x} \frac{\cos t\, dt}{t}$. $\qquad\qquad$ *Ans.* $\ln 2.$

33. Evaluate $\displaystyle\lim_{x \to 0} \int_x^{2x} \frac{e^{-t}}{t}\, dt$. $\qquad\qquad$ *Ans.* $\ln 2.$

34. Evaluate $\displaystyle\lim_{x \to 0} \frac{1}{x} \int_0^x \frac{\sin t}{t}\, dt$. $\qquad\qquad$ *Ans.* $1.$

35. Evaluate $\displaystyle\lim_{x \to 0} \frac{1}{x^2} \int_0^x \frac{1 - \cos t}{t}\, dt$. $\qquad\qquad$ *Ans.* $\tfrac{1}{4}.$

36. Evaluate $\displaystyle\int_2^\infty \frac{dx}{\sqrt{x^4 + 1}} \cdot \left(\frac{1}{\sqrt{x^4 + 1}} = \frac{1}{x^2} \cdot \frac{1}{\sqrt{1 + x^{-4}}} \right.$; substitute x^{-4} for x in Ex. 10, page 441.) $\qquad\qquad$ *Ans.* $0.497.$

In Exs. 37–39, expand the integrand in powers of $\dfrac{1}{x}$. (Cf. Ex. 36.)

37. Find the area under the curve $y = \dfrac{1}{x^2 - 1}$, to the right of $x = 100$.

$\qquad\qquad\qquad\qquad\qquad\qquad\qquad$ *Ans.* $0.010\ 000\ 333\ 353.$

38. Find the area under the curve $y = \dfrac{1}{x^4 + x^2}$, to the right of $x = 10$.

$\qquad\qquad\qquad\qquad\qquad\qquad\qquad$ *Ans.* $0.000\ 331.$

39. For the curve $x^2 y = 1$, show that from $x = 100$ to $x = 200$ the arc exceeds the chord by one ten-trillionth of its length.

241. *Summation of Power Series*

The general problem, given a power series, to find the sum of the series in terms of known functions, is naturally incapable of solution. Even if the sum does happen to be expressible in terms of known functions, the actual determination of that sum may be prohibitively difficult.

There are instances in which the application of our knowledge of the basic series in § 229 will yield the desired sum.

Example (a). Sum the series $\displaystyle\sum_{n=0}^\infty \frac{(-1)^n (n + 2) x^n}{n!}$.

We start with a known series suggested by the series to be summed. We know that

(1) $$e^{-x} = \sum_{n=0}^\infty \frac{(-1)^n x^n}{n!},$$

for all finite x.

The series to be summed has a factor $(n + 2)$ in the numerator. Such a factor can be introduced by differentiation of x^{n+2}. Therefore we first introduce a factor x^2 on both sides of equation (1) to obtain

$$(2) \qquad x^2 e^{-x} = \sum_{n=0}^{\infty} \frac{(-1)^n x^{n+2}}{n!}.$$

Then differentiation of each member of equation (2) yields

$$(3) \qquad e^{-x}(2x - x^2) = \sum_{n=0}^{\infty} \frac{(-1)^n (n + 2) x^{n+1}}{n!},$$

whereupon the desired sum is obtained by division of both members of (3) by x,

$$(4) \qquad e^{-x}(2 - x) = \sum_{n=0}^{\infty} \frac{(-1)^n (n + 2) x^n}{n!},$$

valid for all finite x.

Example (b). Sum the series $\displaystyle\sum_{n=0}^{\infty} \frac{(-1)^n x^{2n}}{(n + 1)(n + 3)}.$

A factor $(n + 1)$ can be introduced into the denominator by integrating $x^n \, dx$, a factor $(n + 3)$ by integrating $x^{n+2} \, dx$. But, in this instance, we can start off with a factor $(n + 1)$ in the denominator by using the basic series

$$(5) \qquad \ln (1 + x) = \sum_{n=1}^{\infty} \frac{(-1)^{n+1} x^n}{n}, \qquad |x| < 1,$$

and shifting index from n to $(n + 1)$ to obtain

$$(6) \qquad \ln (1 + x) = \sum_{n=0}^{\infty} \frac{(-1)^n x^{n+1}}{n + 1}.$$

To get the desired power x^{n+2} into the numerator, we multiply throughout by x, obtaining

$$(7) \qquad x \ln (1 + x) = \sum_{n=0}^{\infty} \frac{(-1)^n x^{n+2}}{n + 1}.$$

Then an integration yields

$$\int x \ln (1 + x) \, dx = C + \sum_{n=0}^{\infty} \frac{(-1)^n x^{n+3}}{(n + 1)(n + 3)},$$

or

(8) $$\frac{1}{2} (x^2 - 1) \ln (1 + x) - \frac{1}{4} (x - 1)^2 = C + \sum_{n=0}^{\infty} \frac{(-1)^n x^{n+3}}{(n + 1)(n + 3)}.$$

Put $x = 0$ to obtain C. Thus we find that $C = -\frac{1}{4}$. Therefore we now have

(9) $$\frac{1}{2} (x^2 - 1) \ln (1 + x) - \frac{1}{4} x^2 + \frac{1}{2} x = \sum_{n=0}^{\infty} \frac{(-1)^n x^{n+3}}{(n + 1)(n + 3)}.$$

To obtain the desired power x^{2n} on the right, we first divide by x^3, exclude $x = 0$, and write

(10) $$\frac{x^2 - 1}{2x^3} \ln (1 + x) - \frac{1}{4x} + \frac{1}{2x^2} = \sum_{n=0}^{\infty} \frac{(-1)^n x^n}{(n + 1)(n + 3)}.$$

Finally, we replace x by x^2, thus obtaining the desired sum

(11) $$\frac{x^4 - 1}{2x^6} \ln (1 + x^2) - \frac{1}{4x^2} + \frac{1}{2x^4} = \sum_{n=0}^{\infty} \frac{(-1)^n x^{2n}}{(n + 1)(n + 3)},$$

$$0 < |x| < 1.$$

Note the implication that the left member, near $x = 0$, is an indeterminate form, as $x \to 0$, with limit $\frac{1}{3}$ ($n = 0$ term on the right).

EXERCISES

Sum the given series with the aid of the basic series in § 229.

1. $$\sum_{n=0}^{\infty} \frac{(n + 1)(n + 2)x^n}{n!} \cdot$$ Start with the series for $x^2 e^x$. *Ans.* $e^x(x^2 + 4x + 2)$.

2. $$\sum_{n=0}^{\infty} \frac{(-1)^n (n + 2)(n + 3)x^n}{n!}.$$

3. $$\sum_{n=0}^{\infty} \frac{x^{n+4}}{n!(n + 2)}.$$

4. $$\sum_{n=0}^{\infty} \frac{(-1)^n x^{2n+3}}{(2n)!(2n + 2)} \cdot$$ Start with the series for $x \cos x$.

Ans. $x(x \sin x + \cos x - 1)$.

5. $\displaystyle\sum_{n=0}^{\infty} \frac{(-1)^n x^{2n+5}}{(2n+1)!(2n+3)}.$ *Ans.* $x^2(\sin x - x \cos x).$

6. $\displaystyle\sum_{n=0}^{\infty} (n+2)(n+1)x^{n+2}.$ *Ans.* $\dfrac{2x^2}{(1-x)^3}.$

7. $\displaystyle\sum_{n=0}^{\infty} \frac{(n+3)(n-1)x^{n+1}}{n+1}.$ *Ans.* $4 \ln (1-x) + \dfrac{x}{(1-x)^2}.$

8. $\displaystyle\sum_{n=0}^{\infty} (-1)^n(n+1)(n+2)x^{2n+1}.$ *Ans.* $\dfrac{2x}{(1+x^2)^3}.$

9. $\displaystyle\sum_{n=0}^{\infty} \frac{(-1)^n(n+4)x^{n+3}}{n!(n+3)}.$ *Ans.* $2 + e^{-x}(x^3 - x^2 - 2x - 2).$

10. $\displaystyle\sum_{n=1}^{\infty} \frac{(-1)^{n-1}x^n}{n(n+1)}.$ *Ans.* $\dfrac{1+x}{x} \ln (1+x) - 1.$

11. $\displaystyle\sum_{n=0}^{\infty} \frac{1}{n!(n+3)}.$ First sum the series $\displaystyle\sum_{n=0}^{\infty} \frac{x^{n+3}}{n!(n+3)}$ and then put $x = 1.$

Ans. $e - 2.$

12. $\displaystyle\sum_{n=0}^{\infty} \frac{(-1)^n}{n!(n+3)}.$ See Ex. 11.   *Ans.* $2 - 5e^{-1}.$

13. $\displaystyle\sum_{n=0}^{\infty} \frac{(-1)^n(n+1)}{4^n(2n)!}.$ *Ans.* $\cos \frac{1}{2} - \frac{1}{4} \sin \frac{1}{2}.$

14. $\displaystyle\sum_{n=0}^{\infty} \frac{n+3}{2^{2n}n!}.$ **15.** $\displaystyle\sum_{n=0}^{\infty} \frac{(-1)^n}{n!(n+4)}.$

16. $\displaystyle\sum_{n=1}^{\infty} \frac{(-1)^n(2n+3)}{2^{2n}(2n+1)!}.$ *Ans.* $\cos \frac{1}{2} + 4 \sin \frac{1}{2} - 3.$

242. *The Function erf x*

The purpose of this section is to convince the student that a nonelementary function is not necessarily difficult to study or to use.

It has long been conventional to use the term *elementary function* to designate any function normally studied in the first two years of collegiate mathematics. For example, polynomials, exponentials, logarithms, trigonometric and inverse trigonometric functions are elementary. **All functions obtained from them by a finite number of applications of the elementary operations of addition, subtraction, multiplication, division, extraction of roots, and raising to powers are elementary.** Finally, we include such functions as sin (sin x) in which the argument in a function previously classed as elementary is replaced by an elementary function. A function which is not elementary is, of course, called nonelementary.

The error function, abbreviated erf, is defined by

$$(1) \qquad \operatorname{erf} x = \frac{2}{\sqrt{\pi}} \int_0^x e^{-\beta^2} \, d\beta.$$

This function appears frequently in the solution of problems in heat conduction and many other physical applications. Its name comes from the use in statistics of a function closely related to (1).

We shall now show that the nonelementary function erf x is as easily handled as are the elementary functions.

From (1) it follows at once that, if

$$y = \operatorname{erf} x,$$
$$(2) \qquad \frac{dy}{dx} = \frac{2}{\sqrt{\pi}} e^{-x^2}.$$

We know from (1) that erf $0 = 0$. In § 203 we found that

$$\int_0^\infty e^{-\beta^2} \, d\beta = \frac{\sqrt{\pi}}{2}.$$

Therefore $\lim_{x \to \infty} \operatorname{erf} x = 1$, which also indicates why the constant $2/\sqrt{\pi}$ was inserted in the definition of erf x.

Next let us obtain the Maclaurin series for erf x. We know that

$$e^z = \sum_{n=0}^{\infty} \frac{z^n}{n!}$$

and therefore that

$$(3) \qquad e^{-\beta^2} = \sum_{n=0}^{\infty} \frac{(-1)^n \beta^{2n}}{n!}.$$

By employing (3) on the right in (1) we get

$$(4) \qquad \operatorname{erf} x = \frac{2}{\sqrt{\pi}} \sum_{n=0}^{\infty} \frac{(-1)^n x^{2n+1}}{(2n+1)n!},$$

an expansion valid for all finite x.

Next let us treat the problem of integrating the error function. Consider the integral

$$(5) \qquad \int_0^x \operatorname{erf} y \, dy.$$

Since we already know, by (2) above, how to differentiate erf x, let us try integration by parts. With the choice shown in the table, this integration by parts at once yields the result

erf y	dy
$\dfrac{2}{\sqrt{\pi}} e^{-y^2} \, dy$	y

$$(6) \qquad \int_0^x \operatorname{erf} y \, dy = \left[y \operatorname{erf} y \right]_0^x - \frac{2}{\sqrt{\pi}} \int_0^x y e^{-y^2} \, dy.$$

The integral on the right in (6) is elementary. It follows that

$$\int_0^x \operatorname{erf} y \, dy = x \operatorname{erf} x - 0 + \frac{1}{\sqrt{\pi}} \left[e^{-y^2} \right]_0^x,$$

or

$$(7) \qquad \int_0^x \operatorname{erf} y \, dy = x \operatorname{erf} x - \frac{1}{\sqrt{\pi}} (1 - e^{-x^2}).$$

From (7) the indefinite integral of erf x also follows. It may be written in the form

$$(8) \qquad \int \operatorname{erf} x \, dx = x \operatorname{erf} x + \frac{1}{\sqrt{\pi}} e^{-x^2} + C.$$

We have now found for erf x its derivative, integral, Maclaurin series, value at $x = 0$, and its limit as $x \to \infty$. Other properties are also easily obtained. See, for instance, Exs. 1–12 below.

EXERCISES

1. Show that, for all real x, $|\operatorname{erf} x| < 1$.

2. Evaluate $\displaystyle\int_0^x y \operatorname{erf} y \, dy.$ $\qquad$ *Ans.* $\dfrac{1}{2}\left(x^2 - \dfrac{1}{2} \right) \operatorname{erf} x + \dfrac{x e^{-x^2}}{2\sqrt{\pi}}.$

3. Evaluate $\displaystyle\int_0^x y^2 \operatorname{erf} y \, dy.$ $\qquad$ *Ans.* $\dfrac{1}{3} x^3 \operatorname{erf} x + \dfrac{1}{3\sqrt{\pi}} (x^2 e^{-x^2} - 1 + e^{-x^2}).$

4. Show that erf x is an odd function of x.

5. Sketch the curve $y = \operatorname{erf} x$.

6. Show that for $x > 0$, $\operatorname{erf} x > \dfrac{2}{\sqrt{\pi}}\left(x - \dfrac{1}{3} x^3 \right)$. You may use the inequality obtained in § 79.

7. Show that $\displaystyle\operatorname*{Lim}_{x \to 0} \frac{\operatorname{erf} x}{x} = \frac{2}{\sqrt{\pi}}.$

8. Show that $\lim\limits_{x \to \infty} [x(1 - \text{erf } x)] = 0$.

9. Use the result in Ex. 8 to aid you in obtaining the area in the first quadrant bounded by the curve $y = \text{erf } x$ and its asymptote $y = 1$.

$$Ans. \ \frac{1}{\sqrt{\pi}}.$$

10. Evaluate $\displaystyle\int_0^x \text{erf}^2 \beta \, d\beta$. *Ans.* $x \, \text{erf}^2 x + \dfrac{2}{\sqrt{\pi}} e^{-x^2} \text{erf } x - \dfrac{2}{\sqrt{2\pi}} \text{erf } (x \sqrt{2})$.

11. Find the area in the first quadrant bounded by the curve $y = \text{erf } x$, the x-axis, and the ordinate $x = c$.   *Ans.* Use equation (7) of this section.

12. Show that you can determine the centroid of the area in Ex. 11 with the aid of Exs. 2 and 10 above.

13. The sine-integral function Si (x) is defined by

$$\text{Si } (x) = \int_0^x \frac{\sin \beta}{\beta} \, d\beta.$$

Study Si (x) in a manner parallel to our study of erf x above. Show, among other things that

$$\int_0^x \text{Si } (y) \, dy = x \, \text{Si } (x) - 1 + \cos x.$$

14. Define the function $g(x)$ by

$$g(x) = \int_1^x \frac{d\beta}{\beta}$$

and study its properties without using your previous knowledge that $g(x) = \ln x$.

15. Define $h(x)$ by

$$h(x) = \int_0^x \frac{d\beta}{\sqrt{1 - \beta^2}}$$

and study it from this definition without directly employing your knowledge that $h(x) = \text{Arcsin } x$.

16. Define $\varphi(x)$ by

$$\varphi(x) = \int_0^x \frac{d\beta}{1 + \beta^2}$$

and study it from this definition without directly employing your knowledge that $\varphi(x) = \text{Arctan } x$.

17. Define $\psi(x)$ by

$$\psi(x) = \int_0^x e^{\alpha^2} \, d\alpha$$

and study the function $\psi(x)$.

APPROXIMATE INTEGRATION

243. *Approximate Computation of Definite Integrals*

Theorem 19, page 107, exhibits the limit of a sum as a definite integral:

$$\operatorname*{Lim}_{n \to \infty} \sum_{i=1}^{n} f(x_i)\, \Delta x = \int_{a}^{b} f(x)\, dx.$$

This method of evaluating the limit may fail, however, for either of two principal reasons:

(*a*) It may not be possible to evaluate the integral in terms of known functions; or

(*b*) The function may have been determined empirically, so that no formula for it is available.

Under (*a*), we have just seen that the difficulty may frequently be overcome by expanding the integrand in a suitable power series and integrating term by term. But it is not always possible to find a power series convergent at both limits; if this is possible, the series may converge so slowly as to be useless.

Under (*b*), we may plot the points corresponding to the given (x, y)-pairs and find the equation of a curve which will pass more or less closely through the given points. (There are several well-known methods for doing this; the process is called *curve fitting*.) Then we may find the area under the approximation curve in the usual way. But in a given problem, this method may be more trouble than it is worth; or, when a curve has been fitted, we may wish to have an independent means of checking the result.

In any of the above situations, we must have recourse to some form of approximate integration other than that of § 240. In addition to integrating machines, various analytic methods are known.

244. *Simpson's Rule*

When we are unable to evaluate the limit of a sum of n rectangles as $n \to \infty$, one way of approximating the result would be to evaluate the sum itself for a reasonably large value of n—e.g., $n = 10$, in Fig. 57, page 106. That is, measure or compute the successive ordinates, multiply by Δx to find the areas of the rectangles, and add the areas by simple arithmetic. Since the error is a rather small fraction of the total, this gives a moderately good approximation. But we can easily do better.

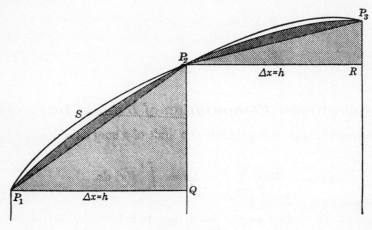

Figure 235

Figure 235 shows a magnification of the top parts of two adjacent elementary strips. Consider the left-hand one, bounded by the arc P_1SP_2. The line P_1Q is the top of our usual rectangular element. If we replace this by the *chord* P_1P_2, thus replacing the rectangle by a trapezoid, we add to the counted area the triangle P_1QP_2, greatly improving the approximation. This method, leading to the "trapezoidal rule" stated below, is sufficiently accurate for many purposes, and is therefore quite often used. But we can do much better than this.

Consider the two adjacent strips simultaneously, and pass a parabola with vertical axis through the three consecutive division-points P_1, P_2, P_3; i.e., replace the broken line $P_1P_2P_3$ by a *parabolic arc*. This adds to the count the narrow darker areas, again greatly improving the approximation.[*]

To put this into effect, take the coordinates of P_1, P_2, P_3 as (x_0, y_0), $(x_0 + h, y_1)$, $(x_0 + 2h, y_2)$, where temporarily, to simplify the writing, we put $\Delta x = h$. The equation

$$(1) \qquad\qquad y - y_0 = a(x - x_0)^2 + b(x - x_0)$$

---

[*] The curve in the figure is of quite unusual shape, with two inflection points close together. Ordinarily, the error by this method would be relatively much smaller than it appears to be in the figure. See Example (a), § 245.

represents a parabola with vertical axis (since the only terms appearing are x^2, x, y, and constant), and it passes through (x_0, y_0). Substituting $(x_0 + h, y_1)$ and $(x_0 + 2h, y_2)$, we get

$$y_1 - y_0 = ah^2 + bh,$$
$$y_2 - y_0 = 4ah^2 + 2bh.$$

Now let us compute the area under the parabola (1) from $x = x_0$ to $x = x_0 + 2h$:

$$A_1 = \int_{x_0}^{x_0+2h} y \, dx = \int_{x_0}^{x_0+2h} [a(x - x_0)^2 + b(x - x_0) + y_0] \, dx$$

$$= \left[\frac{a(x - x_0)^3}{3} + \frac{b(x - x_0)^2}{2} + y_0 x \right]_{x_0}^{x_0+2h}$$

$$= \tfrac{8}{3} ah^3 + 2bh^2 + 2y_0 h$$

$$= \frac{h}{3} (8ah^2 + 6bh + 6y_0)$$

$$= \frac{h}{3} [(4ah^2 + 2bh) + 4(ah^2 + bh) + 6y_0]$$

$$= \frac{h}{3} [y_2 - y_0 + 4(y_1 - y_0) + 6y_0]$$

$$= \frac{h}{3} (y_0 + 4y_1 + y_2).$$

Replacing h by Δx, we find

(2) $$A_1 = \int_{x_0}^{x_0+2\Delta x} y \, dx = \frac{\Delta x}{3} (y_0 + 4y_1 + y_2).$$

Now divide the whole area from $x = a$ to $x = b$ into an *even number n* of strips, each of width Δx, and integrate over two strips at a time, starting with $x_0 = a$:

$$A_1 = \int_{a}^{a+2\Delta x} y \, dx = \frac{\Delta x}{3} (y_0 + 4y_1 + y_2),$$

$$A_2 = \int_{a+2\Delta x}^{a+4\Delta x} y \, dx = \frac{\Delta x}{3} (y_2 + 4y_3 + y_4),$$

$$A_3 = \int_{a+4\Delta x}^{a+6\Delta x} y \, dx = \frac{\Delta x}{3} (y_4 + 4y_5 + y_6),$$

$$\cdots$$

$$A_{\frac{1}{2}n} = \int_{a+(n-2)\Delta x}^{b} y \, dx = \frac{\Delta x}{3} (y_{n-2} + 4y_{n-1} + y_n).$$

Adding all these, we obtain the approximate formula called *Simpson's rule*:

$$\int_{a}^{b} y \, dx = \frac{\Delta x}{3} (y_0 + 4y_1 + 2y_2 + 4y_3 + 2y_4 + \cdots + 4y_{n-1} + y_n).$$

Although we shall not take time either to derive or to apply it, the reader may wish to have available, for possible future reference, the approximate formula known as the *trapezoidal rule*:

$$\int_a^b y\, dx = \frac{\Delta x}{2}\,(y_0 + 2y_1 + 2y_2 + 2y_3 + \cdots + 2y_{n-1} + y_n).$$

The notation is the same as in Simpson's rule, except that here the number of divisions need not be even.

245. *Applications*

We have developed Simpson's rule in connection with plane area. But, of course, the rule applies quite independently of the physical meaning of the integral, since any function of one variable may be interpreted as the ordinate of a plane curve, so that its integral becomes the area under that curve.

Example (*a*). Compute ln 2 from the fact that

$$\int_0^1 \frac{dx}{1 + x} = \Big[\ln\,(1 + x)\Big]_0^1 = \ln 2.$$

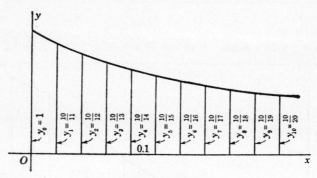

Figure 236

Let us apply Simpson's rule with $n = 10$, $\Delta x = 0.1$, so that*

$$y_0 = \frac{1}{1}, \qquad y_1 = \frac{1}{1.1} = \frac{10}{11}, \qquad y_2 = \frac{1}{1.2} = \frac{10}{12}, \text{ etc.:}$$

$$\int_0^1 \frac{dx}{1 + x} = \frac{1}{30}\left[\frac{10}{10} + \frac{40}{11} + \frac{20}{12} + \frac{40}{13} + \frac{20}{14} + \frac{40}{15} + \frac{20}{16}\right.$$
$$\left. + \frac{40}{17} + \frac{20}{18} + \frac{40}{19} + \frac{10}{20}\right],$$

(1) $$A = \frac{1}{3}\left[\frac{1}{10} + \frac{4}{11} + \frac{1}{6} + \frac{4}{13} + \frac{1}{7} + \frac{4}{15} + \frac{1}{8} + \frac{4}{17} + \frac{1}{9} + \frac{4}{19} + \frac{1}{20}\right];$$

* Here and in a number of the exercises following, a table of reciprocals is handy; see, for instance, the *Macmillan Logarithmic and Trigonometric Tables*, Revised, New York, The Macmillan Co., p. 94.

$$A = \tfrac{1}{3}[0.100\ 000$$
$$0.363\ 636$$
$$0.166\ 667$$
$$0.307\ 692$$
$$0.142\ 857$$
$$0.266\ 667$$
$$0.125\ 009$$
$$0.235\ 294$$
$$0.111\ 111$$
$$0.210\ 526$$
$$0.050\ 000$$
$$\overline{2.079\ 450]} = 0.693\ 15.$$

If we were to keep the (quite untrustworthy) sixth place, the answer would be 0.693 150. The correct value is 0.693 147. Thus, with a six-place table of reciprocals, Simpson's rule produces an error of three in the sixth place. The trapezoidal rule gives an error of six in the fourth place.

Example (*b*). Find the area under the curve determined by the following set of empirical data:

x	0	1	2	3	4	5	6	7	8
y	0	0.38	0.68	1.13	1.47	1.78	2.18	2.60	2.84

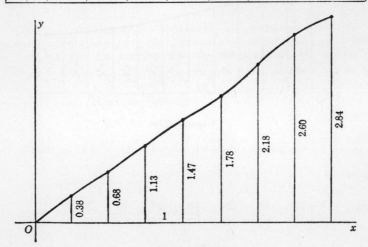

Figure 237

With $n = 8$, $\Delta x = 1$, we have

$$(2)\quad A = \int_0^8 y\ dx = \tfrac{1}{3}[0 + 1.52 + 1.36 + 4.52 + 2.94 + 7.12$$
$$+ 4.36 + 10.40 + 2.84];$$

$$A = \tfrac{1}{3}(35.06) = 11.69.$$

The points, when plotted, follow fairly closely a straight line. The equation of this line, fitted to the data by the method of averages, is

$$y = 0.363x.$$

Using this in (2), we get

$$A = \int_0^8 y\, dx = 0.363 \left[\frac{x^2}{2}\right]_0^8 = 11.62,$$

a difference of 0.6 of 1%.

EXERCISES

1. Evaluate $\int_1^2 \dfrac{dx}{1+x}$ with $n = 10$.

2. Check the answers to Ex. 1 and Example (a) by evaluating $\int_2^3 \dfrac{dx}{1+x}$ with $n = 10$.

3. Evaluate $\int_0^1 \dfrac{dx}{1+x^2}$ with $n = 10$. 　　　　　　*Ans.* $\dfrac{\pi}{4} = 0.78540$.

4. Evaluate $\int_0^1 e^{-x^2}\, dx$ with $n = 10$. 　　　　　　*Ans.* 0.7468.

5. Evaluate $\int_0^1 x^2 e^{-x^2}\, dx$ with $n = 10$. 　　　　　　*Ans.* 0.1895.

6. Check Ex. 5 by means of Ex. 4. (Integrate by parts.)

7. Show, by computation with power series, that the answer given in Ex. 4 is correct to four decimal places.

8. Show, by computation with power series, that the answer given in Ex. 5 is correct to four decimal places.

9. Check the answers to Ex. 1 and Example (a), § 245, by setting $x = 0.2$ in Ex. 3, page 457.

10. Evaluate $\int_0^{\frac{1}{2}} \dfrac{dx}{\sqrt{1-x^2}}$ with $n = 4$. 　　　　*Ans.* $\dfrac{\pi}{6} = 0.5236$.

11. Evaluate $\int_0^1 \sqrt{1+x^4}\, dx$ with $n = 10$. 　　　　*Ans.* 1.090.

In Exs. 12–17, find the area under the curve determined by the given data.*

12.

x	2	4	6	8	10
v	3.4	4.8	5.9	6.9	7.8

Ans. 46.53.

* In some cases, the answers are given to a number of places not justified by the data. This is done in order to show the difference in results by Simpson's rule and by using the fitted equation: Exs. 12–17 vs. Exs. 18–23.

13.

P	100	200	300	400	500
Q	95	185	270	350	415

Ans. 106,330.

14.

t	1	2	3	4	5
x	1.10	4.35	10.05	17.15	26.25

Ans. 44.43.

15.

x	8	10	12	14	16	18	20
y	26	115	227	358	515	684	880

Ans. 4679.

16.

x	0.6	0.8	1.0	1.2	1.4
y	0.161	0.374	0.806	1.302	2.150

Ans. 0.708.

17.

x	1	2	3	4	5	6	7
y	1.82	4.19	6.90	9.21	11.65	14.36	16.72

Ans. 55.56.

In Exs. 18–23, the given equation has been fitted to the data by the method of of averages. Check the answer to the previous exercise by using the empirical formula.

18. Ex. 12: (a) $v^2 = 5.93x$; (b) by a variation of the same method, $v^2 = 5.90x$.
Ans. (a) 46.74; (b) 46.63.

19. Ex. 13: $Q = 0.95P - 0.000\,0005P^3$.   *Ans.* 106,200.

20. Ex. 14: $x = 1.071t^2$.   *Ans.* 44.29.

21. Ex. 15: $y = 2.55x^2 - 140.02$.   *Ans.* 4679.

22. Ex. 16: $y = 0.773x^3$.   *Ans.* 0.717.

23. Ex. 17: (a) $y = 2.49x - 0.69$; (b) by a slight variation of the method, $y = 2.48x - 0.66$.   *Ans.* (a) 55.62; (b) 55.56.

24. Draw a smooth curve through the points

x	0	3	5	7	9	11	12
y	0	0.59	1.56	2.83	4.36	6.05	6.90

and find the area under the curve, taking $n = 6$.

25. Solve Ex. 24 with $n = 12$.

26. Solve Ex. 24, using the fitted formula $y = 0.072x^2 - 0.002x^3$. Compare the results of Exs. 24–26.

27. Draw a smooth curve, on a large scale, through the points

x	0	50	100	150	220	300	500
y	0	22.8	49.8	85.0	128.6	192.4	328.4

and find the area under the curve, taking $n = 10$.

28. Solve Ex. 27, using the fitted formula $y = 0.233x^{1.171}$.

29. The velocity of a body, sliding from rest down a smooth inclined plane, is observed at the ends of successive seconds as shown in the table:

t	1	2	3	4	5	6	7	8
v	1.31	2.52	3.52	4.72	5.87	7.02	8.17	9.42

Find the distance traveled in 8 sec.   *Ans.* 37.8 ft

30. In Ex. 29, the fitted formula is $v = 1.1784t$. Check the answer.   *Ans.* 37.7 ft

DIFFERENTIAL EQUATIONS

OF THE FIRST ORDER

246. *Definitions*

A *differential equation* is an equation containing derivatives or differentials. Many examples have arisen in our previous work: for instance,

$$x - yy' = 0, \qquad (\S\ 33)$$

$$y'' = -\frac{a^2}{y^3}, \qquad (\S\ 33)$$

$$r\frac{dh}{dr} + 2h = 0, \qquad (\S\ 42)$$

$$\frac{d^2y}{dx^2} = -k^2y, \qquad \text{(page 121)}$$

$$\frac{\partial^2 u}{\partial x^2} + \frac{\partial^2 u}{\partial y^2} = 0, \qquad \text{(page 362)}$$

$$\frac{\partial^2 u}{\partial x^2} + \frac{\partial^2 u}{\partial y^2} = \frac{\partial u}{\partial t}, \qquad \text{(page 363)}$$

$$x\frac{\partial u}{\partial x} + y\frac{\partial u}{\partial y} + z\frac{\partial u}{\partial z} = 2u. \qquad \text{(page 362)}$$

(1), (2), (3), (4), (5), (6), (7) appear to the left of the corresponding equations.

Equations such as (1)–(4), involving only one independent variable and therefore containing only ordinary derivatives, are called *ordinary differential equations*. Equations containing partial derivatives (two or more independent variables) are *partial differential equations*—for example, (5)–(7).

The *order* of a differential equation is the order of the highest derivative that occurs in it. Thus (1), (3), (7) are of first order; (2), (4), (5), (6) are of second order. The *degree* of an ordinary differential equation is its algebraic degree in the highest-ordered derivative present in the equation.

A study of partial differential equations is beyond the limits of this book. In elementary applications, ordinary equations of first or second order are of predominant importance.

247. *Solutions of a Differential Equation*

A *solution* of a differential equation is *any relation, free from derivatives, which involves one or more of the variables, and which is consistent with the differential equation.* For instance, the equation

$$(1) \qquad \frac{d^2x}{dt^2} + k^2x = 0$$

has the solution

$$(2) \qquad x = A \cos kt + B \sin kt,$$

with A and B arbitrary constants. That (2) is consistent with (1) is easily shown by twice differentiating (2) with respect to t.

In a like manner, the equation

$$(3) \qquad y(3x^2 + y^2)\, dx + (2xy^2 + 1)\, dy = 0$$

has the solution

$$(4) \qquad x^3 + xy^2 + \ln y = c,$$

with c arbitrary. To verify that equation (4) is a solution of (3), eliminate the arbitrary constant by differentiation, obtaining

$$(3x^2 + y^2)\, dx + \left(2xy + \frac{1}{y}\right) dy = 0,$$

and then multiply throughout by y to get equation (3).

Our aim in these concluding chapters is to solve simple ordinary differential equations and to treat a few elementary applications which involve them.

By analogy with the integral calculus, a solution of a differential equation is often called an *integral* of the equation, and the arbitrary constants are called *constants of integration.*

248. *General Solutions; Particular Solutions*

Under certain rather broad conditions, a differential equation of order n can be shown to have a solution involving n distinct arbitrary constants. Such a solution is called the *general solution.* Some differential equations have solutions which are not special cases of the general solution, but such matters are beyond a brief introduction to the subject. For the differential equations to be solved in this book, every solution is a special case (some choice of the arbitrary constants) of the general solution.

A *particular solution* is any solution, not general, of the differential equation. The particular solutions used most frequently contain no arbitrary constants. For equation (1) of § 247, some particular solutions are:

$$x = \cos kt,$$
$$x = 3 \cos kt - 2 \sin kt, \text{ etc.}$$

In applied problems involving differential equations, we are in most cases concerned with a particular solution. Nevertheless the determination of the general solution is usually a necessary preliminary step,* after which the required particular solution is found by determining the arbitrary constant from given data, called *initial conditions*, or *boundary conditions*.

249. *Separation of Variables*

The general equation of the first order and first degree is

(1) $$M \, dx + N \, dy = 0,$$

where M and N may be functions of both x and y. Some equations of the type (1) are so simple that they can be put in the form

(2) $$A(x) \, dx + B(y) \, dy = 0;$$

i.e., the variables can be separated. Then the solution can be written down at once. For it is only a matter of finding a function F whose total differential is the left member of (2). Then $F = c$, where c is an arbitrary constant, is the desired result.

Example (a). Solve the equation

(3) $$2(y + 3) \, dx - xy \, dy = 0.$$

Separation of the variables leads to

$$\frac{2dx}{x} - \frac{y \, dy}{y + 3} = 0,$$

or

(4) $$\frac{2dx}{x} - \left[1 - \frac{3}{y + 3}\right] dy = 0.$$

Hence we could write the solution as

(5) $$2 \ln x - y + 3 \ln (y + 3) = c.$$

Although (5) is a correct solution, the presence of two logarithmic terms suggests that we put the arbitrary constant in logarithmic form also. Thus, directly from (4) we may write the solution in the form

(6) $$2 \ln x - y + 3 \ln (y + 3) + \ln c_1 = 0,$$

where c_1 is an arbitrary constant different from the c of (5).
From (6) we get

$$y = 2 \ln x + 3 \ln (y + 3) + \ln c_1,$$

* As a rule, this is not true when we are dealing with a partial differential equation.

from which it follows that

(7) $$e^y = c_1 x^2 (y + 3)^3,$$

which is more compact than (5).

Of course (5) can be transformed into (7) easily. From (5)

$$y + c = 2 \ln x + 3 \ln (y + 3),$$

or

$$e^{y+c} = x^2 (y + 3)^3.$$

Now we put

$$e^c = \frac{1}{c_1}$$

and arrive at (7).

The problem of changing one form of solution into another form is one which arises frequently when two or more persons solve the same differential equation and a check on the results is desired. Unless the use to which the solution will be put is known, there is little reason for preference for one form over another, except for considerations of compactness, symmetry, and other esthetic qualities. It is essentially a matter of individual inclination.

Example (*b*). Solve the equation

$$(x^2 - 1) \, dx + xy \, dy = 0.$$

At once, we perform the separation of variables, obtaining

$$\frac{x^2 - 1}{x} \, dx + y \, dy = 0,$$

or

$$2 \left(x - \frac{1}{x} \right) dx + 2y \, dy = 0.$$

Thus the required solution is

$$x^2 - 2 \ln x + y^2 = 2 \ln c,$$

or

$$x^2 + y^2 = 2 \ln (cx).$$

EXERCISES

In Exs. 1–28 obtain the general solution.

1. $(1 - x)y' = y^2$.   *Ans.* $y \ln [c(1 - x)] = 1$.
2. $\sin x \sin y \, dx + \cos x \cos y \, dy = 0$.   *Ans.* $\sin y = c \cos x$.
3. $xy^3 \, dx + e^{x^2} \, dy = 0$.   *Ans.* $e^{-x^2} + y^{-2} = c$.
4. $2y \, dx = 3x \, dy$.   *Ans.* $x^2 = cy^3$.
5. $my \, dx = nx \, dy$.   *Ans.* $x^m = cy^n$.

6. $y' = xy^2$.   *Ans.* $y(x^2 + c) + 2 = 0$.

7. $\dfrac{dV}{dP} = \dfrac{-V}{P}$.   *Ans.* $PV = C$.

8. $ye^{2x}\, dx = (4 + e^{2x})\, dy$.   *Ans.* $c^2y^2 = 4 + e^{2x}$.

9. $dr = b(\cos\theta\, dr + r\sin\theta\, d\theta)$.   *Ans.* $r = c(1 - b\cos\theta)$.

10. $xy\, dx - (x + 2)\, dy = 0$.   *Ans.* $e^x = cy(x + 2)^2$.

11. $x^2\, dx + y(x - 1)\, dy = 0$.   *Ans.* $(x + 1)^2 + y^2 + 2\ln[c(x - 1)] = 0$.

12. $(xy + x)\, dx = (x^2y^2 + x^2 + y^2 + 1)\, dy$.

                 Ans. $\ln(x^2 + 1) = y^2 - 2y + 4\ln[c(y + 1)]$.

13. $x\cos^2 y\, dx + \tan y\, dy = 0$.   *Ans.* $x^2 + \tan^2 y = c^2$.

14. $xy^3\, dx + (y + 1)e^{-x}\, dy = 0$.   *Ans.* $e^x(x - 1) = \dfrac{1}{y} + \dfrac{1}{2y^2} + c$.

15. $\dfrac{d\theta}{dz} = z(1 - z^2)\sec^2\theta$.   *Ans.* $2\theta + \sin 2\theta = c - (1 - z^2)^2$.

16. $\dfrac{dx}{dt} = \sin^2 x\cos^3 t$.   *Ans.* $3\cot x + 3\sin t - \sin^3 t + c = 0$.

17. $\alpha\, d\beta + \beta\, d\alpha + \alpha\beta(d\alpha + d\beta) = 0$.   *Ans.* $\alpha\beta = ce^{-(\alpha+\beta)}$.

18. $\cos y\, dx = x\, dy$.   *Ans.* $x = c(\sec y + \tan y)$.

19. $(1 + \ln x)\, dx + (1 + \ln y)\, dy = 0$.   *Ans.* $x\ln x + y\ln y = c$.

20. $x\, dx - \sqrt{a^2 - x^2}\, dy = 0$.

    Ans. $y - c = -\sqrt{a^2 - x^2}$, the lower half of the circle $x^2 + (y - c)^2 = a^2$.

21. $x\, dx + \sqrt{a^2 - x^2}\, dy = 0$.

    Ans. $y - c = \sqrt{a^2 - x^2}$, the upper half of the circle $x^2 + (y - c)^2 = a^2$.

22. $a^2\, dx = x\sqrt{x^2 - a^2}\, dy$.   *Ans.* $x = a\sec\dfrac{y + c}{a}$.

23. $y\, dx = (e^{3x} + 1)\, dy$.   *Ans.* $y^3(1 + e^{-3x}) = c^3$.

24. $y\ln x\ln y\, dx + dy = 0$.   *Asn.* $x\ln x + \ln\ln y = x + c$.

25. $(x^2 + 1)\, dy + (y^2 + 1)\, dx = 0$. See also Ex. 29, below.

         Ans. $\operatorname{Arctan} y + \operatorname{Arctan} x = \operatorname{Arctan} c$.

26. $(y^2 + 9)\, dx = (x^2 + 9)\, dy$. See also Ex. 30, below.

      Ans. $\operatorname{Arctan}\dfrac{x}{3} - \operatorname{Arctan}\dfrac{y}{3} = \operatorname{Arctan}\dfrac{c}{3}$.

27. $\sqrt{1 - x^2}\, dy + \sqrt{1 - y^2}\, dx = 0$. See Ex. 31 below.

      Ans. $\operatorname{Arcsin} y + \operatorname{Arcsin} x = \operatorname{Arcsin} c$.

28. $\sqrt{4 - x^2}\, dy - \sqrt{4 - y^2}\, dx = 0$. See Ex. 32 below.

      Ans. $\operatorname{Arcsin}\dfrac{y}{2} - \operatorname{Arcsin}\dfrac{x}{2} = \operatorname{Arcsin}\dfrac{c}{2}$.

29. Show that the answer to Ex. 25 can be put in the form $c(1 - xy) = x + y$.

30. Show that the answer to Ex. 26 can be put in the form $c(9 + xy) = 9(x - y)$.

31. Show that the answer to Ex. 27 can be put in the form $x^2 + 2kxy + y^2 = 1 - k^2$, where $k = \sqrt{1 - c^2}$.

32. Show that the answer to Ex. 28 can be put in the form $x^2 - kxy + y^2 = 4 - k^2$, where $k = \sqrt{4 - c^2}$.

In Exs. 33–38 obtain the particular solution satisfying the boundary condition indicated.

33. $xyy' - y^2 = 1$; when $x = 2$, $y = 1$.   *Ans.* $x^2 - 2y^2 = 2$.

34. $\dfrac{dr}{dt} = -2rt$; when $t = 0$, $r = r_0$.   *Ans.* $r = r_0 e^{-t^2}$.

35. $xy^2\, dx + e^x\, dy = 0$; when $x \to \infty$, $y \to \frac{1}{2}$.   *Ans.* $y = \dfrac{e^x}{2e^x - x - 1}$.

36. $(2a^2 - r^2)\, dr = r^3 \sin\theta\, d\theta$; when $\theta = 0$, $r = a$.

$$\text{\textit{Ans.}}\ \ a^2 + r^2 \ln\frac{r}{a} = r^2 \cos\theta.$$

37. $y' = xe^{-y-x^2}$; when $x = 0$, $y = 0$.   *Ans.* $2e^y = 3 - e^{-x^2}$.

38. $v\dfrac{dv}{dx} = g$; when $x = x_0$, $v = v_0$.   *Ans.* $v^2 - v_0^2 = 2g(x - x_0)$.

250. *Homogeneous Functions*

Polynomials in which all terms are of the same degree, such as

(1)
$$\begin{aligned} x^2 - 3xy + 4y^2, \\ x^3 + y^3, \\ x^4y + 7y^5, \end{aligned}$$

are called *homogeneous* polynomials. We wish now to extend that concept of homogeneity so that it will apply to functions other than polynomials.

If we assign a physical dimension, say length, to each variable x and y in the polynomials in (1), then each polynomial itself also has a physical dimension, length to some power. This suggests the desired generalization. If, when certain variables are thought of as lengths, a function has physical dimension length to the kth power, then we shall call that function homogeneous of degree k in those variables. For example, the function

$$x^3 e^{\frac{x}{y}} - 4y^2 \sqrt{x^2 + y^2}$$

is of dimension (length)^3 when x and y are lengths. Therefore that function is said to be homogeneous of degree 3 in x and y.

We permit the degree k to be any number. The function $\sqrt{x + 4y}$ is called homogeneous of degree $\frac{1}{2}$ in x and y. The function

$$\frac{x}{\sqrt{x^2 + y^2}}$$

is homogeneous of degree zero in x and y.

A formal definition of homogeneity follows: *The function $f(x, y)$ is said to be homogeneous of degree k in x and y if, and only if,*

(2)
$$f(\lambda x, \lambda y) = \lambda^k f(x, y).$$

The definition is easily extended to functions of more than two variables.

For the function

$$f(x, y) = x^3 e^{\frac{x}{y}} - 4y^2 \sqrt{x^2 + y^2}$$

considered above, the formal definition of homogeneity leads us to consider

$$f(\lambda x, \lambda y) = \lambda^3 x^3 e^{\frac{\lambda x}{\lambda y}} - 4\lambda^2 y^2 \sqrt{\lambda^2 x^2 + \lambda^2 y^2}.$$

But we see at once that

$$f(\lambda x, \lambda y) = \lambda^3 f(x, y);$$

hence $f(x, y)$ is homogeneous of degree 3 in x and y, as stated previously.

The following theorems prove useful in the next section.

THEOREM 50. *If $M(x, y)$ and $N(x, y)$ are both homogeneous and of the same degree, the function $\dfrac{M(x, y)}{N(x, y)}$ is homogeneous of degree zero.*

THEOREM 51. *If $f(x, y)$ is homogeneous of degree zero in x and y, $f(x, y)$ is a function of $\dfrac{y}{x}$ alone.*

Proof of Theorem 50 is left to the student.

Proof of Theorem 51: Let us put $y = vx$. Then Theorem 51 states that if $f(x, y)$ is homogeneous of degree zero, $f(x, y)$ is a function of v alone. Now

$$(3) \qquad\qquad f(x, y) = f(x, vx) = x^0 f(1, v) = f(1, v),$$

in which the x is now playing the role taken by λ in the definition (2) above. By (3), $f(x, y)$ depends on v alone as stated in Theorem 51.

ORAL EXERCISES

Determine in each exercise whether the function is homogeneous or not. If it is homogeneous, state the degree of the function.

1. $x^2 - 2xy - y^2$.

2. $x^3 - 4x^2 + y^3$.

3. $3x + \sqrt{x^2 - y^2}$.

4. $\dfrac{3x + 2y}{\sqrt{x^2 + y^2}}$.

5. $(x^3 - y^3)e^{\frac{x}{y}} + (x^2 + 4y^2)^{\frac{3}{2}}$.

6. $\sqrt{x + y}$.

7. $x \sin \dfrac{y}{x} - y \sin \dfrac{x}{y}$.

8. $3x^2 - \dfrac{x^3}{y} \text{Arctan} \dfrac{x}{y}$.

9. e^x.

10. $\ln x$.

11. $e^{\frac{x}{y}}$.

12. $\ln \dfrac{x}{y}$.

13. $x \tan \dfrac{y}{x}$.

14. $x \ln x - y \ln y$.

15. $xe^x \tan \dfrac{y}{x}$.

16. $x \ln x - x \ln y$.

17. $\dfrac{x - y}{x^2 + y^2}$.

18. $\dfrac{a^2 - 2x^2}{(a^2 - x^2)^{\frac{3}{2}}}$.

251. *Equations with Homogeneous Coefficients*

Suppose the coefficients M and N in an equation of the first order and first degree,

(1) $$M(x, y)\, dx + N(x, y)\, dy = 0,$$

are both homogeneous functions and are of the *same degree* in x and y. By Theorems 50 and 51 of § 250, the ratio M/N is a function of y/x alone. Hence equation (1) may be put in the form

(2) $$\frac{dy}{dx} + g\left(\frac{y}{x}\right) = 0.$$

This suggests the introduction of a new variable v by putting $y = vx$. Then (2) becomes

(3) $$x\frac{dv}{dx} + v + g(v) = 0,$$

in which the variables are separable. We can obtain the solution of (3) by the method of § 249, insert y/x for v, and thus arrive at the solution of (1). We have shown that the substitution $y = vx$ will transform equation (1) into an equation, in v and x, in which the variables are separable.

The above method of attack would have been equally successful had we used $x = vy$ to obtain from (1) an equation in y and v.

Example. Solve the equation

(4) $$(x^2 - xy + y^2)\, dx - xy\, dy = 0.$$

Since the coefficients in (4) are both homogeneous and of degree two in x and y, let us put $y = vx$. Then (4) becomes

$$(x^2 - x^2v + x^2v^2)\, dx - x^2v(v\, dx + x\, dv) = 0,$$

from which the factor x^2 should be removed at once. That done, we have to solve

$$(1 - v + v^2)\, dx - v(v\, dx + x\, dv) = 0,$$

or

$$(1 - v)\, dx - xv\, dv = 0.$$

Hence we separate variables to get

$$\frac{dx}{x} + \frac{v\, dv}{v - 1} = 0.$$

Then from

$$\frac{dx}{x} + \left[1 + \frac{1}{v - 1} \right] dv = 0$$

the solution is seen to be

$$\ln x + v + \ln (v - 1) = \ln c,$$

or

$$x(v - 1)e^v = c.$$

In terms of the original variables the solution is

$$x\left(\frac{y}{x} - 1 \right) e^{\frac{y}{x}} = c,$$

or

$$(y - x)e^{\frac{y}{x}} = c.$$

EXERCISES

In Exs. 1–21 obtain the general solution.

1. $(x - 2y)\,dx + (2x + y)\,dy = 0.$ *Ans.* $\ln (x^2 + y^2) + 4 \text{ Arctan } \frac{y}{x} = c.$

2. $xy\,dx - (x^2 + 2y^2)\,dy = 0.$ *Ans.* $x^2 = 4y^2 \ln \frac{y}{c}.$

3. $2(2x^2 + y^2)\,dx - xy\,dy = 0.$ *Ans.* $x^4 = c^2(4x^2 + y^2).$

4. $(2x^2 + xy - 2y^2)\,dx = (x^2 - 4xy)\,dy.$ *Ans.* $\text{Arctan } \frac{y}{x} = 2 \ln \frac{x^2 + y^2}{cx}.$

5. $(x^2 + 2y^2)\,dx - xy\,dy = 0.$ *Ans.* $x^4 = c^2(x^2 + y^2).$

6. $(x - y)(4x + y)\,dx + x(5x - y)\,dy = 0.$ *Ans.* $x(y + x)^2 = c(y - 2x).$

7. $(5v - u)\,du + (3v - 7u)\,dv = 0.$ *Ans.* $(3v + u)^2 = c(v - u).$

8. $(x^2 + 2xy - 4y^2)\,dx - (x^2 - 8xy - 4y^2)\,dy = 0.$

Ans. $x^2 + 4y^2 = c(x + y).$

9. $(x^2 + y^2)\,dx - xy\,dy = 0.$ *Ans.* $y^2 = 2x^2 \ln \frac{x}{c}.$

10. $x(x^2 + y^2)^2(y\,dx - x\,dy) + y^6\,dy = 0.$ *Ans.* $(x^2 + y^2)^3 = 6y^6 \ln \frac{c}{y}.$

11. $(x^2 + y^2)\,dx + xy\,dy = 0.$ *Ans.* $x^2(x^2 + 2y^2) = c^4.$

12. $xy\,dx - (x + 2y)^2\,dy = 0.$ *Ans.* $y^3(x + y) = ce^{\frac{x}{y}}.$

13. $v^2\,dx + x(x + v)\,dv = 0.$ *Ans.* $xv^2 = c(x + 2v).$

14. $\left(x \csc \frac{y}{x} - y \right) dx + x\,dy = 0.$ *Ans.* $\ln \frac{x}{c} = \cos \frac{y}{x}.$

15. $x\,dx + \sin^2 \frac{y}{x} [y\,dx - x\,dy] = 0.$ *Ans.* $4x \ln \frac{x}{c} - 2y + x \sin \frac{2y}{x} = 0.$

16. $(x - y \ln y + y \ln x) \, dx + x(\ln y - \ln x) \, dy = 0.$
$$\textit{Ans. } (x - y) \ln x + y \ln y = cx + y.$$

17. $\left(x - y \operatorname{Arctan} \dfrac{y}{x} \right) dx + x \operatorname{Arctan} \dfrac{y}{x} \, dy = 0.$

$$\textit{Ans. } 2y \operatorname{Arctan} \left(\frac{y}{x} \right) = x \ln \left[\frac{c^2(x^2 + y^2)}{x^4} \right].$$

18. $y^2 \, dy = x(x \, dy - y \, dx)e^{\frac{x}{y}}.$
$$\textit{Ans. } y \ln \frac{y}{c} = (y - x)e^{\frac{x}{y}}.$$

19. $t(s^2 + t^2) \, ds - s(s^2 - t^2) \, dt = 0.$
$$\textit{Ans. } s^2 = -2t^2 \ln (cst)$$

20. $y \, dx = (x + \sqrt{y^2 - x^2}) \, dy.$
$$\textit{Ans. } \operatorname{Arcsin} \left(\frac{x}{y} \right) = \ln \frac{y}{c}.$$

21. $(3x^2 - 2xy + 3y^2) \, dx = 4xy \, dy.$
$$\textit{Ans. } (y - x)(y + 3x)^3 = cx^3.$$

22. Prove that, with the aid of the substitution $y = vx$, you can solve any equation of the form

$$y^n f(x) \, dx + H(x, y)(y \, dx - x \, dy) = 0,$$

where $H(x, y)$ is homogeneous in x and y.

In Exs. 23–35 find the particular solution indicated.

23. $(x - y) \, dx + (3x + y) \, dy = 0;$ when $x = 2, y = -1.$
$$\textit{Ans. } 2(x + 2y) + (x + y) \ln (x + y) = 0.$$

24. $(y - \sqrt{x^2 + y^2}) \, dx - x \, dy = 0;$ when $x = \sqrt{3}, y = 1.$
$$\textit{Ans. } x^2 = 9 - 6y.$$

25. $(y + \sqrt{x^2 + y^2}) \, dx - x \, dy = 0;$ when $x = \sqrt{3}, y = 1.$
$$\textit{Ans. } x^2 = 2y + 1.$$

26. $\left(x \cos^2 \dfrac{y}{x} - y \right) dx + x \, dy = 0;$ when $x = 1, y = \dfrac{\pi}{4}.$ $\quad \textit{Ans. } \tan \dfrac{y}{x} = \ln \dfrac{e}{x}.$

27. $(y^2 + 7xy + 16x^2) \, dx + x^2 \, dy = 0;$ when $x = 1, y = 1.$
$$\textit{Ans. } x - y = 5(y + 4x) \ln x.$$

28. $y^2 \, dx + (x^2 + 3xy + 4y^2) \, dy = 0;$ when $x = 2, y = 1.$
$$\textit{Ans. } 4(2y + x) \ln y = 2y - x.$$

29. $xy \, dx + 2(x^2 + 2y^2) \, dy = 0;$ when $x = 0, y = 1.$ $\quad \textit{Ans. } y^4(3x^2 + 4y^2) = 4.$

30. $y(2x^2 - xy + y^2) \, dx - x^2(2x - y) \, dy = 0;$ when $x = 1, y = \frac{1}{2}.$
$$\textit{Ans. } y^2 \ln x = 2y^2 + xy - x^2.$$

31. $y(9x - 2y) \, dx - x(6x - y) \, dy = 0;$ when $x = 1, y = 1.$
$$\textit{Ans. } 3x^3 - x^2y - 2y^2 = 0.$$

32. $y(x^2 + y^2) \, dx + x(3x^2 - 5y^2) \, dy = 0;$ when $x = 2, y = 1.$
$$\textit{Ans. } 2y^5 - 2x^2y^3 + 3x = 0.$$

33. $(16x + 5y) \, dx + (3x + y) \, dy = 0;$ the curve to pass through the point $(1, -3).$ $\qquad \textit{Ans. } y + 3x = (y + 4x) \ln (y + 4x).$

34. $v(3x + 2v) \, dx - x^2 \, dv = 0;$ when $x = 1, v = 2.$ $\quad \textit{Ans. } 2x^3 + 2x^2v - 3v = 0.$

35. $(3x^2 - 2y^2)y' = 2xy;$ when $x = 0, y = -1.$ $\qquad \textit{Ans. } x^2 = 2y^2(y + 1).$

36. If $y' = F(ax + by + c)$, show that the substitution $ax + by + c = v$ produces an equation in which the variables can be separated.

37. Solve the equation $dy = (4x + y)^2 \, dx$. (Ex. 36.)

38. $y' = 2(3x + y)^2 - 1$; when $x = 0$, $y = 1$.

Ans. 4 Arctan $(3x + y) = 8x + \pi$.

252. *Exact Equations*

In § 249 it was noticed that when an equation can be put in the form

$$A(x) \, dx + B(y) \, dy = 0,$$

the general solution may be determined by integration; that is, by finding a function whose differential is $A(x) \, dx + B(y) \, dy$.

That idea can be extended to some equations of the form

(1) $$M(x, y) \, dx + N(x, y) \, dy = 0$$

in which separation of variables may not be possible. Suppose that a function $F(x, y)$ can be found which has for its total differential the expression $M \, dx + N \, dy$; i.e.,

(2) $$dF = M \, dx + N \, dy.$$

Then certainly

(3) $$F(x, y) = c$$

is the general solution of (1). For, from (3) it follows that

$$dF = 0,$$

or, in view of (2),

$$M \, dx + N \, dy = 0,$$

as desired.

Two things, then, are needed: first, to find out under what conditions on M and N a function F exists such that its total differential is exactly $M \, dx + N \, dy$; second, if those conditions are satisfied, actually to determine the function F. If there exists a function F such that $M \, dx + N \, dy$ is exactly the total differential of F, we call equation (1) an *exact equation*.

If the equation

(1) $$M \, dx + N \, dy = 0$$

is exact, then by definition F exists such that

$$dF = M \, dx + N \, dy.$$

But, from calculus,

$$dF = \frac{\partial F}{\partial x} \, dx + \frac{\partial F}{\partial y} \, dy,$$

so

$$M = \frac{\partial F}{\partial x}, \qquad N = \frac{\partial F}{\partial y}.$$

These two equations lead to

$$\frac{\partial M}{\partial y} = \frac{\partial^2 F}{\partial y\, \partial x} \quad \text{and} \quad \frac{\partial N}{\partial x} = \frac{\partial^2 F}{\partial x\, \partial y}.$$

Again from calculus

$$\frac{\partial^2 F}{\partial y\, \partial x} = \frac{\partial^2 F}{\partial x\, \partial y},$$

provided these partial derivatives are continuous. Therefore, if (1) is an exact equation, then

(4)
$$\frac{\partial M}{\partial y} = \frac{\partial N}{\partial x}.$$

Thus, for (1) to be exact, it is necessary that (4) be satisfied.

Let us now show that if condition (4) is satisfied, then (1) is an exact equation. Let $\varphi(x, y)$ be a function for which

$$\frac{\partial \varphi}{\partial x} = M.$$

The function φ is the result of integrating $M\, dx$ with respect to x while holding y constant. Now

$$\frac{\partial^2 \varphi}{\partial y\, \partial x} = \frac{\partial M}{\partial y};$$

hence, if (4) is satisfied, then also

(5)
$$\frac{\partial^2 \varphi}{\partial x\, \partial y} = \frac{\partial N}{\partial x}.$$

Let us integrate both sides of this last equation with respect to x, holding y fixed. In the integration with respect to x the "arbitrary constant" may be any function of y. Let us call it $B'(y)$, for ease in indicating its integral. Then integration of (5) with respect to x yields

(6)
$$\frac{\partial \varphi}{\partial y} = N + B'(y).$$

Now a function F can be exhibited, namely,

$$F = \varphi(x, y) - B(y),$$
for which

$$\begin{aligned}
dF &= \frac{\partial \varphi}{\partial x}\, dx + \frac{\partial \varphi}{\partial y}\, dy - B'(y)\, dy \\
&= M\, dx + [N + B'(y)]\, dy - B'(y)\, dy \\
&= M\, dx + N\, dy.
\end{aligned}$$

Hence, equation (1) is exact. We have completed a proof of the theorem stated below.

THEOREM 52. *If M, N, $\dfrac{\partial M}{\partial y}$, and $\dfrac{\partial N}{\partial x}$ are continuous functions of x and y, then a necessary and sufficient condition that*

$$(1) \qquad\qquad M\, dx + N\, dy = 0$$

be an exact equation is that

$$(4) \qquad\qquad \frac{\partial M}{\partial y} = \frac{\partial N}{\partial x}.$$

Furthermore, the proof contains the germ of a method for obtaining the solution, a method used in Examples (*a*) and (*b*) below. It will be found, however, that with a little practice the solutions of very many exact equations can be written down by inspection. See Examples (*c*) and (*d*). No matter what method is used, the result should be checked by differentiation.

It is natural when an equation is not exact to attempt to make it exact by the introduction of an appropriate factor, which is then called an *integrating factor*. An important application of integrating factors appears in § 253.

Example (a). Solve the equation

$$(7) \qquad\qquad 3x(xy - 2)\, dx + (x^3 + 2y)\, dy = 0.$$

First, from the fact that

$$\frac{\partial M}{\partial y} = 3x^2 \quad \text{and} \quad \frac{\partial N}{\partial x} = 3x^2,$$

we conclude that equation (7) is exact. Therefore, its solution is $F = c$, where

$$(8) \qquad\qquad \frac{\partial F}{\partial x} = M = 3x^2 y - 6x,$$

and

$$(9) \qquad\qquad \frac{\partial F}{\partial y} = N = x^3 + 2y.$$

Let us attempt to determine F from equation (8). Integration of both sides of (8) with respect to x, holding y constant, yields

$$(10) \qquad\qquad F = x^3 y - 3x^2 + T(y),$$

where the usual arbitrary constant in indefinite integration is now necessarily a function $T(y)$, as yet unknown. In order to determine $T(y)$, we use the fact that the function F of equation (10) must also satisfy equation (9). Hence

$$x^3 + T'(y) = x^3 + 2y,$$

so that
$$T'(y) = 2y.$$

No arbitrary constant is needed in obtaining $T(y)$, since one is being introduced on the right in the solution $F = c$. Then
$$T(y) = y^2,$$
and from (10)
$$F = x^3y - 3x^2 + y^2.$$

Finally, the solution of equation (7) is seen to be
$$x^3y - 3x^2 + y^2 = c,$$
a result which is easily checked by differentiation.

Example (b). Solve the equation

(11) $$(2x^3 - xy^2 - 2y + 3)\, dx - (x^2y + 2x)\, dy = 0.$$

Here
$$\frac{\partial M}{\partial y} = -2xy - 2 = \frac{\partial N}{\partial x}$$

so that the equation (11) is exact.

The solution of (11) is $F = c$, where

(12) $$\frac{\partial F}{\partial x} = 2x^3 - xy^2 - 2y + 3$$

and

(13) $$\frac{\partial F}{\partial y} = -x^2y - 2x.$$

Because (13) is simpler than (12), and for variety's sake, let us start the determination of F from equation (13).

At once, from (13)
$$F = -\tfrac{1}{2}x^2y^2 - 2xy + Q(x),$$

where $Q(x)$ will be determined from (12). The latter yields
$$-xy^2 - 2y + Q'(x) = 2x^3 - xy^2 - 2y + 3,$$
$$Q'(x) = 2x^3 + 3.$$
Therefore
$$Q(x) = \tfrac{1}{2}x^4 + 3x,$$

and the desired solution of (11) is
$$-\tfrac{1}{2}x^2y^2 - 2xy + \tfrac{1}{2}x^4 + 3x = \tfrac{1}{2}c,$$
or
$$x^4 - x^2y^2 - 4xy + 6x = c.$$

Example (*c*). Solve the equation of Example (*a*) by inspection. Suppose that we have tested

(7) $$3x(xy - 2) \, dx + (x^3 + 2y) \, dy = 0$$

and found that it is exact. Then we may write down the general solution by inspection; that is, by careful observation of the left member of (7), we shall find a function of which it is the total differential.

First, the term $3x^2y \, dx$ suggests the differential of x^3y. Hence we search (7) for the necessary companion term $x^3 \, dy$ and group the two terms. Any term such as $-6x \, dx$, which contains only one variable, is an exact differential as it stands. Thus we are led to rewrite equation (7) as

$$(3x^2y \, dx + x^3 \, dy) - 6x \, dx + 2y \, dy = 0,$$

from which the general solution

$$x^3y - 3x^2 + y^2 = c$$

is evident.

Example (*d*). Solve the equation

(11) $$(2x^3 - xy^2 - 2y + 3) \, dx - (x^2y + 2x) \, dy = 0$$

of Example (*b*) by inspection.

The grouping

$$2x^3 \, dx - (xy^2 \, dx + x^2y \, dy) - (2y \, dx + 2x \, dy) + 3dx = 0$$

leads at once to the result

$$\tfrac{1}{2}x^4 - \tfrac{1}{2}x^2y^2 - 2xy + 3x = \tfrac{1}{2}c,$$

or

$$x^4 - x^2y^2 - 4xy + 6x = c.$$

EXERCISES

Test each of the following equations for exactness and solve the equation. Those of the equations which are not exact may, of course, be solved by methods of the preceding sections.

1. $(x + y) \, dx + (x - y) \, dy = 0$.   *Ans.* $x^2 + 2xy - y^2 = c$.

2. $(6x + y^2) \, dx + y(2x - 3y) \, dy = 0$.   *Ans.* $3x^2 + xy^2 - y^3 = c$.

3. $(2xy - 3x^2) \, dx + (x^2 + y) \, dy = 0$.   *Ans.* $x^2y - x^3 + \tfrac{1}{2}y^2 = c$.

4. $(y^2 - 2xy + 6x) \, dx - (x^2 - 2xy + 2) \, dy = 0$.

    Ans. $xy^2 - x^2y + 3x^2 - 2y = c$.

5. $(2xy - y) \, dx + (x^2 + x) \, dy = 0$.   *Ans.* $y(x + 1)^3 = cx$.

6. $v(2uv^2 - 3) \, du + (3u^2v^2 - 3u + 4v) \, dv = 0$.   *Ans.* $v(u^2v^2 - 3u + 2v) = c$.

7. $(\cos 2y - 3x^2y^2) \, dx + (\cos 2y - 2x \sin 2y - 2x^3y) \, dy = 0$.

    Ans. $\tfrac{1}{2} \sin 2y + x \cos 2y - x^3y^2 = c$.

8. $(1 + y^2) \, dx + (x^2y + y) \, dy = 0$.   *Ans.* $2 \, \text{Arctan} \, x + \ln (1 + y^2) = c$.

9. $(1 + y^2 + xy^2) \, dx + (x^2y + y + 2xy) \, dy = 0.$ $Ans. \; 2x + y^2(1 + x)^2 = c.$

10. $(w^3 + wz^2 - z) \, dw + (z^3 + w^2z - w) \, dz = 0.$ $Ans. \; (w^2 + z^2)^2 = 4wz + c.$

11. $(2xy - \tan y) \, dx + (x^2 - x \sec^2 y) \, dy = 0.$ $Ans. \; x^2y - x \tan y = c.$

12. $(\cos x \cos y - \cot x) \, dx - \sin x \sin y \, dy = 0.$

$Ans. \; \sin x \cos y = \ln \, (c \sin x).$

13. $(r + \sin \theta - \cos \theta) \, dr + r(\sin \theta + \cos \theta) \, d\theta = 0.$

$Ans. \; r^2 + 2r(\sin \theta - \cos \theta) = c.$

14. $x(3xy - 4y^3 + 6) \, dx + (x^3 - 6x^2y^2 - 1) \, dy = 0.$

$Ans. \; x^3y - 2x^2y^3 + 3x^2 - y = c.$

15. $(\sin \theta - 2r \cos^2 \theta) \, dr + r \cos \theta(2r \sin \theta + 1) \, d\theta = 0.$

$Ans. \; r \sin \theta - r^2 \cos^2 \theta = c.$

16. $[2x + y \cos \, (xy)] \, dx + x \cos \, (xy) \, dy = 0.$ $Ans. \; x^2 + \sin \, (xy) = c.$

17. $2xy \, dx + (y^2 + x^2) \, dy = 0.$ $Ans, \; y(3x^2 + y^2) = c.$

18. $2xy \, dx + (y^2 - x^2) \, dy = 0.$ $Ans. \; x^2 + y^2 = cy.$

19. $[2xy \cos \, (x^2) - 2xy + 1] \, dx + [\sin \, (x^2) - x^2] \, dy = 0.$

$Ans. \; y[\sin \, (x^2) - x^2] = c - x.$

20. $(2x - 3y) \, dx + (2y - 3x) \, dy = 0.$ $Ans. \; x^2 + y^2 - 3xy = c.$

21. Do Ex. 20 by a second method.

22. $(xy^2 + y - x) \, dx + x(xy + 1) \, dy = 0.$ $Ans. \; x^2y^2 + 2xy - x^2 = c.$

23. $3y(x^2 - 1) \, dx + (x^3 + 8y - 3x) \, dy = 0;$ when $x = 0, \; y = 1.$

$Ans. \; xy(x^2 - 3) = 4(1 - y^2).$

24. $(1 - xy)^{-2} \, dx + [y^2 + x^2(1 - xy)^{-2}] \, dy = 0;$ when $x = 4, \; y = 1.$

$Ans. \; xy^4 - y^3 + 3xy - 3x - 3 = 0.$

25. $(ye^{xy} - 2y^3) \, dx + (xe^{xy} - 6xy^2 - 2y) \, dy = 0;$ when $x = 0, \; y = 2.$

$Ans. \; e^{xy} = 2xy^3 + y^2 - 3.$

253. *The Linear Equation of Order One*

A very important concept is that of the linearity or nonlinearity of a differential equation. An equation is said to be *linear* if each term of the equation is either linear in all the dependent variables and their various derivatives or does not contain any of them. Otherwise the equation is said to be *nonlinear*. Such a term as $y \dfrac{dy}{dx}$ is of degree two in y and its derivative together and is therefore nonlinear.

An equation which is linear and of order one in the dependent variable y must by definition be of the form

$$(1) \qquad\qquad A(x) \, dy + B(x)y \, dx = C(x) \, dx.$$

By dividing each member of equation (1) by $A(x)$, we obtain

$$(2) \qquad\qquad dy + P(x)y \, dx = Q(x) \, dx,$$

which we choose as the standard form for the linear equation of order one.

For the moment, suppose that there exists for equation (2) an integrating factor $v(x)$, a function of x alone. Then

$$(3) \qquad\qquad v \, dy + vP(x)y \, dx = vQ(x) \, dx$$

must be an exact equation. But (3) is easily put in the form

$$M \, dx + N \, dy = 0$$

with

$$M = vPy - vQ,$$

and

$$N = v,$$

in which v, P, and Q are functions of x alone.

Therefore, if equation (3) is to be exact, it follows from the requirement $\dfrac{\partial M}{\partial y} = \dfrac{\partial N}{\partial x}$ that v must satisfy the equation

$$(4) \qquad\qquad vP = \frac{dv}{dx}.$$

From (4) v may be obtained readily, for

$$P \, dx = \frac{dv}{v},$$

so that

$$\ln v = \int P \, dx,$$

or

$$(5) \qquad\qquad v = e^{\int P \, dx}.$$

That is, if the equation (2) has an integrating factor independent of y, then that factor must be as given by equation (5).

It remains to be shown that the v given by equation (5) is actually an integrating factor of

$$(2) \qquad\qquad dy + P(x)y \, dx = Q(x) \, dx.$$

Let us apply the factor throughout (2), obtaining

$$(6) \qquad\qquad e^{\int P \, dx} \, dy + Pe^{\int P \, dx}y \, dx = Qe^{\int P \, dx} \, dx.$$

The left member of (6) is the differential of the product

$$ye^{\int P \, dx};$$

the right member of (6) is an exact differential, since it is independent of y. Hence equation (6) is exact, which is what we wished to show.

Of course one integrating factor is sufficient. Hence we may use in the exponent $\left(\displaystyle\int P \, dx \right)$ any function whose differential is $P \, dx$.

With an integrating factor at hand we can lay down the following rule for integrating any linear equation of order one:

(a) Put the equation into standard form:

$$dy + Py\ dx = Q\ dx;$$

(b) Obtain the integrating factor $e^{\int P\ dx}$;
(c) Apply the integrating factor to the equation in its standard form;
(d) Solve the resultant exact equation.

Note, in integrating the exact equation, that *the integral of the left member is always the product of the dependent variable and the integrating factor used.*
Example (a). Solve the equation

$$2(y - 4x^2)\ dx + x\ dy = 0.$$

The equation is linear in y. When put in standard form it becomes

(7)
$$dy + \frac{2}{x}\ y\ dx = 8x\ dx.$$

Then an integrating factor is

$$e^{\int \frac{2dx}{x}} = e^{2\ln x} = (e^{\ln x})^2 = x^2.$$

Next we apply the integrating factor to (7), thus obtaining the exact equation

(8)
$$x^2\ dy + 2xy\ dx = 8x^3\ dx.$$

The solution of (8) is

(9)
$$x^2 y = 2x^4 + c$$

and should be checked, particularly since verification of the result is so easy.

From (9) we get (8) by differentiation. Then the original differential equation follows from (8) by a simple adjustment. Hence (9) is a solution of the original equation.

Example (b). Solve the equation

$$y\ dx + (3x - xy + 2)\ dy = 0.$$

Since the product $y\ dy$ occurs here, the equation is not linear in y. It is, however, linear in x. Therefore we arrange the terms as in

$$y\ dx + (3 - y)x\ dy = -2\ dy$$

and pass to the standard form,

(10)
$$dx + \left(\frac{3}{y} - 1\right) x\ dy = -\frac{2}{y}\ dy.$$

Now

$$\int \left(\frac{3}{y} - 1\right) dy = 3\ln y - y + c_1,$$

so that an integrating factor for equation (10) is

$$e^{3 \ln y - y} = e^{3 \ln y} \cdot e^{-y} = (e^{\ln y})^3 \cdot e^{-y} = y^3 e^{-y}.$$

Application of this integrating factor to equation (10) leads to the exact equation

$$y^3 e^{-y} \, dx + y^2 (3 - y) e^{-y} x \, dy = -2y^2 e^{-y} \, dy,$$

from which we get

$$xy^3 e^{-y} = -2 \int y^2 e^{-y} \, dy$$
$$= 2y^2 e^{-y} + 4y e^{-y} + 4 e^{-y} + c.$$

Thus we may write the solution as

$$xy^3 = 2y^2 + 4y + 4 + ce^y.$$

EXERCISES

In Exs. 1–25 find the general solution.

1. $(x^4 + 2y) \, dx - x \, dy = 0.$ *Ans.* $2y = x^4 + cx^2.$

2. $(3xy + 3y - 4) \, dx + (x + 1)^2 \, dy = 0.$

Ans. $y = 2(x + 1)^{-1} + c(x + 1)^{-3}.$

3. $y' = \csc x - y \cot x.$ *Ans.* $y \sin x = x + c.$

4. $t \dfrac{dx}{dt} = 6te^{2t} + x(2t - 1).$ *Ans.* $xt = (3t^2 + c)e^{2t}.$

5. $dy = (x - 3y) \, dx.$ *Ans.* $9y = 3x - 1 + ce^{-3x}.$

6. $(3x - 1)y' = 6y - 10(3x - 1)^{\frac{1}{3}}.$ *Ans.* $y = 2(3x - 1)^{\frac{1}{3}} + c(3x - 1)^2.$

7. $(y - 2) \, dx + (3x - y) \, dy = 0.$ *Ans.* $12x = 3y + 2 + c(y - 2)^{-3}.$

8. $(2xy + x^2 + x^4) \, dx - (1 + x^2) \, dy = 0.$

Ans. $y = (1 + x^2)(c + x - \text{Arctan } x).$

9. $y' = x - 2xy.$ Solve by two methods. *Ans.* $2y = 1 + ce^{-x^2}.$

10. $(y - \cos^2 x) \, dx + \cos x \, dy = 0.$ *Ans.* $y(\sec x + \tan x) = c + x - \cos x.$

11. $y' = x - 2y \cot 2x.$ *Ans.* $4y \sin 2x = c + \sin 2x - 2x \cos 2x.$

12. $(y - x + xy \cot x) \, dx + x \, dy = 0.$ *Ans.* $xy \sin x = c + \sin x - x \cos x.$

13. $\dfrac{dy}{dx} - my = c_1 e^{mx},$ where c_1 and m are constants. *Ans.* $y = (c_1 x + c_2)e^{mx}.$

14. $\dfrac{dy}{dx} - m_2 y = c_1 e^{m_1 x},$ where c_1, m_1, m_2 are constants and $m_1 \neq m_2.$

Ans. $y = c_3 e^{m_1 x} + c_2 e^{m_2 x},$ where $c_3 = \dfrac{c_1}{m_1 - m_2}.$

15. $v \, dx + (2x + 1 - vx) \, dv = 0.$ *Ans.* $xv^2 = v + 1 + ce^v.$

16. $x(x^2 + 1)y' + 2y = (x^2 + 1)^3.$ *Ans.* $x^2 y = \frac{1}{4}(x^2 + 1)^3 + c(x^2 + 1).$

17. $2x(y - x^2) \, dx + dy = 0.$ *Ans.* $y = x^2 - 1 + ce^{-x^2}.$

18. $(1 + xy) \, dx - (1 + x^2) \, dy = 0.$ *Ans.* $y = x + c(1 + x^2)^{\frac{1}{2}}.$

19. $2y \, dx = (x^2 - 1)(dx - dy).$ *Ans.* $(x - 1)y = (x + 1)[c + x - 2 \ln (x + 1)].$

20. $dx - (1 + 2x \tan y) \, dy = 0.$ *Ans.* $2x \cos^2 y = y + c + \sin y \cos y.$

21. $(1 + \cos x)y' = \sin x(\sin x + \sin x \cos x - y).$
$$Ans.\ y = (1 + \cos x)(c + x - \sin x).$$

22. $y' = 1 + 3y \tan x.$ *Ans.* $3y \cos^3 x = c + 3 \sin x - \sin^3 x.$

23. $(x^2 + a^2) \, dy = 2x[(x^2 + a^2)^2 + 3y] \, dx;$ a is constant.
$$Ans.\ y = (x^2 + a^2)^2[c(x^2 + a^2) - 1].$$

24. $(x + a)y' = bx - ny;$ a, b, n are constants with $n \neq 0, n \neq -1.$
$$Ans.\ n(n + 1)y = b(nx - a) + c(x + a)^{-n}.$$

25. Solve the equation of Ex. 24 for the exceptional cases $n = 0$ and $n = -1.$
$$Ans.\ \text{If } n = 0,\ y = bx + c - ab \ln (x + a).$$
$$\text{If } n = -1,\ y = ab + c(x + a) + b(x + a) \ln (x + a).$$

26. In the standard form $dy + Py \, dx = Q \, dx$ put $y = vw$, thus obtaining

$$w(dv + Pv \, dx) + v \, dw = Q \, dx.$$

Then, by first choosing v so that
$$dv + Pv \, dx = 0$$

and later determining w, show how to complete the solution of

$$dy + Py \, dx = Q \, dx.$$

In Exs. 27–33 find the particular solution indicated.

27. $(2x + 3)y' = y + (2x + 3)^{\frac{1}{2}};$ when $x = -1, y = 0.$
$$Ans.\ 2y = (2x + 3)^{\frac{1}{2}} \ln (2x + 3).$$

28. $y' = x^3 - 2xy;$ when $x = 1, y = 1.$ *Ans.* $2y = x^2 - 1 + 2e^{1-x^2}.$

29. $L\dfrac{di}{dt} + Ri = E$, where L, R, and E are constants; when $t = 0, i = 0.$

$$Ans.\ i = \frac{E}{R} \left(1 - e^{-\frac{Rt}{L}}\right).$$

30. $L\dfrac{di}{dt} + Ri = E \sin \omega t;$ when $t = 0, i = 0.$

$$Ans.\ \text{Let } Z^2 = R^2 + \omega^2 L^2.\ \text{Then } i = EZ^{-2}(R \sin \omega t - \omega L \cos \omega t + \omega L e^{-\frac{Rt}{L}}).$$

31. Find that solution of $y' = 2(2x - y)$ which passes through the point $(0, -1).$
$$Ans.\ y = 2x - 1.$$

32. Find that solution of $y' = 2(2x - y)$ which passes through the point $(0, 1).$
$$Ans.\ y = 2x - 1 + 2e^{-2x}.$$

33. $(1 + t^2) \, ds + 2t[st^2 - 3(1 + t^2)^2] \, dt = 0;$ when $t = 0, s = 2.$
$$Ans.\ s = (1 + t^2)(3 - e^{-t^2}).$$

ELEMENTARY APPLICATIONS

254. *Velocity of Escape from the Earth*

Many physical problems involve differential equations of order one and degree one.

First consider the problem of determining the velocity of a particle projected in a radial direction outward from the earth and acted upon by only one force, the gravitational attraction of the earth.

We shall assume an initial velocity in a radial direction so that the motion of the particle takes place entirely on a line through the center of the earth.

According to the Newtonian law of gravitation the acceleration of the particle will be inversely proportional to the square of the distance from the particle to the center of the earth. Let r be that variable distance, and let R be the radius of the earth. If t represents time, v the velocity of the particle, a its acceleration, and k the constant of proportionality in the Newtonian law, then

$$a = \frac{dv}{dt} = \frac{k}{r^2}.$$

The acceleration is negative because the velocity is decreasing. Hence the constant k is negative. When $r = R$, then $a = -g$, the acceleration at the surface of the earth. Thus

$$-g = \frac{k}{R^2},$$

from which

$$a = -\frac{gR^2}{r^2}.$$

We wish to express the acceleration in terms of the velocity and the distance. We have $a = \frac{dv}{dt}$ and $v = \frac{dr}{dt}$. Hence

$$a = \frac{dv}{dt} = \frac{dr}{dt}\frac{dv}{dr} = v\frac{dv}{dr},$$

so that the differential equation for the velocity is now seen to be

(1) $$v\frac{dv}{dr} = -\frac{gR^2}{r^2}.$$

The method of separation of variables applies to equation (1) and leads at once to the solution

$$v^2 = \frac{2gR^2}{r} + C.$$

Suppose the particle leaves the earth's surface with the velocity v_0. Then $v = v_0$ when $r = R$, from which the constant C is easily determined to be

$$C = v_0{}^2 - 2gR.$$

Thus a particle projected in a radial direction outward from the earth's surface with an initial velocity v_0 will travel with a velocity v given by the equation

(2) $$v^2 = \frac{2gR^2}{r} + v_0{}^2 - 2gR.$$

It is of considerable interest to determine whether the particle will escape from the earth. Now at the surface of the earth, at $r = R$, the velocity is positive, $v = v_0$. An examination of the right member of equation (2) shows that the velocity of the particle will remain positive if, and only if,

(3) $$v_0{}^2 - 2gR \geqq 0.$$

For, if the inequality (3) is satisfied, the velocity given by equation (2) will remain positive, since it cannot vanish, is continuous, and is positive at $r = R$. On the other hand, if the inequality (3) is not satisfied, then $v_0{}^2 - 2gR < 0$ and there will be a critical value of r for which the right member of equation (2) is zero. That is, the particle would stop, the velocity would change from positive to negative, and the particle would return to the earth.

A particle projected from the earth with a velocity v_0 such that $v_0 \geqq \sqrt{2gR}$ will escape from the earth. Hence, the minimum such velocity of projection,

(4) $$v_e = \sqrt{2gR},$$

is called the *velocity of escape*.

The radius of the earth is approximately $R = 3960$ miles. The acceleration of gravity at the surface of the earth is approximately $g = 32.16$ ft. per sec. per sec., or $g = 6.09(10)^{-3}$ mi. per sec. per sec. For the earth the velocity of escape is easily found to be $v_e = 6.95$ mi. per sec.

Of course the gravitational pull of other celestial bodies, the moon, the sun, Mars, Venus, etc., has been neglected in the idealized problem treated here. It is not difficult to see that such approximations are justified, since we are interested in only the critical initial velocity v_e. Whether the particle actually recedes from the earth forever or becomes, for instance, a satellite of some heavenly body, is of no consequence in the present problem.

If in this study we happen to be thinking of the particle as an idealization of a ballistic type rocket, then other elements must be considered. Air resistance in the first few miles may not be negligible. Methods for disposing of such difficulties are not suitable topics for discussion here.

It must be realized that the formula $v_e = \sqrt{2gR}$ applies equally well for the velocity of escape from the other members of the solar system, so long as R and g are given their appropriate values.

255. *Newton's Law of Cooling*

Experiment has shown that under certain conditions a good approximation to the temperature of an object can be obtained by using Newton's law of cooling: The temperature of a body changes at a rate which is proportional to the difference in temperature between the outside medium and the body itself. We assume here that the constant of proportionality is the same whether the temperature is increasing or decreasing.

Suppose, for instance, that a thermometer, which has been at the reading 70° F inside a house, is placed outside where the air temperature is 10° F. Three minutes later it is found that the thermometer reading is 25° F. We wish to predict the thermometer reading at various later times.

Let u (°F) represent the temperature of the thermometer at time t(min.), the time being measured from the instant the thermometer is placed outside. We are given that when $t = 0$, $u = 70$, and when $t = 3$, $u = 25$.

According to Newton's law the time-rate of change of temperature, du/dt, is proportional to the temperature difference $(u - 10)$. Since the thermometer temperature is decreasing, it is convenient to choose $(-k)$ as the constant of proportionality. Thus the u is to be determined from the differential equation

$$(1) \qquad \frac{du}{dt} = -k(u - 10),$$

together with the conditions

$$(2) \qquad \text{When } t = 0, \quad u = 70$$

and

$$(3) \qquad \text{When } t = 3, \quad u = 25.$$

We need to know the thermometer reading at two different times because there are two constants to be determined, the k in equation (1) and the "arbitrary" constant which occurs in the solution of the differential equation (1).

From equation (1) it follows at once that

$$u = 10 + Ce^{-kt}.$$

Then condition (2) yields $70 = 10 + C$ from which $C = 60$, so that we have

$$(4) \qquad u = 10 + 60e^{-kt}.$$

The value of k will be determined now by using the condition (3). Putting $t = 3$ and $u = 25$ into equation (4), we get

$$25 = 10 + 60e^{-3k},$$

from which $e^{-3k} = \frac{1}{4}$, so that $k = \frac{1}{3} \ln 4$.

Thus the temperature u is given by the equation

(5) $$u = 10 + 60e^{-\frac{t}{3} \ln 4}.$$

Since $\ln 4 = 1.39$, equation (5) may be replaced by

(6) $$u = 10 + 60e^{-0.46t},$$

which is convenient when a table of values of e^{-x} is available.

Suppose the thermometer can be read only to the nearest degree and that we wish to know when the reading will first reach $10°$ F. Then we need to find the smallest t such that

$$60e^{-0.46t} < 0.5.$$

The result, to the nearest minute, is $t = 10$.

256. *Simple Chemical Conversion*

It is known from the results of chemical experimentation that, in certain reactions in which a substance A is being converted into another substance, the time-rate of change of the amount x of unconverted substance is proportional to x.

Let the amount of unconverted substance be known at some specified time; i.e., let $x = x_0$ at $t = 0$. Then the amount x at any time $t > 0$ is determined by the differential equation

(1) $$\frac{dx}{dt} = -kx$$

together with the condition that $x = x_0$ when $t = 0$. Since the amount x is decreasing as time increases, the constant of proportionality in equation (1) is taken to be $(-k)$.

From equation (1) it follows that

$$x = Ce^{-kt}.$$

But $x = x_0$ when $t = 0$. Hence $C = x_0$. Thus we have the result

(2) $$x = x_0 e^{-kt}.$$

Let us now add another condition which will enable us to determine k. Suppose it is known that at the end of half a minute, at $t = 30$ (sec.), two-thirds of the original amount x_0 has already been converted. Let us determine how much unconverted substance remains at $t = 60$ (sec.).

When two-thirds of the substance has been converted, one-third remains unconverted. Hence $x = x_0/3$ when $t = 30$. Equation (2) now yields the relation

$$\frac{x_0}{3} = x_0 e^{-30k}$$

from which k is easily found to be $(1/30) \ln 3$. Then with t measured in seconds, the amount of unconverted substance is given by the equation

(3) $$x = x_0 e^{-\frac{t}{30} \ln 3}.$$

At $t = 60$,

$$x = x_0 e^{-2 \ln 3} = x_0(3)^{-2} = \frac{x_0}{9}.$$

Hence one-ninth of the original amount of substance A remains unconverted at the end of 1 min.

EXERCISES

1. The radius of the moon is roughly 1080 mi. The acceleration of gravity at the surface of the moon is about $0.165g$, where g is the acceleration of gravity at the surface of the earth. Determine the velocity of escape for the moon.

Ans. 1.5 mi. per sec.

2. Determine to two significant figures the velocity of escape for each of the celestial bodies listed below. The data given are rough and g may be taken to be $6.1(10)^{-3}$ mi. per sec^2.

	Accel. of gravity at surface	*Radius in miles*	*Ans. in mi./sec.*
Venus	$0.85g$	3,800	6.3
Mars	$0.38g$	2,100	3.1
Jupiter	$2.6g$	43,000	37
Sun	$28g$	432,000	380
Ganymede	$0.12g$	1,780	1.6

3. A thermometer reading 18° F is brought into a room the temperature of which is 70° F. One minute later the thermometer reading is 31°F. Determine the temperature reading as a function of time, and in particular find the temperature reading 5 min. after the thermometer is first brought into the room.

Ans. $u = 70 - 52e^{-0.29t}$; when $t = 5$, $u = 58$.

4. A thermometer reading 75° F is taken out where the temperature is 20° F. The reading is 30° F 4 min. later. Find (a) the thermometer reading 7 min. after the thermometer was brought outside, and (b) the time taken for the reading to drop from 75° F to within a half-degree of the air temperature.

Ans. (a) 23° F; (b) 11.5 min.

5. At 1:00 P.M. a thermometer reading 70° F is taken outside where the air temperature is −10° F, ten below zero. At 1:02 P.M. the reading is 26° F. At 1:05 P.M. the thermometer is taken back indoors where the air is at 70° F. What is the thermometer reading at 1:09 P.M.?

Ans. 56° F.

6. At 9 A.M. a thermometer reading 70° F is taken outdoors where the temperature is 15° F. At 9.05 A.M. the thermometer reading is 45° F. At 9:10 A.M. the thermometer is taken back indoors where the temperature is fixed at 70° F. Find (a) the reading at 9:20 A.M. and (b) when the reading, to the nearest degree, will show the correct (70° F) indoor temperature.　　　*Ans.* (a) 58° F; (b) 9:46 A.M.

7. At 2:00 P.M. a thermometer reading 80° F is taken outside where the air temperature is 20° F. At 2:03 P.M. the temperature reading yielded by the thermometer is 42° F. Later the thermometer is brought inside where the air is at 80° F. At 2:10 P.M. the reading is 71° F. When was the thermometer brought indoors?

Ans. At 2:05 P.M.

8. Suppose that a chemical reaction proceeds according to the law given in § 256 above. If half the substance A has been converted at the end of 10 sec., find when nine-tenths of the substance will have been converted.　　　*Ans.* 33 sec.

9. The conversion of a substance B follows the law used in § 256 above. If only a fourth of the substance has been converted at the end of 10 sec., find when nine-tenths of the substance will have been converted.　　　*Ans.* 80 sec.

10. For a substance C the time rate of conversion is proportional to the square of the amount x of unconverted substance. Let k be the numerical value of the constant of proportionality and let the amount of unconverted substance be x_0 at time $t = 0$. Determine x for all $t \geqq 0$.

$$\textit{Ans. } x = \frac{x_0}{1 + x_0 kt}.$$

11. Two substances, A and B, are being converted into a single compound C. In the laboratory it has been shown that, for these substances, the following law of conversion holds: The time rate of change of the amount x of compound C is proportional to the product of the amounts of unconverted substances A and B. Assume the units of measure so chosen that one unit of the compound C is formed from the combination of one unit of A together with one unit of B. If at time $t = 0$ there are a units of substance A, b units of substance B, and none of the compound C present, show that the law of conversion may be expressed by the equation

$$\frac{dx}{dt} = k(a - x)(b - x).$$

Solve this equation with the given initial condition.

$$\textit{Ans. } \text{If } b \neq a, \ x = \frac{ab[e^{(b-a)kt} - 1]}{be^{(b-a)kt} - a}; \text{ if } b = a, \ x = \frac{a^2 kt}{akt + 1}.$$

12. In the solution of Ex. 11 above assume that $k > 0$ and investigate the behavior of x as $t \to \infty$.　　　*Ans.* If $b \geqq a$, $x \to a$; if $b \leqq a$, $x \to b$.

13. Radium decomposes at a rate proportional to the quantity of radium present. Suppose that it is found that in 25 years approximately 1.1 per cent of a certain quantity of radium has decomposed. Determine approximately how long it will take for one-half the original amount of radium to decompose.　　　*Ans.* 1600 years.

14. A certain radioactive substance has a half-life of 38 hr. Find how long it takes for 90 per cent of the radioactivity to be dissipated.　　　*Ans.* 126 hr.

15. A bacterial population B is known to have a rate of growth proportional to

B itself. If between noon and 2 p.m. the population triples, at what time, no controls being exerted, should B become 100 times what it was at noon?

Ans. About 8.22 p.m.

16. In the motion of an object through a certain medium (air at certain pressures is an example) the medium furnishes a resisting force proportional to the square of the velocity of the moving object. Suppose a body falls, owing to the action of gravity, through such a medium. Let t represent time, v represent velocity, positive downward. Let g be the usual constant acceleration of gravity, and let w be the weight of the body. Use Newton's law, force equals mass times acceleration, to conclude that the differential equation of the motion is

$$\frac{w}{g}\frac{dv}{dt} = w - kv^2,$$

where kv^2 is the magnitude of the resisting force furnished by the medium.

17. Solve the differential equation of Ex. 16 with the initial condition that $v = v_0$ when $t = 0$. Introduce the constant $a^2 = w/k$ to simplify the formulas.

$$Ans.\ \frac{a+v}{a-v} = \frac{(a+v_0)e^{2gt/a}}{a-v_0}.$$

18. Obtain the dimensions, in some consistent set of units, of the variables and parameters of Exs. 16–17 above.

Ans. t in sec. g in ft./sec.^{2}
v in ft./sec. k in (lb.)(sec.^{2})/(ft.^{2})
w in lb. a in ft./sec.

19. There are mediums which resist motion through them with a force proportional to the first power of the velocity. For such a medium, state and solve problems analogous to Exs. 16–18 above, except that for convenience a constant $b = w/k$ may be introduced to replace the a^2 of Ex. 17. Show that b has the dimensions of a velocity.   *Ans.* $v = b + (v_0 - b)e^{-\frac{gt}{b}}$.

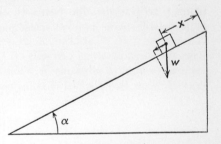

Figure 238

20. Figure 238 shows a weight, w pounds, sliding down an inclined plane which makes an angle α with the horizontal. Assume that no force other than gravity is acting on the weight; i.e., there is no friction, no air resistance, etc. At time $t = 0$, let $x = x_0$ and let the initial velocity be v_0. Determine x for $t > 0$.   *Ans.* $x = \frac{1}{2}gt^2 \sin \alpha + v_0t + x_0$.

21. A long, very smooth board is inclined at an angle of 10° with the horizontal. A weight starts from rest 10 ft. from the bottom of the board and slides downward under the action of gravity alone. Find how long it will take the weight to reach the bottom of the board and determine the terminal speed.

Ans. 1.9 sec. and 10.5 ft./sec.

22. Add to the conditions of Ex. 20 above a retarding force of magnitude kv, where v is the velocity. Determine v and x under the assumption that the weight starts from rest with $x = x_0$. Use the notation $a = kg/w$.

Ans. $v = a^{-1}g \sin \alpha(1 - e^{-at})$; $x = x_0 + a^{-2}g \sin \alpha(-1 + e^{-at} + at)$.

257. *The Catenary*

Let a cable of uniformly distributed weight w (lb. per ft.) be suspended between two supports at points A and B as indicated in Fig. 239. The cable will sag and there will be a lowest point V as indicated in the figure. We wish to determine the curve formed by the suspended cable. That curve is called the *catenary*.

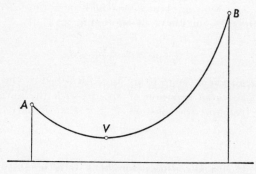

Figure 239

Choose coordinate axes as shown in Fig. 240, the y-axis vertical through the point V, and the x-axis horizontal and passing at a distance y_0 (to be chosen later) below V. Let s represent length (ft.) of the cable measured from V to the variable point P with coordinates (x, y). Then the portion of the cable from V to P is subject to the three forces shown in Fig. 240.

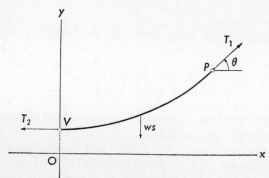

Figure 240

Those forces are: (*a*) the gravitational force ws (lb.) acting downward through the center of gravity of the portion of the cable from V to P, (*b*) the tension T_1 (lb.) acting tangentially at P, and (*c*) the tension T_2 (lb.) acting horizontally (again tangentially) at V. The tension T_1 is a variable; the tension T_2 is constant.

Since equilibrium is assumed, the algebraic sum of the vertical compo-

nents of these forces is zero and the algebraic sum of the horizontal components of these forces is also zero. Therefore, if θ is the angle of inclination,
from the horizontal, of the tangent to the curve at the point (x, y), we have

(1)
$$T_1 \sin \theta - ws = 0$$

and

(2)
$$T_1 \cos \theta - T_2 = 0.$$

But $\tan \theta$ is the slope of the curve of the cable, so that

(3)
$$\tan \theta = \frac{dy}{dx}.$$

We may eliminate the variable tension T_1 from equations (1) and (2)
and obtain

(4)
$$\tan \theta = \frac{ws}{T_2}.$$

The constant T_2/w has the dimension of a length. Put $T_2/w = a$ (ft.).
Then equation (4) becomes

(5)
$$\tan \theta = \frac{s}{a}.$$

From equations (3) and (5) we see that

(6)
$$\frac{s}{a} = \frac{dy}{dx}.$$

Now we know from calculus that, since s is the length of arc of the curve,
then

(7)
$$\frac{ds}{dx} = \sqrt{1 + \left(\frac{dy}{dx}\right)^2}.$$

We need to find a relation between x and y which satisfies (6) and (7)
together with the boundary conditions

(8)
$$\text{When } x = 0, \quad y = y_0 \quad \text{and} \quad \frac{dy}{dx} = 0.$$

Equations (6) and (7) yield

$$\frac{ds}{dx} = \sqrt{1 + \frac{s^2}{a^2}}$$

from which, by Ex. 9, page 186, we obtain

(9)
$$\sinh^{-1} \frac{s}{a} = \frac{x}{a} + C_1.$$

When $x = 0$, $y' = 0$, so that $s = 0$. Therefore $C_1 = 0$ and equation (9) becomes

(10) $$\frac{s}{a} = \sinh \frac{x}{a}.$$

From (6) and (10) it follows with one more integration that

$$y = a \cosh \frac{x}{a} + C_2.$$

But at $x = 0$, $y = y_0$, so $C_2 = y_0 - a$. We may conclude that

(11) $$y = a \cosh \frac{x}{a} + y_0 - a.$$

Then, of course, the sensible choice $y_0 = a$ is made so that the equation of the desired curve (the catenary) is

$$y = a \cosh \frac{x}{a}.$$

258. *Equation of the Tractrix*

By Ex. 21, page 186, the slope of the tractrix at any point is

$$\frac{dy}{dx} = - \frac{y}{\sqrt{a^2 - y^2}}.$$

This gives

$$dx = - \frac{\sqrt{a^2 - y^2}\, dy}{y},$$

so that

$$x = - \sqrt{a^2 - y^2} + a \ln \frac{a + \sqrt{a^2 - y^2}}{y} + C.$$

Since the point $(0, a)$ is on the curve, $C = 0$. Thus

$$x = a \ln \frac{a + \sqrt{a^2 - y^2}}{y} - \sqrt{a^2 - y^2}$$

$$= a \operatorname{sech}^{-1} \frac{y}{a} - \sqrt{a^2 - y^2},$$

by (5), § 98.

LINEAR EQUATIONS

WITH CONSTANT

COEFFICIENTS

259. *The General Linear Equation*

The general linear differential equation of order n may be written

$$(1) \qquad b_0(x) \frac{d^n y}{dx^n} + b_1(x) \frac{d^{n-1}y}{dx^{n-1}} + \cdots + b_{n-1}(x) \frac{dy}{dx} + b_n(x)y = R(x).$$

The functions $R(x)$ and $b_i(x)$; $i = 0, 1, \cdots, n$, are to be independent of the variable y. If $R(x)$ is identically zero, equation (1) is said to be *homogeneous*; if $R(x)$ is not identically zero, equation (1) is called *nonhomogeneous*. Here the word "homogeneous" is being used with reference to the quantities $y, y', y'', \cdots, y^{(n)}$; it has nothing to do with the way in which x enters the equation.

In order to simplify the wording of statements relating to solutions of linear differential equations, we shall adopt a common convention. When a relation $y = f(x)$ is a solution of a linear differential equation, we shall also call $f(x)$ itself a solution of the differential equation.

First we prove that if y_1 and y_2 are solutions of the homogeneous equation

$$(2) \qquad b_0(x)y^{(n)} + b_1(x)y^{(n-1)} + \cdots + b_{n-1}(x)y' + b_n(x)y = 0,$$

and if c_1 and c_2 are constants, then

$$y = c_1 y_1 + c_2 y_2$$

is a solution of equation (2).

The statement that y_1 and y_2 are solutions of (2) means that

$$(3) \qquad b_0 y_1^{(n)} + b_1 y_1^{(n-1)} + \cdots + b_{n-1}y_1' + b_n y_1 = 0$$

and

$$(4) \qquad b_0 y_2^{(n)} + b_1 y_2^{(n-1)} + \cdots + b_{n-1}y_2' + b_n y_2 = 0.$$

Now let us multiply each member of (3) by c_1, each member of (4) by c_2, and add the results. We get

$$(5) \quad b_0[c_1y_1{}^{(n)} + c_2y_2{}^{(n)}] + b_1[c_1y_1{}^{(n-1)} + c_2y_2{}^{(n-1)}] + \cdots$$
$$+ b_{n-1}[c_1y_1' + c_2y_2'] + b_n[c_1y_1 + c_2y_2] = 0.$$

Since $c_1y_1' + c_2y_2' = (c_1y_1 + c_2y_2)'$, etc., equation (5) is neither more nor less than the statement that $c_1y_1 + c_2y_2$ is a solution of equation (2). The proof is completed. The special case $c_2 = 0$ is worth noting; i.e., for a homogeneous linear equation any constant times a solution is also a solution.

In a similar manner, or by iteration of the above result, it can be seen that if y_i; $i = 1, 2, \cdots, k$, are solutions of equation (2) and if c_i; $i = 1, 2, \cdots, k$ are constants, then

$$y = c_1y_1 + c_2y_2 + \cdots + c_ky_k$$

is a solution of equation (2).

260. *Linear Independence*

Given the functions $f_1(x), \cdots, f_n(x)$, then if constants $c_1, c_2, \cdots, c_n$, not all zero, exist such that

$$(1) \qquad\qquad c_1f_1(x) + c_2f_2(x) + \cdots + c_nf_n(x) = 0$$

identically in some interval $a \leq x \leq b$, then the functions $f_1(x)$, $f_2(x)$, $\cdots, f_n(x)$ are said to be *linearly dependent*. If no such relation exists, the functions are said to be *linearly independent*. That is, the functions f_1, f_2, $\cdots, f_n$ are linearly independent when equation (1) implies that

$$c_1 = c_2 = \cdots = c_n = 0.$$

If the functions of a set are linearly dependent, then at least one of them is a linear combination of the others; if they are linearly independent, then none of them is a linear combination of the others.

The functions $\cos \omega t$, $\sin \omega t$, $\sin (\omega t + \alpha)$, in which t is the variable and ω and α are constants, are linearly dependent because there exist constants c_1, c_2, c_3 such that

$$c_1 \cos \omega t + c_2 \sin \omega t + c_3 \sin (\omega t + \alpha) = 0$$

for all t. Indeed, one set of such constants is $c_1 = \sin \alpha$, $c_2 = \cos \alpha$, $c_3 = -1$.

One of the best-known sets of n linearly independent functions of x is the set $1, x, x^2, \cdots, x^{n-1}$. The linear independence of the powers of x follows at once from the fact that if $c_1, c_2, \cdots, c_n$ are not all zero, the equation

$$c_1 + c_2x + \cdots + c_nx^{n-1} = 0$$

can have at most $(n - 1)$ distinct roots and so cannot vanish identically in any interval.

261. *General Solution of a Homogeneous Equation*

Let y_1, y_2, $\cdots$, y_n be linearly independent solutions of the homogeneous equation

$$(1) \qquad b_0(x)y^{(n)} + b_1(x)y^{(n-1)} + \cdots + b_{n-1}(x)y' + b_n(x)y = 0.$$

Then the general solution of equation (1) is

$$(2) \qquad y = c_1 y_1 + c_2 y_2 + \cdots + c_n y_n$$

where c_1, c_2, $\cdots$, c_n are arbitrary constants.

262. *General Solution of a Nonhomogeneous Equation*

Let y_p be any particular solution (not necessarily involving any arbitrary constants) of the equation

$$(1) \qquad b_0 y^{(n)} + b_1 y^{(n-1)} + \cdots + b_{n-1}y' + b_n y = R(x)$$

and let y_c be a solution of the corresponding homogeneous equation

$$(2) \qquad b_0 y^{(n)} + b_1 y^{(n-1)} + \cdots + b_{n-1}y' + b_n y = 0.$$

Then

$$(3) \qquad y = y_c + y_p$$

is a solution of equation (1). For, using the y of equation (3) we see that

$$
\begin{aligned}
b_0 y^{(n)} + \cdots + b_n y &= (b_0 y_c^{(n)} + \cdots + b_n y_c) \\
&\quad + (b_0 y_p^{(n)} + \cdots + b_n y_p) \\
&= 0 + R(x) = R(x).
\end{aligned}
$$

If y_1, y_2, $\cdots$, y_n are linearly independent solutions of equation (2), then

$$(4) \qquad y_c = c_1 y_1 + c_2 y_2 + \cdots + c_n y_n,$$

in which the c's are arbitrary constants, is the general solution of equation (2). The right member of equation (4) is called the *complementary function* for equation (1).

The general solution of the nonhomogeneous equation (1) is the sum of the complementary function and any particular solution.

263. *Differential Operators*

Let D denote differentiation with respect to x, D^2 differentiation twice with respect to x, and so on; i.e., for integral k,

$$D^k y = \frac{d^k y}{dx^k}.$$

The expression

(1) $$A = a_0 D^n + a_1 D^{n-1} + \cdots + a_{n-1}D + a_n$$

is called a differential operator of order n. It may be defined as that operator which, when applied to any function* y, yields the result

(2) $$Ay = a_0 \frac{d^n y}{dx^n} + a_1 \frac{d^{n-1}y}{dx^{n-1}} + \cdots + a_{n-1}\frac{dy}{dx} + a_n y.$$

The coefficients $a_0, a_1, \cdots, a_n$ in the operator A may be functions of x, but in this book the only operators used will be those with constant coefficients.

Since for purposes of addition and multiplication the operators with constant coefficients behave just as algebraic polynomials behave, it is legitimate to use the tools of elementary algebra. In particular, synthetic division may be used to factor operators with constant coefficients.

EXERCISES

Perform the indicated multiplications in Exs. 1–4.

1. $(2D + 1)(D - 4)$.   *Ans.* $2D^2 - 7D - 4$.
2. $(3D - 2)(3D + 2)$.   *Ans.* $9D^2 - 4$.
3. $(D - 2)(D^2 + 2D + 5)$.   *Ans.* $D^3 + D - 10$.
4. $(D + 1)(D - 2)^2$.   *Ans.* $D^3 - 3D^2 + 4$.

In Exs. 5–16 factor each of the operators.

5. $2D^2 - 5D - 3$.   *Ans.* $(D - 3)(2D + 1)$.
6. $3D^2 + 7D + 2$.
7. $D^3 - 4D^2 + D + 6$.   *Ans.* $(D + 1)(D - 2)(D - 3)$.
8. $2D^3 - 7D^2 + 2D + 3$.
9. $D^4 - 9D^2$.   *Ans.* $D^2(D - 3)(D + 3)$.
10. $D^3 - 3D + 2$.
11. $D^3 - 19D - 30$.   *Ans.* $(D + 2)(D + 3)(D - 5)$.
12. $4D^3 - 8D^2 - 11D - 3$.
13. $2D^4 - 11D^3 + 18D^2 - 4D - 8$.   *Ans.* $(D - 2)^3(2D + 1)$.
14. $2D^4 + 9D^3 + 6D^2 - 20D - 24$.
15. $D^4 + D^3 + 7D^2 + 9D - 18$.   *Ans.* $(D - 1)(D + 2)(D^2 + 9)$.
16. $D^3 + D - 10$.   *Ans.* $(D - 2)(D^2 + 2D + 5)$.

264. Some Properties of Differential Operators

Since, for constant m and integral k,

(1) $$D^k e^{mx} = m^k e^{mx},$$

it is easy to find the effect an operator has upon e^{mx}. Let $f(D)$ be a polynomial in D with constant coefficients,

(2) $$f(D) = a_0 D^n + a_1 D^{n-1} + \cdots + a_{n-1}D + a_n.$$

* The function y is assumed to possess as many derivatives as may be encountered in whatever operations take place.

Then
$$f(D)e^{mx} = a_0 m^n e^{mx} + a_1 m^{n-1} e^{mx} + \cdots + a_{n-1} m e^{mx} + a_n e^{mx},$$

so that

(3)
$$f(D)e^{mx} = e^{mx}f(m).$$

If m is a root of the equation $f(m) = 0$, then in view of equation (3), $f(D)e^{mx} = 0$.

Example. Let $f(D) = 2D^2 + 5D - 12$. Then the equation $f(m) = 0$ is

$$2m^2 + 5m - 12 = 0,$$

or

$$(m + 4)(2m - 3) = 0,$$

of which the roots are $m_1 = -4$ and $m_2 = \frac{3}{2}$.

With the aid of equation (3) above it can be seen that

$$(2D^2 + 5D - 12)e^{-4x} = 0$$

and that

$$(2D^2 + 5D - 12)e^{\frac{3}{2}x} = 0.$$

In other words, $y_1 = e^{-4x}$ and $y_2 = e^{\frac{3}{2}x}$ are solutions of the differential equation

$$(2D^2 + 5D - 12)y = 0.$$

Next consider the effect of the operator $(D - m)$ on the product of e^{mx} and a power of x. Since

$$(D - m)(x^k e^{mx}) = kx^{k-1}e^{mx} + mx^k e^{mx} - mx^k e^{mx},$$

we get

$$(D - m)(x^k e^{mx}) = kx^{k-1}e^{mx}.$$

Then

$$(D - m)^2(x^k e^{mx}) = k(D - m)(x^{k-1}e^{mx})$$
$$= k(k - 1)x^{k-2}e^{mx}.$$

Repeating the operation, we are led to

$$(D - m)^k(x^k e^{mx}) = k(k - 1) \cdots 2 \cdot 1 x^0 e^{mx}$$
$$= k!e^{mx}.$$

But $(D - m)e^{mx} = 0$. Therefore, for all $n > k$,

(4)
$$(D - m)^n(x^k e^{mx}) = 0.$$

It will be convenient to think of the exponent of x in (4) as varying rather than the exponent of the operator $(D - m)$. Hence we rewrite (4) as

(5) $(D - m)^n(x^k e^{mx}) = 0$ **for** $k = 0, 1, 2, \cdots, (n - 1)$.

Equation (5) forms the basis for all the solutions obtained in this chapter.

265. *The Auxiliary Equation; Distinct Roots*

Any linear homogeneous differential equation with constant coefficients,

$$(1) \qquad a_0 \frac{d^n y}{dx^n} + a_1 \frac{d^{n-1}y}{dx^{n-1}} + \cdots + a_{n-1}\frac{dy}{dx} + a_n y = 0,$$

may be written in the form

$$(2) \qquad\qquad\qquad f(D)y = 0,$$

where $f(D)$ is a linear differential operator. As we saw in the preceding section, if m is any root of the algebraic equation $f(m) = 0$, then

$$f(D)e^{mx} = 0,$$

which means simply that $y = e^{mx}$ is a solution of equation (2). The equation

$$(3) \qquad\qquad\qquad f(m) = 0$$

is called the *auxiliary equation* associated with (1) or (2).

The auxiliary equation for (1) is of degree n. Let its roots be m_1, m_2, $\cdots$, m_n. If those roots are all real and distinct, then the n solutions $y = e^{m_1 x}$, $y = e^{m_2 x}$, $\cdots$, $y = e^{m_n x}$ are linearly independent and the general solution of (1) can be written down at once. It is

$$y = c_1 e^{m_1 x} + c_2 e^{m_2 x} + \cdots + c_n e^{m_n x},$$

where c_1, c_2, $\cdots$, c_n are arbitrary constants.

Repeated roots of the auxiliary equation will be treated in the next section.

Imaginary roots will be avoided until § 268 where the corresponding solutions will be put into a desirable form.

Example (a). Solve the equation

$$\frac{d^3 y}{dx^3} - 4 \frac{d^2 y}{dx^2} + \frac{dy}{dx} + 6y = 0.$$

First write the auxiliary equation

$$m^3 - 4m^2 + m + 6 = 0,$$

whose roots $m = -1, 2, 3$ may be obtained by synthetic division. Then the general solution is seen to be

$$y = c_1 e^{-x} + c_2 e^{2x} + c_3 e^{3x}.$$

Example (b). Solve the equation

$$(3D^3 + 5D^2 - 2D)y = 0.$$

The auxiliary equation is

$$3m^3 + 5m^2 - 2m = 0$$

and its roots are $m = 0$, -2, $\frac{1}{3}$. Using the fact that $e^{0x} = 1$, the desired solution may be written

$$y = c_1 + c_2 e^{-2x} + c_3 e^{\frac{1}{3}x}.$$

Example (c). Solve the equation

$$\frac{d^2x}{dt^2} - 4x = 0$$

together with the conditions: when $t = 0$, $x = 0$ and $\dfrac{dx}{dt} = 3$.

The auxiliary equation is

$$m^2 - 4 = 0,$$

with roots $m = 2$, -2. Hence the general solution of the differential equation is

$$x = c_1 e^{2t} + c_2 e^{-2t}.$$

It remains to enforce the conditions at $t = 0$. Now

$$\frac{dx}{dt} = 2c_1 e^{2t} - 2c_2 e^{-2t}.$$

Thus the condition that $x = 0$ when $t = 0$ requires that

$$0 = c_1 + c_2$$

while the condition that $\dfrac{dx}{dt} = 3$ when $t = 0$ requires that

$$3 = 2c_1 - 2c_2.$$

From the simultaneous equations for c_1 and c_2 we conclude that $c_1 = \frac{3}{4}$ and $c_2 = -\frac{3}{4}$. Therefore

$$x = \tfrac{3}{4}(e^{2t} - e^{-2t}),$$

which can also be put in the form

$$x = \tfrac{3}{2} \sinh (2t).$$

EXERCISES

In Exs. 1–22 find the general solution. When the operator D is used it is implied that the independent variable is x.

1. $(D^2 - D - 2)y = 0$.   Ans. $y = c_1 e^{-x} + c_2 e^{2x}$.
2. $(D^2 + 3D)y = 0$.
3. $(D^2 - D - 6)y = 0$.   Ans. $y = c_1 e^{-2x} + c_2 e^{3x}$.
4. $(D^2 + 5D + 6)y = 0$.
5. $(D^3 + 2D^2 - 15D)y = 0$.   Ans. $y = c_1 + c_2 e^{3x} + c_3 e^{-5x}$.
6. $(D^3 + 2D^2 - 8D)y = 0$.

7. $(D^3 - D^2 - 4D + 4)y = 0.$ *Ans.* $y = c_1e^{-2x} + c_2e^x + c_3e^{2x}.$
8. $(D^3 - 3D^2 - D + 3)y = 0.$
9. $(4D^3 - 13D + 6)y = 0.$ *Ans.* $y = c_1e^{\frac{1}{2}x} + c_2e^{\frac{3}{2}x} + c_3e^{-2x}.$
10. $(4D^3 - 49D - 60)y = 0.$

11. $\dfrac{d^3x}{dt^3} - 2\dfrac{d^2x}{dt^2} - 3\dfrac{dx}{dt} = 0.$ *Ans.* $x = c_1 + c_2e^{-t} + c_3e^{3t}.$

12. $\dfrac{d^3x}{dt^3} - 7\dfrac{dx}{dt} + 6x = 0.$

13. $(10D^3 + D^2 - 7D + 2)y = 0.$ *Ans.* $y = c_1e^{-x} + c_2e^{\frac{1}{2}x} + c_3e^{\frac{2}{5}x}.$
14. $(4D^3 - 13D - 6)y = 0.$
15. $(D^3 - 5D - 2)y = 0.$ *Ans.* $y = c_1e^{-2x} + c_2e^{(1+\sqrt{2})x} + c_3e^{(1-\sqrt{2})x}.$
16. $(D^3 - 3D^2 - 3D + 1)y = 0.$
17. $(4D^4 - 15D^2 + 5D + 6)y = 0.$ *Ans.* $y = c_1e^{-2x} + c_2e^{-\frac{1}{2}x} + c_3e^{\frac{3}{2}x} + c_4e^x.$
18. $(D^4 - 2D^3 - 13D^2 + 38D - 24)y = 0.$
19. $(6D^4 + 23D^3 + 28D^2 + 13D + 2)y = 0.$
20. $(4D^4 - 45D^2 - 70D - 24)y = 0.$
21. $(D^2 - 4aD + 3a^2)y = 0,$ a real $\neq 0.$
22. $[D^2 - (a + b)D + ab]y = 0,$ a and b real and unequal.

In Exs. 23–24 find the particular solution indicated.

23. $(D^2 - 2D - 3)y = 0;$ when $x = 0,$ $y = 0,$ and $y' = -4.$
$$\text{\textit{Ans.} } y = e^{-x} - e^{3x}.$$
24. $(D^2 - D - 6)y = 0;$ when $x = 0,$ $y = 0$ and when $x = 1,$ $y = e^3.$
$$\text{\textit{Ans.} } y = (e^{3x} - e^{-2x})/(1 - e^{-5}).$$

In Exs. 25–29, find for $x = 1$ the y value for the particular solution required.

25. $(D^2 - 2D - 3)y = 0;$ when $x = 0,$ $y = 4$ and $y' = 0.$
$$\text{\textit{Ans.} When } x = 1,\ y = e^3 + 3e^{-1} = 21.2.$$
26. $(D^3 - 4D)y = 0;$ when $x = 0,$ $y = 0,$ $y' = 0,$ and $y'' = 2.$
$$\text{\textit{Ans.} When } x = 1,\ y = \sinh^2 1.$$
27. $(D^2 - D - 6)y = 0;$ when $x = 0,$ $y = 3$ and $y' = -1.$
$$\text{\textit{Ans.} When } x = 1,\ y = 20.4.$$
28. $(D^2 + 3D - 10)y = 0;$ when $x = 0,$ $y = 0$ and when $x = 2,$ $y = 1.$
$$\text{\textit{Ans.} When } x = 1,\ y = 0.135.$$
29. $(D^3 - 2D^2 - 5D + 6)y = 0;$ when $x = 0,$ $y = 1,$ $y' = -7,$ and $y'' = -1.$
$$\text{\textit{Ans.} When } x = 1,\ y = -19.8.$$

266. The Auxiliary Equation; Repeated Roots

Suppose that in the equation

(1) $$f(D)y = 0$$

the operator $f(D)$ has repeated factors; that is, the auxiliary equation $f(m) = 0$ has repeated roots. Then the method of the previous section does not yield the general solution. Let the auxiliary equation have three equal roots $m_1 = b$, $m_2 = b$, $m_3 = b$. The corresponding part of the solution yielded by the method of § 265 is

$$y = c_1 e^{bx} + c_2 e^{bx} + c_3 e^{bx},$$

or

(2) $$y = (c_1 + c_2 + c_3)e^{bx}.$$

Now (2) can be replaced by

(3) $$y = c_4 e^{bx}$$

with $c_4 = c_1 + c_2 + c_3$. Thus, corresponding to the three roots under consideration, this method has yielded only the solution (3). The difficulty is present, of course, because the three solutions corresponding to the roots $m_1 = m_2 = m_3 = b$ are not linearly independent.

What is needed is a method for obtaining n linearly independent solutions corresponding to n equal roots of the auxiliary equation. Suppose the auxiliary equation $f(m) = 0$ has the n equal roots

$$m_1 = m_2 = \cdots = m_n = b.$$

Then the operator $f(D)$ must have a factor $(D - b)^n$. We wish to find n linearly independent y's for which

(4) $$(D - b)^n y = 0.$$

Turning to the result (5) near the end of § 264 and writing $m = b$, we find that

(5) $$(D - b)^n (x^k e^{bx}) = 0 \text{ for } k = 0, 1, 2, \cdots, (n - 1).$$

The functions $y_k = x^k e^{bx}$; $k = 0, 1, 2, \cdots, (n - 1)$ are linearly independent because, aside from the common factor e^{bx}, they contain only the respective powers $x^0, x^1, x^2, \cdots, x^{n-1}$.

The general solution of equation (4) is

(6) $$y = c_1 e^{bx} + c_2 x e^{bx} + \cdots + c_n x^{n-1} e^{bx}.$$

Furthermore, if $f(D)$ contains the factor $(D - b)^n$, then the equation

(1) $$f(D)y = 0$$

can be written

(7) $$g(D)(D - b)^n y = 0$$

where $g(D)$ contains all the factors of $f(D)$ except for $(D - b)^n$. Then any solution of

(4) $$(D - b)^n y = 0$$

is also a solution of (7) and therefore of (1).

Now we are in a position to write the solution of equation (1) whenever the auxiliary equation has only real roots. Each root of the auxiliary equation is either distinct from all the other roots or it is one of a set of equal roots. Corresponding to a root m_i distinct from all others there is the solution

$$(8) \qquad\qquad y_i = c_i e^{m_i x}$$

and corresponding to n equal roots $m_1, m_2, \cdots, m_n$ each equal to b, there is the solution

$$(9) \qquad\qquad y = c_1 e^{bx} + c_2 x e^{bx} + \cdots + c_n x^{n-1} e^{bx}.$$

The sum of such solutions (8) and (9) yields the proper number of solutions, a number equal to the order of the differential equation, because there is one solution corresponding to each root of the auxiliary equation. The solutions thus obtained can be proved to be linearly independent.

Example (a). Solve the equation

$$(10) \qquad\qquad (D^4 - 7D^3 + 18D^2 - 20D + 8)y = 0.$$

With the aid of synthetic division it is easily seen that the auxiliary equation

$$m^4 - 7m^3 + 18m^2 - 20m + 8 = 0$$

has the roots $m = 1, 2, 2, 2$. Then the general solution of equation (10) is

$$y = c_1 e^x + c_2 e^{2x} + c_3 x e^{2x} + c_4 x^2 e^{2x},$$

or

$$y = c_1 e^x + (c_2 + c_3 x + c_4 x^2) e^{2x}.$$

Example (b). Solve the equation

$$\frac{d^4 y}{dx^4} + 2 \frac{d^3 y}{dx^3} + \frac{d^2 y}{dx^2} = 0.$$

The auxiliary equation is

$$m^4 + 2m^3 + m^2 = 0$$

with roots $m = 0, 0, -1, -1$. Hence the desired solution is

$$y = c_1 + c_2 x + c_3 e^{-x} + c_4 x e^{-x}.$$

EXERCISES

In Exs. 1–20 find the general solution.

1. $(4D^2 - 4D + 1)y = 0$.   *Ans.* $y = (c_1 + c_2 x) e^{\frac{1}{2}x}$.
2. $(D^2 + 6D + 9)y = 0$.
3. $(D^3 - 4D^2 + 4D)y = 0$.   *Ans.* $y = c_1 + (c_2 + c_3 x) e^{2x}$.
4. $(9D^3 + 6D^2 + D)y = 0$.
5. $(2D^4 - 3D^3 - 2D^2)y = 0$.   *Ans.* $y = c_1 + c_2 x + c_3 e^{2x} + c_4 e^{-\frac{1}{2}x}$.

6. $(2D^4 - 5D^3 - 3D^2)y = 0.$

7. $(D^3 + 3D^2 - 4)y = 0.$ $Ans.\ y = c_1e^x + (c_2 + c_3x)e^{-2x}.$

8. $(4D^3 - 27D + 27)y = 0.$

9. $(D^3 + 3D^2 + 3D + 1)y = 0.$ $Ans.\ y = (c_1 + c_2x + c_3x^2)e^{-x}.$

10. $(D^3 + 6D^2 + 12D + 8)y = 0.$

11. $(D^5 - D^3)y = 0.$ $Ans.\ y = c_1 + c_2x + c_3x^2 + c_4e^x + c_5e^{-x};$

$\quad$ or $y = c_1 + c_2x + c_3x^2 + c_6 \cosh x + c_7 \sinh x.$

12. $(D^5 - 16D^3)y = 0.$

13. $(4D^4 + 4D^3 - 3D^2 - 2D + 1)y = 0.$

$\quad Ans.\ y = (c_1 + c_2x)e^{\frac{1}{2}x} + (c_3 + c_4x)e^{-x}.$

14. $(4D^4 - 4D^3 - 23D^2 + 12D + 36)y = 0.$

15. $(D^4 + 3D^3 - 6D^2 - 28D - 24)y = 0.$

$\quad Ans.\ y = c_1e^{3x} + (c_2 + c_3x + c_4x^2)e^{-2x}.$

16. $(27D^4 - 18D^2 + 8D - 1)y = 0.$

17. $(4D^5 - 23D^3 - 33D^2 - 17D - 3)y = 0.$

$\quad Ans.\ y = c_1e^{3x} + (c_2 + c_3x)e^{-x} + (c_4 + c_5x)e^{-\frac{1}{2}x}.$

18. $(4D^5 - 15D^3 - 5D^2 + 15D + 9)y = 0.$

19. $(D^4 - 5D^2 - 6D - 2)y = 0.$

$\quad Ans.\ y = (c_1 + c_2x)e^{-x} + c_3e^{(1+\sqrt{3})x} + c_4e^{(1-\sqrt{3})x}.$

20. $(D^5 - 5D^4 + 7D^3 + D^2 - 8D + 4)y = 0.$

In Exs. 21–26, find the particular solution indicated.

21. $(D^2 + 4D + 4)y = 0$; when $x = 0$, $y = 1$ and $y' = -1$.

22. The equation of Ex. 21 with the conditions that the graph of the solution pass through the points $(0, 2)$ and $(2, 0)$. $\qquad Ans.\ y = (2 - x)e^{-2x}.$

23. $(D^3 - 3D - 2)y = 0$; when $x = 0$, $y = 0$, $y' = 9$, $y'' = 0$.

$\qquad Ans.\ y = 2e^{2x} + (3x - 2)e^{-x}.$

24. $(D^4 + 3D^3 + 2D^2)y = 0$; when $x = 0$, $y = 0$, $y' = 4$, $y'' = -6$, $y''' = 14$.

$\qquad Ans.\ y = 2(x + e^{-x} - e^{-2x}).$

25. The equation of Ex. 24 with the conditions: when $x = 0$, $y = 0$, $y' = 3$, $y'' = -5$, $y''' = 9$. $\qquad Ans.\ y = 2 - e^{-x} - e^{-2x}.$

26. $(D^3 + D^2 - D - 1)y = 0$; when $x = 0$, $y = 1$, when $x = 2$, $y = 0$, and also as $x \to \infty$, $y \to 0$. $\qquad Ans.\ y = \frac{1}{2}(2 - x)e^{-x}.$

In Exs. 27–29 find for $x = 2$ the y value for the particular solution required.

27. $(4D^2 - 4D + 1)y = 0$; when $x = 0$, $y = -2$, $y' = 2$.

$\qquad Ans.\ When\ x = 2,\ y = 4e.$

28. $(D^3 + 2D^2)y = 0$; when $x = 0$, $y = -3$, $y' = 0$, $y'' = 12$.

$\qquad Ans.\ When\ x = 2,\ y = 3e^{-4} + 6.$

29. $(D^3 + 5D^2 + 3D - 9)y = 0$; when $x = 0$, $y = -1$, when $x = 1$, $y = 0$, and also as $x \to \infty$, $y \to 0$. $\qquad Ans.\ When\ x = 2,\ y = e^{-6}.$

267. *A Definition of e^z for Imaginary z*

It is evident that such a symbol as $e^{(2+3i)}$, where $i = \sqrt{-1}$, has no meaning from the standpoint of elementary algebra; that is, it would be meaningless to speak of "e used as a factor $(2 + 3i)$ times." Furthermore, no such simple extension of the meaning of an exponent as saves the day for the symbols $e^{\frac{1}{2}}$, e^{-2}, $e^{\frac{2}{3}}$, etc., is available for $e^{(2+3i)}$. Let us search for a reasonable definition for e^z, where z is imaginary.

Let $z = \alpha + i\beta$ with α and β real. Since it is desirable to have the ordinary laws of exponents remain valid, it is wise to require that

$$(1) \qquad\qquad e^{\alpha+i\beta} = e^{\alpha} \cdot e^{i\beta}.$$

To e^{α} with α real we attach its usual meaning.

Now consider $e^{i\beta}$, β real. In Chapter 31 it was shown that for all real x

$$(2) \qquad\qquad e^x = \sum_{n=0}^{\infty} \frac{x^n}{n!}.$$

If we now tentatively put $x = i\beta$ in (2) as a definition of $e^{i\beta}$, we get

$$(3) \qquad e^{i\beta} = 1 + \frac{i\beta}{1!} + \frac{i^2\beta^2}{2!} + \frac{i^3\beta^3}{3!} + \frac{i^4\beta^4}{4!} + \cdots + \frac{i^n\beta^n}{n!} + \cdots.$$

Separating the even powers of β from the odd powers of β in (3) yields

$$(4) \qquad e^{i\beta} = 1 + \frac{i^2\beta^2}{2!} + \frac{i^4\beta^4}{4!} + \cdots + \frac{i^{2k}\beta^{2k}}{(2k)!} + \cdots$$
$$+ \frac{i\beta}{1!} + \frac{i^3\beta^3}{3!} + \cdots + \frac{i^{2k+1}\beta^{2k+1}}{(2k+1)!} + \cdots,$$

or

$$(4) \qquad e^{i\beta} = \sum_{k=0}^{\infty} \frac{i^{2k}\beta^{2k}}{(2k)!} + \sum_{k=0}^{\infty} \frac{i^{2k+1}\beta^{2k+1}}{(2k+1)!}.$$

Now $i^{2k} = (-1)^k$, so that we may write

$$(5) \qquad e^{i\beta} = 1 - \frac{\beta^2}{2!} + \frac{\beta^4}{4!} + \cdots + \frac{(-1)^k\beta^{2k}}{(2k)!} + \cdots$$
$$+ i\left[\frac{\beta}{1!} - \frac{\beta^3}{3!} + \cdots + \frac{(-1)^k\beta^{2k+1}}{(2k+1)!} + \cdots \right],$$

or

$$(5) \qquad e^{i\beta} = \sum_{k=0}^{\infty} \frac{(-1)^k\beta^{2k}}{(2k)!} + i\sum_{k=0}^{\infty} \frac{(-1)^k\beta^{2k+1}}{(2k+1)!}.$$

But the series on the right in (5) are precisely those for $\cos\beta$ and $\sin\beta$ as developed in Chapter 31. Hence we are led to the tentative result

$$(6) \qquad\qquad e^{i\beta} = \cos\beta + i\sin\beta.$$

The student should realize that the manipulations above have no meaning in themselves at this stage (assuming that infinite series with complex terms are not a part of the content of elementary mathematics). What has been accomplished is this: The formal manipulations above have suggested the meaningful definition (6). Combining (6) with (1), we now put forward a reasonable *definition* of $e^{\alpha+i\beta}$, namely,

(7) $$e^{\alpha+i\beta} = e^{\alpha}(\cos \beta + i \sin \beta), \ \alpha \text{ and } \beta \text{ real}.$$

Replacing β by $-\beta$ in (7) yields a result which is of value to us in the next section,

$$e^{\alpha-i\beta} = e^{\alpha}(\cos \beta - i \sin \beta).$$

It is interesting and important that with the definition (7) the function e^z for complex z retains many of the properties possessed by the function e^x for real x. Such matters are often studied in detail in books on complex variables.* Here we need in particular to know that if

$$y = e^{(a+ib)x},$$

a, b, and x real, then

$$(D - a - ib)y = 0.$$

The result desired follows at once by differentiation, with respect to x, of the function

$$y = e^{ax}(\cos bx + i \sin bx).$$

268. *The Auxiliary Equation; Imaginary Roots*

Consider a differential equation $f(D)y = 0$ for which the auxiliary equation $f(m) = 0$ has real coefficients. From elementary algebra we know that if the auxiliary equation has any imaginary roots, those roots must occur in conjugate pairs. Thus if

$$m_1 = a + ib$$

is a root of the equation $f(m) = 0$, with a and b real and $b \neq 0$, then

$$m_2 = a - ib$$

is also a root of $f(m) = 0$. It must be kept in mind that this result is a consequence of the reality of the coefficients in the equation $f(m) = 0$. Imaginary roots do not necessarily appear in pairs in an algebraic equation whose coefficients involve imaginaries.

We can now construct in usable form solutions of

(1) $$f(D)y = 0$$

corresponding to imaginary roots of $f(m) = 0$. For, since $f(m)$ is assumed to have real coefficients, any imaginary roots appear in conjugate pairs $m_1 = a + ib$ and $m_2 = a - ib$. Then, according to the preceding section,

---

* For example, R. V. Churchill, *Complex Variables and Applications*, 2nd ed., New York, McGraw-Hill Book Co., 1960, pp. 46–49.

equation (1) is satisfied by

(2) $$y = c_1 e^{(a+ib)x} + c_2 e^{(a-ib)x}.$$

Taking x to be real along with a and b, we get from (2) the result

(3) $$y = c_1 e^{ax}(\cos bx + i \sin bx) + c_2 e^{ax}(\cos bx - i \sin bx).$$

Now (3) may be written

$$y = (c_1 + c_2)e^{ax} \cos bx + i(c_1 - c_2)e^{ax} \sin bx.$$

Finally, let $c_1 + c_2 = c_3$, and $i(c_1 - c_2) = c_4$ where c_3 and c_4 are new arbitrary constants. Then equation (1) is seen to have the solutions

(4) $$\boldsymbol{y = c_3 e^{ax} \cos bx + c_4 e^{ax} \sin bx,}$$

corresponding to the two roots $m_1 = a + ib$ and $m_2 = a - ib(b \neq 0)$ of the auxiliary equation.

Taking a, b, x, and y to be real, it follows readily from equation (4) that c_3 and c_4 are real. But $c_1 + c_2 = c_3$, and $i(c_1 - c_2) = c_4$, so that $c_1 = \frac{1}{2}(c_3 - ic_4)$ and $c_2 = \frac{1}{2}(c_3 + ic_4)$. Hence, if $c_4 \neq 0$, the c_1 and c_2 are conjugate complex numbers.

The reduction of the solution (2) above to the desirable form (4) has been done once and that is enough. Whenever a pair of conjugate imaginary roots of the auxiliary equation appears, we write down at once in the form given on the right in equation (4) the particular solution corresponding to those two roots.

Example (a). Solve the equation

$$(D^3 - 3D^2 + 9D + 13)y = 0.$$

For the auxiliary equation

$$m^3 - 3m^2 + 9m + 13 = 0$$

one root, $m_1 = -1$, is easily found. When the factor $(m + 1)$ is removed by synthetic division, it is seen that the other two roots are solutions of the quadratic

$$m^2 - 4m + 13 = 0.$$

Those roots are found to be $m_2 = 2 + 3i$ and $m_3 = 2 - 3i$. The auxiliary equation has the roots $m = -1, 2 \pm 3i$. Hence the general solution of the differential equation is

$$y = c_1 e^{-x} + c_2 e^{2x} \cos 3x + c_3 e^{2x} \sin 3x.$$

Repeated imaginary roots lead to solutions analogous to those brought in by repeated real roots. For instance, if the roots $m = a \pm ib$ occur three times, then the corresponding six linearly independent solutions of the differential equation are those appearing in the expression

$$(c_1 + c_2 x + c_3 x^2)e^{ax} \cos bx + (c_4 + c_5 x + c_6 x^2)e^{ax} \sin bx.$$

Example (b). Solve the equation

$$(D^4 + 8D^2 + 16)y = 0.$$

The auxiliary equation $m^4 + 8m^2 + 16 = 0$ may be written

$$(m^2 + 4)^2 = 0$$

so that its roots are seen to be $m = \pm 2i,\ \pm 2i$. The roots $m_1 = 2i$ and $m_2 = -2i$ each occur twice. Thinking of $2i$ as $0 + 2i$ and recalling that $e^{0x} = 1$, we write the solution of the differential equation as

$$y = (c_1 + c_2 x) \cos 2x + (c_3 + c_4 x) \sin 2x.$$

In such exercises as those below a fine check can be obtained by direct substitution of the result and its appropriate derivatives into the differential equation. The verification is particularly effective because the operations performed in the check are so different from those performed in obtaining the solution.

EXERCISES

Find the general solution except where the exercise stipulates otherwise.

1. Verify directly that the relation

(4) $y = c_3 e^{ax} \cos bx + c_4 e^{ax} \sin bx$

satisfies the equation

$$[(D - a)^2 + b^2]y = 0.$$

2. $(D^2 - 2D + 5)y = 0$. Verify your answer.
$\qquad\qquad\qquad\qquad$ *Ans.* $y = c_1 e^x \cos 2x + c_2 e^x \sin 2x.$

3. $(D^2 - 2D + 2)y = 0.$

4. $(D^2 + 9)y = 0$. Verify your answer. $\qquad$ *Ans.* $y = c_1 \cos 3x + c_2 \sin 3x.$

5. $(D^2 - 9)y = 0.$ $\qquad\qquad\qquad$ *Ans.* $y = c_1 \cosh 3x + c_2 \sinh 3x.$

6. $(D^2 + 6D + 13)y = 0$. Verify your answer.

7. $(D^2 - 4D + 7)y = 0.$ $\qquad$ *Ans.* $y = c_1 e^{2x} \cos \sqrt{3}\, x + c_2 e^{2x} \sin \sqrt{3}\, x.$

8. $(D^3 + 2D^2 + D + 2)y = 0$. Verify your answer.

9. $(D^2 - 1)y = 0$; when $x = 0$, $y = y_0$ and $y' = 0.$ $\qquad$ *Ans.* $y = y_0 \cosh x.$

10. $(D^2 + 1)y = 0$; when $x = 0$, $y = y_0$ and $y' = 0.$ $\qquad$ *Ans.* $y = y_0 \cos x.$

11. $(D^4 + 2D^3 + 10D^2)y = 0$. *Ans.* $y = c_1 + c_2 x + c_3 e^{-x} \cos 3x + c_4 e^{-x} \sin 3x.$

12. $(D^3 + 7D^2 + 19D + 13)y = 0$; when $x = 0$, $y = 0$, $y' = 2$, and $y'' = -12.$
$\qquad\qquad\qquad\qquad\qquad\qquad$ *Ans.* $y = e^{-3x} \sin 2x.$

13. $(D^5 + D^4 - 7D^3 - 11D^2 - 8D - 12)y = 0.$
$\qquad\qquad$ *Ans.* $y = c_1 \cos x + c_2 \sin x + c_3 e^{-2x} + c_4 x e^{-2x} + c_5 e^{3x}.$

14. $(D^4 - 2D^3 + 2D^2 - 2D + 1)y = 0$. Verify your answer.

15. $(D^4 + 18D^2 + 81)y = 0.$ $\qquad$ *Ans.* $y = (c_1 + c_2 x) \cos 3x + (c_3 + c_4 x) \sin 3x.$

16. $(2D^4 + 11D^3 - 4D^2 - 69D + 34)y = 0$. Verify your answer.

17. $(D^6 + 9D^4 + 24D^2 + 16)y = 0.$
$\qquad\qquad$ *Ans.* $y = c_1 \cos x + c_2 \sin x + (c_3 + c_4 x) \cos 2x + (c_5 + c_6 x) \sin 2x.$

18. $(2D^3 - D^2 + 36D - 18)y = 0.$

$$Ans. \; y = c_1 e^{\frac{x}{2}} + c_2 \cos (3\sqrt{2}\,x) + c_3 \sin (3\sqrt{2}\,x).$$

19. $\dfrac{d^2x}{dt^2} + k^2x = 0,$ k real; when $t = 0,$ $x = 0$ and $\dfrac{dx}{dt} = v_0.$ Verify your result completely.

$$Ans. \; x = \frac{v_0}{k} \sin kt.$$

20. $(D^3 + D^2 + 4D + 4)y = 0;$ when $x = 0,$ $y = 0,$ $y' = -1,$ and $y'' = 5.$

$$Ans. \; y = e^{-x} - \cos 2x.$$

21. $\dfrac{d^2x}{dt^2} + 2b\dfrac{dx}{dt} + k^2x = 0,$ $k > b > 0;$ when $t = 0,$ $x = 0$ and $\dfrac{dx}{dt} = v_0.$

$$Ans. \; x = \frac{v_0}{a} e^{-bt} \sin at, \text{ where } a = \sqrt{k^2 - b^2}.$$

MISCELLANEOUS EXERCISES

Obtain the general solution unless otherwise instructed. Your answer can be checked by direct substitution.

1. $(D^3 - D^2 + D - 1)y = 0.$ **2.** $(D^3 + 4D^2 + 5D)y = 0.$

3. $(D^4 - 13D^2 + 36)y = 0.$ **4.** $(D^4 - 5D^3 + 5D^2 + 5D - 6)y = 0.$

5. $(4D^3 + 8D^2 - 11D + 3)y = 0.$ **6.** $(D^3 + D^2 - 16D - 16)y = 0.$

7. $(D^4 - D^3 - 3D^2 + D + 2)y = 0.$

8. $(D^3 - 2D^2 - 3D + 10)y = 0.$ **9.** $(D^5 + D^4 - 6D^3)y = 0.$

10. $(4D^3 + 28D^2 + 61D + 37)y = 0.$

11. $(4D^3 + 12D^2 + 13D + 10)y = 0.$

12. $(18D^3 - 33D^2 + 20D - 4)y = 0.$

13. $(D^2 - D - 6)y = 0;$ when $x = 0,$ $y = 2$ and $y' = 1.$

14. $(D^4 + 6D^3 + 9D^2)y = 0;$ when $x = 0,$ $y = 0,$ $y' = 0,$ and $y'' = 6$ and as $x \to \infty,$ $y' \to 1.$ For this particular solution find the value of y when $x = 1.$

$$Ans. \; y = 1 - e^{-3}.$$

15. $(D^3 + 6D^2 + 12D + 8)y = 0;$ when $x = 0,$ $y = 1,$ $y' = -2,$ and $y'' = 2.$

16. $(8D^3 - 4D^2 - 2D + 1)y = 0.$ **17.** $(D^4 + D^3 - 4D^2 - 4D)y = 0.$

18. $(D^4 - 2D^3 + 5D^2 - 8D + 4)y = 0.$

19. $(D^4 + 2D^2 + 1)y = 0.$ **20.** $(D^4 + 5D^2 + 4)y = 0.$

21. $(D^4 + 3D^3 - 4D)y = 0.$

22. $(D^5 + D^4 - 9D^3 - 13D^2 + 8D + 12)y = 0.$

23. $(D^4 - 11D^3 + 36D^2 - 16D - 64)y = 0.$

24. $(D^2 + 2D + 5)y = 0.$

25. $(D^4 + 4D^3 + 2D^2 - 8D - 8)y = 0.$

26. $(4D^4 - 24D^3 + 35D^2 + 6D - 9)y = 0.$

27. $(4D^4 + 20D^3 + 35D^2 + 25D + 6)y = 0.$

28. $(D^4 - 7D^3 + 11D^2 + 5D - 14)y = 0.$

29. $(D^3 + 5D^2 + 7D + 3)y = 0.$ **30.** $(D^3 - 2D^2 + D - 2)y = 0.$

NONHOMOGENEOUS

EQUATIONS

269. *Construction of a Homogeneous Equation from a Specified Solution*

In preparation for the method of undetermined coefficients (§ 271), it is wise to obtain proficiency in writing down a homogeneous differential equation of which a given relation of proper form is a solution.

Recall that in solutions of homogeneous equations with constant coefficients, a term such as $c_1 e^{ax}$ occurred only when the auxiliary equation $f(m) = 0$ had a root $m = a$ and then the operator $f(D)$ had a factor $(D - a)$. In like manner $c_2 x e^{ax}$ appeared only when $f(D)$ contained the factor $(D - a)^2$, $c_3 x^2 e^{ax}$ only when $f(D)$ contained $(D - a)^3$, etc. Such terms as $ce^{ax} \cos bx$ or $ce^{ax} \sin bx$ correspond to roots $m = a \pm ib$, or to a factor $[(D - a)^2 + b^2]$.

Example (*a*). Find a homogeneous linear equation, with constant coefficients, which has as a particular solution

$$(1) \qquad\qquad y = 7e^{3x} + 2x.$$

First note that the coefficients (7 and 2) are quite irrelevant for the present problem, as long as they are not zero. We shall obtain an equation satisfied by $y = c_1 e^{3x} + c_2 x$, no matter what the constants c_1 and c_2 may be.

A term $c_1 e^{3x}$ occurs along with a root $m = 3$ of the auxiliary equation. The term $c_2 x$ will appear if the auxiliary equation has $m = 0, 0$; that is, a double root $m = 0$. We have recognized that the equation

$$(2) \qquad\qquad D^2(D - 3)y = 0,$$

or

$$(2) \qquad\qquad (D^3 - 3D^2)y = 0$$

has $y = c_1 e^{3x} + c_2 x + c_3$ as its general solution, and therefore that (2) has $y = 7e^{3x} + 2x$ as a particular solution.

Example (*b*). Find a homogeneous linear equation with real, constant coefficients which is satisfied by

$$(3) \qquad\qquad y = 6 + 3xe^x - \cos x.$$

The term 6 is associated with $m = 0$, the term $3xe^x$ with a double root $m = 1, 1$ and the term $(-\cos x)$ with the pair of imaginary roots $m = 0 \pm i$. Hence the auxiliary equation is

$$m(m - 1)^2(m^2 + 1) = 0,$$

or

$$m^5 - 2m^4 + 2m^3 - 2m^2 + m = 0.$$

Therefore the relation (3) is a solution of the differential equation

(4) $$(D^5 - 2D^4 + 2D^3 - 2D^2 + D)y = 0.$$

That is, from the general solution

$$y = c_1 + (c_2 + c_3x)e^x + c_4 \cos x + c_5 \sin x$$

of equation (4), the relation (3) follows by an appropriate choice of the constants: $c_1 = 6$, $c_2 = 0$, $c_3 = 3$, $c_4 = -1$, $c_5 = 0$.

Example (c). Find a homogeneous linear equation with real, constant coefficients which is satisfied by

$$y = 4xe^x \sin 2x.$$

The desired equation must have as its auxiliary equation one with roots $m = 1 \pm 2i$, $1 \pm 2i$. The roots $m = 1 \pm 2i$ correspond to factors

$$(m - 1)^2 + 4,$$

so that the auxiliary equation must be

$$[(m - 1)^2 + 4]^2 = 0,$$

or

$$m^4 - 4m^3 + 14m^2 - 20m + 25 = 0.$$

Hence the desired equation is

$$(D^4 - 4D^3 + 14D^2 - 20D + 25)y = 0.$$

Note that in all such problems a correct (but undesirable) solution may be obtained by inserting additional roots of the auxiliary equation.

ORAL EXERCISES

In Exs. 1–14 obtain in factored form a linear differential equation, with real, constant coefficients which is satisfied by the given relation.

1. $y = 4e^{2x} + 3e^{-x}$.   *Ans.* $(D - 2)(D + 1)y = 0$.
2. $y = 7 - 2x + \frac{1}{2}e^{4x}$.   *Ans.* $D^2(D - 4)y = 0$.
3. $y = -2x + \frac{1}{2}e^{4x}$.   *Ans.* $D^2(D - 4)y = 0$.
4. $y = x^2 - 5 \sin 3x$.   *Ans.* $D^3(D^2 + 9)y = 0$.
5. $y = 2e^x \cos 3x$.
     Ans. $(D - 1 - 3i)(D - 1 + 3i)y = 0$; or $[(D - 1)^2 + 9]y = 0$; or $(D^2 - 2D + 10)y = 0$.

6. $y = 8xe^x + 4e^{-2x}$. 7. $y = 3e^{2x} - e^x$. 8. $y = 2 - e^{-3x}$.
9. $y = x^2 - 4$. 10. $y = \cos x$. 11. $y = \cos x - 4 \sin x$.
12. $y = \sin kx$. 13. $y = 2x \cos x$. 14. $y = 5 \cosh 2x$.

In Exs. 15–30 state the roots of the auxiliary equation for a homogeneous linear equation with real, constant coefficients and containing the given relation as a particular solution.

15. $y = 3xe^{2x}$. *Ans.* $m = 2, 2$.
16. $y = x^2 e^{-x} + 4e^x$. *Ans.* $m = -1, -1, -1, 1$.
17. $y = e^{-x} \cos 4x$. *Ans.* $m = -1 \pm 4i$.
18. $y = 3e^{-x} \cos 4x + 15e^{-x} \sin 4x$. *Ans.* $m = -1 \pm 4i$.
19. $y = x(e^x - 1)$. *Ans.* $m = 1, 1, 0, 0$.
20. $y = 7 + e^{-3x}$. 21. $y = 6x^2 - e^{-4x}$. 22. $y = 3 + 6x^2 - e^{-4x}$.
23. $y = 5 \cos 3x$. 24. $y = 5 \cos 3x - 2 \sin 3x$.
25. $y = x \cos 3x - 2 \sin 3x$. 26. $y = e^{-x}(\sin 2x + \cos 2x)$.
27. $y = e^{-x} \sin 2x$. 28. $y = x^2 - 3x + e^{-3x} + 4e^x \cos 7x$.
29. $y = \sin^3 x$. Use the fact that $\sin^3 x = \frac{1}{4}(3 \sin x - \sin 3x)$.
30. $y = \cos^2 x$.

270. *Solution of a Nonhomogeneous Equation*

Before proceeding to the theoretical basis and the actual working technique of the useful method of undetermined coefficients, let us examine the underlying ideas as applied to a simple numerical example.

Consider the equation

(1) $$D^2(D - 1)y = 3e^x + \sin x.$$

The complementary function may be determined at once from the roots

(2) $$m = 0, 0, 1$$

of the auxiliary equation. The complementary function is

(3) $$y_c = c_1 + c_2 x + c_3 e^x.$$

Since the general solution of (1) is

$$y = y_c + y_p$$

where y_c is as given in (3) and y_p is any particular solution of (1), all that remains is for us to find a particular solution of (1).

The right-hand member of (1),

(4) $$R(x) = 3e^x + \sin x$$

is a particular solution of a homogeneous linear differential equation whose auxiliary equation has the roots

(5) $$m' = 1, \pm i.$$

Therefore the relation (4) is a particular solution of the equation

(6) $$(D - 1)(D^2 + 1)R = 0.$$

We wish to convert (1) into a homogeneous linear differential equation with constant coefficients, because we know how to solve any such equation. But, by (6) the operator $(D - 1)(D^2 + 1)$ will annihilate the right member of (1). Therefore we apply that operator to both sides of equation (1) and get

(7) $$(D - 1)(D^2 + 1)D^2(D - 1)y = 0.$$

Any solution of (1) must be a particular solution of (7). The general solution of (7) can be written down at once from the roots of its auxiliary equation, those roots being the values $m = 0, 0, 1$ from (2) together with the values $m' = 1, \pm i$ from (5). Thus the general solution of (7) is

(8) $$y = c_1 + c_2x + c_3e^x + c_4xe^x + c_5 \cos x + c_6 \sin x.$$

But the desired general solution of (1) is

(9) $$y = y_c + y_p,$$

where

$$y_c = c_1 + c_2x + c_3e^x,$$

the c_1, c_2, c_3 being arbitrary constants as in (8). Thus there must exist a particular solution of (1) containing at most the remaining terms in (8). Using different letters as coefficients to emphasize that they are not arbitrary, we conclude that (1) has a particular solution

(10) $$y_p = Axe^x + B \cos x + C \sin x.$$

It remains only to determine the numerical coefficients A, B, C by direct use of the original equation

(1) $$D^2(D - 1)y = 3e^x + \sin x.$$

From (10) it follows that

$$Dy_p = A(xe^x + e^x) - B \sin x + C \cos x,$$
$$D^2y_p = A(xe^x + 2e^x) - B \cos x - C \sin x,$$
$$D^3y_p = A(xe^x + 3e^x) + B \sin x - C \cos x.$$

Substitution of y_p into (1) then yields

(11) $$Ae^x + (B + C) \sin x + (B - C) \cos x = 3e^x + \sin x.$$

Since (11) is to be an identity and since e^x, $\sin x$, and $\cos x$ are linearly independent, the corresponding coefficients in the two members of (11) must be equal; that is,

$$A = 3,$$
$$B + C = 1,$$
$$B - C = 0.$$

Therefore $A = 3$, $B = \frac{1}{2}$, $C = \frac{1}{2}$. Returning to (10) we find that a particular solution of equation (1) is

$$y_p = 3xe^x + \tfrac{1}{2} \cos x + \tfrac{1}{2} \sin x.$$

The general solution of the original equation

(1) $$D^2(D - 1)y = 3e^x + \sin x$$

is therefore obtained by adding to the complementary function the y_p found above:

(12) $$y = c_1 + c_2x + c_3e^x + 3xe^x + \tfrac{1}{2} \cos x + \tfrac{1}{2} \sin x.$$

A careful analysis of the ideas behind the process used above shows that in order to arrive at the solution (12), we need perform only the following steps:

(a) From (1) find the values of m and m' as exhibited in (2) and (5);

(b) From the values of m and m' write y_c and y_p as in (3) and (10);

(c) Substitute y_p into (1), equate corresponding coefficients, and obtain the numerical values of the coefficients in y_p;

(d) Write the general solution of (1).

271. *The Method of Undetermined Coefficients*

Let us examine the general problem of the type treated in the preceding section. Let $f(D)$ be a polynomial in the operator D. Consider the equation

(1) $$f(D)y = R(x).$$

Let the roots of the auxiliary equation $f(m) = 0$ be

(2) $$m = m_1, m_2, \cdots, m_n.$$

The general solution of (1) is

(3) $$y = y_c + y_p$$

where y_c can be obtained at once from the values of m in (2) and where $y = y_p$ is any particular solution (yet to be obtained) of (1).

Now suppose that the right member $R(x)$ of (1) is itself a particular solution of some homogeneous linear differential equation with constant coefficients,

(4) $$g(D)R = 0,$$

whose auxiliary equation has the roots

(5) $$m' = m'_1, m'_2, \cdots, m'_k.$$

Recall that the values of m' in (5) can be obtained by inspection from $R(x)$.

The differential equation

(6) $$g(D)f(D)y = 0$$

has as the roots of its auxiliary equation the values of m from (2) and m' from (5). Hence the general solution of (6) contains the y_c of (3) and so is of the form

$$y = y_c + y_q.$$

But also any particular solution of (1) must satisfy (6). Now, if

$$f(D)(y_c + y_q) = R(x),$$

then $f(D)y_q = R(x)$ because $f(D)y_c = 0$. Then deleting the y_c from the general solution of (6) leaves a function y_q which for some numerical values of its coefficients must satisfy (1); i.e., the coefficients in y_q can be determined so that $y_q = y_p$. The determination of those numerical coefficients may be accomplished as in the examples below.

It must be kept in mind that the method of this section is applicable when, and only when, the right member of the equation is itself a particular solution of some homogeneous linear differential equation with constant coefficients. Methods which apply to equations with less restricted right-hand members will be found in most books on differential equations. For example, see Rainville's *Elementary Differential Equations*, 2nd ed., New York, 1958, The Macmillan Co., Chapter 11.

Example (a). Solve the equation

(7) $$(D^2 + D - 2)y = 2x - 40 \cos 2x.$$

Here we have

$$m = 1, -2$$

and

$$m' = 0, 0, \pm 2i.$$

Therefore we may write

$$y_c = c_1 e^x + c_2 e^{-2x},$$
$$y_p = A + Bx + C \cos 2x + E \sin 2x,$$

in which c_1 and c_2 are arbitrary constants, while A, B, C, and E are to be determined numerically so that y_p will satisfy the equation (7).

Since

$$Dy_p = B - 2C \sin 2x + 2E \cos 2x$$

and

$$D^2 y_p = -4C \cos 2x - 4E \sin 2x,$$

direct substitution of y_p into (7) yields

(8) $$-4C \cos 2x - 4E \sin 2x + B - 2C \sin 2x + 2E \cos 2x - 2A$$
$$-2Bx - 2C \cos 2x - 2E \sin 2x = 2x - 40 \cos 2x.$$

But (8) is to be an identity in x, so we must equate coefficients of each of the set of linearly independent functions $\cos 2x$, $\sin 2x$, x, 1 appearing in the identity. Thus it follows that

$$-6C + 2E = -40,$$
$$-6E - 2C = 0,$$
$$-2B = 2,$$
$$B - 2A = 0.$$

The above equations determine A, B, C, and E. Indeed, they lead to $A = -\frac{1}{2}$, $B = -1$, $C = 6$, $E = -2$.

Since the general solution of (7) is $y = y_c + y_p$, we can now write

$$y = c_1 e^x + c_2 e^{-2x} - \tfrac{1}{2} - x + 6 \cos 2x - 2 \sin 2x.$$

Example (b). Solve the equation

$$(9) \qquad\qquad (D^2 + 1)y = \sin x.$$

At once $m = \pm i$ and $m' = \pm i$. Therefore

$$y_c = c_1 \cos x + c_2 \sin x,$$
$$y_p = Ax \cos x + Bx \sin x.$$

Now

$$y_p'' = A(-x \cos x - 2 \sin x) + B(-x \sin x + 2 \cos x)$$

so that the requirement that y_p satisfy equation (9) yields

$$-2A \sin x + 2B \cos x = \sin x$$

from which $A = -\frac{1}{2}$ and $B = 0$.

The general solution of (9) is

$$y = c_1 \cos x + c_2 \sin x - \tfrac{1}{2}x \cos x.$$

Example (c). Determine y so that it will satisfy the equation

$$(10) \qquad\qquad y''' - y' = 4e^{-x} + 3e^{2x}$$

together with the conditions that when $x = 0$, $y = 0$, $y' = -1$, and $y'' = 2$.

First we note that $m = 0, 1, -1$, and $m' = -1, 2$. Thus

$$y_c = c_1 + c_2 e^x + c_3 e^{-x},$$
$$y_p = Axe^{-x} + Be^{2x}.$$

Now

$$y_p' = A(-xe^{-x} + e^{-x}) + 2Be^{2x},$$
$$y_p'' = A(xe^{-x} - 2e^{-x}) + 4Be^{2x},$$
$$y_p''' = A(-xe^{-x} + 3e^{-x}) + 8Be^{2x}.$$

Then

$$y_p''' - y_p' = 2Ae^{-x} + 6Be^{2x},$$

so that from (10) we may conclude that $A = 2$ and $B = \frac{1}{2}$.

The general solution of (10) is therefore

(11) $$y = c_1 + c_2 e^x + c_3 e^{-x} + 2xe^{-x} + \tfrac{1}{2} e^{2x}.$$

We must determine c_1, c_2, c_3 so that (11) will satisfy the conditions: when $x = 0$, $y = 0$, $y' = -1$, and $y'' = 2$.

From (11) it follows that

(12) $$y' = c_2 e^x - c_3 e^{-x} - 2xe^{-x} + 2e^{-x} + e^{2x}$$

and

(13) $$y'' = c_2 e^x + c_3 e^{-x} + 2xe^{-x} - 4e^{-x} + 2e^{2x}.$$

We put $x = 0$ in each of (11), (12), and (13) to get the equations for the determination of c_1, c_2, and c_3. These are

$$0 = c_1 + c_2 + c_3 + \tfrac{1}{2},$$
$$-1 = c_2 - c_3 + 3,$$
$$2 = c_2 + c_3 - 2,$$

from which $c_1 = -\tfrac{9}{2}$, $c_2 = 0$, $c_3 = 4$. Therefore the final result is

$$y = -\tfrac{9}{2} + 4e^{-x} + 2xe^{-x} + \tfrac{1}{2} e^{2x}.$$

An important point, sometimes overlooked by students, is that it is the general solution, the y of (11), which must be made to satisfy the boundary conditions.

EXERCISES

Obtain the general solution in Exs. 1–26.

1. $(D^2 + D)y = -\cos x$.   Ans. $y = c_1 + c_2 e^{-x} + \tfrac{1}{2} \cos x - \tfrac{1}{2} \sin x$.
2. $(D^2 - 6D + 9)y = e^x$.   Ans. $y = (c_1 + c_2 x)e^{3x} + \tfrac{1}{4} e^x$.
3. $(D^2 - 2D - 3)y = 27x^2$.   Ans. $y = c_1 e^{-x} + c_2 e^{3x} - 14 + 12x - 9x^2$.
4. $(D^2 - 2D - 3)y = 4 - 8x - 6x^2$.   Ans. $y = c_1 e^{-x} + c_2 e^{3x} + 2x^2$.
5. $(D^2 + 4)y = 15e^x - 8x$.   Ans. $y = c_1 \cos 2x + c_2 \sin 2x + 3e^x - 2x$.
6. $(D^2 + 4)y = 15e^x - 8x^2$.   Ans. $y = c_1 \cos 2x + c_2 \sin 2x + 3e^x - 2x^2 + 1$.
7. $(D^2 + D - 2)y = 12e^{2x}$.   Ans. $y = c_1 e^x + c_2 e^{-2x} + 3e^{2x}$.
8. $(D^2 + D - 2)y = 12e^{-2x}$.   Ans. $y = c_1 e^x + (c_2 - 4x)e^{-2x}$.
9. $(D^2 - 4)y = e^{2x} + 2$.   Ans. $y = c_1 e^{-2x} + (c_2 + \tfrac{1}{4} x)e^{2x} - \tfrac{1}{2}$.
10. $(D^2 - D - 2)y = 6x + 6e^{-x}$.   Ans. $y = c_1 e^{-x} + c_2 e^{2x} - 3x + \tfrac{3}{2} - 2xe^{-x}$.
11. $y'' - 4y' + 3y = 20 \cos x$.   Ans. $y = c_1 e^x + c_2 e^{3x} + 2 \cos x - 4 \sin x$.
12. $y'' - 4y' + 3y = 2 \cos x + 4 \sin x$.   Ans. $y = c_1 e^x + c_2 e^{3x} + \cos x$.
13. $y'' + 2y' + y = 7 + 75 \sin 2x$.
14. $(D^2 + 4D + 5)y = 50x + 13e^{3x}$.
15. $(D^2 + 1)y = \cos x$.   Ans. $y = c_1 \cos x + c_2 \sin x + \tfrac{1}{2} x \sin x$.
16. $(D^2 - 4D + 4)y = e^{2x}$.   Ans. $y = e^{2x}(c_1 + c_2 x + \tfrac{1}{2} x^2)$.
17. $(D^2 - 1)y = e^{-x}(2 \sin x + 4 \cos x)$.   Ans. $y = c_1 e^x + (c_2 - 2 \sin x)e^{-x}$.
18. $(D^2 - 1)y = 8xe^x$.   Ans. $y = c_1 e^{-x} + e^x(c_2 - 2x + 2x^2)$.
19. $(D^3 - D)y = x$.   Ans. $y = c_1 + c_2 e^x + c_3 e^{-x} - \tfrac{1}{2} x^2$.

20. $(D^3 - D^2 + D - 1)y = 4 \sin x$.

21. $(D^3 + D^2 - 4D - 4)y = 3e^{-x} - 4x - 6$.
$$\text{Ans. } y = c_1 e^{2x} + c_2 e^{-2x} + (c_3 - x)e^{-x} + x + \tfrac{1}{2}.$$

22. $(D^4 - 1)y = 7x^2$.   Ans. $y = c_1 e^x + c_2 e^{-x} + c_3 \cos x + c_4 \sin x - 7x^2$.

23. $(D^4 - 1)y = e^{-x}$.   Ans. $y = c_1 e^x + (c_2 - \tfrac{1}{4}x)e^{-x} + c_3 \cos x + c_4 \sin x$.

24. $(D^2 - 1)y = 10 \sin^2 x$. Use the identity $\sin^2 x = \tfrac{1}{2}(1 - \cos 2x)$.
$$\text{Ans. } y = c_1 e^x + c_2 e^{-x} - 5 + \cos 2x.$$

25. $(D^2 + 1)y = 12 \cos^2 x$.   Ans. $y = c_1 \cos x + c_2 \sin x + 6 - 2 \cos 2x$.

26. $(D^2 + 4)y = 4 \sin^2 x$.   Ans. $y = c_1 \cos 2x + c_2 \sin 2x + \tfrac{1}{2}(1 - x \sin 2x)$.

In Exs. 27–31 find the particular solution indicated.

27. $(D^2 + 1)y = 10e^{2x}$; when $x = 0$, $y = 0$ and $y' = 0$.
$$\text{Ans. } y = 2(e^{2x} - \cos x - 2 \sin x).$$

28. $(D^2 - 4)y = 2 - 8x$; when $x = 0$, $y = 0$ and $y' = 5$.

29. $(D^2 + 3D)y = -18x$; when $x = 0$, $y = 0$ and $y' = 5$.
$$\text{Ans. } y = 1 + 2x - 3x^2 - e^{-3x}.$$

30. $(D^2 + 4D + 5)y = 10e^{-3x}$; when $x = 0$, $y = 4$ and $y' = 0$.
$$\text{Ans. } y = e^{-2x}(13 \sin x - \cos x) + 5e^{-3x}.$$

31. $\dfrac{d^2x}{dt^2} + 4\dfrac{dx}{dt} + 5x = 10$; when $t = 0$, $x = 0$ and $\dfrac{dx}{dt} = 0$.
$$\text{Ans. } x = 2(1 - e^{-2t} \cos t - 2e^{-2t} \sin t).$$

In Exs. 32–35 obtain from the particular solution indicated the value of y and the value of y' at $x = 2$.

32. $y'' + 2y' + y = x$; at $x = 0$, $y = -3$ and at $x = 1$, $y = -1$.
$$\text{Ans. At } x = 2, \ y = e^{-2} \text{ and } y' = 1.$$

33. $y'' + 2y' + y = x$; at $x = 0$, $y = -2$ and $y' = 2$.
$$\text{Ans. At } x = 2, \ y = 2e^{-2} \text{ and } y' = 1 - e^{-2}.$$

34. $4y'' + y = 2$; at $x = \pi$, $y = 0$ and $y' = 1$.
$$\text{Ans. At } x = 2, \ y = -0.7635 \text{ and } y' = +0.3012.$$

35. $2y'' - 5y' - 3y = -9x^2 - 1$; at $x = 0$, $y = 1$ and $y' = 0$.
$$\text{Ans. At } x = 2, \ y = 5.64 \text{ and } y' = 5.68.$$

36. $(D^2 + D)y = x + 1$; when $x = 0$, $y = 1$ and when $x = 1$, $y = \tfrac{1}{2}$. Compute the value of y at $x = 4$.   Ans. At $x = 4$, $y = 8 - e^{-1} - e^{-2} - e^{-3}$.

37. $(D^2 + 1)y = x^3$; when $x = 0$, $y = 0$ and when $x = \pi$, $y = 0$. Show that this boundary value problem has no solution.

38. $(D^2 + 1)y = 2 \cos x$; when $x = 0$, $y = 0$ and when $x = \pi$, $y = 0$. Show that this boundary value problem has an unlimited number of solutions and obtain them.   Ans. $y = (x + c) \sin x$.

39. For the equation $(D^3 + D^2)y = 4$ find the solution whose graph has at the origin a point of inflection with a horizontal tangent line.
$$\text{Ans. } y = 4 - 4x + 2x^2 - 4e^{-x}.$$

40. For the equation $(D^2 - D)y = 2 - 2x$ find a particular solution which has at some point (to be determined) on the x-axis an inflection point with a horizontal tangent line.   Ans. The point is $(1, 0)$; the solution is $y = x^2 + 1 - 2e^{x-1}$.

41. $(D^2 + 9)y = \sin 3x$; when $x = 0$, $y = 1$ and when $x = \tfrac{1}{2}\pi$, $y = 1$. Compute the value of y at $x = \tfrac{1}{4}\pi$.   Ans. $x = \tfrac{1}{4}\pi$, $y = -1.3$.

APPLICATIONS

272. *Vibration of a Spring*

Consider a steel spring attached to a rigid support and hanging downward without obstruction. The spring will obey Hooke's law: If the spring is stretched or compressed, its change in length will be proportional to the force exerted upon the spring, and when that force is removed, the spring will return to its original position with its length and other physical properties unchanged.

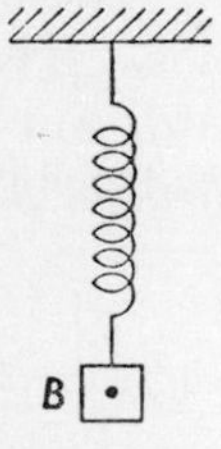

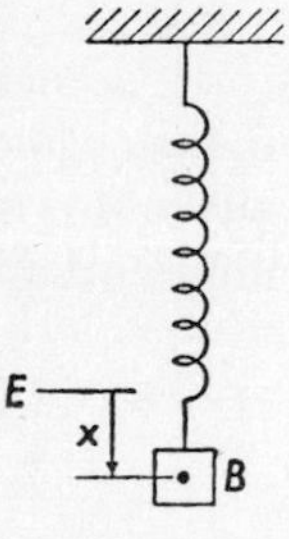

According to Hooke's law there is associated with each spring a numerical constant, the ratio of the force exerted to the displacement produced by that force. Suppose a force of magnitude f pounds stretches the spring s feet. Then the relation

$$(1) \qquad\qquad f = ks$$

Figure 241   Figure 242

defines the spring constant k in the units pounds per foot.

A body B weighing w lb. is attached to the lower end of the spring (Fig. 241) and brought to the point of equilibrium where it can remain at rest. Then suppose that B is pulled down x_0 ft. below the point of equilibrium and suddenly released. Our first problem is to determine the motion of B.

Let us measure time t in seconds, starting with $t = 0$ at the time B is released. Let us also indicate the position of the body B at time t by x, in feet, measured positive downward from the point of equilibrium E (Fig. 242). Then the statement that B was released (i.e., without imparted velocity) from a position x_0 ft. below E can be expressed mathematically by saying that

$$(2) \qquad\qquad \text{When } t = 0, \ x = x_0 \ \text{ and } \ \frac{dx}{dt} = 0.$$

We have used the fact that the motion of B takes place in a straight (vertical) line so that the velocity v is given by

$$v = \frac{dx}{dt}.$$

Let $g = 32$ ft. per sec. per sec. be the magnitude of the acceleration due to gravity. Then B has mass w/g (lb.) (sec.^{2}) per ft. or w/g slugs.

The resultant force F acting upon B at any time is, according to Newton's law,

$$(3) \qquad\qquad F = \frac{w}{g} \frac{d^2x}{dt^2}$$

with F measured positive when it tends to move B in the positive x direction (downward). Let us neglect the force due to air resistance. Then the resultant force acting upon B is the one which by Hooke's law has magnitude $k|x|$, where k is the spring constant. This force is tending to restore equilibrium, to pull B back toward E. Therefore it is opposite in sign to x, so that

$$F = -kx,$$

or

$$(4) \qquad\qquad \frac{w}{g} \frac{d^2x}{dt^2} = -kx.$$

The problem of determining the motion of B is now seen to be one of solving a differential equation with associated boundary conditions. The displacement x from the equilibrium point E (x positive downward) must be a function of the time t such that x satisfies the differential equation

$$(5) \qquad\qquad \frac{w}{g} \frac{d^2x}{dt^2} + kx = 0$$

and the associated conditions:

$$(6) \qquad\qquad \text{When } t = 0,\ x = x_0 \quad \text{and} \quad \frac{dx}{dt} = 0.$$

Let us solve the boundary value problem consisting of (5) and (6). Let $kg/w = \beta^2$. Then (5) may be written

$$\frac{d^2x}{dt^2} + \beta^2 x = 0$$

and we know its general solution to be

$$(7) \qquad\qquad x = c_1 \cos \beta t + c_2 \sin \beta t,$$

where c_1 and c_2 are arbitrary constants. Those constants must be determined to make the function x satisfy the conditions (6). From (7) it follows that

$$(8) \qquad\qquad v = \frac{dx}{dt} = -c_1\beta \sin \beta t + c_2\beta \cos \beta t.$$

Let $t = 0$ in (7) and (8). Then, using the conditions (6), we get $c_1 = x_0$ and $c_2 = 0$.

With c_1 and c_2 known, the relation (7) becomes

(9) $$x = x_0 \cos \beta t$$

where $\beta = \sqrt{kg/w}$. Equation (9) is the solution we have been seeking. That it satisfies (5) and (6) is easily verified.

The motion described by (9) is called simple harmonic motion. It is periodic with period $\dfrac{2\pi}{\beta}$ or $2\pi \left(\dfrac{kg}{w}\right)^{-\frac{1}{2}}$. Its amplitude, the maximum deviation from the point of equilibrium, is $|x_0|$.

Variations of the above problem are obtainable by altering the boundary conditions as in the example below. Note also that the method of solution may be varied a little, replacing (7) by

(10) $$x = c_3 \sin (\beta t + c_4),$$

or by

(11) $$x = c_5 \cos (\beta t + c_6).$$

Equations (10) and (11) have the advantage that each exhibits the amplitude explicitly as is indicated in the exercises below.

Example. A spring is such that it would be stretched 3 in. by a 6-lb. weight. Let a 12-lb. weight B be attached to the spring and pulled down 4 in. below the equilibrium point. If B is started with an upward velocity of 2 ft. per sec., describe the motion of B.

First we determine the spring constant by using the fact that when $f = 6$ (lb.), $s = \frac{3}{12} = \frac{1}{4}$ (ft.). Thus $6 = \frac{1}{4}k$ so that $k = 24$ (lb. per ft.).

With the notation of this section the problem to be solved may be expressed by

(12) $$\frac{12}{32} \frac{d^2x}{dt^2} + 24x = 0$$

together with the conditions:

(13) $$\text{When } t = 0, \ x = \tfrac{1}{3} \quad \text{and} \quad v = -2.$$

Note that the upward velocity (decreasing x) is negative and that the initial value of x must be expressed in feet to be consistent with our use of $g = 32$ (ft. per sec. per sec.).

From (12) we get

$$\frac{d^2x}{dt^2} + 64x = 0$$

so that

$$x = c_1 \cos 8t + c_2 \sin 8t.$$

Then

$$v = -8c_1 \sin 8t + 8c_2 \cos 8t.$$

Hence the conditions on x and v at $t = 0$ lead us to the values $c_1 = \frac{1}{3}$ and $c_2 = -\frac{1}{4}$. Therefore the desired solution is

$$(14) \qquad x = \tfrac{1}{3} \cos 8t - \tfrac{1}{4} \sin 8t.$$

See also Ex. 1 below.

A detailed discussion of the motion is straightforward once (14) has been obtained. In particular it can be shown that the amplitude of the motion is $A = \frac{5}{12}$ (ft.); i.e., B oscillates between points 5 in. above and below E. The period is $\frac{1}{4}\pi$ (sec.).

273. *Damped Vibrations*

The vibration of a spring with a suspended weight is usually retarded by damping forces, of which air resistance is an example. It has been shown by experiment that in many instances such retarding forces are fairly well approximated by a term proportional to the velocity. This retarding force will act upward when B is moving downward $(v > 0)$ and downward when B is moving upward $(v < 0)$. It has a sign opposite to the sign of v.

Thus, with such a resisting medium taken into consideration, the resultant force F of § 272 must be replaced by

$$(1) \qquad F = -kx - bv,$$

where b is a positive constant determined experimentally.

Since

$$F = \frac{w}{g}\frac{d^2x}{dt^2},$$

the differential equation of motion under our present assumptions is

$$(2) \qquad \frac{w}{g}\frac{d^2x}{dt^2} + b\frac{dx}{dt} + kx = 0.$$

In equation (2) put $\beta^2 = \frac{kg}{w}$ and $2\alpha = \frac{bg}{w}$ in order to simplify the writing. Then (2) becomes

$$(3) \qquad \frac{d^2x}{dt^2} + 2\alpha\frac{dx}{dt} + \beta^2 x = 0,$$

which has the auxiliary equation

$$m^2 + 2\alpha m + \beta^2 = 0$$

with roots $m = -\alpha \pm \sqrt{\alpha^2 - \beta^2}$. Often α is small compared to β. Let us assume $\alpha < \beta$ and put

$$\beta^2 - \alpha^2 = \gamma^2$$

so that we have

$$m = -\alpha \pm i\gamma.$$

Then the general solution of (3) is

(4) $$x = e^{-\alpha t}(c_1 \cos \gamma t + c_2 \sin \gamma t)$$

and the arbitrary constants c_1 and c_2 are available for the satisfaction of boundary conditions similar to those of § 272. The factor $e^{-\alpha t}$ is called the *damping factor*. Since $\alpha > 0$, the damping factor approaches zero as $t \to \infty$.

Example. Solve the problem of the example of § 272 with an added damping force of magnitude $0.6|v|$. Such a damping force can be realized by immersing the weight B in a thick liquid.

The problem consists in solving the differential equation

(5) $$\frac{12}{32} \frac{d^2x}{dt^2} + 0.6 \frac{dx}{dt} + 24x = 0$$

together with the conditions

(6) $$\text{when } t = 0, \; x = \tfrac{1}{3} \; \text{ and } \; v = -2.$$

For (5) the auxiliary equation is

$$m^2 + 1.6m + 64 = 0$$

so that $m = -0.80 \pm 8.0i$, in which only two significant figures are retained because of the rough nature of the data and the value of g used. Then

$$x = e^{-0.8t}(c_1 \cos 8t + c_2 \sin 8t),$$
$$v = e^{-0.8t}[(8c_2 - 0.8c_1) \cos 8t - (8c_1 + 0.8c_2) \sin 8t].$$

Because of the conditions (6) we get

$$\tfrac{1}{3} = c_1,$$
$$-2 = 8c_2 - 0.8c_1.$$

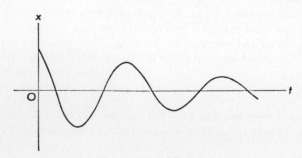

Figure 243

Then $c_1 = 0.33$ and $c_2 = -0.22$.

The desired solution is

(7) $$x = e^{-0.8t}(0.33 \cos 8t - 0.22 \sin 8t),$$

a portion of its graph being shown in Fig. 243.

EXERCISES

In these exercises the notations and approximations (including $g = 32$ ft. per sec. per sec.) of the text are used.

1. Show that the solution (14) of § 272 can be put in the form

$$x = A \cos (8t + \varphi)$$

and that $A = \frac{5}{12}$ (ft.) and $\varphi = \text{Arctan } (\frac{3}{4})$.

In Exs. 2–14 no damping force is present.

2. A spring is such that an 8-lb. weight would stretch it 6 in. Let a 4-lb. weight be attached to the spring, pushed up 2 in. above its equilibrium point, and then released. Describe the motion.   *Ans.* $x = -\frac{1}{6} \cos 11.3t$.

3. If the 4-lb. weight of Ex. 2 starts at the same point, 2 in. above E, but with an upward velocity of 15 ft. per sec., when will the weight reach its lowest point?

4. A spring is such that it is stretched 4 in. by a 10-lb. weight. Suppose the 10-lb. weight to be pulled down 5 in. below E and then given a downward velocity of 15 ft. per sec. Describe the motion.

$$\text{Ans. } x = 0.42 \cos 9.8t + 1.53 \sin 9.8t$$
$$= 1.59 \cos (9.8t - \varphi), \text{ where } \varphi = \text{Arctan } 3.64.$$

5. A spring is such that a 5-lb. weight stretches it 6 in. The 5-lb. weight is attached, the spring reaches equilibrium, then the weight is pulled down 3 in. below the equilibrium point and started off with an upward velocity of 6 ft. per sec. Find an equation giving the position of the weight at all subsequent times.

$$\text{Ans. } x = \frac{1}{4}(\cos 8t - 3 \sin 8t).$$

6. A spring is such that it is stretched 4 in. by an 8-lb. weight. Suppose the weight to be pulled down 6 in. below E and then given an upward velocity of 8 ft. per sec. Describe the motion.   *Ans.* $x = 0.50 \cos 9.8t - 0.82 \sin 9.8t$.

7. Show that the answer to Ex. 6 can be written $x = 0.96 \cos (9.8t + \varphi)$ where $\varphi = \text{Arctan } 1.64$.

8. A spring is stretched 1.5 in. by a 2-lb. weight. Let the weight be pushed up 3 in. above E and then released. Describe the motion.   *Ans.* $x = -\frac{1}{4} \cos 16t$.

9. For the spring and weight of Ex. 8 let the weight be pulled down 4 in. below E and given a downward initial velocity of 8 ft. per sec. Describe the motion.

$$\text{Ans. } x = \frac{1}{3} \cos 16t + \frac{1}{2} \sin 16t.$$

10. Show that the answer to Ex. 9 can be written $x = 0.60 \sin (16t + \varphi)$ where $\varphi = \text{Arctan } \frac{2}{3}$.

11. A spring is stretched 3 in. by a 5-lb. weight. Let the weight be started from E with an upward velocity of 12 ft. per sec. Describe the motion.

$$\text{Ans. } x = -1.06 \sin 11.3t.$$

12. For the spring and weight of Ex. 11, let the weight be pulled down 4 in., below E and then given an upward velocity of 8 ft. per sec. Describe the motion.

$$\text{Ans. } x = 0.33 \cos 11.3t - 0.71 \sin 11.3t.$$

13. Find the amplitude of the motion in Ex. 12.   *Ans.* 0.78 ft.

14. A 20-lb. weight stretches a certain spring 10 in. Let the spring first be compressed 4 in., and then the 20-lb. weight attached and given an initial downward velocity of 8 ft. per sec. Find how far the weight would drop.   *Ans.* 35 in.

15. For the example of § 273 find the time and position of the first stop.

16. For the example of § 273 find the time in which the damping factor $e^{-0.8t}$ drops to one-tenth of its initial value. *Ans.* 2.9 sec.

17. Put (7) of § 273 into the form $x = Ae^{-0.8t} \cos (8t + \varphi)$.

18. A spring is such that a 4-lb. weight stretches it 0.64 ft. The 4-lb. weight is pushed up $\frac{1}{3}$ ft. above the point of equilibrium and then started with a downward velocity of 5 ft. per sec. The motion takes place in a medium which furnishes a damping force of magnitude $\frac{1}{4}|v|$ at all times. Find the equation describing the position of the weight at time t. *Ans.* $x = \frac{1}{3}e^{-t}(2 \sin 7t - \cos 7t)$.

19. A spring is such that a 4-lb. weight stretches it 0.32 ft. The weight is attached to the spring and moves in a medium which furnishes a damping force of magnitude $\frac{3}{2}|v|$. The weight is drawn down $\frac{1}{2}$ ft. below the equilibrium point and given an initial upward velocity of 4 ft. per sec. Find the position of the weight thereafter.

20. A spring is such that a 4-lb. weight stretches the spring 0.4 ft. The 4-lb. weight is attached to the spring (suspended from a fixed support) and the system is allowed to reach equilibrium. Then the weight is started from equilibrium position with an imparted upward velocity of 2 ft. per sec. Assume that the motion takes place in a medium which furnishes a retarding force of magnitude numerically equal to the speed, in feet per second, of the moving weight. Determine the position of the weight as a function of time. *Ans.* $x = -\frac{1}{4}e^{-4t} \sin 8t$.

21. A spring is stretched 6 in. by a 3-lb. weight. The 3-lb. weight is attached to the spring and then started from equilibrium with an imparted upward velocity of 12 ft. per sec. Air resistance furnishes a retarding force equal in magnitude to $0.03|v|$. Find the equation of motion. *Ans.* $x = -1.5e^{-0.16t} \sin 8t$.

22. A spring is stretched 10 in. by a 4-lb. weight. The weight is started 6 in. below the equilibrium point with an upward velocity of 8 ft. per sec. If a resisting medium furnishes a retarding force of magnitude $\frac{1}{4}|v|$, describe the motion.

Ans. $x = e^{-t}[0.50 \cos 6.1t - 1.23 \sin 6.1t]$

23. For Ex. 22 find the times of the first three stops and the position (to the nearest inch) of the weight at each stop.

Ans. $t_1 = 0.3$ sec, $x_1 = -12$ in.; $t_2 = 0.8$ sec.,
$x_2 = +6$ in.; $t_3 = 1.3$ sec., $x_3 = -4$ in.

24. A spring is stretched 4 in. by a 2-lb. weight. The 2-lb. weight is started from the equilibrium point with a downward velocity of 12 ft. per sec. If air resistance furnishes a retarding force of magnitude 0.02 of the velocity, describe the motion.

Ans. $x = 1.22e^{-0.16t} \sin 9.8t$.

274. *Critical Damping*

The problem in damped vibrations which was studied in § 273 was reduced to the problem of solving the equation

(1)
$$\frac{d^2x}{dt^2} + 2\alpha \frac{dx}{dt} + \beta^2 x = 0$$

together with certain initial conditions.

The auxiliary equation for (1) is

$$m^2 + 2\alpha m + \beta^2 = 0$$

and it has the roots

(2) $$m = -\alpha \pm \sqrt{\alpha^2 - \beta^2}.$$

The general solution of equation (1) will assume various forms according to whether the two values of m (a) involve imaginaries, (b) are equal, or (c) are real and distinct.

When $\alpha < \beta$ the roots of the auxiliary equation are imaginary and the solution of equation (1) takes the form

(3) $$x = e^{-\alpha t}(c_1 \cos \gamma t + c_2 \sin \gamma t),$$

or

$$x = Ae^{-\alpha t} \cos (\gamma t + \varphi),$$

in which $\gamma^2 = \beta^2 - \alpha^2$. The motion described by equation (3) is a damped oscillatory motion.

When $\alpha = \beta$, the values of m are real and equal and the solution of equation (1) assumes the form

(4) $$x = (c_3 + c_4 t)e^{-\alpha t}.$$

The motion described by (4) is not oscillatory; it is called *critically damped* motion.

When $\alpha > \beta$ the roots of the auxiliary equation are real and distinct. Then the solution of equation (1) becomes

(5) $$x = e^{-\alpha t}(c_5 e^{\delta t} + c_6 e^{-\delta t})$$

in which $\delta^2 = \alpha^2 - \beta^2$. The motion described by equation (5) is often called *overdamped* motion; the parameter α is larger than it needs to be in order to remove the oscillations.

In Fig. 244 there is a representative graph of each type of motion mentioned above, a damped oscillatory motion, a critically damped one, and an overdamped one.

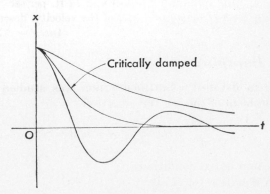

Figure 244

275. *Forced Vibrations*

Suppose next that a spring is supported as in the preceding section but that an additional vertical force is acting upon the weight attached to the spring. The additional force may, for example, be due to the presence of a magnetic field, to motion of the support, etc. The new, impressed force will depend upon time, and we may use $f(t)$ to represent the acceleration which it alone would impart to the weight B. Then the impressed force is $(w/g)f(t)$ and the differential equation with damping taken into consideration, is therefore

$$(1) \qquad \frac{w}{g}\frac{d^2x}{dt^2} + b\frac{dx}{dt} + kx = \frac{w}{g}f(t)$$

or

$$(2) \qquad \frac{d^2x}{dt^2} + 2\alpha\frac{dx}{dt} + \beta^2 x = f(t),$$

where again $2\alpha = \dfrac{bg}{w}$ and $\beta^2 = \dfrac{kg}{w}$.

For $f(t)$ the particular choices $f(t) = A \sin \omega t$, $f(t) = A \cos \omega t$,

$$f(t) = A_1 \cos \omega t + A_2 \sin \omega t,$$

or $f(t) = A \sin (\omega t + \sigma)$, in which A, ω, A_1, A_2, σ are constants, are of special interest in practical work. The fourth of these forms for $f(t)$ includes the others. In § 278 the analogous electromotive forces impressed upon an electric circuit will be considered. Mathematically the problems are the same.

It will be seen in the next section that in undamped motion ($b = 0$), the case $\omega = \beta$ is of particular interest and importance. That case will be avoided in this section.

Example. A spring is such that a 6-lb weight stretches the spring 2 in. There is no appreciable damping present, but the spring and weight are subject to an impressed force such that the equation of motion is

$$(3) \qquad \frac{6}{32}\frac{d^2x}{dt^2} + 36x = -4.60 \sin 4t.$$

The weight B is pulled down 3 in. below the equilibrium point and then released. Describe the motion.

The problem is that of solving

$$(4) \qquad \frac{d^2x}{dt^2} + 192x = -24.5 \sin 4t$$

with the conditions:

$$(5) \qquad \text{When } t = 0, x = 0.25 \quad \text{and} \quad v = 0.$$

The general solution of (4) is easily found to be

(6) $x = c_1 \cos 13.9t + c_2 \sin 13.9t - 0.14 \sin 4t.$

Then

(7) $v = 13.9(-c_1 \sin 13.9t + c_2 \cos 13.9t) - 0.56 \cos 4t.$

Thus the conditions (5) lead to the equations

$$0.25 = c_1$$
$$0 = 13.9c_2 - 0.56,$$

so that $c_1 = 0.25$ and $c_2 = 0.04$.

Therefore the motion under consideration is described by the relation

(8) $x = 0.25 \cos 13.9t + 0.04 \sin 13.9t - 0.14 \sin 4t.$

276. *Resonance*

In the undamped forced vibrations of a spring, equations of the type

(1) $$\frac{d^2x}{dt^2} + \beta^2 x = A \sin \omega t$$

can arise, as was seen in § 275. For equation (1) the roots of the auxiliary equation $m^2 + \beta^2 = 0$ are $m = \pm i\beta$. The right member of (1) is a solution of an equation whose auxiliary equation has roots $m' = \pm i\omega$. Therefore, using the method of undetermined coefficients as in Chapter 37, we can conclude that if $\omega^2 \neq \beta^2$, then (1) has a particular solution of the form

(2) $x_p = a_1 \sin \omega t.$

On the other hand, if $\omega^2 = \beta^2$, then equation (1) has no particular solution of the form (2), but it does have a particular solution of the form

(3) $x_p = b_1 t \cos \beta t.$

Thus, if $\omega^2 \neq \beta^2$, equation (1) has the general solution

(4) $x = c_1 \cos \beta t + c_2 \sin \beta t + Aq \sin \omega t$

where $q = \dfrac{1}{\beta^2 - \omega^2}.$ An important property of the solution (4) is that the numerical value of x is bounded. Indeed, since $|\sin y| \leq 1$ and $|\cos y| \leq 1$, it follows that $|x| \leq |c_1| + |c_2| + |Aq|$. Thus there is a limit to the amplitude of the vibrations.

If $\omega = \beta$, then equation (1) has the general solution

(5) $x = c_1 \cos \beta t + c_2 \sin \beta t - \dfrac{A}{2\beta} t \cos \beta t.$

In (5) the terms $c_1 \cos \beta t$ and $c_2 \sin \beta t$ are bounded, but the term $\dfrac{A}{2\beta} t \cos \beta t$ is unbounded because of the factor t. When $\omega = \beta$ the resulting physical phenomenon (the building up of large amplitudes in the vibration) is called *resonance*.

In actual practice, of course, the amplitude does not exceed all bounds. The elastic limit will be reached and the spring will break, unless before that the weight meets with outside interference such as a floor.

EXERCISES

1. A certain straight-line motion is determined by the differential equation

$$\frac{d^2x}{dt^2} + 2\alpha \frac{dx}{dt} + 169x = 0$$

and the conditions that when $t = 0$, $x = 0$ and $v = 8$ ft. per sec.

(a) Find the value of α which leads to critical damping, determine x in terms of t, and draw the graph for $0 \leqq t \leqq 0.2$.

Ans. $\alpha = 13 \dfrac{1}{\text{sec.}}$, $x = 8te^{-13t}$.

(b) Use $\alpha = 12$. Find x in terms of t and draw the graph.

Ans. $x = 1.6e^{-12t} \sin 5t$.

(c) Use $\alpha = 14$. Find x in terms of t and draw the graph.

Ans. $x = 0.77(e^{-8.8t} - e^{-19.2t})$.

2. A spring is such that a 4-lb. weight stretches it 6 in. There is no appreciable damping present, but an impressed force $\frac{1}{2} \cos 8t$ is acting on the spring. If the 4-lb. weight is started from the equilibrium point with an imparted upward velocity of 4 ft. per sec., determine the position of the weight as a function of time.

Ans. $x = \frac{1}{4}(t - 2) \sin 8t$.

3. A spring is such that a 2-lb. weight stretches it $\frac{1}{2}$ ft. An impressed force $\frac{1}{4} \sin 8t$ and a damping force of magnitude $|v|$ are both acting on the spring. The weight starts $\frac{1}{4}$ ft. below the equilibrium point with an imparted upward velocity of 3 ft. per sec. Find a formula for the position of the weight at time t.

Ans. $x = \frac{3}{32}e^{-8t}(3 - 8t) - \frac{1}{32} \cos 8t$.

4. A spring is such that a 16-lb. weight stretches it 1.5 in. The weight is pulled down to a point 4 in. below the equilibrium point and given an initial downward velocity of 4 ft. per sec. There is no damping force present, but there is an impressed force of $360 \cos 4t$ lb. Find the position and velocity of the weight at time $t = \frac{1}{8}\pi$. sec. *Ans.* At $t = \frac{1}{8}\pi$(sec.), $x = -\frac{8}{3}$ (ft.), $v = -8$ (ft. per sec.).

5. A spring is such that a 4-lb. weight stretches it 6 in. The 4-lb. weight is attached to the vertical spring and reaches its equilibrium point. The weight is then ($t = 0$) drawn downward 3 in. and released. No damping force is present, but there is a simple harmonic exterior force equal to $\sin 8t$ impressed upon the whole system. Find the time for each of the first four stops following $t = 0$. Put the stops in chronological order. *Ans.* $t = \frac{1}{8}\pi, \frac{1}{2}, \frac{1}{4}\pi, \frac{3}{8}\pi$ (sec.).

6. A spring is such that a 2-lb. weight stretches it 6 in. There is a damping force present, with magnitude the same as the magnitude of the velocity. An impressed force $(2 \sin 8t)$ is acting on the spring. If, at $t = 0$, the weight is released from a point 3 in. below the equilibrium point, find its position for $t > 0$.

Ans. $x = (\frac{1}{2} + 4t)e^{-8t} - \frac{1}{4} \cos 8t$.

7. In the example of § 275 change the conditions by imparting to the weight an initial downward velocity of 4 ft. per sec.

Ans. $x = 0.25 \cos 13.9t + 0.33 \sin 13.9t - 0.14 \sin 4t$.

8. Show that the solution to Ex. 7 can be put in the form

$$x = 0.41 \cos (13.9t - \varphi) - 0.14 \sin 4t,$$

where $\varphi = \text{Arctan } (1.32)$. In this form the first term is called the *natural component*, and the second term the *forced component*, of the motion.

9. A spring is such that it is stretched 6 in. by a 12-lb. weight (the spring of the example in § 272). The 12-lb. weight is pulled down 3 in. below the equilibrium point and then released. If no damping is present, but there is an impressed force of magnitude $9 \sin 4t$ lb., describe the motion. Assume that the impressed force acts downward for very small t.   *Ans.* $x = \frac{1}{4} \cos 8t - \frac{1}{4} \sin 8t + \frac{1}{2} \sin 4t$.

10. Show that the answer to Ex. 9 can be written

$$x = \frac{1}{4} \sqrt{2} \cos (8t + \frac{1}{4}\pi) + \frac{1}{2} \sin 4t.$$

11. Alter Ex. 9 by inserting a damping force of magnitude one-half that of the velocity and then determine x.

Ans. $x = e^{-\frac{2t}{3}}(0.30 \cos 8.0t - 0.22 \sin 8.0t) - 0.05 \cos 4t + 0.49 \sin 4t$.

12. A spring is such that a 2-lb. weight stretches it $\frac{1}{2}$ ft. An impressed force $\frac{1}{4} \sin 8t$ is acting upon the spring. If the 2-lb. weight is released from a point 3 in. below the equilibrium point, determine the equation of motion.

Ans. $x = \frac{1}{4}(1 - t) \cos 8t + \frac{1}{32} \sin 8t$.

13. For the motion of Ex. 12 find the first four times at which stops occur and find the position at each stop.

Ans. $t = \pi/8, \pi/4, 1, 3\pi/8$ (sec.) and
$x = -0.15, +0.05, +0.03, +0.04$ (ft.), respectively.

14. Determine the position to be expected, if nothing such as breakage interferes, at the time of the 65th stop, when $t = 8\pi$ (sec.), in Ex. 12.   *Ans.* $x = -6.0$ (ft.).

15. Let the motion of Ex. 12 be retarded by a damping force of magnitude $0.6|v|$. Find the equation of motion.

Ans. $x = 0.30e^{-4.8t} \cos 6.4t + 0.22e^{-4.8t} \sin 6.4t - 0.05 \cos 8t$.

16. Show that (to the nearest 0.01 ft.) whenever $t > 1$ (sec.) the solution of Ex. 15 may be replaced by $x = -0.05 \cos 8t$.

17. Let the motion of Ex. 12 be retarded by a damping force of magnitude $|v|$. Find the equation of motion and also determine its form (to the nearest 0.01 ft.) for $t > 1$ (sec.).

Ans. $x = \frac{9}{32}(8t + 1)e^{-8t} - \frac{1}{32} \cos 8t$; for $t > 1$, $x = -\frac{1}{32} \cos 8t$.

18. Let the motion of Ex. 12 be retarded by a damping force of magnitude $\frac{5}{3}|v|$. Find the equation of motion.   *Ans.* $x = 0.30e^{-\frac{8}{3}t} - 0.03e^{-24t} - 0.02 \cos 8t$.

277. *The Simple Pendulum*

Figure 245

A rod of length L ft. is suspended by one end so that it can swing freely in a vertical plane. Let a weight B (the bob) of w lb. be attached to the free end of the rod, and let the weight of the rod be negligible compared with the weight of the bob.

Let θ (radians) be the angular displacement from the vertical, as shown in Fig. 245, of the rod at time t (sec.). The tangential component of the force w (lb.) is $w \sin \theta$, and it tends to decrease θ. Then, neglecting the weight of the rod and using $s = L\theta$ as a measure of arc length from the vertical position, we may conclude that

$$(1) \qquad\qquad \frac{w}{g}\frac{d^2s}{dt^2} = -w \sin \theta.$$

Since $s = L\theta$ and L is constant, (1) becomes

$$(2) \qquad\qquad \frac{d^2\theta}{dt^2} + \frac{g}{L}\sin \theta = 0.$$

The solution of equation (2) is not elementary; it involves an elliptic integral. If θ is small, however, $\sin \theta$ and θ are nearly equal and (2) is closely approximated by the much simpler equation

$$(3) \qquad\qquad \frac{d^2\theta}{dt^2} + \beta^2\theta = 0; \qquad \beta^2 = \frac{g}{L}.$$

The solution of (3) with pertinent boundary conditions gives usable results whenever those conditions are such that θ remains small, say, $|\theta| < 0.3$ (radians). Recall also that in the derivation, it was assumed that the effect of the weight of the rod is negligible compared with that of the weight of the bob.

EXERCISES

1. A clock has a 6-in. pendulum. The clock ticks once for each time that the pendulum completes a swing, returning to its original position. How many times does the clock tick in 30 sec.?   *Ans.* 38 times.

2. A 6-in. pendulum is released from rest at an angle one-tenth of a radian from the vertical. Using $g = 32$ (ft. per sec. per sec.), describe the motion.
$$\textit{Ans. } \theta = 0.1 \cos 8t \text{ (radians).}$$

3. For the pendulum of Ex. 2 find the maximum angular speed and its first time of occurrence.   *Ans.* 0.8 (rad. per sec.) at 0.2 sec.

4. A 6-in. pendulum is started with a velocity of 1 radian per sec., toward the vertical, from a position 0.1 radian from the vertical. Describe the motion.
$$\textit{Ans. } \theta = \tfrac{1}{10}\cos 8t - \tfrac{1}{8}\sin 8t \text{ (radians).}$$

5. For Ex. 4 find to the nearest degree the maximum angular displacement from the vertical.   *Ans.* 9°.

278. *Electric Circuits*

The basic laws which govern the flow of electric current in a circuit or a network will be given here without derivation. The notation used is common to most texts in electrical engineering; it is:

t (seconds) = time
q (coulombs) = quantity of electricity; e.g., charge on a capacitor
i (amperes) = current, time rate of flow of electricity
e (volts) = electromotive force or voltage
R (ohms) = resistance
L (henrys) = inductance
C (farads) = capacitance.

By the definition of q and i it follows that

$$i = \frac{dq}{dt}.$$

The current at each point in a network may be determined by solving the equations which result from applying Kirchhoff's laws:

(*a*) *The sum of the currents into (or away from) any point is zero,*

and

(*b*) *Around any closed path the sum of the instantaneous voltage drops in a specified direction is zero.*

A circuit is treated as a network containing only one closed path. Figure 246 exhibits an "*RLC* circuit" with some of the customary conventions for indicating various elements.

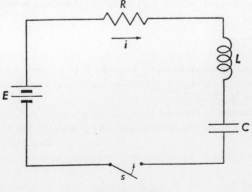

Figure 246

For a circuit Kirchhoff's current law (*a*) indicates merely that the current is the same throughout. That law plays a larger role in networks.

In order to apply Kirchhoff's voltage law (*b*) it is necessary to have the contributions of each of the idealized elements in Fig. 246. The *voltage drop* across the resistance is Ri, that across the inductance is $L\dfrac{di}{dt}$, while the capacitor contributes $\dfrac{1}{C}q$. The impressed electromotive force e ($e = E$, assumed constant in Fig. 246) is contributing a *voltage rise*.

Assume that at time $t = 0$, the switch s shown in Fig. 246 is to be closed. If the capacitor is initially without charge, then $q = 0$ at $t = 0$, while of course $i = 0$ at $t = 0$, since the circuit was not closed until $t = 0$. From Kirchhoff's law (*b*) we get the differential equation

$$L\frac{di}{dt} + Ri + \frac{1}{C}q - E = 0,$$

in which

$$i = \frac{dq}{dt}.$$

The above equations together with the initial conditions

When $t = 0$, $q = 0$ and $i = 0$

constitute the mathematical problem to be solved in connection with Fig. 246. This problem is equivalent to one in damped vibrations. Indeed, the analogies between electrical and mechanical systems are quite useful in practice.

Example. Consider a circuit with the schematic diagram shown in Fig. 247. Here the impressed electromotive force is alternating. It is assumed

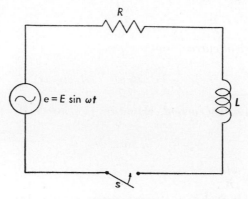

Figure 247

that the switch s is closed at an instant ($t = 0$) when the applied voltage $E \sin \omega t$ is zero.

From Kirchhoff's voltage law it follows that, for $t > 0$,

$$\text{(1)} \qquad L\frac{di}{dt} + Ri = E \sin \omega t,$$

while

$$\text{(2)} \qquad \text{When } t = 0,\ i = 0.$$

Since L, R, E, and ω are constants, equation (1) may be integrated easily by methods developed earlier in this book. The general solution of (1) is

$$\text{(3)} \qquad i = a_1 e^{-\frac{Rt}{L}} + \frac{E}{Z^2}(R \sin \omega t - \omega L \cos \omega t),$$

where a_1 is an arbitrary constant and where $Z = (R^2 + \omega^2 L^2)^{\frac{1}{2}}$. The quantity Z is called the *steady-state impedance* of the circuit.

Since the i of equation (3) is to satisfy (2), it can be seen that $a_1 = \frac{E\omega L}{Z^2}$. Therefore the current in the circuit of Fig. 247 is given by

$$\text{(4)} \qquad i = \frac{E}{Z^2}(R \sin \omega t - \omega L \cos \omega t + \omega L e^{-\frac{Rt}{L}}).$$

For sufficiently large t the last term on the right in (4) is negligible, while the first two terms do not change character with large t. Indeed, the current i may be split into two parts

$$\text{(5)} \qquad i = i_t + i_s,$$

where

$$\text{(6)} \qquad i_t = \frac{E\omega L}{Z^2} e^{-\frac{Rt}{L}},$$

is called the *transient current* and

$$\text{(7)} \qquad i_s = \frac{E}{Z^2}(R \sin \omega t - \omega L \cos \omega t)$$

is called the *steady-state current*. Equation (7) can also be put in the form

$$i_s = \frac{E}{Z} \sin (\omega t - \epsilon),$$

where $\epsilon = \text{Arctan } \frac{\omega L}{R}$.

It is of interest to know the maximum steady-state current, which is easily found to be

$$\text{(8)} \qquad \text{Max } (i_s) = \frac{E}{Z^2}\sqrt{R^2 + \omega^2 L^2} = \frac{E}{Z}.$$

EXERCISES

1. Return to the example of this section, but assume that the switch is closed when the impressed electromotive force is at its maximum. That is, use Fig. 247, page 548, with the replacement $e = E \cos \omega t$ and close the switch at $t = 0$ again, assuming that $i = 0$ when $t = 0$. Find i, i_t, i_s, and max (i_s).

$$Ans.\; i = \frac{E}{Z^2} (\omega L \sin \omega t + R \cos \omega t - Re^{-\frac{Rt}{L}});\; i_t = -\frac{ER}{Z^2} e^{-\frac{Rt}{L}};$$

$$i_s = EZ^{-2}(\omega L \sin \omega t + R \cos \omega t);\; \max\; (i_s) = \frac{E}{Z}.$$

2. In the RL circuit of Fig. 247, page 548, replace the alternating-current element with a direct-current element E. Assume that the switch s is closed at $t = 0$ and that $i = 0$ when $t = 0$. Determine the current i and note its steady-state and transient terms.

3. Figure 248 shows an RC circuit with an alternating-current element inserted. Assume that the switch is closed at $t = 0$ at which time $q = 0$ and $i = 0$. Use the notation $Z^2 = R^2 + (\omega C)^{-2}$, where Z is the steady-state impedance of this circuit. Find i for $t > 0$.

$$Ans.\; i = EZ^{-2}[R \sin \omega t + (\omega C)^{-1} \cos \omega t - (\omega C)^{-1}e^{-\frac{t}{RC}}].$$

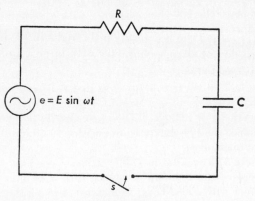

Figure 248

4. In Fig. 248 replace the alternating-current element with a direct-current element $E = 50$ volts and use $R = 10$ ohms, $C = 4(10)^{-4}$ farad. Assume that when the switch s is closed (at $t = 0$) the charge on the capacitor is 0.015 coulomb. Find the initial current in the circuit and the current for $t > 0$.

$$Ans.\; i_0 = 1.25\; (amp.),\; i = 1.25e^{-250t}.$$

5. In Fig. 248 replace $E \sin \omega t$ with $110 \cos 377t$ and use $R = 12$ ohms, $C = 3(10)^{-4}$ farad. Show that the impressed voltage $110 \cos 377t$ is ordinary 60-cycle alternating voltage. Assuming hat $q = 0$ when $t = 0$, find the current i for $t > 0$. $Ans.\; i = 5.94 \cos 377t - 4.38 \sin 377t + 3.23e^{-278t}$.

6. Figure 249 shows an RLC circuit with an alternating-current element. Show that the impressed electromotive force $E \sin 377t$ is ordinary 60-cycle alternating voltage. Using the values $E = 110$, $R = 100$, $L = 0.10$, $C = 5(10)^{-5}$, and assuming that when $t = 0$, $q = 0$ and $i = 0$, find the current i for $t > 0$.

$$Ans.\ i = 1.08 \sin 377t + 0.16 \cos 377t - 1.17e^{-276t} + 1.01e^{-724t}.$$

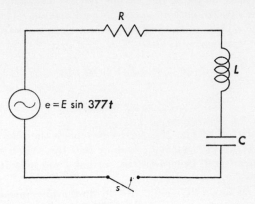

Figure 249

7. In Ex. 6 replace the 100-ohm resistance with a 10-ohm resistance, leaving everything else unchanged. Then compute the current i.

$$Ans.\ i = 3.28 \sin 377t + 5.03 \cos 377t - 5.03e^{-50t} \cos 444t - 3.34e^{-50t} \sin 444t.$$

8. In Ex. 6 replace the 100-ohm resistance with a 40-ohm resistance, and the 0.10-henry inductance with a 0.02-henry inductance, leaving everything else unchanged. Then compute the current i.

$$Ans.\ i = 1.20 \sin 377t + 1.36 \cos 377t - [1.36 + 1.82(10)^3 t]e^{-1000t}.$$

9. In Fig. 249 replace the electromotive force by $e = E \cos 377t$. Use the values $E = 110$, $R = 100$, $L = 0.10$, $C = 5(10)^{-5}$, as in Ex. 6, and compute q and i for $t > 0$, assuming that when $t = 0$, $q = 0$ and $i = 0$.

$$Ans.\ i = 1.08 \cos 377t - 0.16 \sin 377t + 0.86e^{-276t} - 1.94e^{-724t}.$$

10. In Ex. 9 replace the 100-ohm resistance with a 10-ohm resistance, leaving the rest of the problem unchanged.

$$Ans.\ i = 3.28 \cos 377t - 5.03 \sin 377t - 3.28e^{-50t} \cos 444t + 6.37e^{-50t} \sin 444t.$$

11. In Ex. 9 replace the 100-ohm resistance with a 40-ohm resistance and the 0.10-henry inductance with a 0.02-henry inductance, leaving the rest of the problem unchanged. $Ans.\ i = 1.20 \cos 377t - 1.36 \sin 377t - [1.20 - 4.82(10)^3 t]e^{-1000t}.$

12. In Ex. 9 replace the 0.10-henry inductance with 0.01-henry inductance, leaving the rest of the problem unchanged.

$$Ans.\ i = 0.88 \cos 377t - 0.44 \sin 377t + 0.26e^{-204t} - 1.14e^{-9800t}.$$

13. In Fig. 246, page 547, use the values $E = 60$ volts, $R = 8$ ohms, $L = 0.06$ henry, $C = 3(10)^{-4}$ farad, and assume that when $t = 0$, $q = 0$ and $i = 0$. Set up and solve the problem without using the formulas derived in this section. Find the current for $t > 0$. $Ans.\ i = 4.42e^{-66.7t} \sin 226t.$

14. Solve Ex. 13 with the following replacements in the values of the circuit constants: $R = 30$ ohms, $C = 4(10)^{-4}$ farad, (L unchanged).

15. Solve Ex. 13 with the following replacements in the values of the circuit constants: $R = 40$ ohms, $L = 0.02$ henry, $C = 5(10)^{-5}$ farad. $Ans.\ i = 3000te^{-1000t}.$

16. In Ex. 15 find the maximum current. $Ans.\ i_{max} = \dfrac{3}{e}$ (amp.).

TABLES

INDEFINITE INTEGRALS

[In this table, integrals immediately reducible to a standard form (page 234) are omitted.]

1. $\displaystyle\int \frac{x\,dx}{ax + b} = \frac{x}{a} - \frac{b}{a^2} \ln (ax + b) + C.$

2. $\displaystyle\int \frac{x\,dx}{(ax + b)^2} = \frac{b}{a^2(ax + b)} + \frac{1}{a^2} \ln (ax + b) + C.$

3. $\displaystyle\int x(ax + b)^n\,dx = \frac{x(ax + b)^{n+1}}{a(n + 1)} - \frac{(ax + b)^{n+2}}{a^2(n + 1)(n + 2)} + C.$

4. $\displaystyle\int \frac{dx}{x(ax + b)} = \frac{1}{b} \ln \frac{x}{ax + b} + C.$

5. $\displaystyle\int \frac{dx}{x(ax + b)^2} = \frac{1}{b(ax + b)} + \frac{1}{b^2} \ln \frac{x}{ax + b} + C.$

6. $\displaystyle\int \frac{dx}{a^2 - x^2} = \frac{1}{2a} \ln \frac{a + x}{a - x} + C.$ (See page 267.)

7. $\displaystyle\int \frac{dx}{(ax^2 + b)^2} = \frac{x}{2b(ax^2 + b)} + \frac{1}{2b} \int \frac{dx}{ax^2 + b}.$

8. $\displaystyle\int \frac{dx}{x(ax^2 + b)} = \frac{1}{2b} \ln \frac{x^2}{ax^2 + b} + C.$

9. $\displaystyle\int x \sqrt{ax + b}\,dx = \frac{2x}{3a} (ax + b)^{\frac{3}{2}} - \frac{4}{15a^2} (ax + b)^{\frac{5}{2}} + C.$

10. $\displaystyle\int \frac{x\,dx}{\sqrt{ax + b}} = \frac{2x}{a} (ax + b)^{\frac{1}{2}} - \frac{4}{3a^2} (ax + b)^{\frac{3}{2}} + C.$

11. $\displaystyle\int \sqrt{a^2 - x^2}\,dx = \frac{1}{2} x \sqrt{a^2 - x^2} + \frac{1}{2} a^2 \,\text{Arcsin}\, \frac{x}{a} + C.$

12. $\int \sqrt{x^2 \pm a^2}\, dx = \frac{1}{2}x\sqrt{x^2 \pm a^2} \pm \frac{1}{2}a^2 \ln\left(x + \sqrt{x^2 \pm a^2}\right) + C.$

13. $\int \dfrac{dx}{\sqrt{x^2 \pm a^2}} = \ln\left(x + \sqrt{x^2 \pm a^2}\right) + C.$

14. $\int \dfrac{dx}{x\sqrt{a^2 \pm x^2}} = \dfrac{1}{a}\ln\dfrac{x}{a + \sqrt{a^2 \pm x^2}} + C.$

15. $\int \dfrac{dx}{x\sqrt{x^2 - a^2}} = -\dfrac{1}{a}\operatorname{Arcsin}\dfrac{a}{x} + C.$

16. $\int \dfrac{\sqrt{a^2 \pm x^2}}{x}\, dx = \sqrt{a^2 \pm x^2} + a\ln\dfrac{x}{a + \sqrt{a^2 \pm x^2}} + C.$

17. $\int \dfrac{\sqrt{x^2 - a^2}}{x}\, dx = \sqrt{x^2 - a^2} + a\operatorname{Arcsin}\dfrac{a}{x} + C.$

18. $\int (a^2 - x^2)^{\frac{3}{2}}\, dx$

$$= \frac{1}{4}x(a^2 - x^2)^{\frac{3}{2}} + \frac{3}{8}a^2x\sqrt{a^2 - x^2} + \frac{3}{8}a^4\operatorname{Arcsin}\frac{x}{a} + C.$$

19. $\int (x^2 \pm a^2)^{\frac{3}{2}}\, dx = \frac{1}{4}x(x^2 \pm a^2)^{\frac{3}{2}} \pm \frac{3}{8}a^2x\sqrt{x^2 \pm a^2}$

$$+ \tfrac{3}{8}a^4\ln\left(x + \sqrt{x^2 \pm a^2}\right) + C.$$

20. $\int \dfrac{dx}{(a^2 - x^2)^{\frac{3}{2}}} = \dfrac{x}{a^2\sqrt{a^2 - x^2}} + C.$

21. $\int \dfrac{dx}{(x^2 \pm a^2)^{\frac{3}{2}}} = \dfrac{\pm x}{a^2\sqrt{x^2 \pm a^2}} + C.$

22. $\int x^2\sqrt{a^2 - x^2}\, dx$

$$= -\frac{1}{4}x(a^2 - x^2)^{\frac{3}{2}} + \frac{1}{8}a^2x\sqrt{a^2 - x^2} + \frac{1}{8}a^4\operatorname{Arcsin}\frac{x}{a} + C.$$

23. $\int x^3\sqrt{a^2 - x^2}\, dx = \frac{1}{5}(a^2 - x^2)^{\frac{5}{2}} - \frac{1}{3}a^2(a^2 - x^2)^{\frac{3}{2}} + C.$

24. $\int x^2\sqrt{x^2 \pm a^2}\, dx = \frac{1}{4}x(x^2 \pm a^2)^{\frac{3}{2}} \mp \frac{1}{8}a^2x\sqrt{x^2 \pm a^2}$

$$- \tfrac{1}{8}a^4\ln\left(x + \sqrt{x^2 \pm a^2}\right) + C.$$

25. $\int \dfrac{x^2\, dx}{\sqrt{a^2 - x^2}} = -\dfrac{1}{2}x\sqrt{a^2 - x^2} + \dfrac{1}{2}a^2\operatorname{Arcsin}\dfrac{x}{a} + C.$

26. $\int \dfrac{x^3\, dx}{\sqrt{a^2 - x^2}} = -x^2\sqrt{a^2 - x^2} - \dfrac{2}{3}(a^2 - x^2)^{\frac{3}{2}} + C.$

27. $\int \dfrac{x^2\, dx}{\sqrt{x^2 \pm a^2}} = \dfrac{1}{2}x\sqrt{x^2 \pm a^2} \mp \dfrac{1}{2}a^2\ln\left(x + \sqrt{x^2 \pm a^2}\right) + C.$

28. $\int \dfrac{dx}{\sqrt{2ax - x^2}} = 2\operatorname{Arcsin}\sqrt{\dfrac{x}{2a}} + C.$

29. $\displaystyle\int \frac{x^n\,dx}{\sqrt{2ax - x^2}} = -\frac{x^{n-1}\sqrt{2ax - x^2}}{n} + \frac{a(2n - 1)}{n}\int \frac{x^{n-1}\,dx}{\sqrt{2ax - x^2}}.$

30. $\displaystyle\int \sqrt{2ax - x^2}\,dx = \frac{1}{2}(x - a)\sqrt{2ax - x^2} + \frac{1}{2}a^2\,\mathrm{Arcsin}\,\frac{x - a}{a} + C.$

31. $\displaystyle\int \sin^2 x\,dx = \tfrac{1}{2}x - \tfrac{1}{4}\sin 2x + C.$

32. $\displaystyle\int \cos^2 x\,dx = \tfrac{1}{2}x + \tfrac{1}{4}\sin 2x + C.$

33. $\displaystyle\int \sin^n x\,dx = -\frac{\sin^{n-1} x \cos x}{n} + \frac{n - 1}{n}\int \sin^{n-2} x\,dx.$

34. $\displaystyle\int \cos^n x\,dx = \frac{1}{n}\cos^{n-1} x \sin x + \frac{n - 1}{n}\int \cos^{n-2} x\,dx.$

35. $\displaystyle\int \cos^m x \sin^n x\,dx = \frac{\cos^{m-1} x \sin^{n+1} x}{m + n} + \frac{m - 1}{m + n}\int \cos^{m-2} x \sin^n x\,dx.$

36. $\displaystyle\int \cos^m x \sin^n x\,dx$

$$= -\frac{\sin^{n-1} x \cos^{m+1} x}{m + n} + \frac{n - 1}{m + n}\int \cos^m x \sin^{n-2} x\,dx.$$

37. $\displaystyle\int \tan x\,dx = -\ln \cos x + C.$

38. $\displaystyle\int \cot x\,dx = \ln \sin x + C.$

39. $\displaystyle\int \tan^2 x\,dx = \tan x - x + C.$

40. $\displaystyle\int \cot^2 x\,dx = -\cot x - x + C.$

41. $\displaystyle\int \tan^n x\,dx = \frac{\tan^{n-1} x}{n - 1} - \int \tan^{n-2} x\,dx.$

42. $\displaystyle\int \cot^n x\,dx = -\frac{\cot^{n-1} x}{n - 1} - \int \cot^{n-2} x\,dx.$

43. $\displaystyle\int \sec x\,dx = \ln (\sec x + \tan x) + C.$

44. $\displaystyle\int \sec^3 x\,dx = \tfrac{1}{2}\sec x \tan x + \tfrac{1}{2}\ln (\sec x + \tan x) + C.$

45. $\displaystyle\int \csc x\,dx = \ln (\csc x - \cot x) + C.$

46. $\displaystyle\int \csc^3 x\,dx = -\tfrac{1}{2}\csc x \cot x + \tfrac{1}{2}\ln (\csc x - \cot x) + C.$

47. $\displaystyle\int \sec^n x\,dx = \frac{\tan x \sec^{n-2} x}{n - 1} + \frac{n - 2}{n - 1}\int \sec^{n-2} x\,dx.$

48. $\displaystyle\int \csc^n x \, dx = -\frac{\cot x \, \csc^{n-2} x}{n-1} + \frac{n-2}{n-1} \int \csc^{n-2} x \, dx.$

49. $\displaystyle\int x \sin x \, dx = \sin x - x \cos x + C.$

50. $\displaystyle\int x \cos x \, dx = \cos x + x \sin x + C.$

51. $\displaystyle\int x^n \sin x \, dx = -x^n \cos x + n \int x^{n-1} \cos x \, dx.$

52. $\displaystyle\int x^n \cos x \, dx = x^n \sin x - n \int x^{n-1} \sin x \, dx.$

53. $\displaystyle\int x \sin^n x \, dx = \frac{\sin^{n-1} x \, (\sin x - nx \cos x)}{n^2} + \frac{n-1}{n} \int x \sin^{n-2} x \, dx.$

54. $\displaystyle\int x \cos^n x \, dx = \frac{\cos^{n-1} x \, (\cos x + nx \sin x)}{n^2} + \frac{n-1}{n} \int x \cos^{n-2} x \, dx.$

55. $\displaystyle\int \sin mx \sin nx \, dx = \frac{\sin (m-n)x}{2(m-n)} - \frac{\sin (m+n)x}{2(m+n)} + C.$

56. $\displaystyle\int \sin mx \cos nx \, dx = -\frac{\cos (m-n)x}{2(m-n)} - \frac{\cos (m+n)x}{2(m+n)} + C.$

57. $\displaystyle\int \cos mx \cos nx \, dx = \frac{\sin (m-n)x}{2(m-n)} + \frac{\sin (m+n)x}{2(m+n)} + C.$

58. $\displaystyle\int xe^{ax} \, dx = \frac{e^{ax}}{a^2} (ax - 1) + C.$

59. $\displaystyle\int x^2 e^{ax} \, dx = \frac{e^{ax}}{a^3} (a^2x^2 - 2ax + 2) + C.$

60. $\displaystyle\int x^n e^{ax} \, dx = \frac{x^n e^{ax}}{a} - \frac{n}{a} \int x^{n-1} e^{ax} \, dx.$

61. $\displaystyle\int e^{ax} \sin mx \, dx = \frac{e^{ax}(a \sin mx - m \cos mx)}{m^2 + a^2} + C.$

62. $\displaystyle\int e^{ax} \cos mx \, dx = \frac{e^{ax}(m \sin mx + a \cos mx)}{m^2 + a^2} + C.$

63. $\displaystyle\int \sinh x \, dx = \cosh x + C.$

64. $\displaystyle\int \cosh x \, dx = \sinh x + C.$

65. $\displaystyle\int \tanh x \, dx = \ln \cosh x + C.$

66. $\displaystyle\int \sinh^2 x \, dx = \tfrac{1}{2} \sinh x \cosh x - \tfrac{1}{2}x + C.$

67. $\displaystyle\int \cosh^2 x \, dx = \tfrac{1}{2} \sinh x \cosh x + \tfrac{1}{2}x + C.$

68. $\displaystyle\int x \sinh x \, dx = x \cosh x - \sinh x + C.$

69. $\displaystyle\int x \cosh x \, dx = x \sinh x - \cosh x + C.$

70. $\displaystyle\int \ln x \, dx = x \ln x - x + C.$

71. $\displaystyle\int x^n \ln x \, dx = x^{n+1}\left[\frac{\ln x}{n+1} - \frac{1}{(n+1)^2}\right] + C.$

72. $\displaystyle\int (\ln x)^n \, dx = x(\ln x)^n - n \int (\ln x)^{n-1} \, dx.$

Napierian or Natural Logarithms

N	0	1	2	3	4	5	6	7	8	9
0.0		5.395	6.088	6.493	6.781	7.004	7.187	7.341	7.474	7.592
0.1	Take tabular value — 10 7.697	7.793	7.880	7.960	8.034	8.103	8.167	8.228	8.285	8.339
0.2	8.391	8.439	8.486	8.530	8.573	8.614	8.653	8.691	8.727	8.762
0.3	8.796	8.829	8.861	8.891	8.921	8.950	8.978	9.006	9.032	9.058
0.4	9.084	9.108	9.132	9.156	9.179	9.201	9.223	9.245	9.266	9.287
0.5	9.307	9.327	9.346	9.365	9.384	9.402	9.420	9.438	9.455	9.472
0.6	9.489	9.506	9.522	9.538	9.554	9.569	9.584	9.600	9.614	9.629
0.7	9.643	9.658	9.671	9.685	9.699	9.712	9.726	9.739	9.752	9.764
0.8	9.777	9.789	9.802	9.814	9.826	9.837	9.849	9.861	9.872	9.883
0.9	9.895	9.906	9.917	9.927	9.938	9.949	9.959	9.970	9.980	9.990
1.0	0.00000	0995	1980	2956	3922	4879	5827	6766	7696	8618
1.1	9531	*0436	*1333	*2222	*3103	*3976	*4842	*5700	*6551	*7395
1.2	0.1 8232	9062	9885	*0701	*1511	*2314	*3111	*3902	*4686	*5464
1.3	0.2 6236	7003	7763	8518	9267	*0010	*0748	*1481	*2208	*2930
1.4	0.3 3647	4359	5066	5767	6464	7156	7844	8526	9204	9878
1.5	0.4 0547	1211	1871	2527	3178	3825	4469	5108	5742	6373
1.6	7000	7623	8243	8858	9470	*0078	*0682	*1282	*1879	*2473
1.7	0.5 3063	3649	4232	4812	5389	5962	6531	7098	7661	8222
1.8	8779	9333	9884	*0432	*0977	*1519	*2058	*2594	*3127	*3658
1.9	0.6 4185	4710	5233	5752	6269	6783	7294	7803	8310	8813
2.0	9315	9813	*0310	*0804	*1295	*1784	*2271	*2755	*3237	*3716
2.1	0.7 4194	4669	5142	5612	6081	6547	7011	7473	7932	8390
2.2	8846	9299	9751	*0200	*0648	*1093	*1536	*1978	*2418	*2855
2.3	0.8 3291	3725	4157	4587	5015	5442	5866	6289	6710	7129
2.4	7547	7963	8377	8789	9200	9609	*0016	*0422	*0826	*1228
2.5	0.9 1629	2028	2426	2822	3216	3609	4001	4391	4779	5166
2.6	5551	5935	6317	6698	7078	7456	7833	8208	8582	8954
2.7	9325	9695	*0063	*0430	*0796	*1160	*1523	*1885	*2245	*2604
2.8	1.0 2962	3318	3674	4028	4380	4732	5082	5431	5779	6126
2.9	6471	6815	7158	7500	7841	8181	8519	8856	9192	9527
3.0	9861	*0194	*0526	*0856	*1186	*1514	*1841	*2168	*2493	*2817
3.1	1.1 3140	3462	3783	4103	4422	4740	5057	5373	5688	6002
3.2	6315	6627	6938	7248	7557	7865	8173	8479	8784	9089
3.3	9392	9695	9996	*0297	*0597	*0896	*1194	*1491	*1788	*2083
3.4	1.2 2378	2671	2964	3256	3547	3837	4127	4415	4703	4990
3.5	5276	5562	5846	6130	6413	6695	6976	7257	7536	7815
3.6	8093	8371	8647	8923	9198	9473	9746	*0019	*0291	*0563
3.7	1.3 0833	1103	1372	1641	1909	2176	2442	2708	2972	3237
3.8	3500	3763	4025	4286	4547	4807	5067	5325	5584	5841
3.9	6098	6354	6609	6864	7118	7372	7624	7877	8128	8379
4.0	8629	8879	9128	9377	9624	9872	*0118	*0364	*0610	*0854
4.1	1.4 1099	1342	1585	1828	2070	2311	2552	2792	3031	3270
4.2	3508	3746	3984	4220	4456	4692	4927	5161	5395	5629
4.3	5862	6094	6326	6557	6787	7018	7247	7476	7705	7933
4.4	8160	8387	8614	8840	9065	9290	9515	9739	9962	*0185
4.5	1.5 0408	0630	0851	1072	1293	1513	1732	1951	2170	2388
4.6	2606	2823	3039	3256	3471	3687	3902	4116	4330	4543
4.7	4756	4969	5181	5393	5604	5814	6025	6235	6444	6653
4.8	6362	7070	7277	7485	7691	7898	8104	8309	8515	8719
4.9	8924	9127	9331	9534	9737	9939	*0141	*0342	*0543	*0744
5.0	1.6 0944	1144	1343	1542	1741	1939	2137	2334	2531	2728
N	0	1	2	3	4	5	6	7	8	9

This and following tables are from *The Macmillan Logarithmic and Trigonometric Tables*, edited by E. R. Hedrick, copyright 1913 and 1920 by The Macmillan Company and used with the permission of the latter.

Napierian or Natural Logarithms

N	0	1	2	3	4	5	6	7	8	9
5.0	1.6 0944	1144	1343	1542	1741	1939	2137	2334	2531	2728
5.1	2924	3120	3315	3511	3705	3900	4094	4287	4481	4673
5.2	4866	5058	5250	5441	5632	5823	6013	6203	6393	6582
5.3	6771	6959	7147	7335	7523	7710	7896	8083	8269	8455
5.4	8640	8825	9010	9194	9378	9562	9745	9928	*0111	*0293
5.5	1.7 0475	0656	0838	1019	1199	1380	1560	1740	1919	2098
5.6	2277	2455	2633	2811	2988	3166	3342	3519	3695	3871
5.7	4047	4222	4397	4572	4746	4920	5094	5267	5440	5613
5.8	5786	5958	6130	6302	6473	6644	6815	6985	7156	7326
5.9	7495	7665	7834	8002	8171	8339	8507	8675	8842	9009
6.0	9176	9342	9509	9675	9840	*0006	*0171	*0336	*0500	*0665
6.1	1.8 0829	0993	1156	1319	1482	1645	1808	1970	2132	2294
6.2	2455	2616	2777	2938	3098	3258	3418	3578	3737	3895
6.3	4055	4214	4372	4530	4688	4845	5003	5160	5317	5473
6.4	5630	5786	5942	6097	6253	6408	6563	6718	6872	7026
6.5	7180	7334	7487	7641	7794	7947	8099	8251	8403	8555
6.6	8707	8858	9010	9160	9311	9462	9612	9762	9912	*0061
6.7	1.9 0211	0360	0509	0658	0806	0954	1102	1250	1398	1545
6.8	1692	1839	1986	2132	2279	2425	2571	2716	2862	3007
6.9	3152	3297	3442	3586	3730	3874	4018	4162	4305	4448
7.0	4591	4734	4876	5019	5161	5303	5445	5586	5727	5869
7.1	6009	6150	6291	6431	6571	6711	6851	6991	7130	7269
7.2	7408	7547	7685	7824	7962	8100	8238	8376	8513	8650
7.3	8787	8924	9061	9198	9334	9470	9606	9742	9877	*0013
7.4	2.0 0148	0283	0418	0553	0687	0821	0956	1089	1223	1357
7.5	1490	1624	1757	1890	2022	2155	2287	2419	2551	2683
7.6	2815	2946	3078	3209	3340	3471	3601	3732	3862	3992
7.7	4122	4252	4381	4511	4640	4769	4898	5027	5156	5284
7.8	5412	5540	5668	5796	5924	6051	6179	6306	6433	6560
7.9	6686	6813	6939	7065	7191	7317	7443	7568	7694	7819
8.0	7944	8069	8194	8318	8443	8567	8691	8815	8939	9063
8.1	9186	9310	9433	9556	9679	9802	9924	*0047	*0169	*0291
8.2	2.1 0413	0535	0657	0779	0900	1021	1142	1263	1384	1505
8.3	1626	1746	1866	1986	2106	2226	2346	2465	2585	2704
8.4	2823	2942	3061	3180	3298	3417	3535	3653	3771	3889
8.5	4007	4124	4242	4359	4476	4593	4710	4827	4943	5060
8.6	5176	5292	5409	5524	5640	5756	5871	5987	6102	6217
8.7	6332	6447	6562	6677	6791	6905	7020	7134	7248	7361
8.8	7475	7589	7702	7816	7929	8042	8155	8267	8380	8493
8.9	8605	8717	8830	8942	9054	9165	9277	9389	9500	9611
9.0	9722	9834	9944	*0055	*0166	*0276	*0387	*0497	*0607	*0717
9.1	2.2 0827	0937	1047	1157	1266	1375	1485	1594	1703	1812
9.2	1920	2029	2138	2246	2354	2462	2570	2678	2786	2894
9.3	3001	3109	3216	3324	3431	3538	3645	3751	3858	3965
9.4	4071	4177	4284	4390	4496	4601	4707	4813	4918	5024
9.5	5129	5234	5339	5444	5549	5654	5759	5863	5968	6072
9.6	6176	6280	6384	6488	6592	6696	6799	6903	7006	7109
9.7	7213	7316	7419	7521	7624	7727	7829	7932	8034	8136
9.8	8238	8340	8442	8544	8646	8747	8849	8950	9051	9152
9.9	9253	9354	9455	9556	9657	9757	9858	9958	*0058	*0158
10.0	2.3 0259	0358	0458	0558	0658	0757	0857	0956	1055	1154
N	0	1	2	3	4	5	6	7	8	9

Values and Logarithms of Hyperbolic Functions

x	e^x Value	e^x Log$_{10}$	e^{-x} Value	Sinh x Value	Sinh x Log$_{10}$	Cosh x Value	Cosh x Log$_{10}$	Tanh x Value
0.00	1.0000	.00000	1.0000	0.0000	$-\infty$	1.0000	.00000	.00000
0.01	1.0101	.00434	.99005	0.0100	.00001	1.0001	.00002	.01000
0.02	1.0202	.00869	.98020	0.0200	.30106	1.0002	.00009	.02000
0.03	1.0305	.01303	.97045	0.0300	.47719	1.0005	.00020	.02999
0.04	1.0408	.01737	.96079	0.0400	.60218	1.0008	.00035	.03998
0.05	1.0513	.02171	.95123	0.0500	.69915	1.0013	.00054	.04996
0.06	1.0618	.02606	.94176	0.0600	.77841	1.0018	.00078	.05993
0.07	1.0725	.03040	.93239	0.0701	.84545	1.0025	.00106	.06989
0.08	1.0833	.03474	.92312	0.0801	.90355	1.0032	.00139	.07983
0.09	1.0942	.03909	.91393	0.0901	.95483	1.0041	.00176	.08976
0.10	1.1052	.04343	.90484	0.1002	.00072	1.0050	.00217	.09967
0.11	1.1163	.04777	.89583	0.1102	.04227	1.0061	.00262	.10956
0.12	1.1275	.05212	.88692	0.1203	.08022	1.0072	.00312	.11943
0.13	1.1388	.05646	.87810	0.1304	.11517	1.0085	.00366	.12927
0.14	1.1503	.06080	.86936	0.1405	.14755	1.0098	.00424	.13909
0.15	1.1618	.06514	.86071	0.1506	.17772	1.0113	.00487	.14889
0.16	1.1735	.06949	.85214	0.1607	.20597	1.0128	.00554	.15865
0.17	1.1853	.07383	.84366	0.1708	.23254	1.0145	.00625	.16838
0.18	1.1972	.07817	.83527	0.1810	.25762	1.0162	.00700	.17808
0.19	1.2092	.08252	.82696	0.1911	.28136	1.0181	.00779	.18775
0.20	1.2214	.08686	.81873	0.2013	.30392	1.0201	.00863	.19738
0.21	1.2337	.09120	.81058	0.2115	.32541	1.0221	.00951	.20697
0.22	1.2461	.09554	.80252	0.2218	.34592	1.0243	.01043	.21652
0.23	1.2586	.09989	.79453	0.2320	.36555	1.0266	.01139	.22603
0.24	1.2712	.10423	.78663	0.2423	.38437	1.0289	.01239	.23550
0.25	1.2840	.10857	.77880	0.2526	.40245	1.0314	.01343	.24492
0.26	1.2969	.11292	.77105	0.2629	.41986	1.0340	.01452	.25430
0.27	1.3100	.11726	.76338	0.2733	.43663	1.0367	.01564	.26362
0.28	1.3231	.12160	.75578	0.2837	.45282	1.0395	.01681	.27291
0.29	1.3364	.12595	.74826	0.2941	.46847	1.0423	.01801	.28213
0.30	1.3499	.13029	.74082	0.3045	.48362	1.0453	.01926	.29131
0.31	1.3634	.13463	.73345	0.3150	.49830	1.0484	.02054	.30044
0.32	1.3771	.13897	.72615	0.3255	.51254	1.0516	.02187	.30951
0.33	1.3910	.14332	.71892	0.3360	.52637	1.0549	.02323	.31852
0.34	1.4049	.14766	.71177	0.3466	.53981	1.0584	.02463	.32748
0.35	1.4191	.15200	.70469	0.3572	.55290	1.0619	.02607	.33638
0.36	1.4333	.15635	.69768	0.3678	.56564	1.0655	.02755	.34521
0.37	1.4477	.16069	.69073	0.3785	.57807	1.0692	.02907	.35399
0.38	1.4623	.16503	.68386	0.3892	.59019	1.0731	.03063	.36271
0.39	1.4770	.16937	.67706	0.4000	.60202	1.0770	.03222	.37136
0.40	1.4918	.17372	.67032	0.4108	.61358	1.0811	.03385	.37995
0.41	1.5068	.17806	.66365	0.4216	.62488	1.0852	.03552	.38847
0.42	1.5220	.18240	.65705	0.4325	.63594	1.0895	.03723	.39693
0.43	1.5373	.18675	.65051	0.4434	.64677	1.0939	.03897	.40532
0.44	1.5527	.19109	.64404	0.4543	.65738	1.0984	.04075	.41364
0.45	1.5683	.19543	.63763	0.4653	.66777	1.1030	.04256	.42190
0.46	1.5841	.19978	.63128	0.4764	.67797	1.1077	.04441	.43008
0.47	1.6000	.20412	.62500	0.4875	.68797	1.1125	.04630	.43820
0.48	1.6161	.20846	.61878	0.4986	.69779	1.1174	.04822	.44624
0.49	1.6323	.21280	.61263	0.5098	.70744	1.1225	.05018	.45422
0.50	1.6487	.21715	.60653	0.5211	.71692	1.1276	.05217	.46212

Values and Logarithms of Hyperbolic Functions

x	e^x Value	e^x Log₁₀	e^{-x} Value	Sinh x Value	Sinh x Log₁₀	Cosh x Value	Cosh x Log₁₀	Tanh x Value
0.50	1.6487	.21715	.60653	0.5211	.71692	1.1276	.05217	.46212
0.51	1.6653	.22149	.60050	0.5324	.72624	1.1329	.05419	.46995
0.52	1.6820	.22583	.59452	0.5438	.73540	1.1383	.05625	.47770
0.53	1.6989	.23018	.58860	0.5552	.74442	1.1438	.05834	.48538
0.54	1.7160	.23452	.58275	0.5666	.75330	1.1494	.06046	.49299
0.55	1.7333	.23886	.57695	0.5782	.76204	1.1551	.06262	.50052
0.56	1.7507	.24320	.57121	0.5897	.77065	1.1609	.06481	.50798
0.57	1.7683	.24755	.56553	0.6014	.77914	1.1669	.06703	.51536
0.58	1.7860	.25189	.55990	0.6131	.78751	1.1730	.06929	.52267
0.59	1.8040	.25623	.55433	0.6248	.79576	1.1792	.07157	.52990
0.60	1.8221	.26058	.54881	0.6367	.80390	1.1855	.07389	.53705
0.61	1.8404	.26492	.54335	0.6485	.81194	1.1919	.07624	.54413
0.62	1.8589	.26926	.53794	0.6605	.81987	1.1984	.07861	.55113
0.63	1.8776	.27361	.53259	0.6725	.82770	1.2051	.08102	.55805
0.64	1.8965	.27795	.52729	0.6846	.83543	1.2119	.08346	.56490
0.65	1.9155	.28229	.52205	0.6967	.84308	1.2188	.08593	.57167
0.66	1.9348	.28663	.51685	0.7090	.85063	1.2258	.08843	.57836
0.67	1.9542	.29098	.51171	0.7213	.85809	1.2330	.09095	.58498
0.68	1.9739	.29532	.50662	0.7336	.86548	1.2402	.09351	.59152
0.69	1.9937	.29966	.50158	0.7461	.87278	1.2476	.09609	.59798
0.70	2.0138	.30401	.49659	0.7586	.88000	1.2552	.09870	.60437
0.71	2.0340	.30835	.49164	0.7712	.88715	1.2628	.10134	.61068
0.72	2.0544	.31269	.48675	0.7838	.89423	1.2706	.10401	.61691
0.73	2.0751	.31703	.48191	0.7966	.90123	1.2785	.10670	.62307
0.74	2.0959	.32138	.47711	0.8094	.90817	1.2865	.10942	.62915
0.75	2.1170	.32572	.47237	0.8223	.91504	1.2947	.11216	.63515
0.76	2.1383	.33006	.46767	0.8353	.92185	1.3030	.11493	.64108
0.77	2.1598	.33441	.46301	0.8484	.92859	1.3114	.11773	.64693
0.78	2.1815	.33875	.45841	0.8615	.93527	1.3199	.12055	.65271
0.79	2.2034	.34309	.45384	0.8748	.94190	1.3286	.12340	.65841
0.80	2.2255	.34744	.44933	0.8881	.94846	1.3374	.12627	.66404
0.81	2.2479	.35178	.44486	0.9015	.95498	1.3464	.12917	.66959
0.82	2.2705	.35612	.44043	0.9150	.96144	1.3555	.13209	.67507
0.83	2.2933	.36046	.43605	0.9286	.96784	1.3647	.13503	.68048
0.84	2.3164	.36481	.43171	0.9423	.97420	1.3740	.13800	.68581
0.85	2.3396	.36915	.42741	0.9561	.98051	1.3835	.14099	.69107
0.86	2.3632	.37349	.42316	0.9700	.98677	1.3932	.14400	.69626
0.87	2.3869	.37784	.41895	0.9840	.99299	1.4029	.14704	.70137
0.88	2.4109	.38218	.41478	0.9981	.99916	1.4128	.15009	.70642
0.89	2.4351	.38652	.41066	1.0122	.00528	1.4229	.15317	.71139
0.90	2.4596	.39087	.40657	1.0265	.01137	1.4331	.15627	.71630
0.91	2.4843	.39521	.40252	1.0409	.01741	1.4434	.15939	.72113
0.92	2.5093	.39955	.39852	1.0554	.02341	1.4539	.16254	.72590
0.93	2.5345	.40389	.39455	1.0700	.02937	1.4645	.16570	.73059
0.94	2.5600	.40824	.39063	1.0847	.03530	1.4753	.16888	.73522
0.95	2.5857	.41258	.38674	1.0995	.04119	1.4862	.17208	.73978
0.96	2.6117	.41692	.38289	1.1144	.04704	1.4973	.17531	.74428
0.97	2.6379	.42127	.37908	1.1294	.05286	1.5085	.17855	.74870
0.98	2.6645	.42561	.37531	1.1446	.05864	1.5199	.18181	.75307
0.99	2.6912	.42995	.37158	1.1598	.06439	1.5314	.18509	.75736
1.00	2.7183	.43429	.36788	1.1752	.07011	1.5431	.18839	.76159

TABLES

Values and Logarithms of Hyperbolic Functions

x	e^x Value	e^x Log₁₀	e^{-x} Value	Sinh x Value	Sinh x Log₁₀	Cosh x Value	Cosh x Log₁₀	Tanh x Value
1.00	2.7183	.43429	.36788	1.1752	.07011	1.5431	.18839	.76159
1.01	2.7456	.43864	.36422	1.1907	.07580	1.5549	.19171	.76576
1.02	2.7732	.44298	.36059	1.2063	.08146	1.5669	.19504	.76987
1.03	2.8011	.44732	.35701	1.2220	.08708	1.5790	.19839	.77391
1.04	2.8292	.45167	.35345	1.2379	.09268	1.5913	.20176	.77789
1.05	2.8577	.45601	.34994	1.2539	.09825	1.6038	.20515	.78181
1.06	2.8864	.46035	.34646	1.2700	.10379	1.6164	.20855	.78566
1.07	2.9154	.46470	.34301	1.2862	.10930	1.6292	.21197	.78946
1.08	2.9447	.46904	.33960	1.3025	.11479	1.6421	.21541	.79320
1.09	2.9743	.47338	.33622	1.3190	.12025	1.6552	.21886	.79688
1.10	3.0042	.47772	.33287	1.3356	.12569	1.6685	.22233	.80050
1.11	3.0344	.48207	.32956	1.3524	.13111	1.6820	.22582	.80406
1.12	3.0649	.48641	.32628	1.3693	.13649	1.6956	.22931	.80757
1.13	3.0957	.49075	.32303	1.3863	.14186	1.7093	.23283	.81102
1.14	3.1268	.49510	.31982	1.4035	.14720	1.7233	.23636	.81441
1.15	3.1582	.49944	.31664	1.4208	.15253	1.7374	.23990	.81775
1.16	3.1899	.50378	.31349	1.4382	.15783	1.7517	.24346	.82104
1.17	3.2220	.50812	.31037	1.4558	.16311	1.7662	.24703	.82427
1.18	3.2544	.51247	.30728	1.4735	.16836	1.7808	.25062	.82745
1.19	3.2871	.51681	.30422	1.4914	.17360	1.7957	.25422	.83058
1.20	3.3201	.52115	.30119	1.5095	.17882	1.8107	.25784	.83365
1.21	3.3535	.52550	.29820	1.5276	.18402	1.8258	.26146	.83668
1.22	3.3872	.52984	.29523	1.5460	.18920	1.8412	.26510	.83965
1.23	3.4212	.53418	.29229	1.5645	.19437	1.8568	.26876	.84258
1.24	3.4556	.53853	.28938	1.5831	.19951	1.8725	.27242	.84546
1.25	3.4903	.54287	.28650	1.6019	.20464	1.8884	.27610	.84828
1.26	3.5254	.54721	.28365	1.6209	.20975	1.9045	.27979	.85106
1.27	3.5609	.55155	.28083	1.6400	.21485	1.9208	.28349	.85380
1.28	3.5966	.55590	.27804	1.6593	.21993	1.9373	.28721	.85648
1.29	3.6328	.56024	.27527	1.6788	.22499	1.9540	.29093	.85913
1.30	3.6693	.56458	.27253	1.6984	.23004	1.9709	.29467	.86172
1.31	3.7062	.56893	.26982	1.7182	.23507	1.9880	.29842	.86428
1.32	3.7434	.57327	.26714	1.7381	.24009	2.0053	.30217	.86678
1.33	3.7810	.57761	.26448	1.7583	.24509	2.0228	.30594	.86925
1.34	3.8190	.58195	.26185	1.7786	.25008	2.0404	.30972	.87167
1.35	3.8574	.58630	.25924	1.7991	.25505	2.0583	.31352	.87405
1.36	3.8962	.59064	.25666	1.8198	.26002	2.0764	.31732	.87639
1.37	3.9354	.59498	.25411	1.8406	.26496	2.0947	.32113	.87869
1.38	3.9749	.59933	.25158	1.8617	.26990	2.1132	.32495	.88095
1.39	4.0149	.60367	.24908	1.8829	.27482	2.1320	.32878	.88317
1.40	4.0552	.60801	.24660	1.9043	.27974	2.1509	.33262	.88535
1.41	4.0960	.61236	.24414	1.9259	.28464	2.1700	.33647	.88749
1.42	4.1371	.61670	.24171	1.9477	.28952	2.1894	.34033	.88960
1.43	4.1787	.62104	.23931	1.9697	.29440	2.2090	.34420	.89167
1.44	4.2207	.62538	.23693	1.9919	.29926	2.2288	.34807	.89370
1.45	4.2631	.62973	.23457	2.0143	.30412	2.2488	.35196	.89569
1.46	4.3060	.63407	.23224	2.0369	.30896	2.2691	.35585	.89765
1.47	4.3492	.63841	.22993	2.0597	.31379	2.2896	.35976	.89958
1.48	4.3929	.64276	.22764	2.0827	.31862	2.3103	.36367	.90147
1.49	4.4371	.64710	.22537	2.1059	.32343	2.3312	.36759	.90332
1.50	4.4817	.65144	.22313	2.1293	.32823	2.3524	.37151	.90515

Values and Logarithms of Hyperbolic Functions

x	e^x Value	e^x Log₁₀	e^{-x} Value	Sinh x Value	Sinh x Log₁₀	Cosh x Value	Cosh x Log₁₀	Tanh x Value
1.50	4.4817	.65144	.22313	2.1293	.32823	2.3524	.37151	.90515
1.51	4.5267	.65578	.22091	2.1529	.33303	2.3738	.37545	.90694
1.52	4.5722	.66013	.21871	2.1768	.33781	2.3955	.37939	.90870
1.53	4.6182	.66447	.21654	2.2008	.34258	2.4174	.38334	.91042
1.54	4.6646	.66881	.21438	2.2251	.34735	2.4395	.38730	.91212
1.55	4.7115	.67316	.21225	2.2496	.35211	2.4619	.39126	.91379
1.56	4.7588	.67750	.21014	2.2743	.35686	2.4845	.39524	.91542
1.57	4.8066	.68184	.20805	2.2993	.36160	2.5073	.39921	.91703
1.58	4.8550	.68619	.20598	2.3245	.36633	2.5305	.40320	.91860
1.59	4.9037	.69053	.20393	2.3499	.37105	2.5538	.40719	.92015
1.60	4.9530	.69487	.20190	2.3756	.37577	2.5775	.41119	.92167
1.61	5.0028	.69921	.19989	2.4015	.38048	2.6013	.41520	.92316
1.62	5.0531	.70356	.19790	2.4276	.38518	2.6255	.41921	.92462
1.63	5.1039	.70790	.19593	2.4540	.38987	2.6499	.42323	.92606
1.64	5.1552	.71224	.19398	2.4806	.39456	2.6746	.42725	.92747
1.65	5.2070	.71659	.19205	2.5075	.39923	2.6995	.43129	.92886
1.66	5.2593	.72093	.19014	2.5346	.40391	2.7247	.43532	.93022
1.67	5.3122	.72527	.18825	2.5620	.40857	2.7502	.43937	.93155
1.68	5.3656	.72961	.18637	2.5896	.41323	2.7760	.44341	.93286
1.69	5.4195	.73396	.18452	2.6175	.41788	2.8020	.44747	.93415
1.70	5.4739	.73830	.18268	2.6456	.42253	2.8283	.45153	.93541
1.71	5.5290	.74264	.18087	2.6740	.42717	2.8549	.45559	.93665
1.72	5.5845	.74699	.17907	2.7027	.43180	2.8818	.45966	.93786
1.73	5.6407	.75133	.17728	2.7317	.43643	2.9090	.46374	.93906
1.74	5.6973	.75567	.17552	2.7609	.44105	2.9364	.46782	.94023
1.75	5.7546	.76002	.17377	2.7904	.44567	2.9642	.47191	.94138
1.76	5.8124	.76436	.17204	2.8202	.45028	2.9922	.47600	.94250
1.77	5.8709	.76870	.17033	2.8503	.45488	3.0206	.48009	.94361
1.78	5.9299	.77304	.16864	2.8806	.45948	3.0492	.48419	.94470
1.79	5.9895	.77739	.16696	2.9112	.46408	3.0782	.48830	.94576
1.80	6.0496	.78173	.16530	2.9422	.46867	3.1075	.49241	.94681
1.81	6.1104	.78607	.16365	2.9734	.47325	3.1371	.49652	.94783
1.82	6.1719	.79042	.16203	3.0049	.47783	3.1669	.50064	.94884
1.83	6.2339	.79476	.16041	3.0367	.48241	3.1972	.50476	.94983
1.84	6.2965	.79910	.15882	3.0689	.48698	3.2277	.50889	.95080
1.85	6.3598	.80344	.15724	3.1013	.49154	3.2585	.51302	.95175
1.86	6.4237	.80779	.15567	3.1340	.49610	3.2897	.51716	.95268
1.87	6.4883	.81213	.15412	3.1671	.50066	3.3212	.52130	.95359
1.88	6.5535	.81647	.15259	3.2005	.50521	3.3530	.52544	.95449
1.89	6.6194	.82082	.15107	3.2341	.50976	3.3852	.52959	.95537
1.90	6.6859	.82516	.14957	3.2682	.51430	3.4177	.53374	.95624
1.91	6.7531	.82950	.14808	3.3025	.51884	3.4506	.53789	.95709
1.92	6.8210	.83385	.14661	3.3372	.52338	3.4838	.54205	.95792
1.93	6.8895	.83819	.14515	3.3722	.52791	3.5173	.54621	.95873
1.94	6.9588	.84253	.14370	3.4075	.53244	3.5512	.55038	.95953
1.95	7.0287	.84687	.14227	3.4432	.53696	3.5855	.55455	.96032
1.96	7.0993	.85122	.14086	3.4792	.54148	3.6201	.55872	.96109
1.97	7.1707	.85556	.13946	3.5156	.54600	3.6551	.56290	.96185
1.98	7.2427	.85990	.13807	3.5523	.55051	3.6904	.56707	.96259
1.99	7.3155	.86425	.13670	3.5894	.55502	3.7261	.57126	.96331
2.00	7.3891	.86859	.13534	3.6269	.55953	3.7622	.57544	.96403

Values and Logarithms of Hyperbolic Functions

x	e^x Value	e^x Log₁₀	e^{-x} Value	Sinh x Value	Sinh x Log₁₀	Cosh x Value	Cosh x Log₁₀	Tanh x Value
2.00	7.3891	.86859	.13534	3.6269	.55953	3.7622	.57544	.96403
2.01	7.4633	.87293	.13399	3.6647	.56403	3.7987	.57963	.96473
2.02	7.5383	.87727	.13266	3.7028	.56853	3.8355	.58382	.96541
2.03	7.6141	.88162	.13134	3.7414	.57303	3.8727	.58802	.96609
2.04	7.6906	.88596	.13003	3.7803	.57753	3.9103	.59221	.96675
2.05	7.7679	.89030	.12873	3.8196	.58202	3.9483	.59641	.96740
2.06	7.8460	.89465	.12745	3.8593	.58650	3.9867	.60061	.96803
2.07	7.9248	.89899	.12619	3.8993	.59099	4.0255	.60482	.96865
2.08	8.0045	.90333	.12493	3.9398	.59547	4.0647	.60903	.96926
2.09	8.0849	.90768	.12369	3.9806	.59995	4.1043	.61324	.96986
2.10	8.1662	.91202	.12246	4.0219	.60443	4.1443	.61745	.97045
2.11	8.2482	.91636	.12124	4.0635	.60890	4.1847	.62167	.97103
2.12	8.3311	.92070	.12003	4.1056	.61337	4.2256	.62589	.97159
2.13	8.4149	.92505	.11884	4.1480	.61784	4.2669	.63011	.97215
2.14	8.4994	.92939	.11765	4.1909	.62231	4.3085	.63433	.97269
2.15	8.5849	.93373	.11648	4.2342	.62677	4.3507	.63856	.97323
2.16	8.6711	.93808	.11533	4.2779	.63123	4.3932	.64278	.97375
2.17	8.7583	.94242	.11418	4.3221	.63569	4.4362	.64701	.97426
2.18	8.8463	.94676	.11304	4.3666	.64015	4.4797	.65125	.97477
2.19	8.9352	.95110	.11192	4.4116	.64460	4.5236	.65548	.97526
2.20	9.0250	.95545	.11080	4.4571	.64905	4.5679	.65972	.97574
2.21	9.1157	.95979	.10970	4.5030	.65350	4.6127	.66396	.97622
2.22	9.2073	.96413	.10861	4.5494	.65795	4.6580	.66820	.97668
2.23	9.2999	.96848	.10753	4.5962	.66240	4.7037	.67244	.97714
2.24	9.3933	.97282	.10646	4.6434	.66684	4.7499	.67668	.97759
2.25	9.4877	.97716	.10540	4.6912	.67128	4.7966	.68093	.97803
2.26	9.5831	.98151	.10435	4.7394	.67572	4.8437	.68518	.97846
2.27	9.6794	.98585	.10331	4.7880	.68016	4.8914	.68943	.97888
2.28	9.7767	.99019	.10228	4.8372	.68459	4.9395	.69368	.97929
2.29	9.8749	.99453	.10127	4.8868	.68903	4.9881	.69794	.97970
2.30	9.9742	.99888	.10026	4.9370	.69346	5.0372	.70219	.98010
2.31	10.074	.00322	.09926	4.9876	.69789	5.0868	.70645	.98049
2.32	10.176	.00756	.09827	5.0387	.70232	5.1370	.71071	.98087
2.33	10.278	.01191	.09730	5.0903	.70675	5.1876	.71497	.98124
2.34	10.381	.01625	.09633	5.1425	.71117	5.2388	.71923	.98161
2.35	10.486	.02059	.09537	5.1951	.71559	5.2905	.72349	.98197
2.36	10.591	.02493	.09442	5.2483	.72002	5.3427	.72776	.98233
2.37	10.697	.02928	.09348	5.3020	.72444	5.3954	.73203	.98267
2.38	10.805	.03362	.09255	5.3562	.72885	5.4487	.73630	.98301
2.39	10.913	.03796	.09163	5.4109	.73327	5.5026	.74056	.98335
2.40	11.023	.04231	.09072	5.4662	.73769	5.5569	.74484	.98367
2.41	11.134	.04665	.08982	5.5221	.74210	5.6119	.74911	.98400
2.42	11.246	.05099	.08892	5.5785	.74652	5.6674	.75338	.98431
2.43	11.359	.05534	.08804	5.6354	.75093	5.7235	.75766	.98462
2.44	11.473	.05968	.08716	5.6929	.75534	5.7801	.76194	.98492
2.45	11.588	.06402	.08629	5.7510	.75975	5.8373	.76621	.98522
2.46	11.705	.06836	.08543	5.8097	.76415	5.8951	.77049	.98551
2.47	11.822	.07271	.08458	5.8689	.76856	5.9535	.77477	.98579
2.48	11.941	.07705	.08374	5.9288	.77296	6.0125	.77906	.98607
2.49	12.061	.08139	.08291	5.9892	.77737	6.0721	.78334	.98635
2.50	12.182	.08574	.08208	6.0502	.78177	6.1323	.78762	.98661

Values and Logarithms of Hyperbolic Functions

x	e^x Value	e^x Log₁₀	e^{-x} Value	Sinh x Value	Sinh x Log₁₀	Cosh x Value	Cosh x Log₁₀	Tanh x Value
2.50	12.182	.08574	.08208	6.0502	.78177	6.1323	.78762	.98661
2.51	12.305	.09008	.08127	6.1118	.78617	6.1931	.79191	.98688
2.52	12.429	.09442	.08046	6.1741	.79057	6.2545	.79619	.98714
2.53	12.554	.09877	.07966	6.2369	.79497	6.3166	.80048	.98739
2.54	12.680	.10311	.07887	6.3004	.79937	6.3793	.80477	.98764
2.55	12.807	.10745	.07808	6.3645	.80377	6.4426	.80906	.98788
2.56	12.936	.11179	.07730	6.4293	.80816	6.5066	.81335	.98812
2.57	13.066	.11614	.07654	6.4946	.81256	6.5712	.81764	.98835
2.58	13.197	.12048	.07577	6.5607	.81695	6.6365	.82194	.98858
2.59	13.330	.12482	.07502	6.6274	.82134	6.7024	.82623	.98881
2.60	13.464	.12917	.07427	6.6947	.82573	6.7690	.83052	.98903
2.61	13.599	.13351	.07353	6.7628	.83012	6.8363	.83482	.98924
2.62	13.736	.13785	.07280	6.8315	.83451	6.9043	.83912	.98946
2.63	13.874	.14219	.07208	6.9008	.83890	6.9729	.84341	.98966
2.64	14.013	.14654	.07136	6.9709	.84329	7.0423	.84771	.98987
2.65	14.154	.15088	.07065	7.0417	.84768	7.1123	.85201	.99007
2.66	14.296	.15522	.06995	7.1132	.85206	7.1831	.85631	.99026
2.67	14.440	.15957	.06925	7.1854	.85645	7.2546	.86061	.99045
2.68	14.585	.16391	.06856	7.2583	.86083	7.3268	.86492	.99064
2.69	14.732	.16825	.06788	7.3319	.86522	7.3998	.86922	.99083
2.70	14.880	.17260	.06721	7.4063	.86960	7.4735	.87352	.99101
2.71	15.029	.17694	.06654	7.4814	.87398	7.5479	.87783	.99118
2.72	15.180	.18128	.06587	7.5572	.87836	7.6231	.88213	.99136
2.73	15.333	.18562	.06522	7.6338	.88274	7.6991	.88644	.99153
2.74	15.487	.18997	.06457	7.7112	.88712	7.7758	.89074	.99170
2.75	15.643	.19431	.06393	7.7894	.89150	7.8533	.89505	.99186
2.76	15.800	.19865	.06329	7.8683	.89588	7.9316	.89936	.99202
2.77	15.959	.20300	.06266	7.9480	.90026	8.0106	.90367	.99218
2.78	16.119	.20734	.06204	8.0285	.90463	8.0905	.90798	.99233
2.79	16.281	.21168	.06142	8.1098	.90901	8.1712	.91229	.99248
2.80	16.445	.21602	.06081	8.1919	.91339	8.2527	.91660	.99263
2.81	16.610	.22037	.06020	8.2749	.91776	8.3351	.92091	.99278
2.82	16.777	.22471	.05961	8.3586	.92213	8.4182	.92522	.99292
2.83	16.945	.22905	.05901	8.4432	.92651	8.5022	.92953	.99306
2.84	17.116	.23340	.05843	8.5287	.93088	8.5871	.93385	.99320
2.85	17.288	.23774	.05784	8.6150	.93525	8.6728	.93816	.99333
2.86	17.462	.24208	.05727	8.7021	.93963	8.7594	.94247	.99346
2.87	17.637	.24643	.05670	8.7902	.94400	8.8469	.94679	.99359
2.88	17.814	.25077	.05613	8.8791	.94837	8.9352	.95110	.99372
2.89	17.993	.25511	.05558	8.9689	.95274	9.0244	.95542	.99384
2.90	18.174	.25945	.05502	9.0596	.95711	9.1146	.95974	.99396
2.91	18.357	.26380	.05448	9.1512	.96148	9.2056	.96405	.99408
2.92	18.541	.26814	.05393	9.2437	.96584	9.2976	.96837	.99420
2.93	18.728	.27248	.05340	9.3371	.97021	9.3905	.97269	.99431
2.94	18.916	.27683	.05287	9.4315	.97458	9.4844	.97701	.99443
2.95	19.106	.28117	.05234	9.5268	.97895	9.5791	.98133	.99454
2.96	19.298	.28551	.05182	9.6231	.98331	9.6749	.98565	.99464
2.97	19.492	.28985	.05130	9.7203	.98768	9.7716	.98997	.99475
2.98	19.688	.29420	.05079	9.8185	.99205	9.8693	.99429	.99485
2.99	19.886	.29854	.05029	9.9177	.99641	9.9680	.99861	.99496
3.00	20.086	.30288	.04979	10.018	.00078	10.068	.00293	.99505

Four Place Trigonometric Functions

[Characteristics of Logarithms omitted—determine by the usual rule from the value]

Radians	Degrees	Sine Value	Sine Log₁₀	Tangent Value	Tangent Log₁₀	Cotangent Value	Cotangent Log₁₀	Cosine Value	Cosine Log₁₀		
.0000	0° 00′	.0000	—	.0000	—			1.0000	.0000	90° 00′	1.5708
.0029	10	.0029	.4637	.0029	.4637	343.77	.5363	1.0000	.0000	50	1.5679
.0058	20	.0058	.7648	.0058	.7648	171.89	.2352	1.0000	.0000	40	1.5650
.0087	30	.0087	.9408	.0087	.9409	114.59	.0591	1.0000	.0000	30	1.5621
.0116	40	.0116	.0658	.0116	.0658	85.940	.9342	.9999	.0000	20	1.5592
.0145	50	.0145	.1627	.0145	.1627	68.750	.8373	.9999	.0000	10	1.5563
.0175	1° 00′	.0175	.2419	.0175	.2419	57.290	.7581	.9998	.9999	89° 00′	1.5533
.0204	10	.0204	.3088	.0204	.3089	49.104	.6911	.9998	.9999	50	1.5504
.0233	20	.0233	.3668	.0233	.3669	42.964	.6331	.9997	.9999	40	1.5475
.0262	30	.0262	.4179	.0262	.4181	38.188	.5819	.9997	.9999	30	1.5446
.0291	40	.0291	.4637	.0291	.4638	34.368	.5362	.9996	.9998	20	1.5417
.0320	50	.0320	.5050	.0320	.5053	31.242	.4947	.9995	.9998	10	1.5388
.0349	2° 00′	.0349	.5428	.0349	.5431	28.636	.4569	.9994	.9997	88° 00′	1.5359
.0378	10	.0378	.5776	.0378	.5779	26.432	.4221	.9993	.9997	50	1.5330
.0407	20	.0407	.6097	.0407	.6101	24.542	.3899	.9992	.9996	40	1.5301
.0436	30	.0436	.6397	.0437	.6401	22.904	.3599	.9990	.9996	30	1.5272
.0465	40	.0465	.6677	.0466	.6682	21.470	.3318	.9989	.9995	20	1.5243
.0495	50	.0494	.6940	.0495	.6945	20.206	.3055	.9988	.9995	10	1.5213
.0524	3° 00′	.0523	.7188	.0524	.7194	19.081	.2806	.9986	.9994	87° 00′	1.5184
.0553	10	.0552	.7423	.0553	.7429	18.075	.2571	.9985	.9993	50	1.5155
.0582	20	.0581	.7645	.0582	.7652	17.169	.2348	.9983	.9993	40	1.5126
.0611	30	.0610	.7857	.0612	.7865	16.350	.2135	.9981	.9992	30	1.5097
.0640	40	.0640	.8059	.0641	.8067	15.605	.1933	.9980	.9991	20	1.5068
.0669	50	.0669	.8251	.0670	.8261	14.924	.1739	.9978	.9990	10	1.5039
.0698	4° 00′	.0698	.8436	.0699	.8446	14.301	.1554	.9976	.9989	86° 00′	1.5010
.0727	10	.0727	.8613	.0729	.8624	13.727	.1376	.9974	.9989	50	1.4981
.0756	20	.0756	.8783	.0758	.8795	13.197	.1205	.9971	.9988	40	1.4952
.0785	30	.0785	.8946	.0787	.8960	12.706	.1040	.9969	.9987	30	1.4923
.0814	40	.0814	.9104	.0816	.9118	12.251	.0882	.9967	.9986	20	1.4893
.0844	50	.0843	.9256	.0846	.9272	11.826	.0728	.9964	.9985	10	1.4864
.0873	5° 00′	.0872	.9403	.0875	.9420	11.430	.0580	.9962	.9983	85° 00′	1.4835
.0902	10	.0901	.9545	.0904	.9563	11.059	.0437	.9959	.9982	50	1.4806
.0931	20	.0929	.9682	.0934	.9701	10.712	.0299	.9957	.9981	40	1.4777
.0960	30	.0958	.9816	.0963	.9836	10.385	.0164	.9954	.9980	30	1.4748
.0989	40	.0987	.9945	.0992	.9966	10.078	.0034	.9951	.9979	20	1.4719
.1018	50	.1016	.0070	.1022	.0093	9.7882	.9907	.9948	.9977	10	1.4690
.1047	6° 00′	.1045	.0192	.1051	.0216	9.5144	.9784	.9945	.9976	84° 00′	1.4661
.1076	10	.1074	.0311	.1080	.0336	9.2553	.9664	.9942	.9975	50	1.4632
.1105	20	.1103	.0426	.1110	.0453	9.0098	.9547	.9939	.9973	40	1.4603
.1134	30	.1132	.0539	.1139	.0567	8.7769	.9433	.9936	.9972	30	1.4573
.1164	40	.1161	.0648	.1169	.0678	8.5555	.9322	.9932	.9971	20	1.4544
.1193	50	.1190	.0755	.1198	.0786	8.3450	.9214	.9929	.9969	10	1.4515
.1222	7° 00′	.1219	.0859	.1228	.0891	8.1443	.9109	.9925	.9968	83° 00′	1.4486
.1251	10	.1248	.0961	.1257	.0995	7.9530	.9005	.9922	.9966	50	1.4457
.1280	20	.1276	.1060	.1287	.1096	7.7704	.8904	.9918	.9964	40	1.4428
.1309	30	.1305	.1157	.1317	.1194	7.5958	.8806	.9914	.9963	30	1.4399
.1338	40	.1334	.1252	.1346	.1291	7.4287	.8709	.9911	.9961	20	1.4370
.1367	50	.1363	.1345	.1376	.1385	7.2687	.8615	.9907	.9959	10	1.4341
.1396	8° 00′	.1392	.1436	.1405	.1478	7.1154	.8522	.9903	.9958	82° 00′	1.4312
.1425	10	.1421	.1525	.1435	.1569	6.9682	.8431	.9899	.9956	50	1.4283
.1454	20	.1449	.1612	.1465	.1658	6.8269	.8342	.9894	.9954	40	1.4254
.1484	30	.1478	.1697	.1495	.1745	6.6912	.8255	.9890	.9952	30	1.4224
.1513	40	.1507	.1781	.1524	.1831	6.5606	.8169	.9886	.9950	20	1.4195
.1542	50	.1536	.1863	.1554	.1915	6.4348	.8085	.9881	.9948	10	1.4166
.1571	9° 00′	.1564	.1943	.1584	.1997	6.3138	.8003	.9877	.9946	81° 00′	1.4137
		Value Log₁₀ Cosine		Value Log₁₀ Cotangent		Value Log₁₀ Tangent		Value Log₁₀ Sine		Degrees	Radians

Four Place Trigonometric Functions

[Characteristics of Logarithms omitted—determine by the usual rule from the value]

Radians	Degrees	Sine Value	Sine Log₁₀	Tangent Value	Tangent Log₁₀	Cotangent Value	Cotangent Log₁₀	Cosine Value	Cosine Log₁₀		
.1571	9° 00'	.1564	.1943	.1584	.1997	6.3138	.8003	.9877	.9946	81° 00'	1.4137
.1600	10	.1593	.2022	.1614	.2078	6.1970	.7922	.9872	.9944	50	1.4108
.1629	20	.1622	.2100	.1644	.2158	6.0844	.7842	.9868	.9942	40	1.4079
.1658	30	.1650	.2176	.1673	.2236	5.9758	.7764	.9863	.9940	30	1.4050
.1687	40	.1679	.2251	.1703	.2313	5.8708	.7687	.9858	.9938	20	1.4021
.1716	50	.1708	.2324	.1733	.2389	5.7694	.7611	.9853	.9936	10	1.3992
.1745	10° 00'	.1736	.2397	.1763	.2463	5.6713	.7537	.9848	.9934	80° 00'	1.3963
.1774	10	.1765	.2468	.1793	.2536	5.5764	.7464	.9843	.9931	50	1.3934
.1804	20	.1794	.2538	.1823	.2609	5.4845	.7391	.9838	.9929	40	1.3904
.1833	30	.1822	.2606	.1853	.2680	5.3955	.7320	.9833	.9927	30	1.3875
.1862	40	.1851	.2674	.1883	.2750	5.3093	.7250	.9827	.9924	20	1.3846
.1891	50	.1880	.2740	.1914	.2819	5.2257	.7181	.9822	.9922	10	1.3817
.1920	11° 00'	.1908	.2806	.1944	.2887	5.1446	.7113	.9816	.9919	79° 00'	1.3788
.1949	10	.1937	.2870	.1974	.2953	5.0658	.7047	.9811	.9917	50	1.3759
.1978	20	.1965	.2934	.2004	.3020	4.9894	.6980	.9805	.9914	40	1.3730
.2007	30	.1994	.2997	.2035	.3085	4.9152	.6915	.9799	.9912	30	1.3701
.2036	40	.2022	.3058	.2065	.3149	4.8430	.6851	.9793	.9909	20	1.3672
.2065	50	.2051	.3119	.2095	.3212	4.7729	.6788	.9787	.9907	10	1.3643
.2094	12° 00'	.2079	.3179	.2126	.3275	4.7046	.6725	.9781	.9904	78° 00'	1.3614
.2123	10	.2108	.3238	.2156	.3336	4.6382	.6664	.9775	.9901	50	1.3584
.2153	20	.2136	.3296	.2186	.3397	4.5736	.6603	.9769	.9899	40	1.3555
.2182	30	.2164	.3353	.2217	.3458	4.5107	.6542	.9763	.9896	30	1.3526
.2211	40	.2193	.3410	.2247	.3517	4.4494	.6483	.9757	.9893	20	1.3497
.2240	50	.2221	.3466	.2278	.3576	4.3897	.6424	.9750	.9890	10	1.3468
.2269	13° 00'	.2250	.3521	.2309	.3634	4.3315	.6366	.9744	.9887	77° 00'	1.3439
.2298	10	.2278	.3575	.2339	.3691	4.2747	.6309	.9737	.9884	50	1.3410
.2327	20	.2306	.3629	.2370	.3748	4.2193	.6252	.9730	.9881	40	1.3381
.2356	30	.2334	.3682	.2401	.3804	4.1653	.6196	.9724	.9878	30	1.3352
.2385	40	.2363	.3734	.2432	.3859	4.1126	.6141	.9717	.9875	20	1.3323
.2414	50	.2391	.3786	.2462	.3914	4.0611	.6086	.9710	.9872	10	1.3294
.2443	14° 00'	.2419	.3837	.2493	.3968	4.0108	.6032	.9703	.9869	76° 00'	1.3265
.2473	10	.2447	.3887	.2524	.4021	3.9617	.5979	.9696	.9866	50	1.3235
.2502	20	.2476	.3937	.2555	.4074	3.9136	.5926	.9689	.9863	40	1.3206
.2531	30	.2504	.3986	.2586	.4127	3.8667	.5873	.9681	.9859	30	1.3177
.2560	40	.2532	.4035	.2617	.4178	3.8208	.5822	.9674	.9856	20	1.3148
.2589	50	.2560	.4083	.2648	.4230	3.7760	.5770	.9667	.9853	10	1.3119
.2618	15° 00'	.2588	.4130	.2679	.4281	3.7321	.5719	.9659	.9849	75° 00'	1.3090
.2647	10	.2616	.4177	.2711	.4331	3.6891	.5669	.9652	.9846	50	1.3061
.2676	20	.2644	.4223	.2742	.4381	3.6470	.5619	.9644	.9843	40	1.3032
.2705	30	.2672	.4269	.2773	.4430	3.6059	.5570	.9636	.9839	30	1.3003
.2734	40	.2700	.4314	.2805	.4479	3.5656	.5521	.9628	.9836	20	1.2974
.2763	50	.2728	.4359	.2836	.4527	3.5261	.5473	.9621	.9832	10	1.2945
.2793	16° 00'	.2756	.4403	.2867	.4575	3.4874	.5425	.9613	.9828	74° 00'	1.2915
.2822	10	.2784	.4447	.2899	.4622	3.4495	.5378	.9605	.9825	50	1.2886
.2851	20	.2812	.4491	.2931	.4669	3.4124	.5331	.9596	.9821	40	1.2857
.2880	30	.2840	.4533	.2962	.4716	3.3759	.5284	.9588	.9817	30	1.2828
.2909	40	.2868	.4576	.2994	.4762	3.3402	.5238	.9580	.9814	20	1.2799
.2938	50	.2896	.4618	.3026	.4808	3.3052	.5192	.9572	.9810	10	1.2770
.2967	17° 00'	.2924	.4659	.3057	.4853	3.2709	.5147	.9563	.9806	73° 00'	1.2741
.2996	10	.2952	.4700	.3089	.4898	3.2371	.5102	.9555	.9802	50	1.2712
.3025	20	.2979	.4741	.3121	.4943	3.2041	.5057	.9546	.9798	40	1.2683
.3054	30	.3007	.4781	.3153	.4987	3.1716	.5013	.9537	.9794	30	1.2654
.3083	40	.3035	.4821	.3185	.5031	3.1397	.4969	.9528	.9790	20	1.2625
.3113	50	.3062	.4861	.3217	.5075	3.1084	.4925	.9520	.9786	10	1.2595
.3142	18° 00'	.3090	.4900	.3249	.5118	3.0777	.4882	.9511	.9782	72° 00'	1.2566
		Value Cosine	Log₁₀	Value Cotangent	Log₁₀	Value Tangent	Log₁₀	Value Sine	Log₁₀	Degrees	Radians

Four Place Trigonometric Functions

[Characteristics of Logarithms omitted—determine by the usual rule from the value]

Radians	Degrees	Sine Value	Sine Log₁₀	Tangent Value	Tangent Log₁₀	Cotangent Value	Cotangent Log₁₀	Cosine Value	Cosine Log₁₀		
.3142	18° 00′	.3090	.4900	.3249	.5118	3.0777	.4882	.9511	.9782	72° 00′	1.2566
.3171	10	.3118	.4939	.3281	.5161	3.0475	.4839	.9502	.9778	50	1.2537
.3200	20	.3145	.4977	.3314	.5203	3.0178	.4797	.9492	.9774	40	1.2508
.3229	30	.3173	.5015	.3346	.5245	2.9887	.4755	.9483	.9770	30	1.2479
.3258	40	.3201	.5052	.3378	.5287	2.9600	.4713	.9474	.9765	20	1.2450
.3287	50	.3228	.5090	.3411	.5329	2.9319	.4671	.9465	.9761	10	1.2421
.3316	19° 00′	.3256	.5126	.3443	.5370	2.9042	.4630	.9455	.9757	71° 00′	1.2392
.3345	10	.3283	.5163	.3476	.5411	2.8770	.4589	.9446	.9752	50	1.2363
.3374	20	.3311	.5199	.3508	.5451	2.8502	.4549	.9436	.9748	40	1.2334
.3403	30	.3338	.5235	.3541	.5491	2.8239	.4509	.9426	.9743	30	1.2305
.3432	40	.3365	.5270	.3574	.5531	2.7980	.4469	.9417	.9739	20	1.2275
.3462	50	.3393	.5306	.3607	.5571	2.7725	.4429	.9407	.9734	10	1.2246
.3491	20° 00′	.3420	.5341	.3640	.5611	2.7475	.4389	.9397	.9730	70° 00′	1.2217
.3520	10	.3448	.5375	.3673	.5650	2.7228	.4350	.9387	.9725	50	1.2188
.3549	20	.3475	.5409	.3706	.5689	2.6985	.4311	.9377	.9721	40	1.2159
.3578	30	.3502	.5443	.3739	.5727	2.6746	.4273	.9367	.9716	30	1.2130
.3607	40	.3529	.5477	.3772	.5766	2.6511	.4234	.9356	.9711	20	1.2101
.3636	50	.3557	.5510	.3805	.5804	2.6279	.4196	.9346	.9706	10	1.2072
.3665	21° 00′	.3584	.5543	.3839	.5842	2.6051	.4158	.9336	.9702	69° 00′	1.2043
.3694	10	.3611	.5576	.3872	.5879	2.5826	.4121	.9325	.9697	50	1.2014
.3723	20	.3638	.5609	.3906	.5917	2.5605	.4083	.9315	.9692	40	1.1985
.3752	30	.3665	.5641	.3939	.5954	2.5386	.4046	.9304	.9687	30	1.1956
.3782	40	.3692	.5673	.3973	.5991	2.5172	.4009	.9293	.9682	20	1.1926
.3811	50	.3719	.5704	.4006	.6028	2.4960	.3972	.9283	.9677	10	1.1897
.3840	22° 00′	.3746	.5736	.4040	.6064	2.4751	.3936	.9272	.9672	68° 00′	1.1868
.3869	10	.3773	.5767	.4074	.6100	2.4545	.3900	.9261	.9667	50	1.1839
.3898	20	.3800	.5798	.4108	.6136	2.4342	.3864	.9250	.9661	40	1.1810
.3927	30	.3827	.5828	.4142	.6172	2.4142	.3828	.9239	.9656	30	1.1781
.3956	40	.3854	.5859	.4176	.6208	2.3945	.3792	.9228	.9651	20	1.1752
.3985	50	.3881	.5889	.4210	.6243	2.3750	.3757	.9216	.9646	10	1.1723
.4014	23° 00′	.3907	.5919	.4245	.6279	2.3559	.3721	.9205	.9640	67° 00′	1.1694
.4043	10	.3934	.5948	.4279	.6314	2.3369	.3686	.9194	.9635	50	1.1665
.4072	20	.3961	.5978	.4314	.6348	2.3183	.3652	.9182	.9629	40	1.1636
.4102	30	.3987	.6007	.4348	.6383	2.2998	.3617	.9171	.9624	30	1.1606
.4131	40	.4014	.6036	.4383	.6417	2.2817	.3583	.9159	.9618	20	1.1577
.4160	50	.4041	.6065	.4417	.6452	2.2637	.3548	.9147	.9613	10	1.1548
.4189	24° 00′	.4067	.6093	.4452	.6486	2.2460	.3514	.9135	.9607	66° 00′	1.1519
.4218	10	.4094	.6121	.4487	.6520	2.2286	.3480	.9124	.9602	50	1.1490
.4247	20	.4120	.6149	.4522	.6553	2.2113	.3447	.9112	.9596	40	1.1461
.4276	30	.4147	.6177	.4557	.6587	2.1943	.3413	.9100	.9590	30	1.1432
.4305	40	.4173	.6205	.4592	.6620	2.1775	.3380	.9088	.9584	20	1.1403
.4334	50	.4200	.6232	.4628	.6654	2.1609	.3346	.9075	.9579	10	1.1374
.4363	25° 00′	.4226	.6259	.4663	.6687	2.1445	.3313	.9063	.9573	65° 00′	1.1345
.4392	10	.4253	.6286	.4699	.6720	2.1283	.3280	.9051	.9567	50	1.1316
.4422	20	.4279	.6313	.4734	.6752	2.1123	.3248	.9038	.9561	40	1.1286
.4451	30	.4305	.6340	.4770	.6785	2.0965	.3215	.9026	.9555	30	1.1257
.4480	40	.4331	.6366	.4806	.6817	2.0809	.3183	.9013	.9549	20	1.1228
.4509	50	.4358	.6392	.4841	.6850	2.0655	.3150	.9001	.9543	/ 10	1.1199
.4538	26° 00′	.4384	.6418	.4877	.6882	2.0503	.3118	.8988	.9537	64° 00′	1.1170
.4567	10	.4410	.6444	.4913	.6914	2.0353	.3086	.8975	.9530	50	1.1141
.4596	20	.4436	.6470	.4950	.6946	2.0204	.3054	.8962	.9524	40	1.1112
.4625	30	.4462	.6495	.4986	.6977	2.0057	.3023	.8949	.9518	30	1.1083
.4654	40	.4488	.6521	.5022	.7009	1.9912	.2991	.8936	.9512	20	1.1054
.4683	50	.4514	.6546	.5059	.7040	1.9768	.2960	.8923	.9505	10	1.1025
.4712	27° 00′	.4540	.6570	.5095	.7072	1.9626	.2928	.8910	.9499	63° 00′	1.0996
		Value Log₁₀ Cosine		Value Log₁₀ Cotangent		Value Log₁₀ Tangent		Value Log₁₀ Sine		Degrees	Radians

Four Place Trigonometric Functions

[Characteristics of Logarithms omitted—determine by the usual rule from the value]

Radians	Degrees	Sine Value	Log₁₀	Tangent Value	Log₁₀	Cotangent Value	Log₁₀	Cosine Value	Log₁₀		
.4712	27° 00′	.4540	.6570	.5095	.7072	1.9626	.2928	.8910	.9499	63° 00′	1.0996
.4741	10	.4566	.6595	.5132	.7103	1.9486	.2897	.8897	.9492	50	1.0966
.4771	20	.4592	.6620	.5169	.7134	1.9347	.2866	.8884	.9486	40	1.0937
.4800	30	.4617	.6644	.5206	.7165	1.9210	.2835	.8870	.9479	30	1.0908
.4829	40	.4643	.6668	.5243	.7196	1.9074	.2804	.8857	.9473	20	1.0879
.4858	50	.4669	.6692	.5280	.7226	1.8940	.2774	.8843	.9466	10	1.0850
.4887	28° 00′	.4695	.6716	.5317	.7257	1.8807	.2743	.8829	.9459	62° 00′	1.0821
.4916	10	.4720	.6740	.5354	.7287	1.8676	.2713	.8816	.9453	50	1.0792
.4945	20	.4746	.6763	.5392	.7317	1.8546	.2683	.8802	.9446	40	1.0763
.4974	30	.4772	.6787	.5430	.7348	1.8418	.2652	.8788	.9439	30	1.0734
.5003	40	.4797	.6810	.5467	.7378	1.8291	.2622	.8774	.9432	20	1.0705
.5032	50	.4823	.6833	.5505	.7408	1.8165	.2592	.8760	.9425	10	1.0676
.5061	29° 00′	.4848	.6856	.5543	.7438	1.8040	.2562	.8746	.9418	61° 00′	1.0647
.5091	10	.4874	.6878	.5581	.7467	1.7917	.2533	.8732	.9411	50	1.0617
.5120	20	.4899	.6901	.5619	.7497	1.7796	.2503	.8718	.9404	40	1.0588
.5149	30	.4924	.6923	.5658	.7526	1.7675	.2474	.8704	.9397	30	1.0559
.5178	40	.4950	.6946	.5696	.7556	1.7556	.2444	.8689	.9390	20	1.0530
.5207	50	.4975	.6968	.5735	.7585	1.7437	.2415	.8675	.9383	10	1.0501
.5236	30° 00′	.5000	.6990	.5774	.7614	1.7321	.2386	.8660	.9375	60° 00′	1.0472
.5265	10	.5025	.7012	.5812	.7644	1.7205	.2356	.8646	.9368	50	1.0443
.5294	20	.5050	.7033	.5851	.7673	1.7090	.2327	.8631	.9361	40	1.0414
.5323	30	.5075	.7055	.5890	.7701	1.6977	.2299	.8616	.9353	30	1.0385
.5352	40	.5100	.7076	.5930	.7730	1.6864	.2270	.8601	.9346	20	1.0356
.5381	50	.5125	.7097	.5969	.7759	1.6753	.2241	.8587	.9338	10	1.0327
.5411	31° 00′	.5150	.7118	.6009	.7788	1.6643	.2212	.8572	.9331	59° 00′	1.0297
.5440	10	.5175	.7139	.6048	.7816	1.6534	.2184	.8557	.9323	50	1.0268
.5469	20	.5200	.7160	.6088	.7845	1.6426	.2155	.8542	.9315	40	1.0239
.5498	30	.5225	.7181	.6128	.7873	1.6319	.2127	.8526	.9308	30	1.0210
.5527	40	.5250	.7201	.6168	.7902	1.6212	.2098	.8511	.9300	20	1.0181
.5556	50	.5275	.7222	.6208	.7930	1.6107	.2070	.8496	.9292	10	1.0152
.5585	32° 00′	.5299	.7242	.6249	.7958	1.6003	.2042	.8480	.9284	58° 00′	1.0123
.5614	10	.5324	.7262	.6289	.7986	1.5900	.2014	.8465	.9276	50	1.0094
.5643	20	.5348	.7282	.6330	.8014	1.5798	.1986	.8450	.9268	40	1.0065
.5672	30	.5373	.7302	.6371	.8042	1.5697	.1958	.8434	.9260	30	1.0036
.5701	40	.5398	.7322	.6412	.8070	1.5597	.1930	.8418	.9252	20	1.0007
.5730	50	.5422	.7342	.6453	.8097	1.5497	.1903	.8403	.9244	10	.9977
.5760	33° 00′	.5446	.7361	.6494	.8125	1.5399	.1875	.8387	.9236	57° 00′	.9948
.5789	10	.5471	.7380	.6536	.8153	1.5301	.1847	.8371	.9228	50	.9919
.5818	20	.5495	.7400	.6577	.8180	1.5204	.1820	.8355	.9219	40	.9890
.5847	30	.5519	.7419	.6619	.8208	1.5108	.1792	.8339	.9211	30	.9861
.5876	40	.5544	.7438	.6661	.8235	1.5013	.1765	.8323	.9203	20	.9832
.5905	50	.5568	.7457	.6703	.8263	1.4919	.1737	.8307	.9194	10	.9803
.5934	34° 00′	.5592	.7476	.6745	.8290	1.4826	.1710	.8290	.9186	56° 00′	.9774
.5963	10	.5616	.7494	.6787	.8317	1.4733	.1683	.8274	.9177	50	.9745
.5992	20	.5640	.7513	.6830	.8344	1.4641	.1656	.8258	.9169	40	.9716
.6021	30	.5664	.7531	.6873	.8371	1.4550	.1629	.8241	.9160	30	.9687
.6050	40	.5688	.7550	.6916	.8398	1.4460	.1602	.8225	.9151	20	.9657
.6080	50	.5712	.7568	.6959	.8425	1.4370	.1575	.8208	.9142	10	.9628
.6109	35° 00′	.5736	.7586	.7002	.8452	1.4281	.1548	.8192	.9134	55° 00′	.9599
.6138	10	.5760	.7604	.7046	.8479	1.4193	.1521	.8175	.9125	50	.9570
.6167	20	.5783	.7622	.7089	.8506	1.4106	.1494	.8158	.9116	40	.9541
.6196	30	.5807	.7640	.7133	.8533	1.4019	.1467	.8141	.9107	30	.9512
.6225	40	.5831	.7657	.7177	.8559	1.3934	.1441	.8124	.9098	20	.9483
.6254	50	.5854	.7675	.7221	.8586	1.3848	.1414	.8107	.9089	10	.9454
.6283	36° 00′	.5878	.7692	.7265	.8613	1.3764	.1387	.8090	.9080	54° 00′	.9425
		Value Cosine	Log₁₀	Value Cotangent	Log₁₀	Value Tangent	Log₁₀	Value Sine	Log₁₀	Degrees	Radians

Four Place Trigonometric Functions

[Characteristics of Logarithms omitted—determine by the usual rule from the value]

Radians	Degrees	Sine Value	Sine Log₁₀	Tangent Value	Tangent Log₁₀	Cotangent Value	Cotangent Log₁₀	Cosine Value	Cosine Log₁₀		
.6283	36° 00′	.5878	.7692	.7265	.8613	1.3764	.1387	.8090	.9080	54° 00′	.9425
.6312	10	.5901	.7710	.7310	.8639	1.3680	.1361	.8073	.9070	50	.9396
.6341	20	.5925	.7727	.7355	.8666	1.3597	.1334	.8056	.9061	40	.9367
.6370	30	.5948	.7744	.7400	.8692	1.3514	.1308	.8039	.9052	30	.9338
.6400	40	.5972	.7761	.7445	.8718	1.3432	.1282	.8021	.9042	20	.9308
.6429	50	.5995	.7778	.7490	.8745	1.3351	.1255	.8004	.9033	10	.9279
.6458	37° 00′	.6018	.7795	.7536	.8771	1.3270	.1229	.7986	.9023	53° 00′	.9250
.6487	10	.6041	.7811	.7581	.8797	1.3190	.1203	.7969	.9014	50	.9221
.6516	20	.6065	.7828	.7627	.8824	1.3111	.1176	.7951	.9004	40	.9192
.6545	30	.6088	.7844	.7673	.8850	1.3032	.1150	.7934	.8995	30	.9163
.6574	40	.6111	.7861	.7720	.8876	1.2954	.1124	.7916	.8985	20	.9134
.6603	50	.6134	.7877	.7766	.8902	1.2876	.1098	.7898	.8975	10	.9105
.6632	38° 00′	.6157	.7893	.7813	.8928	1.2799	.1072	.7880	.8965	52° 00′	.9076
.6661	10	.6180	.7910	.7860	.8954	1.2723	.1046	.7862	.8955	50	.9047
.6690	20	.6202	.7926	.7907	.8980	1.2647	.1020	.7844	.8945	40	.9018
.6720	30	.6225	.7941	.7954	.9006	1.2572	.0994	.7826	.8935	30	.8988
.6749	40	.6248	.7957	.8002	.9032	1.2497	.0968	.7808	.8925	20	.8959
.6778	50	.6271	.7973	.8050	.9058	1.2423	.0942	.7790	.8915	10	.8930
.6807	39° 00′	.6293	.7989	.8098	.9084	1.2349	.0916	.7771	.8905	51° 00′	.8901
.6836	10	.6316	.8004	.8146	.9110	1.2276	.0890	.7753	.8895	50	.8872
.6865	20	.6338	.8020	.8195	.9135	1.2203	.0865	.7735	.8884	40	.8843
.6894	30	.6361	.8035	.8243	.9161	1.2131	.0839	.7716	.8874	30	.8814
.6923	40	.6383	.8050	.8292	.9187	1.2059	.0813	.7698	.8864	20	.8785
.6952	50	.6406	.8066	.8342	.9212	1.1988	.0788	.7679	.8853	10	.8756
.6981	40° 00′	.6428	.8081	.8391	.9238	1.1918	.0762	.7660	.8843	50° 00′	.8727
.7010	10	.6450	.8096	.8441	.9264	1.1847	.0736	.7642	.8832	50	.8698
.7039	20	.6472	.8111	.8491	.9289	1.1778	.0711	.7623	.8821	40	.8668
.7069	30	.6494	.8125	.8541	.9315	1.1708	.0685	.7604	.8810	30	.8639
.7098	40	.6517	.8140	.8591	.9341	1.1640	.0659	.7585	.8800	20	.8610
.7127	50	.6539	.8155	.8642	.9366	1.1571	.0634	.7566	.8789	10	.8581
.7156	41° 00′	.6561	.8169	.8693	.9392	1.1504	.0608	.7547	.8778	49° 00′	.8552
.7185	10	.6583	.8184	.8744	.9417	1.1436	.0583	.7528	.8767	50	.8523
.7214	20	.6604	.8198	.8796	.9443	1.1369	.0557	.7509	.8756	40	.8494
.7243	30	.6626	.8213	.8847	.9468	1.1303	.0532	.7490	.8745	30	.8465
.7272	40	.6648	.8227	.8899	.9494	1.1237	.0506	.7470	.8733	20	.8436
.7301	50	.6670	.8241	.8952	.9519	1.1171	.0481	.7451	.8722	10	.8407
.7330	42° 00′	.6691	.8255	.9004	.9544	1.1106	.0456	.7431	.8711	48° 00′	.8378
.7359	10	.6713	.8269	.9057	.9570	1.1041	.0430	.7412	.8699	50	.8348
.7389	20	.6734	.8283	.9110	.9595	1.0977	.0405	.7392	.8688	40	.8319
.7418	30	.6756	.8297	.9163	.9621	1.0913	.0379	.7373	.8676	30	.8290
.7447	40	.6777	.8311	.9217	.9646	1.0850	.0354	.7353	.8665	20	.8261
.7476	50	.6799	.8324	.9271	.9671	1.0786	.0329	.7333	.8653	10	.8232
.7505	43° 00′	.6820	.8338	.9325	.9697	1.0724	.0303	.7314	.8641	47° 00′	.8203
.7534	10	.6841	.8351	.9380	.9722	1.0661	.0278	.7294	.8629	50	.8174
.7563	20	.6862	.8365	.9435	.9747	1.0599	.0253	.7274	.8618	40	.8145
.7592	30	.6884	.8378	.9490	.9772	1.0538	.0228	.7254	.8606	30	.8116
.7621	40	.6905	.8391	.9545	.9798	1.0477	.0202	.7234	.8594	20	.8087
.7650	50	.6926	.8405	.9601	.9823	1.0416	.0177	.7214	.8582	10	.8058
.7679	44° 00′	.6947	.8418	.9657	.9848	1.0355	.0152	.7193	.8569	46° 00′	.8029
.7709	10	.6967	.8431	.9713	.9874	1.0295	.0126	.7173	.8557	50	.7999
.7738	20	.6988	.8444	.9770	.9899	1.0235	.0101	.7153	.8545	40	.7970
.7767	30	.7009	.8457	.9827	.9924	1.0176	.0076	.7133	.8532	30	.7941
.7796	40	.7030	.8469	.9884	.9949	1.0117	.0051	.7112	.8520	20	.7912
.7825	50	.7050	.8482	.9942	.9975	1.0058	.0025	.7092	.8507	10	.7883
.7854	45° 00′	.7071	.8495	1.0000	.0000	1.0000	.0000	.7071	.8495	45° 00′	.7854
		Value Cosine	Log₁₀ Cosine	Value Cotangent	Log₁₀ Cotangent	Value Tangent	Log₁₀ Tangent	Value Sine	Log₁₀ Sine	Degrees	Radians

Radian Measure—Trigonometric Functions

x Radians	Sin x	Cos x	Tan x	Equivalent of x	x Radians	Sin x	Cos x	Tan x	Equivalent of x
.00	.00000	1.0000	.00000	0° 00'.0	.50	.47943	.87758	.54630	28° 38'.9
.01	.01000	.99995	.01000	0° 34'.4	.51	.48818	.87274	.55936	29° 13'.3
.02	.02000	.99980	.02000	1° 08'.8	.52	.49688	.86782	.57256	29° 47'.6
.03	.03000	.99955	.03001	1° 43'.1	.53	.50553	.86281	.58592	30° 22'.0
.04	.03999	.99920	.04002	2° 17'.5	.54	.51414	.85771	.59943	30° 56'.4
.05	.04998	.99875	.05004	2° 51'.9	.55	.52269	.85252	.61311	31° 30'.8
.06	.05996	.99820	.06007	3° 26'.3	.56	.53119	.84726	.62695	32° 05'.1
.07	.06994	.99755	.07011	4° 00'.6	.57	.53963	.84190	.64097	32° 39'.5
.08	.07991	.99680	.08017	4° 35'.0	.58	.54802	.83646	.65517	33° 13'.9
.09	.08988	.99595	.09024	5° 09'.4	.59	.55636	.83094	.66956	33° 48'.3
.10	.09983	.99500	.10033	5° 43'.8	.60	.56464	.82534	.68414	34° 22'.6
.11	.10978	.99396	.11045	6° 18'.2	.61	.57287	.81965	.69892	34° 57'.0
.12	.11971	.99281	.12058	6° 52'.5	.62	.58104	.81388	.71391	35° 31'.4
.13	.12963	.99156	.13074	7° 26'.9	.63	.58914	.80803	.72911	36° 05'.8
.14	.13954	.99022	.14092	8° 01'.3	.64	.59720	.80210	.74454	36° 40'.2
.15	.14944	.98877	.15114	8° 35'.7	.65	.60519	.79608	.76020	37° 14'.5
.16	.15932	.98723	.16138	9° 10'.0	.66	.61312	.78999	.77610	37° 48'.9
.17	.16918	.98558	.17166	9° 44'.4	.67	.62099	.78382	.79225	38° 23'.3
.18	.17903	.98384	.18197	10° 18'.8	.68	.62879	.77757	.80866	38° 57'.7
.19	.18886	.98200	.19232	10° 53'.2	.69	.63654	.77125	.82534	39° 32'.0
.20	.19867	.98007	.20271	11° 27'.5	.70	.64422	.76484	.84229	40° 06'.4
.21	.20846	.97803	.21314	12° 01'.9	.71	.65183	.75836	.85953	40° 40'.8
.22	.21823	.97590	.22362	12° 36'.3	.72	.65938	.75181	.87707	41° 15'.2
.23	.22798	.97367	.23414	13° 10'.7	.73	.66687	.74517	.89492	41° 49'.6
.24	.23770	.97134	.24472	13° 45'.1	.74	.67429	.73847	.91309	42° 23'.9
.25	.24740	.96891	.25534	14° 19'.4	.75	.68164	.73169	.93160	42° 58'.3
.26	.25708	.96639	.26602	14° 53'.8	.76	.68892	.72484	.95045	43° 32'.7
.27	.26673	.96377	.27676	15° 28'.2	.77	.69614	.71791	.96967	44° 07'.1
.28	.27636	.96106	.28755	16° 02'.6	.78	.70328	.71091	.98926	44° 41'.4
.29	.28595	.95824	.29841	16° 36'.9	.79	.71035	.70385	1.0092	45° 15'.8
.30	.29552	.95534	.30934	17° 11'.3	.80	.71736	.69671	1.0296	45° 50'.2
.31	.30506	.95233	.32033	17° 45'.7	.81	.72429	.68950	1.0505	46° 24'.6
.32	.31457	.94924	.33139	18° 20'.1	.82	.73115	.68222	1.0717	46° 59'.0
.33	.32404	.94604	.34252	18° 54'.5	.83	.73793	.67488	1.0934	47° 38'.3
.34	.33349	.94275	.35374	19° 28'.8	.84	.74464	.66746	1.1156	48° 07'.7
.35	.34290	.93937	.36503	20° 03'.2	.85	.75128	.65998	1.1383	48° 42'.1
.36	.35227	.93590	.37640	20° 37'.6	.86	.75784	.65244	1.1616	49° 16'.5
.37	.36162	.93233	.38786	21° 12'.0	.87	.76433	.64483	1.1853	49° 50'.8
.38	.37092	.92866	.39941	21° 46'.3	.88	.77074	.63715	1.2097	50° 25'.2
.39	.38019	.92491	.41105	22° 20'.7	.89	.77707	.62941	1.2346	50° 59'.6
.40	.38942	.92106	.42279	22° 55'.1	.90	.78333	.62161	1.2602	51° 34'.0
.41	.39861	.91712	.43463	23° 29'.5	.91	.78950	.61375	1.2864	52° 08'.3
.42	.40776	.91309	.44657	24° 03'.9	.92	.79560	.60582	1.3133	52° 42'.7
.43	.41687	.90897	.45862	24° 38'.2	.93	.80162	.59783	1.3409	53° 17'.1
.44	.42594	.90475	.47078	25° 12'.6	.94	.80756	.58979	1.3692	53° 51'.5
.45	.43497	.90045	.48306	25° 47'.0	.95	.81342	.58168	1.3984	54° 25'.9
.46	.44395	.89605	.49545	26° 21'.4	.96	.81919	.57352	1.4284	55° 00'.2
.47	.45289	.89157	.50797	26° 55'.7	.97	.82489	.56530	1.4592	55° 34'.6
.48	.46178	.88699	.52061	27° 30'.1	.98	.83050	.55702	1.4910	56° 09'.0
.49	.47063	.88233	.53339	28° 04'.5	.99	.83603	.54869	1.5237	56° 43'.4
.50	.47943	.87758	.54630	28° 38'.9	1.00	.84147	.54030	1.5574	57° 17'.7

TABLES

Radian Measure—Trigonometric Functions

x Radians	Sin x	Cos x	Tan x	Equivalent of x	x Radians	Sin x	Cos x	Tan x	Equivalent of x
1.00	.84147	.54030	1.5574	57° 17'.7	1.30	.96356	.26750	3.6021	74° 29'.1
1.01	.84683	.53186	1.5922	57° 52'.1	1.31	.96618	.25785	3.7471	75° 08'.4
1.02	.85211	.52337	1.6281	58° 26'.5	1.32	.96872	.24818	3.9033	75° 37'.8
1.03	.85730	.51482	1.6652	59° 00'.9	1.33	.97115	.23848	4.0723	76° 12'.2
1.04	.86240	.50622	1.7036	59° 35'.3	1.34	.97348	.22875	4.2556	76° 46'.6
1.05	.86742	.49757	1.7433	60° 09'.6	1.35	.97572	.21901	4.4552	77° 21'.0
1.06	.87236	.48887	1.7844	60° 44'.0	1.36	.97786	.20924	4.6734	77° 55'.3
1.07	.87720	.48012	1.8270	61° 18'.4	1.37	.97991	.19945	4.9131	78° 29'.7
1.08	.88196	.47133	1.8712	61° 52'.8	1.38	.98185	.18964	5.1774	79° 04'.1
1.09	.88663	.46249	1.9171	62° 27'.1	1.39	.98370	.17981	5.4707	79° 38'.5
1.10	.89121	.45360	1.9648	63° 01'.5	1.40	.98545	.16997	5.7979	80° 12'.8
1.11	.89570	.44466	2.0143	63° 35'.9	1.41	.98710	.16010	6.1654	80° 47'.2
1.12	.90010	.43568	2.0660	64° 10'.3	1.42	.98865	.15023	6.5811	81° 21'.6
1.13	.90441	.42666	2.1198	64° 44'.7	1.43	.99010	.14033	7.0555	81° 56'.0
1.14	.90863	.41759	2.1759	65° 19'.0	1.44	.99146	.13042	7.6018	82° 30'.4
1.15	.91276	.40849	2.2345	65° 53'.4	1.45	.99271	.12050	8.2381	83° 04'.7
1.16	.91680	.39934	2.2958	66° 27'.8	1.46	.99387	.11057	8.9886	83° 39'.1
1.17	.92075	.39015	2.3600	67° 02'.2	1.47	.99492	.10063	9.8874	84° 13'.5
1.18	.92461	.38092	2.4273	67° 36'.5	1.48	.99588	.09067	10.983	84° 47'.9
1.19	.92837	.37166	2.4979	68° 10'.9	1.49	.99674	.08071	12.350	85° 22'.2
1.20	.93204	.36236	2.5722	68° 45'.3	1.50	.99749	.07074	14.101	85° 56'.6
1.21	.93562	.35302	2.6503	69° 19'.7	1.51	.99815	.06076	16.428	86° 31'.0
1.22	.93910	.34365	2.7328	69° 54'.1	1.52	.99871	.05077	19.670	87° 05'.4
1.23	.94249	.33424	2.8198	70° 28'.4	1.53	.99917	.04079	24.498	87° 39'.8
1.24	.94578	.32480	2.9119	71° 02'.8	1.54	.99953	.03079	32.461	88° 14'.1
1.25	.94898	.31532	3.0096	71° 37'.2	1.55	.99978	.02079	48.078	88° 48'.5
1.26	.95209	.30582	3.1133	72° 11'.6	1.56	.99994	.01080	92.621	89° 22'.9
1.27	.95510	.29628	3.2236	72° 45'.9	*1.57	*1.0000	*.00080	*1255.8	89° 57'.3
1.28	.95802	.28672	3.3413	73° 20'.3	1.58	.99996	−.00920	−108.65	90° 31'.6
1.29	.96084	.27712	3.4672	73° 54'.7	1.59	.99982	−.01920	−52.067	91° 06'.0
1.30	.96356	.26750	3.6021	74° 29'.1	1.60	.99957	−.02920	−34.233	91° 40'.4

π radians = 180°   1 radian = 57° 17' 44''.806 = 57.°2957795
π = 3.14159265   3600'' = 60' = 1° = 0.01745329 radian
*1 right angle = 90° = $\pi/2$ radians = 1.5707963 radians

INDEX